MW00399316

Introduction to
Fluid Mechanics

Introduction to
Fluid Mechanics

STEPHEN WHITAKER

Professor of Chemical Engineering
University of California at Davis

KRIEGER PUBLISHING COMPANY
MALABAR, FLORIDA

Original Edition 1968
Reprint Edition 1981 w/corrections
Reissued 1992 w/minor corrections

Printed and Published by
KRIEGER PUBLISHING COMPANY
KRIEGER DRIVE
MALABAR, FLORIDA 32950

Copyright © 1968 by
PRENTICE HALL, INC.
Transferred to Stephen Whitaker 1976
Reprinted by arrangement with author

Library of Congress Cataloging-In-Publication Data
Whitaker, Stephen.
    Introduction to Fluid Mechanics.

    Reprint. Originally published: Englewood Cliffs, N.J. :
Prentice-Hall (Prentice-Hall international series in the
physical and chemical engineering sciences.
    Includes bibliographical references and index.
    1. Fluid dynamics.   I. Title.   II. Series: Prentice-
Hall international series in the physical and chemical engi-
neering sciences.
[QA911.W38 1981]   532'.05   81-1620
ISBN 0-89464-785-7   AACR2

10   9   8

Preface

This book is intended for use in an introductory course in fluid mechanics. The student is expected to have completed two years of college mathematics and to be familiar with ordinary differential equations, partial differentiation, multiple integrals, Taylor series, and the basic elements of vector analysis.

The book is based primarily on a common core fluid mechanics course in which the author participated while at Northwestern University. There, each department (with the exception of Electrical Engineering) offered advanced undergraduate courses in fluid mechanics, and it was necessary to provide a rigorous foundation in the common core course. The first eight chapters are the result of experience in teaching that course. They can be covered satisfactorily in approximately 40 lectures, and thus can be used in either a three-unit semester course or a four-unit quarter course.

Chapters 9, 10, and 11 were added to provide flexibility for those persons who may wish to use the book in a terminal course. Under these circumstances it may be necessary to delete some material in Chapters 1–8; however, certain sections must be covered if subsequent material is to be understood. These sections are marked with an asterisk.

Vector notation is used freely throughout the text, not because it leads to elegance or rigor but simply because fundamental concepts are best expressed in a form which attempts to connect them with reality.

A variety of people contributed in innumerable ways to the completion of this text; they have the author's thanks. Special appreciation is due Professor John C. Slattery of Northwestern University, for the origin of the text rests largely on an endless series of conversations with him regarding the problems of teaching fluid mechanics to undergraduates.

Davis, California   STEPHEN WHITAKER

Contents

 *Sections marked with an asterisk must be covered if subsequent material is to be
understood.

† The general form of Newton's law of viscosity is listed in the previous section.
‡ This section requires supplementary discussion if it is presented independently of the previous section.

Nomenclature[†]

Roman Letters

a   acceleration vector (82)

A cross-sectional area, portion of a closed surface (33)

$A_e(t)$ area of entrances and exits (214)

$A_s(t)$ area of solid moving surfaces (214)

A_s area of solid fixed surfaces (214)

A^* characteristic area (287)

$\mathscr{A}$ area of a closed surface fixed in space (33)

$\mathscr{A}_a(t)$ area of an arbitrary closed surface moving in space (33)

$\mathscr{A}_m(t)$ area of a closed material surface (33)

b width (47)

b   arbitrary constant vector (86)

C constant of integration (41)

C_D drag coefficient (304)

C_d discharge coefficient (333)

C_c contraction coefficient (334)

c wave speed (372), velocity of sound (399)

c_p constant pressure heat capacity per unit mass (402)

c_v constant volume heat capacity per unit mass (402)

D tube diameter (5)

d   rate of strain tensor in Gibbs notation (133)

d_{ij} rate of strain tensor in index notation (133)

e internal energy per unit mass (392)

$\mathbf{e}_{(i)}$ unit base vectors for rectangular, Cartesian coordinate system (26)

[†] Page number in parentheses indicates where the symbol is first defined.

$\dot{E}_v$	rate of viscous dissipation (227)	N_{Fr}	Froude number (165)
E_{sp}	specific energy (360)	N_{ca}	cavitation number (22)
f	friction factor (287)	p	absolute pressure (38)
F_D	drag force (286)	p_{vp}	vapor pressure (22)
$\mathbf{F}$	force vector (10)	p_g	gauge pressure (45)
$\mathbf{g}$	gravity vector (34)	p°	stagnation pressure (407)
g	magnitude of gravity vector (41)	p_0	ambient or atmospheric pressure (43)
g_c	gravitational constant (11)	P	dimensionless pressure (160)
h	fluid depth (43), enthalpy per unit mass (394)	$\mathscr{P}$	dimensionless pressure which includes the body force term (160)
h_f	friction head loss (308)	q	volumetric flow rate per unit width (67)
h_m	minor head loss (308)	$\mathbf{q}$	heat flux vector (392)
H_w	change in head caused by a pump or turbine (308)	Q	volumetric flow rate (61)
$\mathbf{i}, \mathbf{j}, \mathbf{k}$	unit base vectors for rectangular, Cartesian coordinate system (24)	$\dot{Q}$	rate of heat transfer (392)
		r, θ, z	cylindrical coordinates (94)
		r, θ, ϕ	spherical coordinates (94)
$\mathbf{I}$	unit tensor (129)	$\mathbf{r}$	spatial position vector (76)
k	thermal conductivity (404)	$\bar{\mathbf{r}}$	position vector locating the center of stress (49)
K	head loss coefficient (311)	$\mathbf{R}$	material position vector (76)
KE^*	characteristic kinetic energy per unit volume (287)	R	dimensionless radius (162), gas constant (402)
ℓ	length (47), Prandtl mixing length (201)	R_h	hydraulic radius (159)
L	length (42)	$\mathscr{R}$	universal gas constant (402), dimensionless ratio of like quantities (162)
L_e	entrance length (171)		
m	mass (402), Ostwald-de Wael model parameter (20)	s	entropy per unit mass (397), arc length (98)
$\dot{m}$	mass flow rate (265)	S	wetted perimeter (351)
M	mass (10), Mach number (403)	$\mathcal{S}$	scalar function (93)
MW	molecular weight (13)	t	time (10)
n	number of moles (9), Ostwald-de Wael model parameter (20), Manning roughness factor (352)	$\mathbf{t}_{(\mathbf{n})}$	stress vector (35)
		$\mathbf{t}_{(\mathbf{n})}^*$	net stress vector (257)
		T_0	Bingham model yield stress (19)
$\mathbf{n}$	outwardly directed unit normal (35)	T	absolute temperature (9)
N_{Re}	Reynolds number (5)	T°	stagnation temperature (407)
$N_{\mathrm{Re},x}$	length Reynolds number (431)	$\mathbf{T}$	total stress tensor in Gibbs notation (112)

T_{ij}	total stress tensor in index notation (115)	κ	compressibility (13), bulk coefficient of viscosity (133)
$\mathcal{T}$	torque vector (48)	λ	wave length (374)
u_0	characteristic velocity (159)	$\boldsymbol{\lambda}$	unit tangent vector (99)
u_∞	velocity far removed from an immersed body (430)	μ	shear coefficient of viscosity (14)
$\mathbf{v}$	fluid velocity vector (77)	μ_{app}	apparent viscosity (19)
$\mathbf{U}$	dimensionless fluid velocity vector (160)	μ_0	Bingham model viscosity (19)
$v_x, v_y,$ v_z	scalar components of $\mathbf{v}$ in rectangular Cartesian co-ordinates (24)	$\mu^{(t)}$ ν	eddy viscosity (200) kinematic viscosity (16)
v	magnitude of fluid velocity vector (222)	π ρ	3.1416... density (2)
v^+	dimensionless fluid velocity (206)	σ $\boldsymbol{\tau}$	surface tension (21) viscous stress tensor in Gibbs notation (130)
$\mathbf{v}_r$	relative fluid velocity vector (156)	τ_{ij}	viscous stress tensor in index notation (130)
V	volume (54)	$\overline{\boldsymbol{\tau}}^{(t)}$	turbulent stress tensor (194)
$\mathcal{V}$	control volume fixed in space (33)	τ_0 ϕ	wall shear stress (205) gravitational potential function (40)
$\mathcal{V}_a(t)$	arbitrary volume moving in space (33)	Φ	viscous dissipation function (223)
$\mathcal{V}_m(t)$	material volume (33)	ψ	stream function (102)
$\mathbf{w}$	arbitrary velocity vector (79)	ω	angular velocity (178)
$\dot{W}$	rate of work (227)	$\boldsymbol{\omega}$	vorticity vector (152)
x, y, z	rectangular, Cartesian coor-dinates (24)	$\boldsymbol{\Omega}$	vorticity tensor in Gibbs notation (152)
X, Y, Z	dimensionless rectangular, Cartesian coordinates (164)	Ω_{ij}	vorticity tensor in index nota-tion (138)
y^+	dimensionless distance (206)		

Greek Letters

α_{ij}	direction cosine (118)
β	coefficient of expansion (13)
γ	specific gravity (55), ratio of specific heats (402)
δ	boundary layer thickness (426)
δ_{ij}	Kronecker delta (130)
ε/D	relative roughness (293)
η	length (47)
θ	angle (47)
Θ	dimensionless time (160)

Mathematical Symbols

∇	"del" vector operator (40)
∇^2	the Laplacian (154)
$\dfrac{D}{Dt}$	material derivative (78)
$\dfrac{d}{dt}$	total derivative (77)
$\dfrac{\partial}{\partial t}$	partial derivative (79)
$\langle\ \rangle$	area or volume average (109)
$\overline{}$	time average (187)

Introduction to Fluid Mechanics

Introduction

1

This chapter is devoted to a brief discussion of the fundamental postulates governing the motion of fluids, the types of flow that are to be investigated, the physical properties of fluids, and vector notation. The first five sections are qualitative and may be read quickly; however, Sec. 1.6 must be studied carefully for we will draw upon that material throughout the remaining chapters.

*1.1 The Continuum Postulate

The object of this text is to formulate the equations governing the motion of a continuum and apply them to the problem of fluid motion. In treating a fluid as a continuum we postulate that functions such as velocity, pressure, density, etc. are continuous point functions. In actual fact this is not true, for the materials we wish to study are made up of molecules. We may speak of the velocity of a molecule with some assurance that this quantity is well defined; however, the velocity at a fixed location in space is rather meaningless from the molecular point of view. We need not be concerned with this dilemma, because the cases we wish to study represent a class of problems for which the distance between molecules is so small that they represent a continuous system.

The density of a fluid may be defined as

$$\rho = \lim_{\Delta V \to 0} \left(\frac{\Delta M}{\Delta V} \right) \tag{1.1-1}$$

where ΔM is the mass contained in a small volume ΔV. As defined by Eq. 1.1-1, the density ρ might be represented by the curve shown in Fig. 1.1-1.

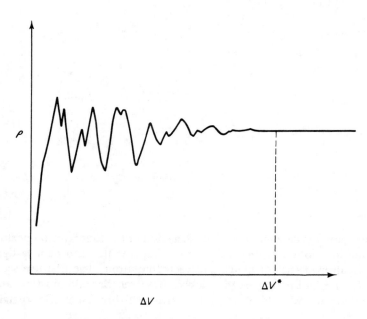

Fig. I.I-I. Density as a function of volume.

The volume ΔV^* is the same order of magnitude as the cube of the mean free path† for gases, and is comparable to the volume of a molecule for liquids. For the continuum approach to hold, we must be dealing with systems that have dimensions much larger than either the mean free path or the molecular diameter. Since both these quantities are generally quite small, we can expect satisfactory results for a great many practical situations. Two examples where the continuum approach must be used with caution are the following: the motion of a spacecraft through the upper atmosphere; the motion of a gas through the pores of a catalyst pellet such as those currently used in petroleum refining processes. In the first case, the pressure is very low; thus, the mean free path of the gaseous molecules is large (on the order of 1 ft at 70 mi from

† The mean free path is the average distance traveled by molecules between collisions.

the earth).[1] In the second case, the mean free path of the molecules may be very small (on the order of 10^{-6} cm), yet the pore size in the catalyst pellet may also be extremely small and comparable to the mean free path.[2] In both of these examples, the velocity is *not* a continuous function, and we consider these to be cases of *slip flow*. We use the term "slip flow" because there is not intimate contacting of the fluid molecules with the solid surfaces, and the velocity of the fluid at the solid-fluid interface need not be zero.

*1.2 Types of Flow

We shall examine several types of flow in this text, and the boundaries which divide them into various classes are not always clear. Some distinct differences exist, however, and it will be helpful to discuss them.

Compressible and incompressible flow

Very often a fluid is considered incompressible if its density undergoes "negligible" changes for "appreciable" changes in temperature and pressure. The words negligible and appreciable are rather vague, and they have meaning only in terms of our experience. Thus, the density of water changes by less than 5 per cent in 100°C and less than 1 per cent in 100 atm, and we are inclined to consider water as incompressible. In actual fact water is taken to be an incompressible fluid simply because the types of flows which *generally* occur with water are satisfactorily treated by the incompressible form of the equations of motion. However, if we heat a pan of water on the stove, we note that circulation patterns are set up. They occur because warm water at the bottom of the pan is less dense than the cooler water at the surface, and buoyancy effects give rise to convective flows. Although it is the nonuniform density of the fluid which causes the flow, such a flow is usually not termed "compressible," a term which general usage reserves for flows where the fluid velocity approaches or exceeds sonic velocity (i.e., the speed of sound). This situation is more likely to occur in gases where the sonic velocity is about 1100 ft/sec at normal temperatures and pressures. The "sonic boom" caused by high-speed jet aircraft is an obvious example of the rapid changes in density (and pressure) that occur at a shock wave.

Sonic velocity in water is about 4700 ft/sec; thus, we might expect that compressible flows are less likely to occur. However, the common phenomenon of "water hammer" that occurs when a valve is suddenly closed in a water

1. E. J. Opik, *Physics of Meteor Flight in the Atmosphere* (New York: Interscience Publishers, Inc., 1958), p. 13.
2. P. Emmett, ed., *Catalysis* (New York: Reinhold Publishing Corp., 1955), Vol. 2, p. 126.

line is a case of compressible flow in liquids. The point here is that we must consider whether a given *flow* may be treated as incompressible, *not* whether the *fluid* is incompressible. Compressible flows are treated in Chap. 10.

Laminar and turbulent flow

The distinction between laminar and turbulent flows is somewhat easier to make than the distinction between compressible and incompressible flows.

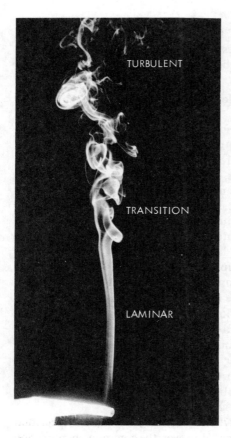

Laminar flow is characterized by smooth motion of one lamina of fluid past another, while turbulent flow is characterized by an irregular and nearly random motion superimposed on the main motion of the fluid. The two types of flow can be observed in the trail of smoke leaving the burning cigarette shown in Fig. 1.2-1. The smoke rises from the cigarette in a smooth, laminar stream for perhaps 1 or 2 in.; however, at that point it generally becomes unstable and a transition to turbulent flow takes place. This is characterized by whirls and a more random motion of the smoke stream as it rises into the air.

The transition from laminar to turbulent flow in tubes was first investigated by Osborne Reynolds,[3] and a sketch of the apparatus used by Reynolds is illustrated in Fig. 1.2-2. The system consisted essentially of a bell-mouthed glass tube into which a dye streak was injected with the water that entered the tube from a reservoir. Reynolds observed two distinct types of flow. In the first, the dye streak maintained its identity and remained in the center of the tube, although it spread slowly

Fig. 1.2-1. Laminar and turbulent flow from a burning cigarette.

3. O. Reynolds, "An Experimental Investigation of the Circumstances which Determine whether the Motion of Water Shall be Direct or Sinuous and the Law of Resistance in Parallel Channels." *Phil. Trans. Roy. Soc. (London) Ser. A*, 1883, 174: 935.

because of molecular diffusion. In the second, the dye streak was soon dispersed throughout the tube when the laminar flow that existed at the entrance of the tube underwent the transition to turbulent flow. The dispersion of the dye streak is similar in some respects to the dispersion of the thin stream of smoke given off by the cigarette. Reynolds found that the

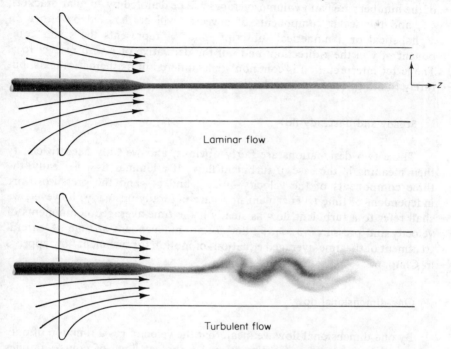

Laminar flow

Turbulent flow

Fig. 1.2-2. Reynolds experimental investigation of the transition to turbulence.

transition conditions could be correlated by a dimensionless group which is now known as the Reynolds number, defined as follows.

$$N_{\mathrm{Re}} = \frac{\rho \langle v_z \rangle D}{\mu} \tag{1.2-1}$$

where ρ = density
  $\langle v_z \rangle$ = average velocity in the z-direction
  D = tube diameter
  μ = viscosity

Reynolds found that the transition took place for values of N_{Re} of about 2100, regardless of the specific values of ρ, $\langle v_z \rangle$, D, and μ. In Chap. 5, we will be able to prove that the Reynolds number is, indeed, the governing parameter for the transition to turbulent flow.

The notation in Eq. 1.2-1 deserves some comment, for it will be used consistently throughout the text. Dimensionless numbers or groups will always be denoted by the letter N with a subscript appropriate to the name of the number; area and volume averages will be denoted by angular brackets, $\langle \rangle$; and the scalar components of a vector will be denoted by either an alphabetical or a numerical subscript. Thus v_z represents the scalar component of $\mathbf{v}$ in the z-direction, and not the derivative of v with respect to z. The latter interpretation is commonly encountered in mathematics texts, but rarely found in books on mechanics.

Steady and unsteady flow

These two designations are fairly obvious, and we only need to clarify their meaning in the case of turbulent flow. If a laminar flow is steady, the three components of the velocity—v_x, v_y, and v_z—and the pressure p are independent of time t. Turbulent flows are naturally unsteady; however, we shall refer to a turbulent flow as steady if the time-averaged components of velocity and pressure—$\bar{v}_x$, $\bar{v}_y$, $\bar{v}_z$, and $\bar{p}$—are independent of time. A careful treatment of the time-averaged equations of motion for turbulent flow appears in Chap. 6.

One-dimensional flow

By one-dimensional flow we mean that the velocity $\mathbf{v}$ is a function of only one spatial coordinate. One-dimensional turbulent flow, of course, implies that the time-averaged velocity $\bar{\mathbf{v}}$ is a function of only one spatial coordinate. The flow in the Reynolds' apparatus is one-dimensional some distance downstream from the entrance (i.e., $\mathbf{v}$ is only a function of r), but at the entrance, $\mathbf{v}$ is a function of r and z and the flow is two-dimensional. Often we approximate two- and three-dimensional flows by one-dimensional models, because the velocity field is easily determined for a one-dimensional flow.

*1.3 The Solution of Flow Problems

In attempting to formulate the equations of fluid motion, we need a clear understanding of the fundamental postulates governing this motion. The student has already made use of Newton's second law to solve problems in statics and dynamics, and it would seem natural to include it as one of the laws or fundamental postulates which govern the motion of fluids. Truesdell[4] has pointed out that the fundamental postulates of continuum mechanics are more appropriately attributed to Euler. We may state Euler's two laws of mechanics as follows.

1. The time rate of change of the momentum of a body equals the force acting on the body.
2. The time rate of change of the angular momentum (moment of momentum) of a body equals the torque acting on the body, where both the torque and the moment are taken with respect to the same fixed point.

These laws apply not only to discrete particles, but also to any arbitrary continuous body. Euler's first law is, of course, the generalization of Newton's second law which states:[†]

> "The change in motion is proportional to the motive force impressed, and it takes place along the right line in which the force is impressed."

Euler's second law is very definitely a separate fundamental postulate of continuum mechanics; however, this concept is not always clearly understood. Confusion arises because the second law may be derived from the first law if all forces are continuous functions of mass (i.e., "body forces") and all torques are the moments of these body forces. When shear stresses are present, however, the second law is independent of the first.

While Euler's first law is most often referred to and known as Newton's second law of motion, its development can actually be attributed to the efforts of a number of scientists and engineers starting with Newton and ending with Euler. To avoid confusion, we shall refer to these two laws as the *linear momentum principle* and the *angular momentum principle*.

In addition to the two laws of mechanics, we must also make use of the principles of *conservation of mass* and *conservation of energy* to solve problems of fluid motion. The latter principle is required only when the flow is compressible; we shall not encounter this condition until Chap. 10. For reasons which will become apparent when we explore the various forms of these fundamental postulates, we often refer to the two laws of mechanics as the principles of conservation of momentum and conservation of angular momentum, or the balance of momentum and the balance of angular momentum. According to the linear momentum principle, momentum is not conserved for it may increase or decrease depending upon the force that acts upon

---

4. C. Truesdell, "A Program toward Rediscovering the Rational Mechanics of the Age of Reason," *Archives for the History of Exact Science*, 1961, 1:31.

† See Ref. 4, page 6.

the body; however, to apply a force to a body is to supply momentum to the body, and with this in mind we might state these laws as follows:

$$\begin{Bmatrix} \text{the time rate of} \\ \text{change of } \textit{momentum} \\ \text{of the body} \end{Bmatrix} = \begin{Bmatrix} \text{the rate at which } \textit{momentum} \\ \text{is supplied to the body (by} \\ \text{application of a force)} \end{Bmatrix} \qquad (1.3\text{-}1)$$

$$\begin{Bmatrix} \text{the time rate of} \\ \text{change of angular} \\ \text{momentum of the body} \end{Bmatrix} = \begin{Bmatrix} \text{the rate at which } \textit{angular} \\ \textit{momentum} \text{ is supplied to the} \\ \text{body (by application of a torque)} \end{Bmatrix} \qquad (1.3\text{-}2)$$

In both Eqs. 1.3-1 and 1.3-2 the word "body" refers to a fixed quantity of material; therefore, a body always contains the same mass points and is sometimes referred to as a "system." If we compare these equations with the principle of conservation of energy, which states

$$\begin{Bmatrix} \text{the time rate of change} \\ \text{of } \textit{energy} \text{ of the body} \end{Bmatrix} = \begin{Bmatrix} \text{the rate at which } \textit{energy} \\ \text{is supplied to the body} \end{Bmatrix} \qquad (1.3\text{-}3)$$

or the principle of conservation of mass,

$$\begin{Bmatrix} \text{the time rate of change} \\ \text{of } \textit{mass} \text{ of the body} \end{Bmatrix} = \begin{Bmatrix} \text{the rate at which } \textit{mass} \\ \text{is supplied to the body} \end{Bmatrix} \qquad (1.3\text{-}4)$$

we see that the words "mass," "energy," "momentum," and "angular momentum" are interchangeable. For this reason we often speak of the principles of conservation of mass, energy, momentum, and angular momentum, and we make use of mass balances, energy balances, and momentum balances to solve engineering problems. Although the fundamental postulates appear to be very similar when stated in words, we must remember that Eqs. 1.3-1 and 1.3-2 are actually *vector* equations, whereas Eqs. 1.3-3 and 1.3-4 represent *scalar* equations.

The solution of problems only starts with the fundamental postulates, and the four main tools which an engineer uses to reach a final solution are as follows:

1. the fundamental postulates;
2. mathematical analysis;
3. constitutive equations, equations of state, and other experimental information;
4. intuition.

The fundamental postulates are the easiest to deal with because they are comparatively well understood and limited in number. The mathematical analysis required to put these fundamental postulates into useable form is not excessively difficult and has wide applications. For this reason, the student's effort to understand the first two items has applications far beyond the area of fluid mechanics. Constitutive equations describe the response of materials to applied *forces*. Thus Hooke's law, which relates the strain to the applied stress, is a constitutive equation for linearly elastic materials. Newton's law of viscosity (rate of strain proportional to stress), Fourier's law of heat conduction (heat flux proportional to temperature gradient), and Ohm's law (electrical current proportional to potential gradient) are all constitutive equations describing idealized linear behavior. It is unfortunate that these relationships are called "laws" for they are not laws in the sense that the linear momentum principle is a law. The linear momentum principle applies to *all* materials, while constitutive equations such as Hooke's law and Newton's law are merely "rules" which describe the behavior of a particular material. Constitutive equations are generally formulated on the basis of experimental observation, although kinetic theory can be used to derive Newton's law of viscosity for dilute gases.

An equation of state determines the relationship of the thermodynamic pressure, the density, and the temperature. The ideal gas law,

$$pV = n\mathscr{R}T \tag{1.3-5}$$

is a well-known example of an equation of state; however, many other equations of state are available for describing the relationship between pressure and density for nonideal gases and for liquids. Equations of state are determined by experimental observation, although once again the ideal gas law may be derived by kinetic theory for gases at low pressures.

The last category of knowledge that we require in order to solve problems is intuition. In general, simple problems can be solved with practically no intuition, while the more complex problems encountered later in this text require a great deal to obtain even an approximate solution. Birkhoff[5] has written the following regarding intuition and problem solving:

> "...the boundary value problems of rational hydrodynamics are exceedingly difficult, and progress would have been much slower if rigorous mathematics had not been supplemented by various *plausible intuitive hypotheses*. Of these, the following have been especially suggestive:
> I. Intuition suffices for determining which physical variables require consideration.
> II. Small causes produce small effects and infinitesimal causes produce infinitesimal effects.
> III. Symmetric causes produce effects with the same symmetry.
> IV. The flow topology [i.e., the salient characteristics of the flow field] can be guessed by intuition."

5. G. Birkhoff, *Hydrodynamics, A Study in Logic, Fact, and Similitude* (Princeton, N.J.: Princeton University Press, 1960), p. 4.

He goes on to say, "The preceding plausible assumptions are usually made tacitly as a matter of course." Although Birkhoff devotes the first two chapters of his book to an examination of the fallibility of these assumptions, he does not imply that we should refrain from using intuition in solving fluid mechanics problems. Rather he implies that we should understand clearly when intuition is being used.

Throughout this text it will be pointed out to the student how easy it is to make use of these intuitive hypotheses without ever realizing that it is being done. In attacking a problem it is most important to realize clearly in what area one is working, and the student should constantly ask himself the following questions. Am I working with a fundamental postulate at this point? Is this step simply mathematical analysis? Do I need some experimental information here, or is this step I am now making purely intuitive? If it is intuitive, then go on with it, but do not be surprised if the "wrong" answer is obtained. Intuition is only acquired by experience, and that experience requires solving problems and getting the wrong answer in addition to solving problems and getting the right answer.

1.4 Units

The simplest manner of handling units is to define mass, length, and time arbitrarily, and then use the linear momentum principle to define a unit of force. In the cgs system,

$$M = \text{mass (g)}$$
$$\mathbf{v} = \text{velocity (cm/sec)}$$
$$t = \text{time (sec)}$$

We may write Eq. 1.3-1 as

$$\frac{d}{dt}(M\mathbf{v}) = \mathbf{F} \tag{1.4-1}$$

where $M\mathbf{v}$ is the momentum of the body, and $\mathbf{F}$ is the force acting on the body.† We may use Eq. 1.4-1 to define a "dyne" as the unit of force required to give 1 g an acceleration of 1 cm/sec².

$$\frac{d}{dt}(M\mathbf{v}) = \mathbf{F} \tag{1.4-2}$$
$$(1 \text{ g-cm/sec}^2 = 1 \text{ dyne})$$

Note that there is a simple "one-to-one" correspondence between the various terms in the equation; thus, *one* unit of mass multiplied by *one* unit of

† Note that throughout the text boldface type is one of the methods used to indicate vectors.

acceleration gives rise to *one* unit of force. We could speak of force in terms of g-cm/sec², but it is far more convenient to refer to force in terms of dynes. Note that "gram" is a measure of mass, and "dyne" is a measure of force—a wise choice of words. In the English system of units, confusion arises because we make use of the word "pound" to indicate both mass and force—surely an unfortunate choice of words. Let us consider the English system of units to consist of pounds-mass (lb_m), feet (ft), and seconds (sec). In a manner analogous to the cgs system we may define a unit of force as,

$$\frac{d}{dt}(M\mathbf{v}) = \mathbf{F}$$

(1.4-3)

$$(1\ lb_m\text{-ft/sec}^2 = 1\ \text{poundal})$$

Thus, the force required to give a mass of 1 lb_m an acceleration of 1 ft/sec² is 1 poundal; however, we generally do not use the poundal as a unit of force. We choose to work instead with that force exerted by the earth's gravitational field on 1 pound-mass. Thus,

$$\text{unit of force} = (1\ lb_m)\,(32.2\ \text{ft/sec}^2)$$

$$= 32.2\ lb_m\text{-ft/sec}^2$$

(1.4-4)

We call this unit of force, 1 pound-force (lb_f)

$$1\ lb_f = 32.2\ lb_m\text{-ft/sec}^2$$

(1.4-5)

If we wish to use as our units, pound-force, pound-mass, foot, and second, Eq. 1.4-3 must be rewritten

$$\frac{1}{g_c}\frac{d}{dt}(M\mathbf{v}) = \mathbf{F}$$

(1.4-6)

where $g_c = 32.2\ lb_m\text{-ft/}lb_f\text{-sec}^2$

Note that it is simply the lack of a one-to-one correspondence between mass, acceleration, and force which leads to the conversion factor, g_c. Throughout the remainder of this text we will not use the preceding form but will always work in absolute units (dyne, gram, centimeter, second; or poundal, pound-mass, foot, second). In working with this set of units, the conversion factor g_c is not incorporated into the equations written in the text; therefore, the equations take a somewhat simpler form. However, final answers are generally required in pounds-force rather than poundals, and we must use conversion factors to accomplish this change of units. It is useful to note from Eq. 1.4-5 that

$$1 = 32.2\ lb_m\text{-ft/}lb_f\text{-sec}^2$$

Table 1.4-1
UNITS AND CONVERSION FACTORS

Mass	Length	Time
1 lb_m = 453.6 g	1 in. = 2.54 cm	1 min = 60 sec
1 ton (short) = 2000 lb_m	1 ft = 12 in.	1 hr = 60 min
1 ton (long) = 2240 lb_m	1 yd = 3 ft	1 day = 24 hr
1 kg = 1000 g	1 mi = 5280 ft	
1 slug = 32.2 lb_m	1 angstrom (Å) = 10^{-8} cm	
	1 micron (μ) = 10^{-4} cm	

Force	Area	Volume
1 dyne =	1 in.^{2} = 6.45 cm^2	1 in.^{3} = 16.4 cm^3
2.25 $\times$ 10^{-6} lb_f	1 ft^2 = 144 in.^{2}	1 ft^3 = 1728 in.^{3}
1 dyne = 7.23 $\times$ 10^{-5}	1 acre = 4.35 $\times$ 10^4 ft^2	1 gal = 231 in.^{3}
poundal		1 qt (dry) = 1101 cm^3
		1 qt (liquid) = 0.25 gal
		1 bl = 31.5 gal

Pressure	Viscosity	Power
1 atm = 14.7 lb_f/in.^{2}	1 poise = 1 g/cm-sec	1 hp = 3.3 $\times$ 10^4 lb_f-ft/min
1 atm = 29.9 in. of Hg	1 poise = 6.72 $\times$ 10^{-2}	1 lb_f-ft/min = 1.29 $\times$ 10^{-3}Btu/min
1 atm = 33.8 ft of H_2O	lb_m/ft-sec	1 Btu (39°F) = 1055 watt-sec
1 atm = 1.013 $\times$ 10^6	1 poise = 10^2 centipoise	
dyne/cm^2		

and, similarly,

$$1 = 12 \text{ in./ft}$$
$$1 = 1.8°F/°C$$
$$1 = 3600 \text{ sec/hr}$$
etc.

Since $g_c = 32.2$ lb_m-ft/lb_f-sec^2 is also equal to unity (dimensionless), we may multiply any quantity by this number without changing its value—i.e., multiplication by one does not change the value of the quantity.

Table 1.4-1 lists a variety of conversion factors from one set of units to another. A more thorough set of conversion tables can be obtained in the *Handbook of Chemistry and Physics.*[6]

*1.5 Fluid Properties

In the study of single-phase incompressible flow, we need know only the density ρ and the viscosity μ if the fluid is Newtonian. For non-Newtonian fluids, we require additional parameters to characterize the viscous behavior of the fluid.

6. C. D. Hodgman, ed., *Handbook of Chemistry and Physics* (Cleveland, Ohio: Chemical Rubber Publishing Co., 1956).

Density

Table 1.5-1 lists the physical properties of some common liquids. The densities (except that for mercury), range from 50 to 100 lb_m/ft^3. Since the

Table 1.5-1

APPROXIMATE PHYSICAL PROPERTIES OF SOME COMMON LIQUIDS

Substance	T, °F	ρ, lb_m/ft^3	κ, atm^{-1}	β, °K^{-1}
Ethyl alcohol	68	49.2	120×10^{-6}	1.12×10^{-3}
Benzene	68	54.8	90×10^{-6}	1.20×10^{-3}
Carbon tetrachloride	68	128	98×10^{-6}	1.24×10^{-3}
Mercury	68	846	3.9×10^{-6}	0.18×10^{-3}
SAE 30 oil	100	57.5	50×10^{-6}	0.90×10^{-3}
Water	60	62.4	52×10^{-6}	0.21×10^{-3}

compressibility κ, defined as

$$\kappa = \frac{1}{\rho}\left(\frac{\partial \rho}{\partial p}\right)_T \tag{1.5-1}$$

and the coefficient of expansion β, defined as

$$\beta = -\frac{1}{\rho}\left(\frac{\partial \rho}{\partial T}\right)_p \tag{1.5-2}$$

are so small for liquids, we generally do not need to consider the effect of temperature and pressure on density. On the other hand, the density of gases depends strongly on the temperature and pressure. At standard conditions (298°K and 1 atm), the density, compressibility, and coefficient of expansion can be estimated by the ideal gas law as

$$\rho = \frac{p(MW)}{\mathscr{R}T} \tag{1.5-3a}$$

$$\kappa = \frac{1}{p} \tag{1.5-3b}$$

$$\beta = \frac{1}{T} \tag{1.5-3c}$$

where MW is the molecular weight.

Whenever the temperature or pressure are close to the critical values—i.e., the pressure and temperature at the *critical point*—the deviation from ideal gas behavior becomes significant and either experimental data or more sophisticated correlations must be used. There is a great deal of theoretical and experimental information pertaining to the densities and viscosities of gases as a function of pressure and temperature. A summary of this information has been compiled by Reid and Sherwood[7] and an elaborate treatment of the subject is given by Hirschfelder, Curtiss, and Bird.[8]

Viscosity

The distinctive mechanical characteristic of a fluid is that it deforms continuously under the action of a shear stress. Solids, of course, suffer a deformation (or "strain") under the action of a shear stress; however, this deformation is independent of time except for the very slow changes from "creep" phenomena. Fluids, on the other hand, will continue to deform as long as the shear stress is applied.

The rate at which a fluid deforms is given by the rate of change in distance between two neighboring points moving with the fluid divided by the distance between the points. Thus, the rate of deformation is given by the "change in length per unit length per unit time." In solid mechanics, the change in length per unit length is called the *strain*; it is therefore natural to refer to the rate of deformation as the *rate of strain*. However, the student should be forewarned that the terms rate of strain, strain rate, and shear rate (used especially with simple shearing flows) may all be used in discussing the rate of deformation of a fluid.

For Newtonian fluids there is a simple linear relationship between the applied shear stress and the rate of strain. The coefficient relating the shear stress and the rate of strain is called the *coefficient of viscosity* or, more commonly, "the viscosity." The nature of viscosity can best be introduced by describing an experiment often performed to measure the coefficient of viscosity, μ. Consider the fluid motion between two long parallel plates such as those illustrated in Fig. 1.5-1. One of the plates is fixed and the other is

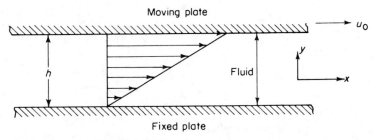

Fig. I.5-I. Velocity distribution between two parallel plates.

7. R. C. Reid and T. K. Sherwood, *The Properties of Gases and Liquids* (New York: McGraw-Hill Book Co., Inc., 1958).

8. J. O. Hirschfelder, C. S. Curtiss, and R. B. Bird, *Molecular Theory of Gases and Liquids* (New York: John Wiley and Sons, Inc., 1954).

moving at a constant velocity u_0 giving rise to the simple shearing flow indicated. This idealized flow can be approximated quite closely in a Couette viscometer, which consists of a pair of coaxial cylinders arranged as illustrated in Fig. 1.5-2. The inner cylinder is fixed and a torque is applied to the outer cylinder causing it to rotate at a steady rate. As h/r_0 becomes small, the curvature of the annular region can be neglected and the flow in a Couette viscometer resembles the rectilinear flow shown in Fig. 1.5-1.

For many fluids, experiments of this kind lead to results similar to those shown in Fig. 1.5-3, where the force per unit area, F/A, required to maintain the motion is plotted as a function of the velocity u_0 divided by the plate spacing h. In a Couette viscometer, the force F is given by the

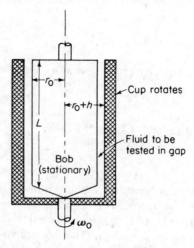

Fig. 1.5-2. Couette viscometer.

applied torque divided by the lever arm $r_0 + h$, and the area A is the area of the outer cylinder. These results may be expressed as

$$\frac{F}{A} = \mu\left(\frac{u_0}{h}\right) \qquad (1.5\text{-}4)$$

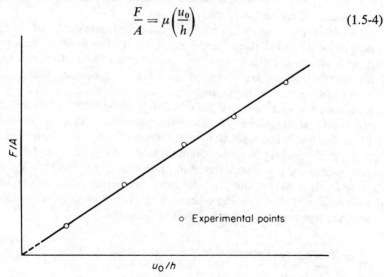

Fig. 1.5-3. Typical results from a Couette viscometer experiment.

where μ is the slope of the line drawn through the experimental points. We will find it convenient to write the force per unit area acting on a surface for which y is constant (henceforth referred to as the y-surface) in the x-direction as

$$\frac{F}{A} = T_{yx} \tag{1.5-5}$$

The velocity gradient may be expressed as a derivative

$$\frac{u_0}{h} = \frac{dv_x}{dy} \tag{1.5-6}$$

and Eq. 1.5-4 takes the form

$$T_{yx} = \mu \frac{dv_x}{dy} \tag{1.5-7}$$

which is Newton's law of viscosity for this particular simple flow.

The subscripts used here deserve some attention. Throughout the text, T with two subscripts will be used to denote the total stress (force per unit area) acting on a surface. The first subscript will indicate the surface upon which the stress is acting; the second will indicate the direction of the stress. Thus, T_{yx} is the stress acting on the y-surface in the x-direction, while T_{xy} is the stress acting on the x-surface in the y-direction. The scalar components of a vector such as the velocity vector $\mathbf{v}$ may be denoted by alphabetic subscripts. Thus, v_x, v_y, and v_z represent the components of the velocity vector in the x-, y-, and z-directions, respectively.

The viscosity of a wide variety of commonly encountered fluids is presented as a function of temperature in Fig. 1.5-4. The fluids we may encounter in practice have viscosities ranging over several orders of magnitude. Common lubricating oils are in the range of 100 centipoise. Water, kerosene, gasoline, and other similar fluids have viscosities on the order of 1 centipoise. Gases such as air, saturated steam, and hydrogen have viscosities nearly three orders of magnitude less than that of water. As we shall see in later studies, the kinematic viscosity, or the ratio of viscosity to the density, is a key physical property in understanding fluid motion. In Fig. 1.5-5, the kinematic viscosity is given as a function of temperature. Here we see that such diverse fluids as water and air have nearly the same order of magnitude for the kinematic viscosity, and, in general, the range of kinematic viscosities is somewhat less than that of the absolute viscosity.

Non-Newtonian fluids

Fluids which exhibit a linear relationship between the shear stress T_{yx} and the shear rate (dv_x/dy) are called Newtonian fluids. Many fluids exhibit

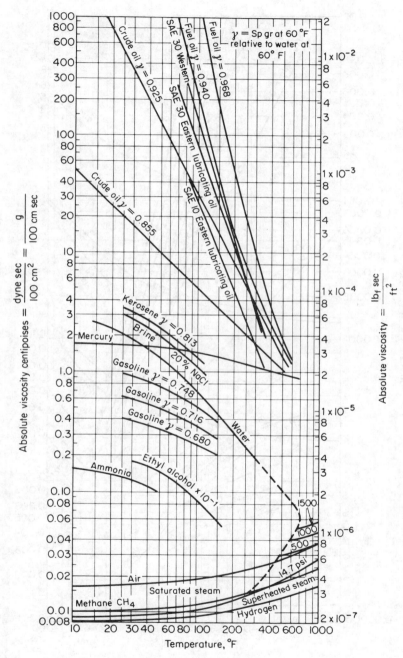

Fig. 1.5-4. Viscosity of fluids.

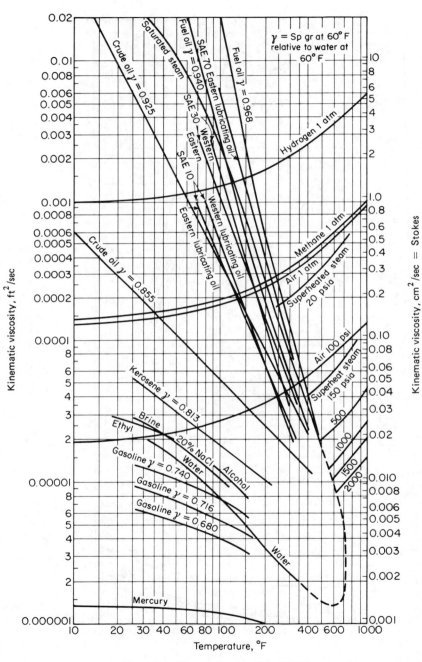

Fig. 1.5-5. Kinematic viscosity of fluids.

this type of behavior; however, there is an important class of fluids which do not. These are called non-Newtonian fluids, and the shear stress-shear rate relationship for some fluids of this type is indicated in Fig. 1.5-6.

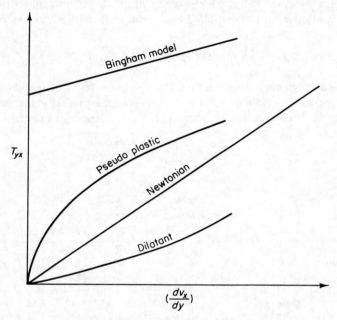

Fig. 1.5-6. Behavior of non-Newtonian fluids.

The curves shown in Fig. 1.5-6 indicate just a few of the many types of non-Newtonian fluid behavior which have been observed experimentally. The slope of these curves is often called the apparent viscosity, and denoted by μ_{app}.

The Bingham model

The Bingham model describes fluids which possess a *yield stress*, i.e., the material will not deform unless the magnitude of the shear stress exceeds some critical value, T_0. Thus, the shear stress-shear rate relationship is given by

$$T_{yx} = \left(\mu_0 + \frac{T_0}{\left| \dfrac{dv_x}{dy} \right|} \right) \frac{dv_x}{dy} \qquad \text{if} \quad |T_{yx}| > T_0 \qquad (1.5\text{-}8a)$$

$$\frac{dv_x}{dy} = 0 \qquad \text{if} \quad |T_{yx}| \leq T_0 \qquad (1.5\text{-}8b)$$

Although no real fluids are described exactly by the Bingham model, several fit the model reasonably well. Ordinary paint behaves somewhat like a Bingham fluid. This characteristic is beneficial, for it means that there is a critical film thickness below which paint will no longer flow under the action of gravity, allowing it to be applied to vertical walls without excessive runoff.

The Ostwald-de Wael model ("power-law" fluid)

Fluids for which the apparent viscosity decreases with increasing shear rate are called *pseudoplastic*. When the apparent viscosity increases with shear rate the fluid is called *dilatant*. This type of behavior may be described by

$$T_{yx} = m \left| \frac{dv_x}{dy} \right|^{n-1} \frac{dv_x}{dy} \qquad (1.5\text{-}9)$$

Table 1.5-3

BINGHAM MODEL PARAMETERS[a]

Fluid	T_0, lbf/ft²	μ_0, lbf-sec/ft²
Water	0	2.09×10^{-5}
Honey	1.2	2.40×10^{-1}
Mayonnaise	0.8	1.32×10^{-2}
Ketchup	0.3	1.74×10^{-3}
Enamels, glossy	0–0.06	$2.93 \times 10^{-3} - 8.15 \times 10^{-3}$
Enamels, semiglossy	0.10–0.25	$2.09 \times 10^{-3} - 7.32 \times 10^{-3}$
Flat or matte paints	0.04–0.21	$1.25 \times 10^{-3} - 2.09 \times 10^{-3}$
Water-dispersible paints	0.02–0.21	$0.42 \times 10^{-3} - 2.93 \times 10^{-3}$
Varnishes	0	$1.88 \times 10^{-3} - 6.06 \times 10^{-3}$

[a] Data taken from F. R. Eirich, ed., *Rheology—Theory and Practice* (New York: Academic Press, 1960), Vol. 3, Chap. 6.

When $n = 1$, this equation reduces to Newton's law of viscosity with $m = \mu$. If $n < 1$, it describes a pseudoplastic fluid, and if $n > 1$, the behavior is dilatant. Some representative values of the Bingham model parameters and the Ostwald-de Wael model parameters are given in Tables 1.5-3 and 4.

Table 1.5-4

OSTWALD-DE WAEL MODEL PARAMETERS[a]

Fluid	Composition by Weight, per cent	m, lbf-secⁿ/ft²	n (dimensionless)
Carboxymethyl cellulose in water	3.0	0.194	0.566
Lime in water	33.0	0.150	0.171
Napalm in kerosene	10	0.089	0.52
Paper pulp	4	0.418	0.575

[a] Data taken from R. B. Bird, W. E. Stewart, and E. N. Lightfoot, *Transport Phenomena* (New York: John Wiley and Sons, Inc., 1960).

The material presented in this section has been brief, but sufficient information has been given for the student to solve some simple non-Newtonian laminar flow problems. Several sources[9-11] are available which provide a thorough discussion of non-Newtonian fluids.

Surface tension

For two phase flows, the surface tension σ may be an important physical property; however, situations where surface tension plays a significant role will not be covered in this text. Even so, it is worthwhile to discuss the subject briefly.

The molecules at an interface between two fluids exist in a state different from that of the molecules in the interior of the fluid. At an air-water interface, for example, the water molecules are (on the average) surrounded by water molecules on only one side, whereas the interior molecules are completely surrounded. Consequently, the configurational energy of the surface molecules differs from that of the interior molecules and the surface exists in a state of tension. This tension is known as the surface or interfacial tension and has units of force per length. A force balance on the spherical drop shown in Fig. 1.5-7 indicates that the pressure in the interior of the drop

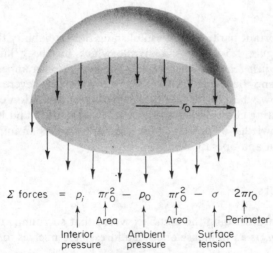

$$\Sigma \text{ forces} = p_i \;\; \pi r_0^2 \;-\; p_0 \;\; \pi r_0^2 \;-\; \sigma \;\; 2\pi r_0$$

	Area		Area		Perimeter
Interior pressure		Ambient pressure		Surface tension	

Fig. 1.5-7. Force balance on a spherical drop.

9. A. B. Metzner, *Advances in Chemical Engineering* (New York: Academic Press, 1960), Vol. 1.

10. R. B. Bird, W. E. Stewart, and E. N. Lightfoot, *Transport Phenomena* (New York: John Wiley and Sons, Inc., 1960), Chaps. 1, 3.

11. A. Fredrickson, *Principles and Applications of Rheology* (Englewood Cliffs, N.J.: Prentice-Hall, Inc., 1964).

p_i is given by

$$p_i = p_0 + \frac{2\sigma}{r_0} \qquad (1.5\text{-}10)$$

where p_0 = ambient pressure

r_0 = radius of the drop

For an arbitrary surface it can be shown[12] that the pressure "jump" or discontinuity is

$$\Delta p = \sigma\left(\frac{1}{r_1} + \frac{1}{r_2}\right) \qquad (1.5\text{-}11)$$

where r_1 and r_2 are the principal radii of curvature. There are some fascinating and important situations where surface tension effects dominate the fluid motion. These cases are best illustrated by the brilliant movie prepared by Professor L. Trefethen,[13] which is both educational and entertaining.

Vapor pressure

Under some conditions, the fluid pressure can become less than the vapor pressure,† p_{vp}, and cavitation may occur. The most common cases are in high-speed pumps and in the wake of a bluff body, such as that shown in Fig. 1.5-8. The cavitation number, N_{ca}, is defined as,

$$N_{\text{ca}} = \frac{p_0 - p_{vp}}{\frac{1}{2}\rho u_0^2} \qquad (1.5\text{-}12)$$

and is an important parameter in establishing the probability that cavitation will occur. Figure 1.5-8 shows a missile which has been launched under water and has just reached the surface. The cavitation numbers range from 1.10 to 0.054, and the results indicate that we can expect severe cavitation for this type of flow when N_{ca} is less than 0.10. Since cavitation can drastically alter the operating characteristics of a centrifugal pump[14] and lead to serious corrosion, knowledge of the vapor pressure of a fluid is an important factor in pump design and operation.

*1.6 Vectors

The task of describing the complex world that surrounds us in terms of *abstract symbols* is an immense one. In addressing ourselves to this problem,

12. R. Aris, *Vectors, Tensors, and the Basic Equations of Fluid Mechanics* (Englewood Cliffs, N.J.: Prentice-Hall, Inc., 1962), Chap. 10.

13. L. Trefethen, "Surface Tension in Fluid Mechanics," distributed by Educational Services, Inc., 47 Galen St., Watertown, Mass. 02172.

† The vapor pressure is the pressure exerted by the vapor in equilibrium with the liquid. Thus, the vapor pressure of water at 100°F is 0.065 atm, and at 212°F it is 1.00 atm.

14. R. H. Sabersky and A. J. Acosta, *Fluid Flow—A First Course in Fluid Mechanics* (New York: The Macmillan Company, 1964), Chap. 10.

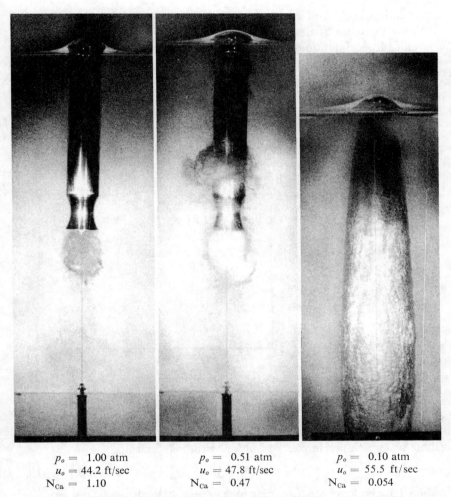

$p_o = 1.00$ atm	$p_o = 0.51$ atm	$p_o = 0.10$ atm
$u_o = 44.2$ ft/sec	$u_o = 47.8$ ft/sec	$u_o = 55.5$ ft/sec
$N_{Ca} = 1.10$	$N_{Ca} = 0.47$	$N_{Ca} = 0.054$

Fig. 1.5-8. Cavitation behind an underwater missile. Photographs courtesy of U.S. Naval Ordnance, Pasadena, Calif. For a detailed discussion see NAVWEPS Report 7735, Part 1, *Water-Exit Behavior of Missiles*, by J. G. Waugh and G. W. Stubstad.

it is wise to use symbols which contain as much information as possible and which relate this information to the physical world as closely as possible. Inasmuch as velocity is a quantity having both magnitude and direction (a vector), we choose a notation which symbolizes this fact and represent the velocity as **v**. Instead of using boldface type† to represent a vector, we could just as well place an arrow over the symbol, $\vec{v}$, or mark it with an asterisk, v^*, etc. Use of boldface type is the traditional method of communicating

† The use of boldface type to indicate vectors is known as Gibbs notation.

information, and, like Pavlov's dogs, we respond to a symbol in boldface type with the thought, "It's a vector."

Our physical notion of a vector is that of a directed line segment, such as that illustrated in Fig. 1.6-1. The vector **v** may be represented in terms of its

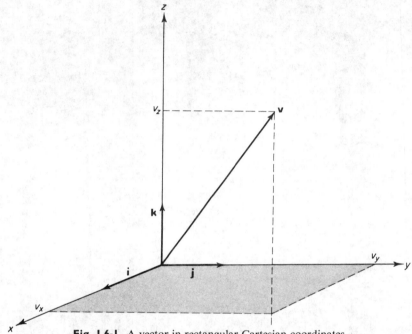

Fig. 1.6-1. A vector in rectangular Cartesian coordinates.

three scalar components v_x, v_y, and v_z by the relationship

$$\mathbf{v} = \mathbf{i}v_x + \mathbf{j}v_y + \mathbf{k}v_z \tag{1.6-1}$$

where **i, j**, and **k** are the three unit base vectors. The three scalar components are the projections of **v** on the three coordinate axes. The scalar (or dot) product between two vectors, **A** and **B**, is defined as

$$\mathbf{A} \cdot \mathbf{B} = AB \cos \theta \tag{1.6-2}$$

where A and B are the magnitudes of the two vectors, and θ is the angle between them. The scalar product of an arbitrary vector and a unit vector yields the projection of the vector on a line defined by the unit vector. For example,

$$\mathbf{v} \cdot \mathbf{i} = v \cos \theta_{vx} = v_x \tag{1.6-3}$$

where θ_{vx} is the angle between the vector **v** and the x-axis.

Aside from the physical significance of a directed line segment, a vector has certain definite transformation properties. These are best examined in two-dimensional form because the algebraic effort associated with a fully three-dimensional rotation can obscure the analysis. A vector in two dimensions is shown in Fig. 1.6-2, and the scalar components are noted for both the

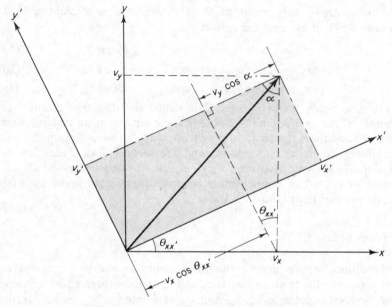

Fig. 1.6-2. Transformation of a vector.

x,y-coordinate system, and the rotated coordinates, x', y'. The four angles associated with the transformation are given by the following expressions:

1. $\theta_{xx'}$, angle between the x-coordinate axis and the x'-coordinate axis;
2. $\theta_{yx'}$, angle between the y-coordinate axis and the x'-coordinate axis;
3. $\theta_{xy'}$, angle between the x-coordinate axis and the y'-coordinate axis;
4. $\theta_{yy'}$, angle between the y-coordinate axis and the y'-coordinate axis.

The subscripts of θ obviously have a definite meaning, and they will be helpful in constructing a compact formulation of the transformation law for vectors. By the construction shown in Fig. 1.6-2 we may write,

$$v_x' = v_x \cos \theta_{xx'} + v_y \cos \alpha \qquad (1.6\text{-}4)$$

and by simple geometrical considerations, the angle α may be expressed

$$\alpha = \frac{\pi}{2} - \theta_{xx'} = \theta_{yx'} \qquad (1.6\text{-}5)$$

Substitution of Eq. 1.6-5 into Eq. 1.6-4 yields

$$v_x' = v_x \cos \theta_{xx'} + v_y \cos \theta_{yx'} \qquad (1.6\text{-}6a)$$

An expression for v_y' may be derived in a similar manner.

$$v_y' = v_x \cos \theta_{xy'} + v_y \cos \theta_{yy'} \qquad (1.6\text{-}6b)$$

The extension of this result to three dimensions is straightforward but tedious; we shall list only the results.

$$v_x' = v_x \cos \theta_{xx'} + v_y \cos \theta_{yx'} + v_z \cos \theta_{zx'} \qquad (1.6\text{-}7a)$$

$$v_y' = v_x \cos \theta_{xy'} + v_y \cos \theta_{yy'} + v_z \cos \theta_{zy'} \qquad (1.6\text{-}7b)$$

$$v_z' = v_x \cos \theta_{xz'} + v_y \cos \theta_{yz'} + v_z \cos \theta_{zz'} \qquad (1.6\text{-}7c)$$

The terms, $\cos \theta_{xx'}$, $\cos \theta_{zy'}$, etc., are called the direction cosines for the rotation, $x, y, z \rightarrow x', y', z'$. We note in these equations an ordered arrangement of subscripts, the first always identical to the subscript on the velocity component in the x, y, z system, and the second always identical to the subscript on the velocity in the x', y', z' system. This order will allow us to express Eqs. 1.6-7 in a much more compact form if we make use of index notation rather than Gibbs notation.

Index notation

Traditionally, we denote the three coordinate axes of a rectangular Cartesian coordinate system as x, y, and z, and the three scalar components of the velocity vector as v_x, v_y, and v_z. It would be just as satisfactory to denote the coordinate axes as x_1, x_2, and x_3, and the scalar components as v_1, v_2, and v_3. Similarly, the base vectors can be expressed as

$$\mathbf{e}_{(1)} = \mathbf{i} \qquad (1.6\text{-}8a)$$

$$\mathbf{e}_{(2)} = \mathbf{j} \qquad (1.6\text{-}8b)$$

$$\mathbf{e}_{(3)} = \mathbf{k} \qquad (1.6\text{-}8c)$$

Using this notation, we may express the vector $\mathbf{v}$ as

$$\mathbf{v} = \mathbf{i}v_x + \mathbf{j}v_y + \mathbf{k}v_z = \mathbf{e}_{(1)}v_1 + \mathbf{e}_{(2)}v_2 + \mathbf{e}_{(3)}v_3 \qquad (1.6\text{-}9)$$

Use of numerical subscripts allows us to express a vector in terms of its scalar components and base vectors as

$$\mathbf{v} = \sum_{i=1}^{3} \mathbf{e}_{(i)}v_i \qquad (1.6\text{-}10)$$

Further simplification results if we accept the convention that repeated subscripts (or *indices*, as the subscripts i are called) are summed from 1 to 3. This is called the *summation convention*, and allows us to write Eq. 1.6-10 as

$$\mathbf{v} = \mathbf{e}_{(i)}v_i \qquad (1.6\text{-}11)$$

Index notation is most useful in dealing directly with the scalar components of vectors. For example, the use of numerical subscripts allows us to express Eqs. 1.6-7 as

$$v_1' = v_1 \cos \theta_{11} + v_2 \cos \theta_{21} + v_3 \cos \theta_{31} \qquad (1.6\text{-}12a)$$

$$v_2' = v_1 \cos \theta_{12} + v_2 \cos \theta_{22} + v_3 \cos \theta_{32} \qquad (1.6\text{-}12b)$$

$$v_3' = v_1 \cos \theta_{13} + v_2 \cos \theta_{23} + v_3 \cos \theta_{33} \qquad (1.6\text{-}12c)$$

where it is understood that the second subscript on θ refers to the primed (') coordinate system. The summation convention can be used to reduce Eqs. 1.6-12 to a more compact form.

$$v_1' = v_i \cos \theta_{i1} \qquad (1.6\text{-}13a)$$

$$v_2' = v_i \cos \theta_{i2} \qquad (1.6\text{-}13b)$$

$$v_3' = v_i \cos \theta_{i3} \qquad (1.6\text{-}13c)$$

Although i was used as the repeated index in each case, any index—such as k, j, n, etc.—could have been used to obtain the same result. Since a repeated index may be represented by any letter, it is often called a *dummy index*. A single, or unrepeated, index is called a *free index*, and it may assume any value from 1 to 3. Using the convention for a free index, we can simplify Eqs. 1.6-13 further by writing

$$v_j' = v_i \cos \theta_{ij} \qquad (1.6\text{-}14)$$

Certainly Eq. 1.6-14 is a far more compact representation of the information presented in Eqs. 1.6-12; however, our objective in introducing this notation is not to produce a "slick" method of writing equations. In the treatment of stress (Chap. 4), in Newton's law of viscosity (Chap. 5), and in the mechanical energy equation (Chap. 7), we shall find index notation invaluable, primarily because it saves us from getting bogged down in a ponderous algebraic effort.

In Gibbs notation, the velocity vector would be expressed as $\mathbf{v}$; however, index notation may be used to express the same vector as v_i. The point to be remembered here is that the *symbol* $\mathbf{v}$ represents three scalar components relative to the x,y,z-coordinate system, and we can represent these three scalar components just as well by the symbol v_i (or v_j, etc.). The advantage of Gibbs notation is that by tradition (certainly not by logic) it gives the feeling of a directed quantity, while index notation gives the feeling of a group of three numbers. The former is more closely related to our physical intuition, while the latter is extremely useful in treating complex vector operations.

If we jump ahead briefly to Chap. 7, we find that in Gibbs notation the viscous dissipation to internal energy is represented by $\nabla \mathbf{v} : \mathbf{T}$,† while the rate

---

† $\mathbf{T}$ represents the total stress *tensor*. Tensors in Gibbs notation will be represented by sans serif type whenever possible.

of surface work per unit volume is $\nabla \cdot (\mathbf{v} \cdot \mathbf{T})$. These two abstract symbols represent two very different physical phenomena, and it is helpful to the student that these symbols actually look different. In index notation, these terms are represented by

$$\left(\frac{\partial v_i}{\partial x_j}\right) T_{ij} \quad \text{and} \quad \frac{\partial}{\partial x_j}(v_i T_{ij})$$

respectively. Although the symbols are indeed different and therefore represent different quantities, the difference is not so apparent, nor so easily grasped by the reader intent on assembling a stream of information into some coherent whole.

Although index notation lacks something in quick visual communication, it is an extremely powerful tool for carrying out complex vector and tensor operations. Therefore, we may sometimes begin an analysis in Gibbs notation, switch to index notation when the going gets tough, and then express our final result in Gibbs notation. This switching of notation should not disturb the student, for it is done in an effort to improve the exposition. Bridgman[15] has pointed out that "mathematics is merely a precise verbalization," and even the nonmathematician is aware that some languages (notations) are more suitable than others for expressing certain thoughts or ideas. For example, the opera singer prefers to sing in Italian because of the soft vowel endings, while the dialectician prefers English for its scope and variety of meaning.[16] Thus, the opera singer may perform in Italian but carry out his contract negotiations in English. Similarly, we will use Gibbs notation for quick visual communication and index notation for the more difficult analytic steps. Although index notation is really unnecessary until we reach Chap. 4, examples and problems will be given throughout the first three chapters in order to accustom the student to it.

PROBLEMS

1-1. The "weight" of an object is defined as the force (in pounds-force) exerted on the object by gravity. If the mass of an object is 10.0 lb_m, what is its weight on the earth and on a planet where the gravitational acceleration is 10 ft/sec²?

 Ans: 3.11 lb_f

1-2. (a) Express in terms of atmospheres the pressure $p = 12.5$ poundals/ft².

 Ans: 1.84×10^{-4} atm

15. P. W. Bridgman, *The Nature of Thermodynamics* (Cambridge, Mass.: Harvard University Press, 1941).
16. D. Conrad, "Lectures on Modern Languages" (from a series of unpublished lectures delivered in Chicago, Ill., in 1962).

(b) Express in square centimeters per second the kinematic viscosity $v = 1.6 \times 10^{-4}$ poise-ft^3/lb$_m$.

Ans: 10^{-2} cm^2/sec

(c) Express in cubic feet per second the volumetric flow rate $Q = 120$ gal/min.

Ans: 0.267 ft^3/sec

1-3. Given the following conditions for flow in a pipe,

$$\langle v_z \rangle = 10 \text{ ft/sec}$$
$$D = 1 \text{ in.}$$
$$\rho = 80 \text{ lb}_m/\text{ft}^3$$
$$\mu = 0.015 \text{ poise}$$

calculate the Reynolds number.

Ans: 6.6×10^4

1-4. On the assumption that $h \ll r_0$ for the Couette viscometer shown in Fig. 1.5-2, derive a relationship between the torque $\mathscr{T}$ required to drive the outer cylinder, and the viscosity μ in terms of r_0, h, L (length of the annular region), and ω_0 (angular velocity).

1-5. Given that T_{yx} is a constant for the plane Couette flow illustrated in Fig. 1.5-1, solve Eq. 1.5-7 subject to the boundary conditions (B.C.),

| B.C. 1: | $v_x = 0,$ | $y = 0$ |
| B.C. 2: | $v_x = u_0,$ | $y = h$ |

to determine the velocity distribution and the relationship between T_{yx} and u_0.

1-6. If the critical stress T_0 for a Bingham fluid is 0.058 lb$_f$/ft^2 and the density is 87 lb$_m$/ft^3, compute the minimum film thickness that would result if this fluid were applied to a vertical wall.

Ans: 0.008 in.

1-7. As an approximation, the fluid motion that occurs when braked automobile tires slide on a wet pavement might be considered comparable to that illustrated in Fig. 1.5-1. If the effective contact area between the tires and the pavement is 48 in.^{2}, and the water film is 0.003 in. thick, express the drag force exerted on the automobile as a function of its velocity u_0. Assuming that this relationship is valid even when u_0 is changing, compute the time and distance required for a 2000 lb$_m$ car to decelerate from 60 mph to 5 mph. Use 0.011 poise for viscosity of water.

1-8. Rework Prob. 1-5 for the case where the temperature distribution in the fluid is

$$T = T_0 - \Delta T\left(\frac{y}{h}\right)$$

and the viscosity is related to the temperature by

$$\mu = \mu_\infty \exp\left(\frac{\Delta E}{RT}\right)$$

This problem requires a numerical integration of Eq. 1.5-7, which is best handled by forming the dimensionless equation

$$\frac{dU_x}{dY} = \exp\left[-\left(\frac{\Delta E}{RT_0}\right)\Big/\left(1 - \frac{\Delta T}{T_0}Y\right)\right]$$

where $U_x = v_x \mu_\infty / hT_{yx}$

$$Y = \frac{y}{h}$$

which is subject to the boundary condition,

B.C. 1: $U_x = 0, \qquad Y = 0$

Some interesting results can be obtained by setting $\Delta E / RT_0$ equal to 5.0, and letting $\Delta T / T_0$ take on the values 0.0, 0.1, 0.2, and 0.3.

1-9. What is the angle between the vector, $\mathbf{A} = 10\mathbf{i} + 5\mathbf{j}$, and the x-axis?

1-10. Given a counterclockwise rotation of 30° around the z-axis as shown in Fig. 1-10, express $\mathbf{i}'$ and $\mathbf{j}'$ in terms of $\mathbf{i}$ and $\mathbf{j}$.

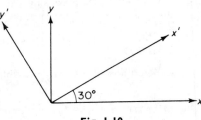

Ans: $\mathbf{i}' = \dfrac{\sqrt{3}}{2}\mathbf{i} + \tfrac{1}{2}\mathbf{j}$

$\mathbf{j}' = -\tfrac{1}{2}\mathbf{i} + \dfrac{\sqrt{3}}{2}\mathbf{j}$

Fig. 1-10

1-11. The three algebraic equations

$$\begin{aligned} x + 5y + 3z &= 10 \\ 2x + 4y + 4z &= 5 \\ 3x + 26y &= 7 \end{aligned}$$

can be expressed in a single equation as

$$a_{ij}x_j = b_i$$

where $x_1 = x$, $x_2 = y$, and $x_3 = z$. List the values of the nine terms represented by a_{ij}, if the three terms represented by b_j are $b_1 = 10$, $b_2 = 5$, and $b_3 = 7$.

1-12. Write out the three scalar components of the vector $\mathbf{A} + \mathbf{B}$. Express the equation

$$\mathbf{C} = \mathbf{A} + \mathbf{B}$$

in index notation.

1-13. The vector $\mathbf{C}$ is defined as a scalar, S, times the vector, $\mathbf{B}$.

$$\mathbf{C} = S\mathbf{B}$$

Write out the scalar components of the vector $\mathbf{C}$ and express this result in index notation.

1-14. Express the scalar $S = \mathbf{C} \cdot (\mathbf{A} + \mathbf{B})$ in index notation.

1-15. Given a second order system a_{ij} such that

$$a_{11} = 6, \qquad a_{12} = 3, \qquad a_{13} = -3$$
$$a_{21} = 5, \qquad a_{22} = 0, \qquad a_{23} = 2$$
$$a_{31} = -4, \qquad a_{32} = 1, \qquad a_{33} = 7$$

Compute the term $a_{1k}a_{2k}$.

Ans: 24.

Fluid Statics and One-Dimensional Laminar Flow

2

In this chapter we shall examine the two simplest types of fluid motion: fluids at rest and steady, one-dimensional, laminar flow. This will serve to introduce the student to some of the fundamental concepts of fluid mechanics, without getting involved in the mathematical details required to examine many of the more complex flows encountered in practice. We will first present a general formulation of the linear momentum principle and then use this result to derive the *equations of fluid statics*, which are simply a special form of the more general *equations of motion* to be presented in Chaps. 4 and 5. The second topic covered in this chapter, one-dimensional laminar flow, is another example of a special form of the general equations of motion.

*2.1 The Material Volume

As previously discussed, the linear momentum principle states that

$$\begin{Bmatrix} \text{the time rate of change} \\ \text{of momentum of the body} \end{Bmatrix} = \begin{Bmatrix} \text{the force acting} \\ \text{on the body} \end{Bmatrix} \quad (2.1\text{-}1)$$

32

The "body" referred to in Eq. 2.1-1 consists of some fixed quantity of material, such as a steel ball moving under the action of the earth's gravitational field, or all the asparagus and butter sauce contained in a sealed polyethylene bag, or a weather balloon filled with helium being bounced around in the turbulent atmosphere. The material within these three systems, or bodies, remains the same; therefore, they may be called material volumes. It follows immediately from the principle of conservation of mass that the mass of a material volume is constant.

In applying Eq. 2.1-1 to a fluid, some conceptual difficulties arise. If we define our system at some time, $t = 0$, as all the material within a sphere of radius r_0, we might imagine that at some other time we could not locate the system with a smooth closed surface, owing to the random motion of the molecules. If we wish to work within the realm of continuum mechanics, and we do, we must restrict ourselves to cases where this random molecular motion can be neglected. As we mentioned in Chap. 1, we may do so when the gross dimensions of the system under consideration are much larger than the mean free path of the molecules in the fluid. Under these conditions, we may correctly speak of a material volume which may be continuously changing size and shape but exchanging no mass with its surroundings. We denote a material volume as $\mathscr{V}_m(t)$, and the surface of a material volume as $\mathscr{A}_m(t)$. The subscript m reminds us that we are discussing a "material" volume and surface, both of which may be functions of time. Later in the text we shall have occasion to discuss volumes fixed in space, designated by $\mathscr{V}$, and volumes which move through space in an arbitrary manner, designated by $\mathscr{V}_a(t)$. The surface areas associated with these volumes are indicated by $\mathscr{A}$ and $\mathscr{A}_a(t)$, respectively. These volumes and the surfaces associated with them are designated by capital script letters to alert the student to their special significance. In addition, it allows us to use the symbol A to indicate cross-sectional areas and *portions of closed surfaces*, while closed surfaces are clearly distinguished by the use of $\mathscr{A}$, $\mathscr{A}_m(t)$, and $\mathscr{A}_a(t)$.

The linear momentum principle

Consider now the differential volume of fluid dV illustrated in Fig. 2.1-1. The mass, dM, contained in this differential volume is given by

$$dM = \rho \, dV \qquad (2.1\text{-}2)$$

and the momentum (mass times velocity) of the differential element is, therefore,

$$dM \, \mathbf{v} = \rho \mathbf{v} \, dV \qquad (2.1\text{-}3)$$

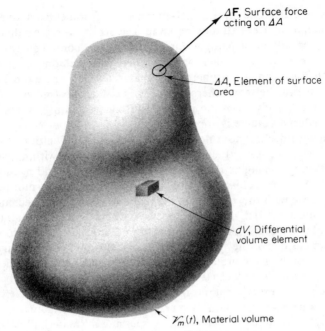

$\Delta \mathbf{F}$, Surface force acting on ΔA

ΔA, Element of surface area

dV, Differential volume element

$\mathscr{V}_m(t)$, Material volume

Fig. 2.1-1. A material volume.

We may now write the momentum of the material volume† as,

$$\{\text{momentum of the material volume}\} = \int_{\mathscr{V}_m(t)} \rho \mathbf{v} \, dV \qquad (2.1\text{-}4)$$

and Eq. 2.1-1 may be written

$$\frac{D}{Dt} \int_{\mathscr{V}_m(t)} \rho \mathbf{v} \, dV = \begin{Bmatrix} \text{force acting} \\ \text{on the material} \\ \text{volume} \end{Bmatrix} \qquad (2.1\text{-}5)$$

The derivative, D/Dt, is called the *material derivative* and will be discussed in detail along with the *total* and *partial time derivatives* in Chap. 3. For the present, it is sufficient to say the material derivative simply indicates that we are taking the time rate of change of a material volume.

The forces acting on a material volume of fluid consist of body forces—such as gravitational, electrostatic, and electromagnetic forces—that act on the mass as a whole and surface forces that act on the bounding surface of the material volume. If the body force per unit mass is represented by $\mathbf{g}$, the total body force is

$$\begin{Bmatrix} \text{body force exerted} \\ \text{on the material} \\ \text{volume} \end{Bmatrix} = \int_{\mathscr{V}_m(t)} \rho \mathbf{g} \, dV \qquad (2.1\text{-}6)$$

† This type of terminology will be used throughout the text instead of the correct statement, *the momentum of the body having a configuration* $\mathscr{V}_m(t)$.

We shall consider only the gravitational body force; **g** will therefore represent the gravity vector. In treating the surface force it will be appropriate to work in terms of the stress vector, $\mathbf{t}_{(n)}$, defined by Eq. 2.1-7.

$$\mathbf{t}_{(n)} = \lim_{\Delta A \to 0} \left(\frac{\Delta \mathbf{F}}{\Delta A} \right) \qquad (2.1\text{-}7)$$

where $\Delta \mathbf{F}$ is the force exerted by the surroundings on the area ΔA.

In general, a scalar or a vector can be specified simply in terms of its spatial coordinates and time; however, this is not the case with the stress vector, for it also depends on the orientation (given by the normal vector **n**) of the surface in question. The subscript **(n)** is thus used in denoting the stress vector. As an example of this dependence upon **n**, we might consider the solid bar under compression illustrated in Fig. 2.1-2. It is appropriate to

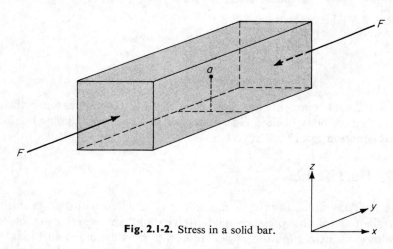

Fig. 2.1-2. Stress in a solid bar.

ask the following questions. What is the temperature in the bar at point a? What is the velocity at point a? What is the density at point a? However, the question—What is the stress at point a?—is incomplete. We must ask: What is the stress at point a for a surface having a normal **n**?

To illustrate this point, we shall consider the state of stress for the plane at point a having a normal $\pm \mathbf{j}$. If the total compressive force acting on the bar is F and the cross-sectional area of the bar is A, then the stress vector at point a for a surface having a normal $\pm \mathbf{j}$ is given by

$$\mathbf{t}_{(\pm \mathbf{j})} = \pm \mathbf{j} \left(\frac{F}{A} \right) \qquad (2.1\text{-}8)$$

where the plus or minus sign on the right-hand side of Eq. 2.1-8 is used depending on whether the normal to the surface is chosen as $\pm \mathbf{j}$. What about the stress at point a acting on the surface having a normal $\pm\mathbf{k}$? In the absence of any ambient pressure, it is obvious that this stress is zero.

$$\mathbf{t}_{(\pm\mathbf{k})} = 0 \qquad (2.1\text{-}9)$$

When discussing the forces exerted by one phase upon another, we can easily become confused as to which phase we are referring. To eliminate this difficulty, we shall adhere to the following convention: $\mathbf{t}_{(\mathbf{n})}$ at a phase interface will refer to the force per unit area exerted *by* the phase into which the normal $\mathbf{n}$ points, *on* the phase for which $\mathbf{n}$ is the outwardly directed normal.

The net surface force acting on the material volume may be represented in terms of the stress vector

$$\left\{ \begin{matrix} \text{surface force exerted} \\ by \text{ the surroundings} \\ on \text{ the material volume} \end{matrix} \right\} = \int_{\mathscr{A}_m(t)} \mathbf{t}_{(\mathbf{n})}\, dA \qquad (2.1\text{-}10)$$

and Eq. 2.1-1 becomes

$$\frac{D}{Dt} \int_{\mathscr{V}_m(t)} \rho\mathbf{v}\, dV = \int_{\mathscr{V}_m(t)} \rho\mathbf{g}\, dV + \int_{\mathscr{A}_m(t)} \mathbf{t}_{(\mathbf{n})}\, dA \qquad (2.1\text{-}11)$$

$$\underbrace{\qquad\qquad}_{\substack{\text{Time rate of change} \\ \text{of momentum}}} \quad \underbrace{\qquad}_{\text{Body force}} \quad \underbrace{\qquad}_{\substack{\text{Surface} \\ \text{force}}}$$

Equation 2.1-11 represents the application of the linear momentum principle to an arbitrary body of fluid. In the next section, we will examine the form of this equation for a fluid at rest.

*2.2   Fluid Statics

In studying fluids at rest an engineer is confronted with two problems: determination of the pressure field in the fluid and application of this knowledge to determine forces and moments on submerged surfaces. We will consider the first problem initially. Application of Eq. 2.1-11 to any body of fluid at rest yields†

$$0 = \int_{\mathscr{V}} \rho\mathbf{g}\, dV + \int_{\mathscr{A}} \mathbf{t}_{(\mathbf{n})}\, dA \qquad (2.2\text{-}1)$$

Note that in this case the limits of integration for the volume and surface integrals are independent of time.

The stress vector for a static fluid

The commonly accepted definition of a fluid is that it will deform *continuously* under the application of a *shear* stress. In light of this definition,

† A scalar zero in a vector equation should be read as the null vector.

the stress on a fluid element at rest must always act *normal* to the surface under consideration. We now wish to apply Eq. 2.2-1 to the tetrahedron shown in Fig. 2.2-1, subject to the restriction that all shear stresses are zero, to prove that the static stress in a fluid is isotropic. The vector forces shown*

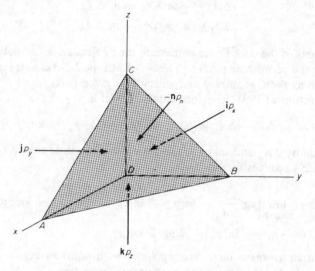

Fig. 2.2-1. Static stress on a tetrahedron.

in Fig. 2.2-1 are all normal to the respective surfaces on which they act, and Table 2.2-1 indicates the force and the outwardly directed unit normal for the four planes making up the tetrahedron.

Table 2.2-1

STATIC STRESS ON A TETRAHEDRON

Plane	Area	Normal	Stress vector
ABC	ΔA_n	$\mathbf{n}$	$-\mathbf{n}p_n$
BCD	ΔA_x	$-\mathbf{i}$	$\mathbf{i}p_x$
ADC	ΔA_y	$-\mathbf{j}$	$\mathbf{j}p_y$
ABD	ΔA_z	$-\mathbf{k}$	$\mathbf{k}p_z$

Application of Eq. 2.2-1 to the tetrahedron, and expression of the area integrals of the stresses in terms of an average stress and an area, yields

$$0 = \rho\mathbf{g}\,\Delta V - \mathbf{n}\langle p_n\rangle\,\Delta A_n + \mathbf{i}\langle p_x\rangle\,\Delta A_x + \mathbf{j}\langle p_y\rangle\,\Delta A_y + \mathbf{k}\langle p_z\rangle\,\Delta A_z \qquad (2.2\text{-}2)$$

---

*Here we have used p_x to represent the pressure acting on the surface area designated by ΔA_x with a similar interpretation applying to p_y and ΔA_y, etc. Both p_x and ΔA_x are *scalar* quantities not to be confused with the component of a *vector* such as $n_x = \mathbf{i}\cdot\mathbf{n}$.

To proceed with our analysis and prove that $p_n = p_x = p_y = p_z$ we must express the areas ΔA_x, ΔA_y, ΔA_z in terms of ΔA_n. These expressions are given by,

$$\Delta A_x = \mathbf{i} \cdot \mathbf{n} \, \Delta A_n = n_x \, \Delta A_n \tag{2.2-3a}$$

$$\Delta A_y = \mathbf{j} \cdot \mathbf{n} \, \Delta A_n = n_y \, \Delta A_n \tag{2.2-3b}$$

$$\Delta A_z = \mathbf{k} \cdot \mathbf{n} \, \Delta A_n = n_z \, \Delta A_n \tag{2.2-3c}$$

i.e., the areas of the coordinate planes are the projections of the oblique area, ΔA_n, onto the coordinate planes. The proof of Eqs. 2.2-3 is a straightforward problem in analytic geometry and will not be given here.

Substitution of Eqs. 2.2-3 into Eq. 2.2-2 yields

$$0 = \rho \mathbf{g} \, \Delta V - \Delta A_n \left[\mathbf{n} \langle p_n \rangle - \mathbf{i} n_x \langle p_x \rangle - \mathbf{j} n_y \langle p_y \rangle - \mathbf{k} n_z \langle p_z \rangle \right] \tag{2.2-4}$$

If we divide by ΔA_n and take the limit $\Delta A_n \to 0$, we note that $\Delta V / \Delta A_n \to 0$, and Eq. 2.2-4 reduces to

$$0 = \lim_{\Delta A_n \to 0} \left\{ \rho \mathbf{g} \frac{\Delta V}{\Delta A_n} - \left[\mathbf{n} \langle p_n \rangle - \mathbf{i} n_x \langle p_x \rangle - \mathbf{j} n_y \langle p_y \rangle - \mathbf{k} n_z \langle p_z \rangle \right] \right\}$$
$$= -\mathbf{n} p_n + \mathbf{i} n_x p_x + \mathbf{j} n_y p_y + \mathbf{k} n_z p_z \tag{2.2-5}$$

Here the area averages have been replaced with point values in accordance with $\Delta V \to 0$. If we express the unit normal $\mathbf{n}$ in terms of its scalar components,

$$\mathbf{n} = \mathbf{i} n_x + \mathbf{j} n_y + \mathbf{k} n_z \tag{2.2-6}$$

we may write Eq. 2.2-5 as

$$0 = \mathbf{i} n_x (p_n - p_x) + \mathbf{j} n_y (p_n - p_y) + \mathbf{k} n_z (p_n - p_z) \tag{2.2-7}$$

Now, if a vector is equal to zero, it readily follows (by forming the dot product with $\mathbf{i}$, $\mathbf{j}$, and $\mathbf{k}$, respectively) that the scalar components of the vector are zero. Thus, Eq. 2.2-7 leads us to the conclusion that $p_x = p_n$, $p_y = p_n$, and $p_z = p_n$, and our proof is complete.

Dropping the subscript n, we express the stress vector acting on any arbitrary surface as

$$\mathbf{t}_{(\mathbf{n})} = -\mathbf{n} p \tag{2.2-8}$$

where $\mathbf{n}$ is the outwardly directed unit normal. Equation 2.2-8 indicates that the magnitude of the stress vector is given by the pressure, and the direction is opposite to that of the unit normal. The minus sign in Eq. 2.2-8 is a manifestation of the convention that $\mathbf{t}_{(\mathbf{n})}$ represents the stress exerted *on* the system *by* the surroundings when $\mathbf{n}$ is the outwardly directed normal for the system.

We now wish to determine the pressure in the fluid illustrated in Fig. 2.2-2. Our first step is to apply Eqs. 2.2-1 and 2.2-8 to the differential volume

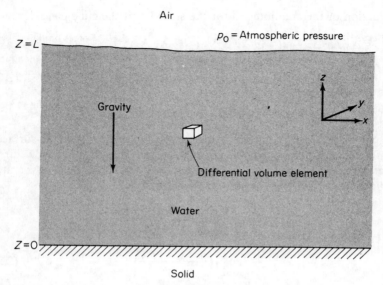

Fig. 2.2-2. A fluid at rest.

element shown in Fig. 2.2-2 and illustrated in detail in Fig. 2.2-3. Taking the differential cube shown in Fig. 2.2-3 to have its sides parallel to the coordinate planes, and designating the lengths of the edges by Δx, Δy and Δz, we may apply Eq. 2.2-1 to this cube to yield

$$0 = \rho \mathbf{g} \, \Delta x \, \Delta y \, \Delta z - \int_{\mathscr{A}} \mathbf{n} p \, dA \qquad (2.2\text{-}9)$$

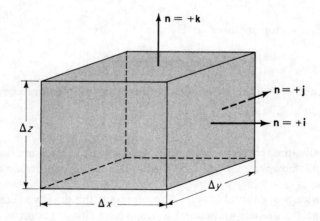

Fig. 2.2-3. Differential volume element.

Evaluation of the area integral for the six sides of the cube gives

$$0 = \rho\mathbf{g}\,\Delta x\,\Delta y\,\Delta z - \left\{(-\mathbf{i}p\,\Delta y\,\Delta z)_x + (\mathbf{i}p\,\Delta y\,\Delta z)_{x+\Delta x}\right.\quad \begin{array}{l}\text{Forces on the}\\ \text{x-surfaces}\end{array}$$

$$+ (-\mathbf{j}p\,\Delta x\,\Delta z)_y + (\mathbf{j}p\,\Delta x\,\Delta z)_{y+\Delta y}\quad \begin{array}{l}\text{Forces on the}\\ \text{y-surfaces}\end{array}\qquad (2.2\text{-}10)$$

$$\left.+ (-\mathbf{k}p\,\Delta x\,\Delta y)_z + (\mathbf{k}p\,\Delta x\,\Delta y)_{z+\Delta z}\right\}\quad \begin{array}{l}\text{Forces on the}\\ \text{z-surfaces}\end{array}$$

The convention used to describe the surfaces is such that an "x-surface" is one for which the x-coordinate is constant and the unit outwardly directed normal takes on the values $\pm\mathbf{i}$. If we divide Eq. 2.2-10 by $\Delta x\,\Delta y\,\Delta z$ and take the limits $\Delta x \to 0$, $\Delta y \to 0$, and $\Delta z \to 0$, we obtain

$$0 = \rho\mathbf{g} - \left\{\lim_{\Delta x\to 0}\left[\mathbf{i}\left(\frac{p|_{x+\Delta x} - p|_x}{\Delta x}\right)\right]\right.$$

$$+ \lim_{\Delta y\to 0}\left[\mathbf{j}\left(\frac{p|_{y+\Delta y} - p|_y}{\Delta y}\right)\right]\qquad (2.2\text{-}11)$$

$$\left.+ \lim_{\Delta z\to 0}\left[\mathbf{k}\left(\frac{p|_{z+\Delta z} - p|_z}{\Delta z}\right)\right]\right\}$$

Each of the limits is the definition of a partial derivative, and Eq. 2.2-12 results from the limiting process.

$$0 = \rho\mathbf{g} - \left(\mathbf{i}\frac{\partial p}{\partial x} + \mathbf{j}\frac{\partial p}{\partial y} + \mathbf{k}\frac{\partial p}{\partial z}\right)\qquad (2.2\text{-}12)$$

This equation may be written in the more compact form,

$$0 = \rho\mathbf{g} - \nabla p\qquad (2.2\text{-}13)$$

where ∇ is a vector operator which takes the form

$$\nabla = \mathbf{i}\frac{\partial}{\partial x} + \mathbf{j}\frac{\partial}{\partial y} + \mathbf{k}\frac{\partial}{\partial z}\qquad (2.2\text{-}14)$$

in rectangular coordinates. In index notation, this result would be expressed,

$$0 = \rho g_i - \frac{\partial p}{\partial x_i}\qquad (2.2\text{-}15)$$

Traditionally, the term ∇p is called the *gradient* of the pressure and denoted by "grad p"; however, the use of the symbol ∇ is more informative and will be used here.

Very often we will find it helpful to represent the gravity vector in terms of the negative of the gradient of a scalar, ϕ. This function is called the gravitational potential function because it represents the gravitational potential energy of the fluid. The gravity vector **g** may be expressed

$$\mathbf{g} = \mathbf{i}g_x + \mathbf{j}g_y + \mathbf{k}g_z \tag{2.2-16}$$

where the scalar components g_x, g_y, and g_z are constants. If we choose ϕ to be given by

$$\phi = -(xg_x + yg_y + zg_z) \tag{2.2-17}$$

it follows that minus the gradient of ϕ is equal to **g**.

$$-\nabla\phi = \left(\mathbf{i}\frac{\partial}{\partial x} + \mathbf{j}\frac{\partial}{\partial y} + \mathbf{k}\frac{\partial}{\partial z}\right)(xg_x + yg_y + zg_z)$$

$$= \mathbf{i}g_x + \mathbf{j}g_y + \mathbf{k}g_z \tag{2.2-18}$$

$$= \mathbf{g}$$

This method of representing **g** is possible only because **g** is a constant vector. Equation 2.2-13 may be written in terms of ϕ.

$$0 = \rho\nabla\phi + \nabla p \tag{2.2-19}$$

If the density is constant, this equation may be written as

$$0 = \nabla(\rho\phi + p) \tag{2.2-20}$$

Since this result holds everywhere in the fluid, the term $\rho\phi + p$ must be a constant, and we may write

$$p = C - \rho\phi \tag{2.2-21}$$

Here we have integrated the equations of fluid statics, and C is the constant of integration. Use of the potential function to obtain the integrated form of Eq. 2.2-13 is satisfying from the mathematical point of view, but the solution of this equation deserves a treatment more closely connected to the student's notion of static fluid systems.

For the system shown in Fig. 2.2-2, the gravity vector is

$$\mathbf{g} = -\mathbf{k}g \tag{2.2-22}$$

where g is the magnitude of the gravity vector. Substitution of Eq. 2.2-22 into Eq. 2.2-13 yields the three scalar equations

$$\frac{\partial p}{\partial x} = 0 \tag{2.2-23a}$$

$$\frac{\partial p}{\partial y} = 0 \tag{2.2-23b}$$

$$\frac{\partial p}{\partial z} = -\rho g \tag{2.2-23c}$$

These three scalar components of the original vector equation are quite obviously expressed by the index notation of Eq. 2.2-15, where $g_1 = g_2 = 0$ and $g_3 = -g$. Integration of Eq. 2.2-23c gives

$$p = -\rho g z + C(x, y) \tag{2.2-24}$$

where the constant of integration may be a function of x and y; however, Eqs. 2.2-23a and b indicate that the pressure is neither a function of x nor y, and we write Eq. 2.2-24

$$p = -\rho g z + C \tag{2.2-25}$$

A single boundary condition is needed in order to determine the constant C and thus specify the pressure everywhere in the fluid. It is obtained by recognizing that the pressure at $z = L$ is the atmospheric pressure p_0. We may write

B.C. 1: $\qquad\qquad p = p_0, \qquad z = L \tag{2.2-26}$

the application of which to Eq. 2.2-25 yields,

$$p|_{z=L} = p_0 = -\rho g L + C \tag{2.2-27}$$

and the constant of integration is

$$C = p_0 + \rho g L \tag{2.2-28}$$

Substitution of C into Eq. 2.2-25 yields the final expression for the pressure.

$$p = p_0 + \rho g (L - z) \tag{2.2-29}$$

This problem is such a simple one that the student can easily have missed the significance of the various steps; therefore, a review will be helpful.

1. The linear momentum principle and Eq. 2.2-8 were applied to a differential volume element to develop the equations of fluid statics.
2. The equations were solved to yield Eq. 2.2-25.
3. A boundary condition was specified and applied to Eq. 2.2-25 to obtain an expression for the pressure.

It may not seem so to the student, but the final step in this general process is usually the most troublesome. The differential equations of motion can be derived once and for all, and methods of solution (for those cases which can be solved) are neatly tabulated in mathematics and fluid mechanics texts; however, boundary conditions are specified mainly on the basis of physical intuition, and thus present a more difficult problem. Things are not quite as bad as they may seem, for there are two rules which guide us in specifying boundary conditions: velocity is a continuous function; the stress vector is a continuous function. Both these ideas follow from the continuum postulate discussed in Sec. 1.1. Boundary condition 1 results from application of the second rule—i.e., pressure is a continuous function for fluids at rest.†

2.3 Barometers

A barometer is a device for measuring the absolute pressure of the atmosphere. The one illustrated in Fig. 2.3-1 consists of a single tube closed at one end and immersed in the barometer fluid. Such a system may be obtained by filling the tube with the barometer fluid (usually mercury), closing the open end (the thumb does nicely), and immersing the tube in the pool of barometer fluid. The fluid vaporizes in the closed end, and the pressure there is the vapor pressure p_{vp}. For mercury the vapor pressure at room temperature is approximately 3×10^{-6} atm and may be considered to be zero. The differential equation for the pressure is

$$\frac{\partial p}{\partial z} = -\rho_{\mathrm{Hg}} g \qquad (2.3\text{-}1)$$

which is integrated to give

$$p = -\rho_{\mathrm{Hg}} g z + C \quad (2.3\text{-}2)$$

The boundary condition is

B.C. 1:

$$p = p_{vp} \approx 0, \qquad z = h \quad (2.3\text{-}3)$$

the application of which to Eq. 2.3-2 gives

$$p = \rho_{\mathrm{Hg}} g (h - z) \qquad (2.3\text{-}4)$$

Since the pressure at $z = 0$ is the atmospheric pressure, p_0, we write

$$p_0 = \rho_{\mathrm{Hg}} g h \qquad (2.3\text{-}5)$$

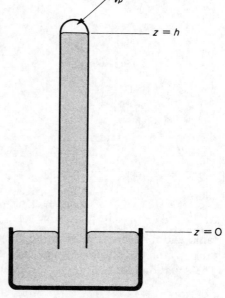

Fig. 2.3-1. Mercury barometer.

Because of the universal use of mercury barometers to measure atmospheric pressure, it is often reported in terms of h, or inches of mercury. Atmospheric pressure varies from day to day, the average being 29.92 in. Hg. This value

† Taking the pressure to be continuous neglects any effect of surface tension at the gas-liquid interface.

is referred to as one *standard atmosphere,* and we may use Eq. 2.3-5 to determine that

$$p_0 \text{ (standard)} = 14.696 \text{ lb}_f/\text{in.}^2$$

This quantity is often written 14.696 psia (pounds per square inch absolute).

2.4 Manometers

Manometers are devices which make use of columns of liquid to determine pressure differences. The simplest type is the U-tube illustrated in Fig. 2.4-1. The manometer fluid must be immiscible with the fluid in the

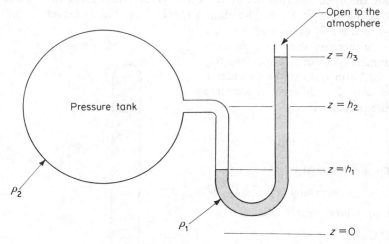

Fig. 2.4-1. U-tube manometer.

tank, and its density, ρ_1, must be greater than the density of the fluid in the tank, ρ_2, or there will be a tendency for it to replace the fluid in the tank. The equations for the pressure in the two fluids are

$$\frac{\partial p_1}{\partial z} = -\rho_1 g \tag{2.4-1}$$

$$\frac{\partial p_2}{\partial z} = -\rho_2 g \tag{2.4-2}$$

The boundary conditions for this system are

B.C. 1: $p_1 = p_0, \quad z = h_3$ (2.4-3)

B.C. 2: $p_2 = p_1, \quad z = h_1$ (2.4-4)

Both these conditions are derived from the notion that the pressure is a continuous function.† Solution of the two differential equations gives

$$p_1 = -\rho_1 g z + C_1 \qquad (2.4\text{-}5)$$

$$p_2 = -\rho_2 g z + C_2 \qquad (2.4\text{-}6)$$

Application of boundary condition 1 gives

$$p_1\big|_{z=h_3} = p_0 = -\rho_1 g h_3 + C_1 \qquad (2.4\text{-}7a)$$

or

$$C_1 = p_0 + \rho_1 g h_3 \qquad (2.4\text{-}7b)$$

and the pressure in fluid 1 is

$$p_1 = p_0 + \rho_1 g(h_3 - z) \qquad (2.4\text{-}8)$$

Application of boundary condition 2 gives

$$p_2\big|_{z=h_1} = -\rho_2 g h_1 + C_2 = p_1\big|_{z=h_1} = p_0 + \rho_1 g(h_3 - h_1) \qquad (2.4\text{-}9a)$$

or

$$C_2 = p_0 + \rho_2 g h_1 + \rho_1 g(h_3 - h_1) \qquad (2.4\text{-}9b)$$

and the pressure in fluid 2 is

$$p_2 = p_0 + \rho_2 g(h_1 - z) + \rho_1 g(h_3 - h_1) \qquad (2.4\text{-}10)$$

The gauge pressure, p_g, is defined as the absolute pressure minus the atmospheric pressure; therefore, the gauge pressure in the tank is

$$p_g = (p_2 - p_0) = \rho_2 g(h_1 - z) + \rho_1 g(h_3 - h_1) \qquad (2.4\text{-}11)$$

If the fluid in the tank is a gas, the density of the manometer fluid will usually be much larger than that of the gas; thus, $\rho_1 \gg \rho_2$, and the gauge pressure is

$$p_g \simeq \rho_1 g(h_3 - h_1) \qquad (2.4\text{-}12)$$

Manometer calculation

The fluid in the tank is a gas and a mercury manometer is used to measure the pressure. The readings on the manometer are

$$\left.\begin{array}{l} h_1 = 3.25\ \text{ft} \\ h_3 = 5.17\ \text{ft} \end{array}\right\} \quad \text{or} \quad (h_3 - h_1) = 1.92\ \text{ft}$$

† Interfacial tensions are obviously being neglected here.

The density of mercury is 13.5 g/cm³, and the gauge pressure is

$$p_g = \left\{(13.5 \text{ g/cm}^3)(32.2 \text{ ft/sec}^2)(1.92 \text{ ft})\right\}$$

Original terms

$$\times \left\{\left(\frac{1 \text{ lb}_m}{453.6 \text{ g}}\right)\left(\frac{\text{lb}_f \text{ sec}^2}{32.2 \text{ lb}_m \text{ ft}}\right)\left(\frac{2.54 \text{ cm}}{\text{in.}}\right)^3\left(\frac{12 \text{ in.}}{\text{ft}}\right)\right\}$$

Conversion factors

$$p_g = \frac{(13.5)(1.92)(2.54)^3(12)}{(453.6)} = 11.2 \text{ lb}_f/\text{in.}^2$$

To distinguish gauge pressure from absolute pressure (psia) we write

$$p_g = 11.2 \text{ psig (pounds per square inch gauge)}$$

*2.5 Forces on Submerged Plane Surfaces

Now that we have learned to determine the pressure field for a fluid at rest, we can direct our attention to the second problem noted in Sec. 2.2, i.e., the calculation of forces on submerged surfaces. According to our previous definition, the force which the surroundings exert on a system is

$$\left\{\begin{matrix}\text{force per unit area} \\ \text{acting on the system}\end{matrix}\right\} = \mathbf{t}_{(n)} = -\mathbf{n}p \quad \text{for a fluid at rest} \quad (2.5\text{-}1)$$

where $\mathbf{n}$ is the outwardly directed unit normal for the system. The total force $\mathbf{F}$ exerted by a fluid at rest on a solid surface is

$$\mathbf{F} = \int_A \mathbf{t}_{(n)} \, dA = -\int_A \mathbf{n}p \, dA \quad (2.5\text{-}2)$$

where it must be remembered that $\mathbf{n}$ is the outwardly directed unit normal for the solid—i.e., our convention is that $\mathbf{n}$ is the unit normal directed *into* the phase which exerts the force. The first step in calculating the force and moment on the gate shown in Fig. 2.5-1 is to determine the pressure in the fluid by means of the differential equation

$$\frac{\partial p}{\partial z} = -\rho g \quad (2.5\text{-}3)$$

and the boundary condition

B.C. 1: $p = p_0, \quad z = L$ (2.5-4)

Thus,

$$p = p_0 + \rho g(L - z) \quad (2.5\text{-}5)$$

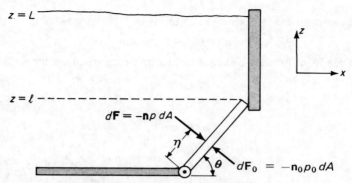

Fig. 2.5-1. Surface force and moment on a gate.

The net surface force exerted on the gate, $\mathbf{F}_{net}$, consists of the force exerted by the liquid and by the surrounding atmosphere,

$$\mathbf{F}_{net} = -\int_A \mathbf{n}p\, dA - \int_A \mathbf{n}_0 p_0\, dA \qquad (2.5\text{-}6)$$

The unit outwardly directed normal in the surrounding atmosphere, $\mathbf{n}_0$, is just equal and opposite to $\mathbf{n}$, and we may write Eq. 2.5-6

$$\mathbf{F}_{net} = -\int_A (p - p_0)\mathbf{n}\, dA \qquad (2.5\text{-}7)$$

If the width of the gate is b, then

$$dA = b\, d\eta$$

where η is the distance measured along the gate from the hinge. The net force is now given by

$$\mathbf{F}_{net} = -\int_{\eta=0}^{\eta=\ell/\sin\theta} \rho g(L-z)\mathbf{n}b\, d\eta \qquad (2.5\text{-}8)$$

In order to evaluate the integral we must either put z in terms of η or η in terms of z. In the latter case we write

$$\eta = \frac{z}{\sin\theta}$$

$$d\eta = \frac{dz}{\sin\theta}$$

and the force becomes

$$\mathbf{F}_{net} = -\frac{1}{\sin\theta}\int_0^\ell \rho g(L-z)\mathbf{n}b\, dz = -\frac{\mathbf{n}}{\sin\theta}\,\rho g b\ell\left(L-\frac{\ell}{2}\right) \qquad (2.5\text{-}9)$$

The unit normal can be expressed in terms of its components

$$\mathbf{n} = \mathbf{i}n_x + \mathbf{j}n_y + \mathbf{k}n_z \qquad (2.5\text{-}10)$$

and we see from Fig. 2.5-2 that these components are given by

$$n_x = -\sin\theta \qquad (2.5\text{-}11a)$$

$$n_y = 0 \qquad (2.5\text{-}11b)$$

$$n_z = \cos\theta \qquad (2.5\text{-}11c)$$

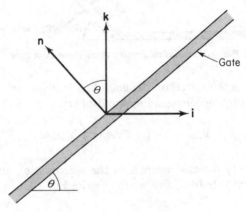

$n_x = \mathbf{i} \cdot \mathbf{n} = \cos(\pi/2 + \theta) = -\sin\theta$
$n_y = \mathbf{j} \cdot \mathbf{n} = 0$
$n_z = \mathbf{k} \cdot \mathbf{n} = \cos\theta$

Fig. 2.5-2. Components of the unit normal.

The net force may be expressed as

$$\mathbf{F}_{\text{net}} = -(\mathbf{i}n_x + \mathbf{k}n_z)\left(\frac{\rho g b \ell}{\sin\theta}\right)\left(L - \frac{\ell}{2}\right) \qquad (2.5\text{-}12)$$

and the components are given by

$$F_{x,\text{net}} = \rho g\left(L - \frac{\ell}{2}\right)b\ell \qquad (2.5\text{-}13a)$$

$$F_{z,\text{net}} = -\rho g \cot\theta\left(L - \frac{\ell}{2}\right)b\ell \qquad (2.5\text{-}13b)$$

The torque, $\mathscr{T}$, on the hinge of the gate is given by

$$\mathscr{T} = \int_0^{\ell/\sin\theta} \mathbf{r} \times \underbrace{[-\mathbf{n}(p - p_0)b]\,d\eta}_{\text{Force}} \qquad (2.5\text{-}14)$$

Moment arm

The position vector $\mathbf{r}$ is best represented in terms of a unit tangent vector to the gate, and the distance measured along the gate, η.

$$\mathbf{r} = \boldsymbol{\lambda}\eta \qquad (2.5\text{-}15)$$

Since $\boldsymbol{\lambda}$ and $\mathbf{n}$ are orthogonal, we may write

$$\mathbf{r} \times \mathbf{n} = \eta\boldsymbol{\lambda} \times \mathbf{n} = -\mathbf{j}\eta \qquad (2.5\text{-}16)$$

and Eq. 2.5-14 takes the form

$$\mathcal{T} = \mathbf{j}\int_0^{\ell/\sin\theta} (p - p_0)b\eta \, d\eta \qquad (2.5\text{-}17)$$

Putting the pressure difference $p - p_0$ in terms of η and integrating, we have

$$\mathcal{T} = \mathbf{j}\left[\frac{\rho g b \ell^2\left(\dfrac{L}{2} - \dfrac{\ell}{3}\right)}{\sin^2\theta}\right] \qquad (2.5\text{-}18)$$

It is often convenient to represent a distributed force in terms of a single resultant force. For this resultant force to describe properly the distributed force system, it must act a point which gives rise to the same torque as the distributed force system. When discussing hydrostatic systems, we call this point the *center of pressure* and denote it by $\bar{\mathbf{r}}$. The position vector locating the center of pressure is determined by solving the equation

$$\bar{\mathbf{r}} \times \mathbf{F} = \mathcal{T} \qquad (2.5\text{-}19)$$

where $\mathcal{T}$ is the torque owing to the distributed force system and $\mathbf{F}$ is the resultant force. Letting

$$\bar{\mathbf{r}} = \boldsymbol{\lambda}\bar{\eta} \qquad (2.5\text{-}20)$$

and substituting Eqs. 2.5-9 and 2.5-18 into Eq. 2.5-19, we locate the center of pressure on the hinged gate.

$$\bar{\eta} = \frac{\ell}{\sin\theta}\left[\frac{\dfrac{L}{2} - \dfrac{\ell}{3}}{L - \dfrac{\ell}{2}}\right] \qquad (2.5\text{-}21)$$

*2.6   Forces on Submerged Curved Surfaces

We first examine the problem of forces on curved submerged surfaces by considering the force on the arbitrary surface shown in Fig. 2.6-1. The force on the surface is

$$\mathbf{F} = -\int_A \mathbf{n}p \, dA \qquad (2.6\text{-}1)$$

where

$$p = p_0 + \rho g(L - z)$$

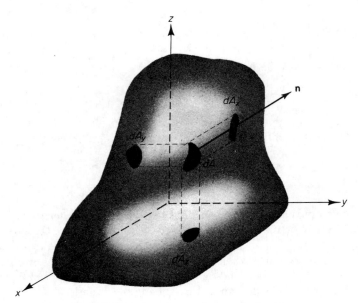

Fig. 2.6-1. Projected areas for a curved surface.

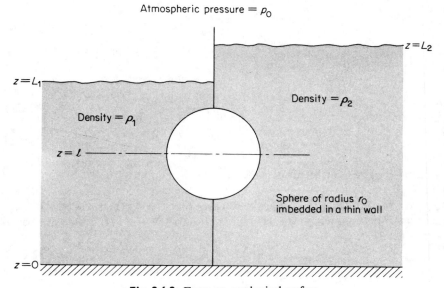

Fig. 2.6-2. Force on a spherical surface.

Since the projection of the surface area element dA on the three coordinate planes is

$$\mathbf{i} \cdot \mathbf{n} \, dA = dA_x \qquad (2.6\text{-}2a)$$

$$\mathbf{j} \cdot \mathbf{n} \, dA = dA_y \qquad (2.6\text{-}2b)$$

$$\mathbf{k} \cdot \mathbf{n} \, dA = dA_z \qquad (2.6\text{-}2c)$$

the surface area may be expressed in terms of the projected areas as

$$\mathbf{n} \, dA = \mathbf{i} \, dA_x + \mathbf{j} \, dA_y + \mathbf{k} \, dA_z \qquad (2.6\text{-}3)$$

The force acting on the solid surface may be written in terms of the projected areas to yield

$$\mathbf{F} = -\mathbf{i} \int_{A_x} p \, dA_x - \mathbf{j} \int_{A_y} p \, dA_y - \mathbf{k} \int_{A_z} p \, dA_z \qquad (2.6\text{-}4)$$

We do this because the pressure is always given in terms of the x, y, and z coordinates; therefore, it is necessary to perform the integration in terms of these coordinates rather than in terms of the surface area. To illustrate the application of these ideas, we consider the system shown in Fig. 2.6-2. The force that the fluids exert on the sphere is

$$\mathbf{F} = -\int_{A_1} \mathbf{n}_1 p_1 \, dA - \int_{A_2} \mathbf{n}_2 p_2 \, dA \qquad (2.6\text{-}5)$$

where $\mathbf{n}_1$ and $\mathbf{n}_2$ are the unit normals directed into fluids 1 and 2, respectively. The pressures in the two fluids are given by

$$p_1 = p_0 + \rho_1 g(L_1 - z) \qquad (2.6\text{-}6)$$

$$p_2 = p_0 + \rho_2 g(L_2 - z) \qquad (2.6\text{-}7)$$

Substitution of Eqs. 2.6-6 and 2.6-7 into Eq. 2.6-5 and taking the scalar product with the unit vector $\mathbf{i}$ give

$$F_x = \mathbf{i} \cdot \mathbf{F} = -\int_{A_1} [p_0 + \rho_1 g(L_1 - z)] \mathbf{i} \cdot \mathbf{n}_1 \, dA$$

$$\qquad\qquad\qquad (2.6\text{-}8)$$

$$-\int_{A_2} [p_0 + \rho_2 g(L_2 - z)] \mathbf{i} \cdot \mathbf{n}_2 \, dA$$

Upon examining Fig. 2.6-3, we see that

$$\mathbf{i} \cdot \mathbf{n}_1 \, dA = -dA_x \qquad (2.6\text{-}9)$$

$$\mathbf{i} \cdot \mathbf{n}_2 \, dA = dA_x \qquad (2.6\text{-}10)$$

Substitution of Eqs. 2.6-9 and 2.6-10 into Eq. 2.6-8 and putting both terms

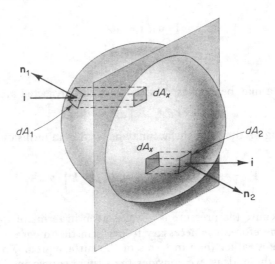

Fig. 2.6-3. Projected areas for a spherical surface.

under the same integral sign,

$$F_x = \int_{A_x} \left\{ [p_0 + \rho_1 g(L_1 - z)] - [p_0 + \rho_2 g(L_2 - z)] \right\} dA_x$$

(2.6-11)

$$= \int_{A_x} [(\rho_1 L_1 - \rho_2 L_2)g + (\rho_2 - \rho_1)gz] \, dA_x$$

Since

$$dA_x = dy \, dz \tag{2.6-12}$$

the force may be written as

$$F_x = \int_{z=\ell-r_0}^{z=\ell+r_0} \int_{y=-\sqrt{r_0^2-(z-\ell)^2}}^{y=+\sqrt{r_0^2-(z-\ell)^2}} [(\rho_1 L_1 - \rho_2 L_2)g + (\rho_2 - \rho_1)gz] \, dy \, dz \quad (2.6\text{-}13)$$

Integration with respect to y gives

$$F_x = 2 \int_{z=\ell-r_0}^{z=\ell+r_0} [(\rho_1 L_1 - \rho_2 L_2)g + (\rho_2 - \rho_1)gz]\sqrt{r_0^2 - (z-\ell)^2} \, dz \quad (2.6\text{-}14)$$

which we may integrate in turn to give

$$F_x = [(\rho_1 L_1 - \rho_2 L_2)g + (\rho_2 - \rho_1)g\ell]\pi r_0^2 \tag{2.6-15}$$

If we add and subtract p_0 from the right-hand side and rearrange the terms we obtain

$$F_x = [p_0 + \rho_1 g(L_1 - \ell)]\pi r_0^2 -- [p_0 + \rho_2 g(L_2 - \ell)]\pi r_0^2 \quad (2.6\text{-}16)$$

Mean pressure   Area   Mean pressure   Area

Thus, the resulting force may be written in terms of the mean pressure acting on the surface multiplied by the projected area of the surface in the direction of the force. We may use this result to quickly determine forces which act perpendicularly to the gravity vector provided the pressure is a *linear* function of z.

*2.7 Buoyancy Forces

The resultant force exerted on a body by a fluid at rest is called the buoyant force. The principle that we wish to prove here is attributed to Archimedes (287–212 BC), who supposedly discovered the phenomenon while entering the pool of a public bath.[1] The principle states that "a body is buoyed up by a force equal to the weight of the displaced fluid." We can easily prove this by applying Eq. 2.6-1 to the solid body illustrated in Fig. 2.7-1. In this case, we consider a solid body which may be separated into two regions by a curve along which

$$\mathbf{k} \cdot \mathbf{n} = 0 \quad (2.7\text{-}1)$$

Thus, the normal to the solid surface lies in the x-y plane along this curve. The analysis can be easily extended to more complex shapes simply by dividing the volume into several sections. If we designate the position of the upper surface by z_2 and the lower surface by z_1, Eq. 2.6-1 may be separated into two parts to give

$$\mathbf{F} = -\int_{A_2} \mathbf{n}_2 p|_{z=z_2}\, dA - \int_{A_1} \mathbf{n}_1 p|_{z=z_1}\, dA \quad (2.7\text{-}2)$$

Taking the dot product of Eq. 2.7-2 with the unit vector $\mathbf{k}$, we get the buoyancy force

$$\mathbf{k} \cdot \mathbf{F} = F_z = -\int_{A_2} p|_{z=z_2}\mathbf{n}_2 \cdot \mathbf{k}\, dA - \int_{A_1} p|_{z=z_1}\mathbf{n}_1 \cdot \mathbf{k}\, dA \quad (2.7\text{-}3)$$

Since $\mathbf{n} \cdot \mathbf{k}\, dA$ is the projection of the surface area on the x-y plane, we may change the variables of integration to

$$\mathbf{k} \cdot \mathbf{n}_2\, dA = dA_z, \quad \text{upper region} \quad (2.7\text{-}4a)$$

$$\mathbf{k} \cdot \mathbf{n}_1\, dA = -dA_z, \quad \text{lower region} \quad (2.7\text{-}4b)$$

1. H. Rouse and S. Ince, *History of Hydraulics* (New York: Dover Publications, Inc., 1963), p. 16.

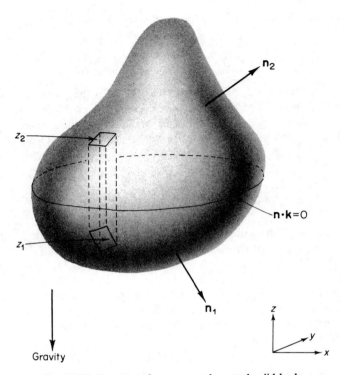

Fig. 2.7-1. Buoyancy force on a submerged solid body.

and Eq. 2.7-3 becomes

$$F_z = -\int_{A_z} p|_{z=z_2}\, dA_z + \int_{A_z} p|_{z=z_1}\, dA_z \tag{2.7-5}$$

Putting both terms under the same integral sign, and noting that

$$p|_{z=z_1} - p|_{z=z_2} = \rho g(z_2 - z_1) \tag{2.7-6}$$

we obtain

$$F_z = \int_{A_z} \rho g(z_2 - z_1)\, dA_z \tag{2.7-7}$$

But ρg is a constant and the volume of the solid V_s is

$$V_s = \int_{A_z} (z_2 - z_1)\, dA_z \tag{2.7-8}$$

and the solid body is buoyed up by the "weight" of the displaced fluid.

$$F_z = \rho g V_s \tag{2.7-9}$$

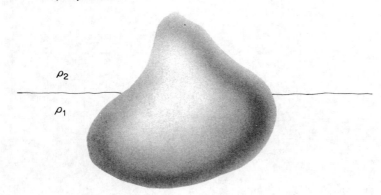

ρ_2

ρ_1

Fig. 2.7-2. Solid body floating at an interface.

The result is not difficult to extend to the case of a solid body at the interface between two fluids. This situation is illustrated in Fig. 2.7-2 and the proof is left to the student.

The hydrometer

A hydrometer uses the buoyancy principle to determine the ratio of densities of two fluids. In general, one of these fluids is water and the ratio of densities, ρ/ρ_{H_2O}, is called the specific gravity, γ.

$$\gamma = \frac{\rho}{\rho_{H_2O}} \qquad (2.7\text{-}10)$$

A hydrometer floating first in water and then in some other fluid is shown in Fig. 2.7-3. If the mass of the hydrometer is M and the density of the air above the liquid is so small that the air contributes a negligible amount to the buoyancy force, then Archimedes' principle yields

$$Mg = \rho_{H_2O}gV_{H_2O} \qquad (2.7\text{-}11)$$

$$Mg = \rho_{oil}gV_{oil} \qquad (2.7\text{-}12)$$

where V_{H_2O} and V_{oil} are the volumes of the displaced water and oil respectively. Division of Eq. 2.7-12 by Eq. 2.7-11 gives

$$1 = \left(\frac{\rho_{oil}}{\rho_{H_2O}}\right)\left(\frac{V_{oil}}{V_{H_2O}}\right) \qquad (2.7\text{-}13)$$

and the specific gravity of the oil is

$$\gamma_{oil} = \frac{V_{H_2O}}{V_{oil}} \qquad (2.7\text{-}14)$$

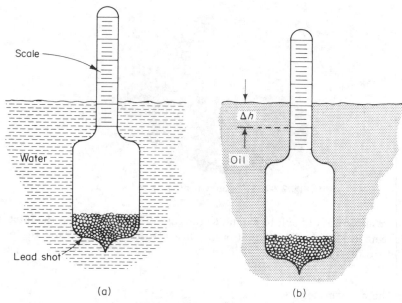

Fig. 2.7-3. A hydrometer.

If the cross-sectional area of the graduated shaft is A then

and
$$V_{oil} = V_{H_2O} + A\,\Delta h \qquad (2.7\text{-}15)$$

$$\gamma_{oil} = \frac{1}{1 + \left(\dfrac{A}{V_{H_2O}}\right)\Delta h} \qquad (2.7\text{-}16)$$

We need to know both the cross-sectional area A and the volume V_{H_2O} in order to determine γ_{oil}. The area A can be measured easily and V_{H_2O} may be determined from Eq. 2.7-11 since the density of water is well known and the mass of the hydrometer is measured easily. Knowing A and V_{H_2O} allows us to mark off a scale on the stem of the hydrometer giving the specific gravity directly.

2.8 One-Dimensional Laminar Flows

If only a single component of the velocity vector is nonzero, the linear momentum principle is easy to apply, provided the flow is laminar and the streamlines are straight. The subject of streamlines will be discussed in detail in Chap. 3; for now, it will suffice to say that for *steady flow*, streamlines are

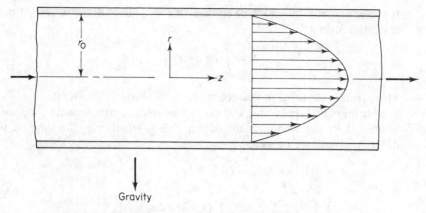

Fig. 2.8-1. Laminar flow in a circular tube.

imaginary lines traced out by particles of fluid. Thus, the streamlines in the Couette viscometer described in Chap. 1 would be concentric circles. For the flow illustrated in Fig. 2.8-1, $v_\theta = v_r = 0$, and v_z is only a function of r; thus a fluid particle would move in a straight line parallel to the z-axis.

We start the analysis with the linear momentum equation

$$\frac{D}{Dt} \int_{\mathscr{V}_{m(t)}} \rho \mathbf{v} \, dV = \int_{\mathscr{V}_{m(t)}} \rho \mathbf{g} \, dV + \int_{\mathscr{A}_{m(t)}} \mathbf{t}_{(n)} \, dA \qquad (2.8\text{-}1)$$

which is to be applied to the differential cylindrical section shown in Fig. 2.8-2. This section of fluid is a material volume, and is therefore continuously deforming; however, the velocity of every fluid particle in this volume is a constant. Thus, the momentum is also constant

$$\int_{\mathscr{V}_{m(t)}} \rho \mathbf{v} \, dV = \text{constant vector} \qquad (2.8\text{-}2)$$

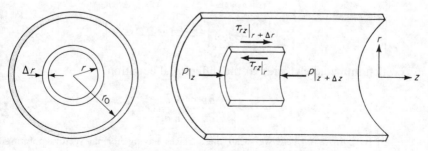

Fig. 2.8-2. Differential material volume element.

58   Fluid Statics and One-Dimensional Laminar Flow   Chap. 2

Inasmuch as the time rate of change of a constant vector is zero, Eq. 2.8-1 takes the form

$$0 = \int_{\mathscr{V}_m(t)} \rho \mathbf{g} \, dV + \int_{\mathscr{A}_m(t)} \mathbf{t}_{(n)} \, dA \qquad (2.8\text{-}3)$$

This result is identical to that for static fluids, but in this case the stress vector has both normal (pressure) and tangential (shear) components. We are only interested in the z-component of Eq. 2.8-3, which may be applied to the differential volume to yield

$$0 = [(p \, 2\pi r \, \Delta r)_z - (p \, 2\pi r \, \Delta r)_{z+\Delta z}] \qquad \text{Forces on the } z\text{-surfaces}$$

$$+ [-(\tau_{rz} \, 2\pi r \, \Delta z)_r + (\tau_{rz} \, 2\pi r \, \Delta z)_{r+\Delta r}] \qquad \text{Forces on the } r\text{-surfaces}$$

(2.8-4)

A very definite sign convention is used with the shear stress, τ_{rz}. On the surface having an outwardly directed normal in the *positive* r-direction, the shear stress τ_{rz} is represented as acting in the *positive* z-direction. On the surface having an outwardly directed normal in the *negative* r-direction, the shear stress is represented as acting in the *negative* z-direction. The actual direction of the shear stress will depend on the specific problem under investigation. For example, if the flow in the tube were reversed, the direction of the shear stress could certainly be reversed. In formulating problems, we must adhere to the sign convention that a positive shear stress acts in the positive coordinate direction on *positive surfaces,*† and in the negative coordinate direction on *negative surfaces.* This scheme is necessary to insure that shear stresses on opposite sides of a differentially thin shell of fluid act in opposite directions, which is, of course, intuitively obvious. A proof will be given in Chap. 4 where stress is studied in detail.

Dividing Eq. 2.8-4 by $2\pi\Delta r\Delta z$ and taking the limits $\Delta r \to 0$ and $\Delta z \to 0$, we get

$$0 = \lim_{\Delta z \to 0} \left[-r\left(\frac{p|_{z+\Delta z} - p|_z}{\Delta z}\right) \right]$$

$$+ \lim_{\Delta r \to 0} \left[\frac{\tau_{rz}r|_{r+\Delta r} - \tau_{rz}r|_r}{\Delta r} \right] \qquad (2.8\text{-}5)$$

which immediately leads to the differential equation

$$0 = -\frac{\partial p}{\partial z} + \frac{1}{r}\frac{\partial}{\partial r}(r\tau_{rz}) \qquad (2.8\text{-}6)$$

† By *positive surfaces* we mean the surfaces having normal vectors pointing in the positive coordinate directions.

Equation 2.8-6 is called the *stress equation of motion*, and it may be expressed in terms of the velocity gradient if Newton's law of viscosity is used.

$$\tau_{rz} = \mu \frac{\partial v_z}{\partial r} \tag{2.8-7}$$

The relationship between the shear stress and the velocity gradient for this flow is very similar to the relationship given in Chap. 1 for plane Couette flow. In Chap. 5, Newton's law of viscosity will be examined in detail; for the present, we must regard Eq. 2.8-7 as an experimentally determined relationship between the shear stress and the velocity gradient for flow in a circular tube.

If the viscosity μ is constant, we may substitute Eq. 2.8-7 into Eq. 2.8-6 to yield

$$\frac{\partial p}{\partial z} = \mu \frac{1}{r} \frac{\partial}{\partial r}\left(r \frac{\partial v_z}{\partial r}\right) \tag{2.8-8}$$

The solution of this equation requires some careful arguments regarding the functional dependence of v_z and p. Because v_θ and v_r are zero,† each fluid particle must move in a straight line along the tube. If the density for this flow is constant, the volumetric flow rate across any section of the tube must remain constant (which follows from the fact that conservation of mass implies conservation of volume, if the density is constant), and we can conclude that the velocity v_z is not a function of z. If, in addition, we assume that the flow is axisymmetric,† v_z is only a function of r.

$$v_z = v_z(r) \tag{2.8-9}$$

The pressure will be a function of r and θ owing to gravitational effects, and it will certainly depend on z. Thus,

$$p = p(r, \theta, z) \tag{2.8-10}$$

However, the effect of gravity will be the same everywhere along the tube, and the pressure gradient will not depend on r and θ. The functional dependence of $\partial p/\partial z$ may be expressed as

$$\frac{\partial p}{\partial z} = f(z) \tag{2.8-11}$$

Examining Eq. 2.8-8 in light of these arguments, we see that the left-hand side is only a function of z while the right-hand side is only a function of r. Keeping in mind that r and z are independent variables, we conclude that

† See Birkhoff's plausible intuitive hypothesis IV, Sec. 1.3.

both sides of Eq. 2.8-8 must be constant,† and we write

$$\mu \frac{1}{r} \frac{d}{dr}\left(r \frac{dv_z}{dr}\right) = -\frac{\Delta p}{L} \qquad (2.8\text{-}12)$$

Here the partial derivatives have been replaced by total derivatives, inasmuch as v_z is only a function of r, and the pressure gradient $\partial p/\partial z$ has been replaced by $-(\Delta p/L)$, where

$$\Delta p = p|_{z=0} - p|_{z=L} \qquad (2.8\text{-}13)$$

Multiplication of Eq. 2.8-12 by $r\,dr$, division by μ, and integration give

$$r \frac{dv_z}{dr} = -\left(\frac{\Delta p}{L}\right)\frac{r^2}{2\mu} + C_1 \qquad (2.8\text{-}14)$$

Dividing by r and integrating again, we have an expression for the velocity profile.

$$v_z = -\left(\frac{\Delta p}{L}\right)\frac{r^2}{4\mu} + C_1 \ln r + C_2 \qquad (2.8\text{-}15)$$

The boundary conditions for this flow are

    B.C. 1: v_z is finite for $0 \le r \le r_0$ (2.8-16a)

    B.C. 2: $v_z = 0$, $r = r_0$ (2.8-16b)

Both these conditions are derived from the idea that the fluid is a continuum; the velocity is therefore a continuous function. The first boundary condition is somewhat unusual in that the velocity is *not* specified at some point; it is simply restricted to a finite value. Boundary conditions of this type are often found in the analysis of fluid motion, heat transfer, and mass transfer. Because the statement is so obvious, it is sometimes overlooked by students unfamiliar with the solution of boundary value problems. Application of boundary condition 1 requires that C_1 be zero, because $\ln r \to -\infty$ as $r \to 0$, and boundary condition 2 yields an expression for C_2,

$$v_z|_{r=r_0} = 0 = -\left(\frac{\Delta p}{L}\right)\frac{r_0^2}{4\mu} + C_2 \qquad (2.8\text{-}17)$$

The velocity may now be given as

$$v_z = \left(\frac{\Delta p}{L}\right)\frac{r_0^2}{4\mu}\left[1 - \left(\frac{r}{r_0}\right)^2\right] \qquad (2.8\text{-}18)$$

indicating that the velocity profile is parabolic.

---

† The arguments presented here are mainly qualitative and should be accepted in that context. A quantitative treatment of this problem is given in Chap. 5.

Eq. 2.8-18 is a very useful result, for it allows us to calculate the flow rate if the dimensions of the system, the pressure drop, and the viscosity are given. The volumetric flow rate is given by

$$Q = \int_0^{2\pi} \int_0^{r_0} v_z \dot{r} \, dr \, d\theta = \frac{\pi r_0^4}{8\mu}\left(\frac{\Delta p}{L}\right) \tag{2.8-19}$$

This relationship between the volumetric flow rate, the radius r_0 and the pressure gradient $\Delta p/L$ is called the Hagen-Poiseuille law in honor of the hydraulician, Hagen, and the physician, Poiseuille, who experimentally established this result in the early part of the nineteenth century.

We see by Eq. 2.8-19 that the flow rate is very sensitive to changes in the pipe radius; thus, a small error in sizing a pipe can lead to an appreciable error in the flow rate or pressure drop. For a given flow rate and a given fluid, specification of the pressure drop (i.e., the pump size) and the pipe size must be made on an economic basis. If a small-diameter pipe is used, the cost of the pipe is small but the cost of the pump is large. An engineer will constantly be confronted with problems of this type which require that an economic constraint be placed on the derived result.

Other quantities of interest can be derived from Eq. 2.8-18. The *maximum velocity*, $v_{z,\max}$, occurs at $r = 0$ and has the value

$$v_{z,\max} = \frac{r_0^2}{4\mu}\left(\frac{\Delta p}{L}\right) \tag{2.8-20}$$

The same conduits are often used to carry different fluids in order that piping costs be minimized and piping layouts simplified. In such cases it is important to know how long it will take before the new fluid being pumped through the conduit arrives at the exit. The maximum velocity can be used to calculate the "breakthrough" time. The *average velocity* $\langle v_z \rangle$† is defined as the volumetric flow rate divided by the cross-sectional area; therefore,

$$\langle v_z \rangle = \frac{Q}{\pi r_0^2} = \left(\frac{r_0^2}{8\mu}\right)\left(\frac{\Delta p}{L}\right)$$

The average velocity is often a useful quantity for sizing pipeline reactors, since the extent of a chemical reaction depends on the time the fluid spends in the reactor. This time is called the average residence time and is given by

$$\text{average residence time} = \frac{L}{\langle v_z \rangle}$$

Application of the Hagen-Poiseuille law is limited to steady, laminar flow; therefore, we must be sure that the flow under consideration is not turbulent.

† Throughout the text, angular brackets $(\langle \, \rangle)$ will be used to denote both volume and area averages.

Calculation of the flow rate should always be accompanied by a determination of the Reynolds number,

$$N_{\text{Re}} = \frac{\rho \langle v_z \rangle D}{\mu}$$

to be sure that it is less than the critical value, 2100.

Knowledge of the stress distribution for laminar flow in a tube is sometimes desired. Rewriting Eq. 2.8-6 in the form

$$\frac{d}{dr}(r\tau_{rz}) = -\left(\frac{\Delta p}{L}\right)r \qquad (2.8\text{-}21)$$

and integrating, we have

$$\tau_{rz} = -\left(\frac{\Delta p}{L}\right)\frac{r}{2} + \frac{C_1}{r} \qquad (2.8\text{-}22)$$

Because the shear stress must always be finite, we may write,

B.C. 1: τ_{rz} is finite for $0 \leq r \leq r_0$

Thus, the constant of integration C_1 is zero, and the shear stress is a linear function of r.

$$\tau_{rz} = -\left(\frac{\Delta p}{L}\right)\frac{r}{2} \qquad (2.8\text{-}23)$$

The fact that τ_{rz} is negative is in keeping with our intuition, because the shear stress acting on the r-surface having a positive outwardly directed normal must certainly act in the negative z-direction if the fluid is flowing in the positive z-direction.

Sample calculation of pressure drop

Oil having a density of 0.87 g/cm³ and a viscosity of 1.3 poises is to be pumped through a smooth pipe 100 ft long with an inner diameter of 2.0 in. We wish to calculate the pressure drop for a volumetric flow rate of 1000 ft³/hr. Rearranging Eq. 2.8-19 gives

$$\Delta p = 8\mu L Q / \pi r_0^4 \qquad (2.8\text{-}24)$$

Substituting the appropriate values and the necessary conversion factors, we get

$$\Delta p = \left\{ \underbrace{\frac{(8)(1.3 \text{ poises})(100 \text{ ft})(1000 \text{ ft}^3/\text{hr})}{(3.14)(1.0 \text{ in.})^4}}_{\text{Original terms}} \right\}$$

$$\times \left\{ \underbrace{\left(\frac{1 \text{ dyne-sec/cm}^2}{\text{poise}}\right)\left(\frac{12 \text{ in.}}{\text{ft}}\right)^4\left(\frac{1 \text{ hr}}{3600 \text{ sec}}\right)}_{\text{Conversion factors}} \right\}$$

$$\Delta p = 1.91 \times 10^6 \text{ dyne/cm}^2$$

If we wish the answer in terms of pounds-force per square inch, we write

$$\Delta p = \left\{ \underbrace{1.91 \times 10^6 \text{ dyne/cm}^2}_{\text{Original term}} \right\} \left\{ \underbrace{\left(\frac{2.25 \times 10^{-6} \text{ lb}_f}{\text{dyne}} \right) \left(\frac{2.54 \text{ cm}}{\text{in.}} \right)^2}_{\text{Conversion factors}} \right\} = 27.6 \text{ lb}_f/\text{in.}^2$$

To complete the solution, we need to verify that the flow is laminar. The Reynolds number is given by

$$N_{\text{Re}} = \frac{\rho \langle v_z \rangle D}{\mu} = \frac{4 \rho Q}{\pi D \mu}$$

$$N_{\text{Re}} = \underbrace{\left\{ \frac{(4)(0.87 \text{ g/cm}^3)(1000 \text{ ft}^3/\text{hr})}{(3.14)(2.0 \text{ in.})(1.3 \text{ poises})} \right\}}_{\text{Original terms}}$$

$$\times \underbrace{\left\{ \left(\frac{1 \text{ hr}}{3600 \text{ sec}} \right) \left(\frac{12 \text{ in.}}{\text{ft}} \right)^3 \left(\frac{2.54 \text{ cm}}{\text{in.}} \right)^2 \left(\frac{1 \text{ poise}}{\text{g/cm-sec}} \right) \right\}}_{\text{Conversion factors}}$$

Carrying out the computation, we have

$$N_{\text{Re}} = 1320$$

Thus, the flow is laminar.

Non-Newtonian flow between two flat plates

Figure 2.8-3 illustrates the flow of a non-Newtonian fluid between two parallel plates, inclined at an angle θ from the horizontal. The velocity profile is indicative of a pseudoplastic "power-law" fluid. Assuming the flow to be one-dimensional and laminar, we apply the x-component of Eq. 2.8-3 to the differential volume shown in Fig. 2.8-3 to obtain

$$0 = (\rho g_x) \Delta x \, \Delta y \, \Delta z \qquad \text{Body force}$$

$$+ \{ p \, \Delta y \, \Delta z |_x - p \, \Delta y \, \Delta z |_{x+\Delta x} \} \qquad \begin{array}{l} \text{Forces on the} \\ x\text{-surfaces} \end{array} \qquad (2.8\text{-}25)$$

$$+ \{ -\tau_{yx} \Delta x \, \Delta z |_y + \tau_{yx} \Delta x \, \Delta z |_{y+\Delta y} \} \qquad \begin{array}{l} \text{Forces on the} \\ y\text{-surfaces} \end{array}$$

Dividing by $\Delta x \, \Delta y \, \Delta z$ and taking the limit as before, we get

$$0 = \rho g \sin \theta - \lim_{\Delta x \to 0} \frac{p|_{x+\Delta x} - p|_x}{\Delta x}$$

$$+ \lim_{\Delta y \to 0} \frac{\tau_{yx}|_{y+\Delta y} - \tau_{yx}|_y}{\Delta y} \qquad (2.8\text{-}26)$$

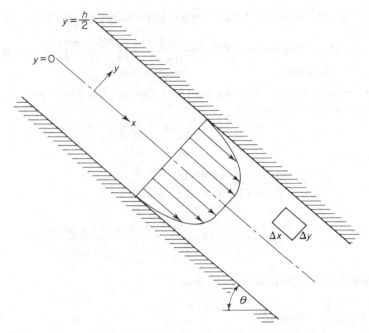

Fig. 2.8-3. Flow between two flat plates.

where g_x has been replaced by $g \sin \theta$. Each limit represents a derivative, and the limiting process gives us

$$0 = \rho g \sin \theta - \frac{\partial p}{\partial x} + \frac{\partial \tau_{yx}}{\partial y} \qquad (2.8\text{-}27)$$

We may also apply the y-component of Eq. 2.8-3 to this flow to obtain

$$0 = -\rho g \cos \theta - \frac{\partial p}{\partial y} \qquad (2.8\text{-}28)$$

Integration of Eq. 2.8-28 gives an expression for the pressure†

$$p(x, y) = -\rho g y \cos \theta + C(x) \qquad (2.8\text{-}29)$$

which leads to the conclusion that $\partial p / \partial x$ is independent of y. Rearranging Eq. 2.8-27 into the form,

$$\frac{\partial p}{\partial x} - \rho g \sin \theta = \frac{\partial \tau_{yx}}{\partial y} \qquad (2.8\text{-}30)$$

† Note that integration of a partial derivative yields a "constant of integration," which may be a function of the other independent variables.

we note that the left-hand side is independent of y. For one-dimensional flow τ_{yx} is independent of x, thus both sides of Eq. 2.8-30 must be equal to a constant. Integration is then straightforward, and we obtain

$$\tau_{yx} = -\left(\frac{\Delta p}{L} + \rho g \sin \theta\right) y + C_1 \qquad (2.8\text{-}31)$$

The boundary condition that we wish to apply to evaluate the constant of integration is that the shear stress is zero at the plane of symmetry, $y = 0$.

B.C. 1: $\tau_{yx} = 0, \qquad y = 0$ (2.8-32)

The easiest way to demonstrate the validity of this condition is to apply Eq. 2.8-3 to the differential volume shown in Fig. 2.8-4. Note that the shear

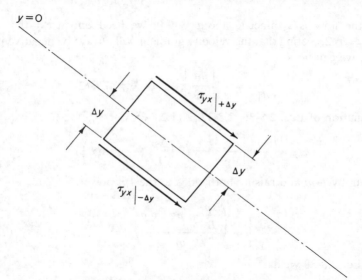

Fig. 2.8-4. Shear stress at a plane of symmetry.

stresses at $y = +\Delta y$ and $y = -\Delta y$ are both acting in the same direction following the assumption of symmetry about the plane $y = 0$, i.e.,

$$\left.\tau_{yx}\right|_{+y} = -\left.\tau_{yx}\right|_{-y} \qquad (2.8\text{-}33)$$

Evaluation of the terms in Eq. 2.8-3 gives

$$0 = (\rho g_x)2\,\Delta x\,\Delta y\,\Delta z \qquad \text{Body force}$$

$$+ 2p\,\Delta y\,\Delta z|_x - 2p\,\Delta y\,\Delta z|_{x+\Delta x} \quad \begin{array}{l}\text{Forces on the}\\ \text{x-surfaces}\end{array} \qquad (2.8\text{-}34)$$

$$+ 2\tau_{yx}|_{y=+\Delta y}\,\Delta x\,\Delta z \qquad \begin{array}{l}\text{Forces on the}\\ \text{y-surfaces}\end{array}$$

If we let Δx and Δz remain finite and allow Δy to go to zero, Eq. 2.8-34 reduces to

$$2\tau_{yx}\big|_{y=0}\,\Delta x\,\Delta z = 0 \tag{2.8-35}$$

and it follows that the shear stress at the plane of symmetry must be zero. Thus, C_1 is zero and the stress distribution is

$$\tau_{yx} = -\left(\frac{\Delta p}{L} + \rho g \sin \theta\right) y \tag{2.8-36}$$

The shear stress for a power-law fluid in one-dimensional flow is given by (see Eq. 1.5-9)

$$\tau_{yx} = m\left|\frac{dv_x}{dy}\right|^{n-1}\left(\frac{dv_x}{dy}\right) \tag{2.8-37}$$

Since the flow is symmetric about $y = 0$, we need only treat the region $0 \le y \le h/2$. Noting that the velocity gradient will always be negative in this region, we can write

$$\frac{dv_x}{dy} = -\left|\frac{dv_x}{dy}\right|, \qquad 0 \le y \le h/2 \tag{2.8-38}$$

Combination of Eqs. 2.8-36, 2.8-37, and 2.8-38 yields

$$\tau_{yx} = -m\left|\frac{dv_x}{dy}\right|^{n} = -\left(\frac{\Delta p}{L} + \rho g \sin \theta\right) y \tag{2.8-39}$$

Dividing by $-m$ and raising both sides to the $1/n$ power,

$$\left|\frac{dv_x}{dy}\right| = \left(\frac{\dfrac{\Delta p}{L} + \rho g \sin \theta}{m}\right)^{1/n} y^{1/n} \tag{2.8-40}$$

Using Eq. 2.8-38 yields

$$\left(\frac{dv_x}{dy}\right) = -\left(\frac{\dfrac{\Delta p}{L} + \rho g \sin \theta}{m}\right)^{1/n} y^{1/n} \tag{2.8-41}$$

This equation may be integrated, subject to the boundary condition

B.C. 1:
$$v_x = 0, \qquad y = \frac{h}{2} \tag{2.8-42}$$

to obtain the velocity distribution

$$v_x = \frac{n}{n+1}\left(\frac{\dfrac{\Delta p}{L} + \rho g \sin \theta}{m}\right)^{1/n}\left(\frac{h}{2}\right)^{(1+n)/n}\left[1 - \left(\frac{2y}{h}\right)^{(1+n)/n}\right] \tag{2.8-43}$$

The volumetric flow rate per unit width $q\dagger$ is readily obtained by integrating Eq. 2.8-43.

$$q = \left(\frac{2n}{2n+1}\right)\left(\frac{\frac{\Delta p}{L} + \rho g \sin \theta}{m}\right)^{1/n} \left(\frac{h}{2}\right)^{(2n+1)/n} \quad (2.8\text{-}44)$$

The velocity profile is somewhat easier to examine if the velocity is made dimensionless by dividing by the average velocity.$\ddagger$

$$U_x = \frac{v_x}{\langle v_x \rangle} = \left(\frac{2n+1}{n+1}\right)(1 - Y^{(n+1)/n}) \quad (2.8\text{-}45)$$

where $Y = 2y/h$, a dimensionless distance. Several velocity profiles, computed from Eq. 2.8-45, are shown in Fig. 2.8-5.

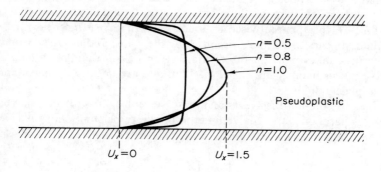

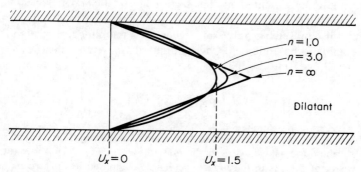

Fig. 2.8-5. Velocity profiles for a power-law fluid flowing between two flat plates.

† The total volumetric flow rate (in cubic feet per second) will always be represented by Q, while the volumetric flow rate per unit width (in cubic feet per second per foot) will be represented by q.

‡ Whenever possible, capital letters will be used to denote dimensionless quantities.

If we compare Eq. 2.8-37 with Newton's law of viscosity, we see that the apparent viscosity is given by

$$\mu_{app} = m \left| \frac{dv_x}{dy} \right|^{n-1} \qquad (2.8\text{-}46)$$

Thus, if $n < 1$ the apparent viscosity decreases with increasing shear rate, and the fluid is called pseudoplastic. Since the shear rate is zero at the centerline and a maximum at the wall, the apparent viscosity becomes increasingly smaller near the wall, and the flow resembles a case where there might be "slip" at the wall. Note in Eq. 2.8-44, that as n becomes small, the volumetric flow rate becomes more sensitive to the channel depth, h. In working with highly pseudoplastic fluids, we must be extremely careful when specifying pipe diameters or channel depths, for a small error in geometry can lead to a large error in the flow rate at a given pressure drop.

If $n > 1$, the apparent viscosity increases with increasing shear rate; thus, the fluid appears to be more viscous near the walls, and a larger proportion of the flow takes place in the central region of the channel. Fluids which behave in this manner are called dilatant, and are not nearly as common as pseudoplastic fluids.

If $n = 1$, the fluid is Newtonian and we replace m with μ. The velocity profile is parabolic, and the volumetric flow rate per unit width is given by

$$q = \frac{h^3}{12\mu}\left(\frac{\Delta p}{L} + \rho g \sin \theta\right) \qquad (2.8\text{-}47)$$

This type of flow is sometimes referred to as "plane" Poiseuille flow.

The methods presented in this section have allowed us to solve some rather important practical problems without recourse to detailed analysis; however, this approach is only useful when the streamlines are straight. Much work remains to be done before we can handle more complex flows.

PROBLEMS

2.1. If the density of fluid 1 is 62.4 lb m/ft³ and the density of fluid 2 is 136.8 lb m/ft, determine the gas pressure in the tank shown in Fig. 2-1. Assume that the density of the gas in the tank is negligible compared to the two manometer fluids.

Ans.: 20.4 psia.

2-2. A simple U-tube manometer can be used to determine the specific gravity γ of fluids which are more dense than water by the arrangement illustrated in Fig. 2-2. Derive an expression for γ in terms of z_1, z_2, and z_3.

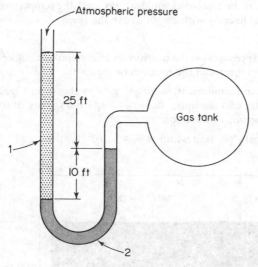

Fig. 2-1

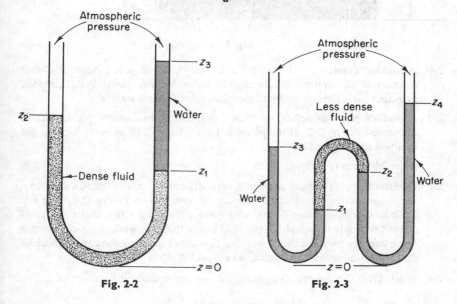

Fig. 2-2   Fig. 2-3

2-3. For fluids with a density close to, but less than, that of water, the specific gravity is best determined in the system shown in Fig. 2-3. Derive an expression for γ in terms of z_1, z_2, z_3 and z_4.

$$Ans.: \quad \gamma = \frac{\rho_1}{\rho_2} = \frac{(z_4 - z_2) - (z_3 - z_1)}{(z_1 - z_2)}$$

2-4. If the air can be treated as an ideal gas, and the temperature of the atmosphere varies linearly with height above the earth,

$$T = T_0 - \alpha z$$

derive an expression for the pressure as a function of z neglecting fluid motion in the atmosphere and the rotation of the earth.

2-5. Two fluids are confined by a hinged gate as shown in Fig. 2-5. If the lower fluid is water and the upper fluid has a specific gravity of 0.8, determine the moment per unit width about point "A."

Ans.: Moment per unit width is 69.4×10^4 lb$_f$-ft/ft.

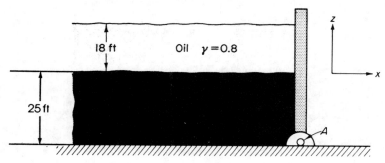

Fig. 2-5

2-6. A wooden sphere ($\rho = 58$ lb$_m$/ft^3) is floating at an air-water interface. What fraction of the sphere is submerged? Solve by first deriving Archimedes' principle for an arbitrary body located at a fluid-fluid interface.

2-7. A wooden plank of density 46 lb$_m$/ft^3 is anchored in a submerged surface as illustrated in Fig. 2-7. If the plank is 1 in. thick and 10 in. wide, what is the moment about point "A"?

Ans.: Moment is 57 lb$_f$-ft.

2-8. Determine both the horizontal and vertical components of the force per unit width exerted by the fluid on the curved gate shown in Fig. 2-8. Use Eq. 2.5-2 to determine these forces, and deduce from the result that the y-component is simply the weight of the fluid above the gate, while the x-component is the average pressure exerted on the gate times the projected area. In order that the units remain consistent, take $\beta = 1$ ft$^{1/2}$.

2-9. Work Prob. 2-8 for the case where the density is a linear function of y.

$$\rho = \rho_0 - \Delta\rho \left(\frac{y}{6 \text{ ft}}\right)$$

where $\Delta\rho = 10$ lb$_m$/ft^3

$\rho_0 = 62.4$ lb$_m$/ft^3

$y = $ ft

Ans.: $f_x = 896$ lb$_f$/ft; $f_y = -2960$ lb$_f$/ft.

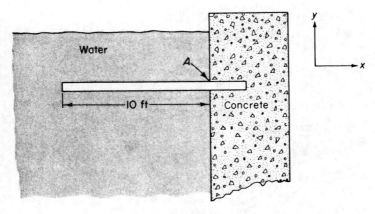

Fig. 2-7

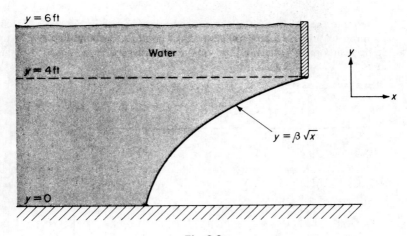

Fig. 2-8

2-10. The spherical tank shown in Fig. 2-10 contains both water and oil at a pressure indicated by the mercury manometer. The mass of each half of the spherical shell is 2000 lb$_m$. If 30 bolts are used to hold the two sections together, what is the force per bolt?

2-11. A weather balloon 10 ft in diameter is filled with 7.0 lb$_m$ of helium. Using the result obtained in Prob. 2-4 with $\alpha = 0.005°K/ft$, determine to what altitude the balloon will rise. Assume that $T_0 = 298°K$, the diameter of the balloon is constant at 10 ft, and the mass of the balloon is 10 lb$_m$.

Given: $R_{air} = 0.0253$ atm ft^3/lb$_m$°R, $R_{He} = 0.182$ atm ft^3/lb$_m$°R.

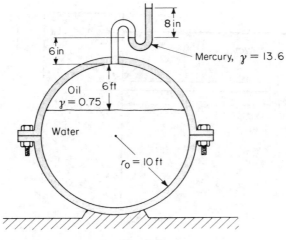

Fig. 2-10

2-12. Determine the thickness t of the concrete dam shown in Fig. 2-12, which is required to produce a zero moment about point B. Assume that the hydrostatic head on the bottom of the dam varies linearly from 80 ft at A to zero at B.

Ans.: $t = 34.1$ ft.

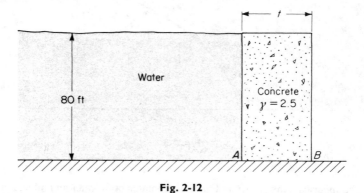

Fig. 2-12

2-13. The micromanometer illustrated in Fig. 2-13 is a useful device for accurately measuring small pressure differences. If the densities of the two manometer fluids are nearly the same ($\rho_1 \approx \rho_2$), measurable values of the distance d can be obtained for very small values of the pressure difference, $p_B - p_A$. Letting A_1 be the cross-sectional area of the reservoirs, and A_2 be the cross-sectional area of the connecting tube, derive an expression for $p_B - p_A$ in terms of ρ_1, ρ_2, g, A_1, A_2, and d.

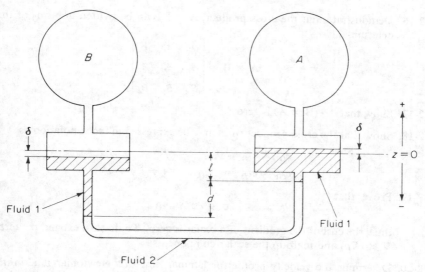

Fig. 2-13

2-14. The *center of stress* (often referred to as the *center of pressure* for hydrostatic systems) is defined as the position at which total force could be applied and still give the same torque as the distributed force system. If we define $\bar{r}$ as the position vector locating the center of stress, the mathematical equivalent of the above definition is

$$\bar{r} \times F = \int_A r \times t_{(n)} \, dA$$

where

$$F = \int_A t_{(n)} \, dA$$

Use these equations to locate the center of stress for the gate shown in Fig. 2-8 when the density is constant.

2-15. Prove the following:

(a) $A \cdot (B \times C) = B \cdot (C \times A) = C \cdot (A \times B)$

(b) $A \times (B \times C) = -(B \times C) \times A = B(A \cdot C) - C(A \cdot B)$

Given that

$$i \times j = k = -j \times i, \quad i \times i = 0$$
$$j \times k = i = -k \times j, \quad j \times j = 0$$
$$k \times i = j = -i \times k, \quad k \times k = 0$$

2-16. Demonstrate that the cross product, $\mathbf{A} \times \mathbf{B}$, can be written in term• of the determinant

$$\mathbf{A} \times \mathbf{B} = \begin{vmatrix} \mathbf{i} & \mathbf{j} & \mathbf{k} \\ A_x & A_y & A_z \\ B_x & B_y & B_z \end{vmatrix}$$

2-17. Show that $\mathbf{A} \cdot (\mathbf{B} \times \mathbf{A})$ is zero.

2-18. Show that the cross product rules may be expressed in index notation as

$$\mathbf{e}_{(i)} \times \mathbf{e}_{(j)} = 0, \qquad i = j$$
$$\mathbf{e}_{(i)} \times \mathbf{e}_{(j)} = \pm \mathbf{e}_{(k)}, \qquad i \neq j \neq k \neq i$$

2-19. Prove that

$$\nabla \times (\nabla p) = 0$$

thus, the curl of the gradient of a scalar is zero. To do this, expand the term $\nabla \times (\nabla p)$ and regroup the scalar components.

2-20. Determine the velocity profile for laminar flow of a Newtonian fluid in the annular region illustrated in Fig. 2-20.

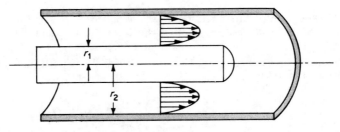

Fig. 2-20

2-21. Derive the flow-rate, pressure-drop relationship for the flow of a power-law fluid through a circular tube. The relationship between shear stress and shear rate is given by

$$\tau_{rz} = m \left| \frac{dv_z}{dr} \right|^{n-1} \left(\frac{dv_z}{dr} \right)$$

for one-dimensional laminar flow in a tube.

Kinematics 3

In the previous chapter, we analyzed the problem of determining the pressure field and surface forces for static fluids, and we determined velocity profiles for one-dimensional laminar flows. In both cases, the linear momentum principle was applied to a differential volume element to derive the appropriate differential equations. These were, in fact, special forms of the more general differential equations of motion, and the derivations were possible only because the acceleration term in the linear momentum equation was zero. To analyze the complex flows commonly encountered in practice, we must be capable of describing the fluid motion in a precise manner. Kinematics is the description of motion per se, and it takes no account of how this motion is brought about. The material presented in this chapter represents a key step toward our objective of deriving the differential equations of motion. In addition, some of the derived results must be used in the formulation of the macroscopic balances treated in Chap. 7.

The student is encouraged not to dismiss these preliminary developments as "mathematical gymnastics" unrelated to the practical application of the final result, for the derived differential equations (Chap. 5) or the macroscopic balances (Chap. 7) cannot be applied to practical problems with any confidence unless the derivation is understood. And the derivation cannot be understood unless the mathematical tools used in the development are mastered.

*3.1   Material and Spatial Coordinates

Our objective in this section is to develop an understanding of *material coordinates* and their relationship to *spatial coordinates*, so that we can adequately describe the motion of a fluid. The term "spatial coordinates" refers to a fixed rectangular coordinate system in which all points may be located. The existence of such a coordinate system follows from the assumption that the space is Euclidean. There are two possible methods of locating or identifying a "particle" of fluid, which may be defined as a differential material volume element, $d\mathcal{V}_m(t)$, i.e. it is a vanishingly small volume of fluid which contains the same material at all times. At some time, t, we may designate the position of a fluid particle in terms of its spatial coordinates—x, y, and z. In this manner, all fluid particles may be located in terms of the spatial coordinates and time. At some reference time, chosen as $t = 0$ for convenience, the position of any fluid particle can be specified as

$$x = X, \qquad y = Y, \qquad z = Z, \qquad \text{at} \quad t = 0$$

At some other time, $t > 0$, the position of this particle may be expressed as

$$x = X + \int_0^t \left(\frac{dx}{dt}\right) dt \qquad (3.1\text{-}1a)$$

$$y = Y + \int_0^t \left(\frac{dy}{dt}\right) dt \qquad (3.1\text{-}1b)$$

$$z = Z + \int_0^t \left(\frac{dz}{dt}\right) dt \qquad (3.1\text{-}1c)$$

We may put this result in more compact vector form by multiplying these three equations by $\mathbf{i}$, $\mathbf{j}$, and $\mathbf{k}$, respectively, and then adding to obtain

$$\mathbf{r} = \mathbf{R} + \int_0^t \left(\frac{d\mathbf{r}}{dt}\right) dt \qquad (3.1\text{-}2)$$

where $\mathbf{r} = \mathbf{i}x + \mathbf{j}y + \mathbf{k}z$
$\mathbf{R} = \mathbf{i}X + \mathbf{j}Y + \mathbf{k}Z$

We shall call $\mathbf{r}$ the *spatial position vector*, because it locates the fluid particle in space, while $\mathbf{R}$ will be called the *material position vector*, because it represents the coordinates used to "tag" or identify a given particle. Notice that the material coordinates do not represent a coordinate system which moves and deforms with the fluid; they simply represent a *specific* set of spatial coordinates—namely, those which the fluid particle occupied at the reference time, $t = 0$. Since no two fluid particles can occupy the same spatial position at the same time, the material position vector uniquely defines a fluid particle. Equation 3.1-2 may be written as

$$\mathbf{r} = \mathbf{r}(\mathbf{R}, t) \tag{3.1-3}$$

which simply expresses the fact that the spatial coordinates of a fluid particle are a function of time and the material coordinates.†

The time rate of change of the spatial position vector for a particular fluid particle is the velocity of that particle. Since this time derivative is evaluated with the material coordinates held constant, it is called a *material derivative*. In keeping with the nomenclature to be established in Sec. 3.2, we write

$$\left(\frac{d\mathbf{r}}{dt}\right)_{\mathbf{R}} = \frac{D\mathbf{r}}{Dt} = \mathbf{v} \tag{3.1-4}$$

*3.2 Time Derivatives

The time derivative of an arbitrary scalar function, $S = S(x, y, z, t)$, is given by

$$\frac{dS}{dt} = \lim_{\Delta t \to 0} \left[\frac{S(t + \Delta t) - S(t)}{\Delta t} \right] \tag{3.2-1}$$

where the spatial dependence of S is understood. For the special case where S is a function of time only, this definition of the derivative is unambiguous. However, if S is a function of the spatial coordinates, the derivative expressed by Eq. 3.2-1 is not well defined until some statement is made about the point in space at which S is measured for the two times, t and $t + \Delta t$.

As our first example, we shall consider a system of particles moving through space, letting x_p represent the x coordinate of the pth particle, as illustrated in Fig. 3.2-1. According to Eq. 3.2-1, we write

$$\frac{dx_p}{dt} = \lim_{\Delta t \to 0} \left[\frac{x_p(t + \Delta t) - x_p(t)}{\Delta t} \right] \tag{3.2-2}$$

$$= v_x, \text{ the velocity of the } p\text{th particle in the}$$
$$x\text{-direction}$$

† Describing the fluid motion in terms of the material coordinates and time is often referred to as the *Lagrangian method*, while the use of spatial coordinates and time is referred to as the *Eulerian method*.

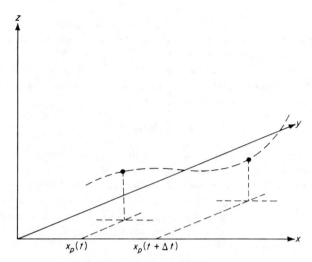

Fig. 3.2-1. Motion of a particle in space.

The derivative given by Eq. 3.2-2 is the time rate of change of a scalar, which is measured as we move *with* the particle—i.e., we might imagine an observer riding on the particle and continuously observing his position along the x-coordinate. This type of derivative, encountered previously in the study of particle dynamics, is called a material derivative and denoted by

$$\frac{Dx_p}{Dt} = \left(\frac{dx_p}{dt}\right)_{\mathbf{R}} = \lim_{\Delta t \to 0}\left[\frac{x_p(t+\Delta t) - x_p(t)}{\Delta t}\right] \qquad (3.2\text{-}3)$$

Material coordinates
held constant

In this particular example, there is no question about the type of derivative we obtain by the limiting process indicated by Eq. 3.2-1. The time derivative of any quantity associated with a particle is necessarily a material derivative, since the quantity can only be measured by an observer or a device which moves with the particle. For example, if we evaluate the time rate of change of the temperature of the pth particle,

$$\frac{dT_p}{dt} = \lim_{\Delta t \to 0}\left[\frac{T_p(t+\Delta t) - T_p(t)}{\Delta t}\right] \qquad (3.2\text{-}4)$$

it is obviously a material derivative.

Consider now the difficulties encountered in specifying the time rate of change of the temperature of a fluid. The derivative

$$\frac{dT}{dt} = \lim_{\Delta t \to 0}\left[\frac{T(t+\Delta t) - T(t)}{\Delta t}\right] \qquad (3.2\text{-}5)$$

is meaningless until we specify where, in space, T is measured. In the previous example, we measured the temperature while moving with a particle; however, the temperature of a fluid may be measured at a point fixed in space by a thermocouple or some other device. If the spatial coordinates are held constant for the limiting process, we write

$$\frac{\partial T}{\partial t} = \left(\frac{dT}{dt}\right)_{\mathbf{r}} = \lim_{\Delta t \to 0}\left[\frac{T(t + \Delta t) - T(t)}{\Delta t}\right] \qquad (3.2\text{-}6)$$

Spatial coordinates
held constant

where $\partial T/\partial t$ is called the *partial derivative*. It is possible, but not practical, to measure the temperature of a fluid with some device which moves with the fluid. Under such conditions the material coordinates would be held constant, and the material derivative DT/Dt would be determined. If $\mathbf{R}$ is held constant, the temperature of a single fluid particle is measured, whereas the temperature of a succession of fluid particles is measured if $\mathbf{r}$ is held constant.

Thus far we have indicated that the time rate of change of a scalar function takes on special meaning when either the spatial or material coordinates are held constant. If neither is held constant, the derivative is meaningful only if either the function depends only on time or the velocity of the point at which the function is measured has been specified.

Before we present specific equations for the material and total derivatives, it will be helpful to give examples of the three types of derivatives by considering a skin diver measuring the water temperature in the Big Sur River. The temperature may be a function of the spatial coordinates, x, y, and z, and time t. If the diver anchors himself at some point in the river, the time rate of change of temperature that he measures is given by

$$\left(\frac{dT}{dt}\right)_{\mathbf{r}} = \left(\frac{\partial T}{\partial t}\right) \qquad (3.2\text{-}7)$$

If he allows himself to drift with the current while he measures the time rate of change of temperature, the material derivative is determined.

$$\left(\frac{dT}{dt}\right)_{\mathbf{R}} = \left(\frac{DT}{Dt}\right) \qquad (3.2\text{-}8)$$

If the skin diver is energetic and moves about with a velocity $\mathbf{w}$ he measures the *total derivative*, dT/dt, which depends on the spatial variations of T, the velocity $\mathbf{w}$, and the partial derivative with respect to time.

We would now like to formulate these ideas in mathematical terms. The temperature is a function of the spatial coordinates and time, and we express this functional dependence as

$$T = T(\mathbf{r}, t) \qquad (3.2\text{-}9)$$

If the material coordinates are to be held constant, we express the spatial coordinates in terms of $\mathbf{R}$ and t by means of Eq. 3.1-3.

$$T = T(\mathbf{r}, t) = T[\mathbf{r}(\mathbf{R}, t), t] \qquad (3.2\text{-}10)$$
$$= T[x(\mathbf{R}, t), y(\mathbf{R}, t), z(\mathbf{R}, t), t]$$

Holding $\mathbf{R}$ constant, we differentiate with respect to time and get

$$\left(\frac{dT}{dt}\right)_{\mathbf{R}} = \frac{DT}{Dt} = \left(\frac{\partial T}{\partial x}\right)\left(\frac{dx}{dt}\right)_{\mathbf{R}} + \left(\frac{\partial T}{\partial y}\right)\left(\frac{dy}{dt}\right)_{\mathbf{R}} + \left(\frac{\partial T}{\partial z}\right)\left(\frac{dz}{dt}\right)_{\mathbf{R}} + \left(\frac{dT}{dt}\right)_{\mathbf{r}}$$
$$(3.2\text{-}11)$$

where the chain rule has been used to obtain the first three terms. This step always presents some difficulties, and it may be helpful to consider it further. If the student has had a course in thermodynamics, he is familiar with functions of several variables. For example, consider the Gibbs free energy, which may be expressed as a function of the temperature, volume, and number of moles, n.

$$G = G(T, V, n) \qquad (3.2\text{-}12)$$

The total derivative is

$$dG = \left(\frac{\partial G}{\partial T}\right)_{v,n} dT + \left(\frac{\partial G}{\partial V}\right)_{T,n} dV + \left(\frac{\partial G}{\partial n}\right)_{T,v} dn \qquad (3.2\text{-}13)$$

There is some curious notation associated with thermodynamics which is rarely encountered elsewhere—i.e., the use of subscripts on the partial derivatives to indicate which variables are being held constant. In some respects, this system is superfluous, because a partial derivative implies that "all other *independent* variables are held constant" during the limiting process. However, in thermodynamics there is a wide choice of independent variables, and the subscripts are used as a reminder that the independent variables are (in this example) T, V, and n. If T, V, and n are functions of time, Eq. 3.2-13 may be divided by dt to obtain

$$\frac{dG}{dt} = \left(\frac{\partial G}{\partial T}\right)_{V,n}\left(\frac{dT}{dt}\right) + \left(\frac{\partial G}{\partial V}\right)_{V,n}\left(\frac{dV}{dt}\right) + \left(\frac{\partial G}{\partial n}\right)_{T,v}\left(\frac{dn}{dt}\right) \qquad (3.2\text{-}14)$$

Under these conditions, the functional dependence of G could have been expressed as

$$G = G[T(t), V(t), n(t)] \qquad (3.2\text{-}15)$$

which is very similar to the functional dependence of T in Eq. 3.2-10 when $\mathbf{R}$ is held constant. The only difference is that the temperature, T, depends explicitly upon time in addition to the implicit time dependence via $x(t)$, $y(t)$, and $z(t)$.

Returning now to Eq. 3.2-11, we note that the derivatives of the spatial coordinates holding **R** constant are the components of the fluid velocity vector **v**, and the derivative of the temperature holding **r** constant is the partial derivative.

$$\frac{DT}{Dt} = \left(\frac{\partial T}{\partial t}\right) + v_x\left(\frac{\partial T}{\partial x}\right) + v_y\left(\frac{\partial T}{\partial y}\right) + v_z\left(\frac{\partial T}{\partial z}\right) \qquad (3.2\text{-}16)$$

Using vector notation, we can express Eq. 3.2-16 as

$$\frac{DT}{Dt} = \frac{\partial T}{\partial t} + \mathbf{v} \cdot \nabla T \qquad (3.2\text{-}17)$$

Noticing the repetition of x, y, and z in the last three terms of Eq. 3.2-16 quite naturally leads us to the use of index notation and the summation convention

$$\frac{DT}{Dt} = \left(\frac{\partial T}{\partial t}\right) + v_i\left(\frac{\partial T}{\partial x_i}\right) \qquad (3.2\text{-}18)$$

If the location of the point at which the temperature is measured varies with time owing to the motion of the skin diver, the material coordinates are no longer held constant. Instead of Eq. 3.2-11, we write

$$\left(\frac{dT}{dt}\right) = \left(\frac{\partial T}{\partial t}\right) + \left(\frac{\partial T}{\partial x}\right)\left(\frac{dx}{dt}\right) + \left(\frac{\partial T}{\partial y}\right)\left(\frac{dy}{dt}\right) + \left(\frac{\partial T}{\partial z}\right)\left(\frac{dz}{dt}\right) \qquad (3.2\text{-}19)$$

where dx/dt, dy/dt, and dz/dt are the components of the velocity vector **w** which describes the diver's motion. In vector form, Eq. 3.2-19 becomes

$$\frac{dT}{dt} = \frac{\partial T}{\partial t} + \mathbf{w} \cdot \nabla T \qquad (3.2\text{-}20)$$

This result is the most general type of time derivative we shall encounter. Equation 3.2-17 is just a special case (i.e., $\mathbf{w} = \mathbf{v}$) of Eq. 3.2-20, as is the partial derivative (i.e., $\mathbf{w} = 0$).

The sky-diver

As an illustration of the application of Eq. 3.2-20, let us consider a sky diver who has mistakenly strapped a dial thermometer instead of his altimeter onto his wrist. His error makes the jump more precarious but allows him to gather some interesting meteorological data. Assume that the air temperature is independent of time and decreases linearly between ground level and an altitude of 10,000 ft. Thus, we may represent the temperature as

$$T = T_0 - \alpha z$$

where $\alpha = 5 \times 10^{-3}°\text{F/ft}$, and Eq. 3.2-20 reduces to

$$\frac{dT}{dt} = -w_z\alpha \tag{3.2-21}$$

In the free-fall stage, the sky diver's velocity is about 200 mph. Hence,

$$\frac{dT}{dt} = -\left\{\left(\frac{-200\text{ mi}}{\text{hr}}\right)\left(\frac{5 \times 10^{-3}°\text{F}}{\text{ft}}\right)\right\}\left\{\left(\frac{5280\text{ ft}}{\text{mi}}\right)\left(\frac{\text{hr}}{3600\text{ sec}}\right)\right\} = 1.47°\text{F/sec}$$

and he experiences a rapid rise in temperature. After the parachute is opened, the velocity decreases to about 5 mph, and the rate of temperature rise is reduced to only $0.037°\text{F/sec}$.

The velocity field

In the study of fluid motion, we will be concerned with fluid acceleration and the forces which give rise to it. The time rate of change of velocity of a fluid particle is the acceleration **a**, given by

$$\mathbf{a} = \left(\frac{d\mathbf{v}}{dt}\right)_{\mathbf{R}} = \frac{D\mathbf{v}}{Dt} \tag{3.2-22}$$

The idea of acceleration is most easily grasped if we picture ourselves as moving with a system and continuously noting the rate at which our velocity is changing. For example, acceleration is vividly experienced as we rapidly pull away from a stoplight in a high-powered, low-slung, sports car. Under these circumstances, we can both "see" the acceleration (by observing our rapidly changing position) and "feel" the acceleration (in terms of the forces required to produce it).

Consider now a person fixed in space observing our sports car as it moves away from the stoplight. It is much more difficult for him to get the feel of the acceleration, for he can only note the velocity and the rate at which the velocity is changing with distance.

We have a similar difficulty in describing fluid acceleration from the point of view of a fixed observer, for the acceleration is *not* expressed as "the time rate of change of the velocity." Let us expand the right-hand side of Eq. 3.2-22 to express the acceleration as

$$\mathbf{a} = \frac{\partial \mathbf{v}}{\partial t} + \mathbf{v} \cdot \nabla\mathbf{v} \tag{3.2-23}$$

$$\underset{\substack{\uparrow \\ \text{Local} \\ \text{acceleration}}}{} \qquad \underset{\substack{\uparrow \\ \text{Convective} \\ \text{acceleration}}}{}$$

Here we see that the acceleration consists of two terms. The first is the rate of change of velocity at a fixed point in space and is called the *local acceleration*. The second is called the *convective acceleration*, and it depends upon both the magnitude of the velocity and the velocity gradients.

An observer riding with a fluid particle would describe his acceleration in terms of a single vector, **a**; the fixed observer would note the velocity, the local time rate of change of velocity, and the velocity gradients, and from these quantities he would deduce the acceleration. Note that if the flow is steady— i.e., **v** is not a function of time—Eq. 3.2-23 indicates that the acceleration is not necessarily zero.

As an example of a steady, accelerating flow, let us consider the flow in the entrance region of the Reynolds apparatus discussed in Sec. 1.2 and reproduced in Fig. 3.2-2. As a fluid particle moves from z to $z + \Delta z$ along the

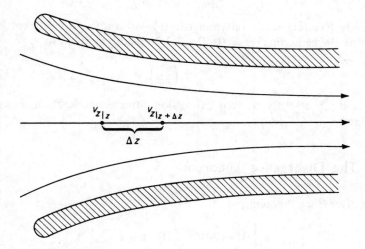

Fig. 3.2-2. Flow in the entrance region of the Reynolds apparatus.

centerline, the velocity changes from

$$v_z|_z \quad \text{to} \quad v_z|_{z+\Delta z}$$

The time required for the particle to move this distance may be denoted by Δt and expressed as

$$\Delta t = \frac{\Delta z}{\bar{v}_z} \tag{3.2-24}$$

Here $\bar{v}_z$ represents some average value of v_z. The acceleration in the

z-direction is the rate at which v_z changes with time and is therefore given by

$$a_z = \lim_{\Delta t \to 0} \left(\frac{v_z|_{z+\Delta z} - v_z|_z}{\Delta t} \right) = \lim_{\Delta z \to 0} \left[\frac{\bar{v}_z (v_z|_{z+\Delta z} - v_z|_z)}{\Delta z} \right]$$

$$= v_z \left(\frac{\partial v_z}{\partial z} \right) \tag{3.2-25}$$

Now let us compare this result with that given by Eq. 3.2-23. Forming the scalar product of Eq. 3.2-23 with $\mathbf{k}$, we have†

$$a_z = \frac{\partial v_z}{\partial t} + \mathbf{v} \cdot \nabla v_z$$

$$= \frac{\partial v_z}{\partial t} + v_r \left(\frac{\partial v_z}{\partial r} \right) + \frac{v_\theta}{r} \left(\frac{\partial v_z}{\partial \theta} \right) + v_z \left(\frac{\partial v_z}{\partial z} \right) \tag{3.2-26}$$

For steady $[(\partial v_z / \partial t) = 0]$, axisymmetric ($v_\theta = 0$ and v_z independent of θ), flow along the centerline ($v_r = 0$), Eq. 3.2-26 readily reduces to

$$a_z = v_z \left(\frac{\partial v_z}{\partial z} \right) \tag{3.2-27}$$

which is the previously derived expression for the acceleration along the centerline.

*3.3   The Divergence Theorem

The divergence theorem,‡

$$\int_{\mathscr{V}} \nabla \cdot \mathbf{G} \, dV = \int_{\mathscr{A}} \mathbf{G} \cdot \mathbf{n} \, dA \tag{3.3-1}$$

is a necessary mathematical tool for developing the differential equations of mass, momentum, and energy. In addition, it is very useful in formulating the macroscopic balances and in solving certain problems. Some of the ideas in this development have already been encountered in the discussion of surface forces and buoyancy effects, presented in Chap. 2. Expansion of Eq. 3.3-1 gives

$$\int_{\mathscr{V}} \left(\frac{\partial G_x}{\partial x} + \frac{\partial G_y}{\partial y} + \frac{\partial G_z}{\partial z} \right) dV = \int_{\mathscr{A}} (G_x \mathbf{i} \cdot \mathbf{n} + G_y \mathbf{j} \cdot \mathbf{n} + G_z \mathbf{k} \cdot \mathbf{n}) \, dA \tag{3.3-2}$$

† Here we have made use of an underived expression for $\mathbf{v} \cdot \nabla$ in cylindrical coordinates.
‡ The divergence theorem is also known as Green's theorem, Gauss' theorem, and Ostrogradsky's theorem.

The proof of this result will be accomplished by first proving that

$$\int_{\mathscr{V}} \left(\frac{\partial G_z}{\partial z}\right) dV = \int_{\mathscr{A}} G_z \mathbf{k} \cdot \mathbf{n} \, dA \qquad (3.3\text{-}3)$$

The volume $\mathscr{V}$ under consideration is illustrated in Fig. 3.3-1, and we presume that the surface may be divided into two regions by a curve along which

$$\mathbf{n} \cdot \mathbf{k} = 0 \qquad (3.3\text{-}4)$$

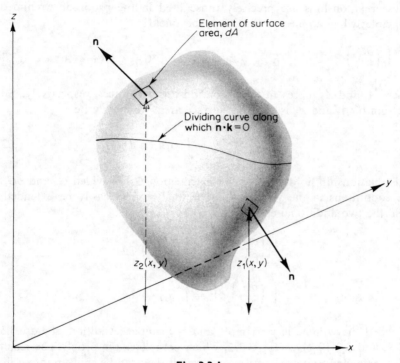

Fig. 3.3-1

where $\mathbf{n}$ is the outwardly directed unit normal. Volumes of this type are called "x-y simple" or "x-y projectable." In the lower region, the position of the surface is designated as $z_1(x, y)$, and in the upper region, $z_2(x, y)$. With this in mind, we write the volume integral on the left-hand side of Eq. 3.3-3 as

$$\int_{\mathscr{V}} \left(\frac{\partial G_z}{\partial z}\right) dV = \int_x \int_y \int_{z_1(x,y)}^{z_2(x,y)} \left(\frac{\partial G_z}{\partial z}\right) dz \, dy \, dx = \int_x \int_y \left[G_z\big|_{z_2(x,y)} - G_z\big|_{z_1(x,y)}\right] dy \, dx$$

$$(3.3\text{-}5)$$

Our limits of integration are now in terms of x and y; however, we wish to change these limits, representing them in terms of the surface area. In the lower region, the projected area $dx\,dy$ is given by

$$dx\,dy = -\mathbf{k} \cdot \mathbf{n}\,dA, \quad \text{Lower region} \qquad (3.3\text{-}6a)$$

while in the upper region,

$$dx\,dy = \mathbf{k} \cdot \mathbf{n}\,dA, \quad \text{Upper region} \qquad (3.3\text{-}6b)$$

These relationships are precisely those used in the proof of Archimedes' principle; when applied to Eq. 3.3-5, they yield

$$\int_{\mathcal{V}} \left(\frac{\partial G_z}{\partial z}\right) dV = \int_{A_2} G_z\big|_{z_2(x,y)} \mathbf{k} \cdot \mathbf{n}\,dA - \int_{A_1} G_z\big|_{z_1(x,y)} (-\mathbf{k} \cdot \mathbf{n})\,dA \quad (3.3\text{-}7)$$

where A_1 and A_2 represent the lower and upper surfaces, respectively. Since the sum of A_1 and A_2 is the total surface area, we may write

$$\int_{\mathcal{V}} \left(\frac{\partial G_z}{\partial z}\right) dV = \int_{\mathcal{A}} G_z \mathbf{k} \cdot \mathbf{n}\,dA \qquad (3.3\text{-}8)$$

This relationship holds for any scalar function G_z, provided G_z and $\partial G_z/\partial z$ are continuous in the volume $\mathcal{V}$. The analysis can easily be extended to yield the two additional equations,

$$\int_{\mathcal{V}} \left(\frac{\partial G_x}{\partial x}\right) dV = \int_{\mathcal{A}} G_x \mathbf{i} \cdot \mathbf{n}\,dA \qquad (3.3\text{-}9)$$

$$\int_{\mathcal{V}} \left(\frac{\partial G_y}{\partial y}\right) dV = \int_{\mathcal{A}} G_y \mathbf{j} \cdot \mathbf{n}\,dA \qquad (3.3\text{-}10)$$

provided the volume is y-z simple and z-x simple. Addition of Eqs. 3.3-8, 3.3-9, and 3.3-10 gives Eq. 3.3-2, which completes the proof. The result is easily extended to more complex volumes if they can be split up into a finite number of auxiliary volumes that meet the requirements of this proof.

Another useful form of the divergence theorem may be obtained by writing

$$\mathbf{G} = S\mathbf{b} \qquad (3.3\text{-}11)$$

where S is an arbitrary scalar, and $\mathbf{b}$ is an arbitrary, *constant* vector. By this we mean that the scalar components of $\mathbf{b}$ can take on any value, but they must be independent of x, y, and z. Substitution of Eq. 3.3-11 into Eq. 3.3-1 yields

$$\int_{\mathcal{V}} \nabla \cdot (S\mathbf{b})\,dV = \int_{\mathcal{A}} S\mathbf{b} \cdot \mathbf{n}\,dA \qquad (3.3\text{-}12)$$

The divergence of a scalar times a vector is given by

$$\mathbf{\nabla} \cdot (S\mathbf{b}) = \mathbf{b} \cdot \mathbf{\nabla} S + S\mathbf{\nabla} \cdot \mathbf{b} \tag{3.3-13}$$

In Gibbs notation, Eq. 3.3-13 may be proved by expanding both sides to show that they they are equal; however, in index notation the proof consists of straightforward product differentiation.

$$\frac{\partial}{\partial x_i} (Sb_i) = b_i \left(\frac{\partial S}{\partial x_i} \right) + S \frac{\partial b_i}{\partial x_i} \tag{3.3-14}$$

Since $\mathbf{b}$ is a constant vector, $\mathbf{\nabla} \cdot \mathbf{b}$ is zero and Eq. 3.3-12 takes the form

$$\int_{\mathcal{V}} \mathbf{b} \cdot \mathbf{\nabla} S \, dV = \int_{\mathcal{A}} S\mathbf{b} \cdot \mathbf{n} \, dA \tag{3.3-15}$$

Putting both integrals on the left-hand side of the equation and removing $\mathbf{b}$ from the integral signs, we get

$$\mathbf{b} \cdot \left[\int_{\mathcal{V}} \mathbf{\nabla} S \, dV - \int_{\mathcal{A}} S\mathbf{n} \, dA \right] = 0 \tag{3.3-16}$$

Since $\mathbf{b}$ is an *arbitrary*, constant vector, the term inside the brackets (which is also a vector) must be zero, and the divergence theorem for a scalar is obtained.

$$\int_{\mathcal{V}} \mathbf{\nabla} S \, dV = \int_{\mathcal{A}} S\mathbf{n} \, dA \tag{3.3-17}$$

The value of this result may be demonstrated by applying it to the linear momentum equation for a static fluid, which, in Chap. 2, was

$$0 = \int_{\mathcal{V}} \rho \mathbf{g} \, dV + \int_{\mathcal{A}} \mathbf{t}_{(n)} \, dA \tag{3.3-18}$$

The stress vector for a static fluid is

$$\mathbf{t}_{(n)} = -\mathbf{n}p$$

and Eq. 3.3-18 becomes

$$0 = \int_{\mathcal{V}} \rho \mathbf{g} \, dV - \int_{\mathcal{A}} p\mathbf{n} \, dA \tag{3.3-19}$$

Application of the divergence theorem for a scalar allows us to transform the area integral to a volume integral; hence, both terms can be put under the same integral sign

$$0 = \int_{\mathcal{V}} (\rho \mathbf{g} - \mathbf{\nabla} p) \, dV \tag{3.3-20}$$

Since the limits of integration are arbitrary, the integrand must be zero, and we obtain the previously derived equation for the pressure.

$$0 = -\nabla p + \rho \mathbf{g} \qquad (3.3\text{-}21)$$

The technique of extracting a differential equation from an arbitrary volume integral is an important one and deserves clarification. For the volume integral to be zero, the integrand must either be identically zero or take on both *plus* and *minus* values. However, if there is some region where the integrand is either positive or negative, we may form the integral over that region and thus violate Eq. 3.3-20. It follows, then, that if the limits of integration are arbitrary and the integral is equal to zero, the integrand must be identically zero. This result requires, of course, that the pressure and density be continuous functions.

*3.4 The Transport Theorem

The objective of this section is to develop a general equation for the time derivative of a volume integral, under conditions such that points on the surface of the volume move with a velocity, $\mathbf{w}$. By our previously discussed nomenclature, this volume is designated as $\mathscr{V}_a(t)$. The velocity $\mathbf{w}$ is a continuous function of the spatial coordinates and time, and may be set equal to the fluid velocity $\mathbf{v}$ as a special case. The volume then moves with the fluid and is a material volume designated by $\mathscr{V}_m(t)$. Under these conditions, we refer to the derived result as the *Reynolds transport theorem*.

Considering the arbitrary volume $\mathscr{V}_a(t)$ illustrated in Fig. 3.4-1, we wish to determine the time derivative of the volume integral of some scalar function, S. By definition,

$$\frac{d}{dt}\int_{\mathscr{V}_a(t)} S\, dV = \lim_{\Delta t \to 0}\left[\frac{\displaystyle\int_{\mathscr{V}_a(t+\Delta t)} S(t+\Delta t)\, dV - \int_{\mathscr{V}_a(t)} S(t)\, dV}{\Delta t}\right] \qquad (3.4\text{-}1)$$

To visualize the process under consideration, we must think of a volume, such as a sphere, moving through space so that the velocity of each point on the surface of the volume is given by $\mathbf{w}$. The velocity $\mathbf{w}$ may be a function of of the spatial coordinates (if the volume is deforming) and time (if the volume is accelerating or decelerating). At each instant of time, we assume that some scalar quantity—such as the density, or the temperature, or a scalar component of the velocity vector—is evaluated and the integral of this quantity over the volume is obtained. The time rate of change of the integral of this scalar, designated by S, is given by Eq. 3.4-1.

As in Sec. 3.2, the time derivative has no meaning unless the position in space at which the function is measured is specified. In this case the information is provided in terms of the velocity $\mathbf{w}$. In a time Δt, the "new" volume

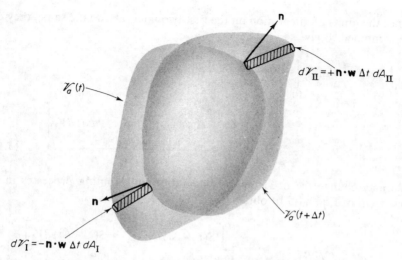

Fig. 3.4-1. The moving volume $\mathscr{V}_a(t)$.

swept out by the moving surface shall be designated by $V_{II}(\Delta t)$, and the "old" volume left behind by $V_I(\Delta t)$. The surface area at time t is represented by $\mathscr{A}_a(t)$, and may be split into two areas—$A_I(t)$ and $A_{II}(t)$—by a curve on the surface along which $\mathbf{n} \cdot \mathbf{w} = 0$. In a manner similar to our derivation of the divergence theorem, we will limit ourselves to the case where a single curve separates the volume into two parts. More complex cases can be reduced to this simple situation by appropriate formation of auxiliary volumes.

Our first step in the derivation of the transport theorem requires that we express the volume, $\mathscr{V}_a(t + \Delta t)$, as

$$\mathscr{V}_a(t + \Delta t) = \mathscr{V}_a(t) + V_{II}(\Delta t) - V_I(\Delta t) \tag{3.4-2}$$

thus allowing us to write the integral in Eq. 3.4-1 as

$$\int_{\mathscr{V}_a(t+\Delta t)} S(t + \Delta t)\, dV = \int_{\mathscr{V}_a(t)} S(t + \Delta t)\, dV + \int_{V_{II}(\Delta t)} S(t + \Delta t)\, dV_{II} - \int_{V_I(\Delta t)} S(t + \Delta t)\, dV_I$$

$$\tag{3.4-3}$$

Substitution of Eq. 3.4-3 into Eq. 3.4-1 yields

$$\frac{d}{dt} \int_{\mathscr{V}_a(t)} S\, dV$$

$$= \lim_{\Delta t \to 0} \left[\frac{\int_{\mathscr{V}_a(t)} S(t + \Delta t)\, dV - \int_{\mathscr{V}_a(t)} S(t)\, dV + \int_{V_{II}(\Delta t)} S(t + \Delta t)\, dV_{II} - \int_{V_I(\Delta t)} S(t + \Delta t)\, dV_I}{\Delta t} \right]$$

$$\tag{3.4-4}$$

Since the limits of integration on the first two integrals are the same, they can be combined to give

$$\frac{d}{dt} \int_{\mathscr{V}_a(t)} S \, dV = \lim_{\Delta t \to 0} \int_{\mathscr{V}_a(t)} \left[\frac{S(t + \Delta t) - S(t)}{\Delta t} \right] dV$$

$$+ \lim_{\Delta t \to 0} \left[\frac{\displaystyle\int_{V_{\mathrm{II}}(\Delta t)} S(t + \Delta t) \, dV_{\mathrm{II}} - \int_{V_{\mathrm{I}}(\Delta t)} S(t + \Delta t) \, dV_{\mathrm{I}}}{\Delta t} \right] \qquad (3.4\text{-}5)$$

We may change the order of the integrating and limiting processes in the first term of Eq. 3.4-5 to obtain

$$\frac{d}{dt} \int_{\mathscr{V}_a(t)} S \, dV = \int_{\mathscr{V}_a(t)} \left(\frac{\partial S}{\partial t} \right) dV + \lim_{\Delta t \to 0} \left[\frac{\displaystyle\int_{V_{\mathrm{II}}(\Delta t)} S(t + \Delta t) \, dV_{\mathrm{II}} - \int_{V_{\mathrm{I}}(\Delta t)} S(t + \Delta t) \, dV_{\mathrm{I}}}{\Delta t} \right] \qquad (3.4\text{-}6)$$

Our next step in this analysis is to change the volume integrals to surface integrals. Examining Fig. 3.4-2, we see that the length L of an oblique

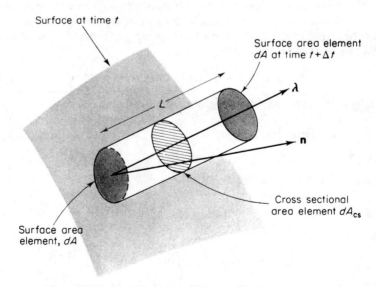

Fig. 3.4-2. Differential volume swept out by a moving surface.

cylinder swept out by a moving surface in a time Δt is

$$L = w \Delta t \qquad (3.4\text{-}7)$$

where w is the magnitude of the velocity vector $\mathbf{w}$. This vector may be written in terms of a unit vector $\boldsymbol{\lambda}$ (which gives the direction) and the magnitude w.

$$\mathbf{w} = \boldsymbol{\lambda} w \qquad (3.4\text{-}8)$$

The volume dV is given by the length times the cross-sectional area, dA_{cs},

$$dV = L \, dA_{cs} \qquad (3.4\text{-}9)$$

However, we seek a relationship between the volume dV and the surface area dA. The relationship between the cross-sectional area of the oblique cylinder and its surface area is

$$dA_{cs} = \pm \cos \theta \, dA \qquad (3.4\text{-}10)$$

where the cosine of θ is given by the scalar product between $\boldsymbol{\lambda}$ and $\mathbf{n}$.

$$\cos \theta = \boldsymbol{\lambda} \cdot \mathbf{n} \qquad (3.4\text{-}11)$$

The use of either the plus or minus sign in Eq. 3.4-10 depends on whether θ is greater or less than $\pi/2$. Equations 3.4-7 through 3.4-11 can be combined to give

$$\begin{aligned} dV &= \pm w \, \Delta t \, \boldsymbol{\lambda} \cdot \mathbf{n} \, dA \\ &= \pm \mathbf{w} \cdot \mathbf{n} \, \Delta t \, dA \end{aligned} \qquad (3.4\text{-}12)$$

Applying this result to the differential volumes, dV_{I} and dV_{II}, we write

$$dV_{\mathrm{I}} = -\mathbf{w} \cdot \mathbf{n} \, \Delta t \, dA_{\mathrm{I}} \qquad (3.4\text{-}13\mathrm{a})$$

$$dV_{\mathrm{II}} = +\mathbf{w} \cdot \mathbf{n} \, \Delta t \, dA_{\mathrm{II}} \qquad (3.4\text{-}13\mathrm{b})$$

Using these results allows us to write the two volume integrals in Eq. 3.4-6 as

$$\int_{V_{\mathrm{II}}(\Delta t)} S(t + \Delta t) \, dV_{\mathrm{II}} = +\Delta t \int_{A_{\mathrm{II}}(t)} S(t + \Delta t)\mathbf{w} \cdot \mathbf{n} \, dA_{\mathrm{II}} \qquad (3.4\text{-}14\mathrm{a})$$

$$\int_{V_{\mathrm{I}}(\Delta t)} S(t + \Delta t) \, dV_{\mathrm{I}} = -\Delta t \int_{A_{\mathrm{I}}(t)} S(t + \Delta t)\mathbf{w} \cdot \mathbf{n} \, dA_{\mathrm{I}} \qquad (3.4\text{-}14\mathrm{b})$$

Substitution of Eqs. 3.4-14 into Eq. 3.4-6 gives

$$\frac{d}{dt} \int_{\mathscr{V}_a(t)} S \, dV = \int_{\mathscr{V}_a(t)} \left(\frac{\partial S}{\partial t} \right) dV$$

$$+ \lim_{\Delta t \to 0} \left[\frac{\Delta t \int_{A_{\mathrm{II}}(t)} S(t + \Delta t)\mathbf{w} \cdot \mathbf{n} \, dA_{\mathrm{II}} + \Delta t \int_{A_{\mathrm{I}}(t)} S(t + \Delta t)\mathbf{w} \cdot \mathbf{n} \, dA_{\mathrm{I}}}{\Delta t} \right]$$

$$(3.4\text{-}15)$$

Taking the limit as indicated, and noting that $A_{\mathrm{I}}(t) + A_{\mathrm{II}}(t) = \mathscr{A}_a(t)$, we finally obtain the general transport theorem

$$\frac{d}{dt}\int_{\mathcal{V}_a(t)} S\, dV = \int_{\mathcal{V}_a(t)} \left(\frac{\partial S}{\partial t}\right) dV + \int_{\mathcal{A}_a(t)} S\mathbf{w}\cdot\mathbf{n}\, dA \qquad \text{General transport theorem} \qquad (3.4\text{-}16)$$

An obvious special case of this result is a volume fixed in space. Then, $\mathbf{w} = 0$ and

$$\frac{d}{dt}\int_{\mathcal{V}} S\, dV = \int_{\mathcal{V}} \left(\frac{\partial S}{\partial t}\right) dV \qquad\qquad (3.4\text{-}17)$$

where the limits of integration have been changed from $\mathcal{V}_a(t)$ to $\mathcal{V}$ to indicate that the volume is fixed in space. The most important use of Eq. 3.4-16 is for material volumes. Then $\mathbf{w}$ is equal to the fluid velocity $\mathbf{v}$ and we write

$$\frac{D}{Dt}\int_{\mathcal{V}_m(t)} S\, dV = \int_{\mathcal{V}_m(t)} \frac{\partial S}{\partial t}\, dV + \int_{\mathcal{A}_m(t)} S\mathbf{v}\cdot\mathbf{n}\, dA \qquad \text{Reynolds transport theorem} \qquad (3.4\text{-}18)$$

This result is referred to as the Reynolds transport theorem. The nomenclature indicates that the volume is a material volume, $\mathcal{V}_m(t)$, the surface is a material surface, $\mathcal{A}_m(t)$, and the time derivative D/Dt is taken with the material coordinates held constant.

This derivation was presented in terms of a scalar S to focus the students' attention on the development of the transport theorem. The extension to integrals of vectors is straightforward. For example, we need only apply the transport theorem to the three scalars, v_x, v_y, and v_z; then we multiply by $\mathbf{i}$, $\mathbf{j}$, and $\mathbf{k}$, respectively, and form the sum to obtain

$$\frac{d}{dt}\int_{\mathcal{V}_a(t)} \mathbf{v}\, dV = \int_{\mathcal{V}_a(t)} \frac{\partial \mathbf{v}}{\partial t}\, dV + \int_{\mathcal{A}_a(t)} \mathbf{v}(\mathbf{w}\cdot\mathbf{n})\, dA \qquad (3.4\text{-}19)$$

In concluding this treatment of the transport theorem, a warning is necessary: Much more satisfactory methods of deriving the transport theorem[1-2] are available through the use of a coordinate transformation from spatial to material coordinates. The development presented here is intuitive in nature inasmuch as the geometry of curved, moving surfaces is more complex than we have intimated.

*3.5 Conservation of Mass

We will now make use of the previous developments to formulate the *continuity equation*, which may be descriptively referred to as the *differential*

1. R. Aris, *Vectors, Tensors, and the Basic Equations of Fluid Mechanics* (Englewood Cliffs, N.J.: Prentice-Hall, Inc., 1962), p. 78.

2. C. Truesdell and R. Toupin, *The Classical Field Theories, Handbuch der Physik,* S. Flügge, ed. (Berlin: Springer-Verlag, 1960), p. 347.

mass balance. The mass M contained in a material volume is given by

$$M = \int_{\mathscr{V}_m(t)} \rho \, dV \qquad (3.5\text{-}1)$$

Since conservation of mass requires that M be a constant, the time rate of change of M must be zero.

$$\left(\frac{dM}{dt}\right)_{\mathbf{R}} = \frac{DM}{Dt} = \frac{D}{Dt}\int_{\mathscr{V}_m(t)} \rho \, dV = 0 \qquad (3.5\text{-}2)$$

Application of the Reynolds transport theorem yields

$$\frac{D}{Dt}\int_{\mathscr{V}_m(t)} \rho \, dV = \int_{\mathscr{V}_m(t)}\left(\frac{\partial\rho}{\partial t}\right) dV + \int_{\mathscr{A}_m(t)} \rho\mathbf{v}\cdot\mathbf{n}\, dA = 0 \qquad (3.5\text{-}3)$$

The divergence theorem may now be used to transform the area integral into a volume integral, allowing both terms to be written under the same integral sign.

$$\frac{D}{Dt}\int_{\mathscr{V}_m(t)} \rho \, dV = \int_{\mathscr{V}_m(t)}\left[\frac{\partial\rho}{\partial t} + \mathbf{\nabla}\cdot(\rho\mathbf{v})\right] dV = 0 \qquad (3.5\text{-}4)$$

Since the limits of integration are arbitrary, the term in brackets must be zero and the continuity equation results

$$\frac{\partial\rho}{\partial t} + \mathbf{\nabla}\cdot(\rho\mathbf{v}) = 0 \qquad (3.5\text{-}5)$$

This equation applies to every point in space, and is subject only to the restriction that the material under consideration is a continuum free from nuclear reaction. Making use of Eq. 3.2-17 for the material derivative of a scalar function, and noting that,

$$\mathbf{\nabla}\cdot(\rho\mathbf{v}) = \mathbf{v}\cdot\mathbf{\nabla}\rho + \rho\mathbf{\nabla}\cdot\mathbf{v} \qquad (3.5\text{-}6)$$

we may write the continuity equation as

$$\frac{D\rho}{Dt} + \rho\mathbf{\nabla}\cdot\mathbf{v} = 0 \qquad (3.5\text{-}7)$$

Equations 3.5-7 and 3.5-5 are entirely equivalent, and the latter is given only to familiarize the student with a commonly used form of the continuity equation. An especially important form of this equation is that for an incompressible flow, for which both Eqs. 3.5-7 and 3.5-5 reduce to

$$\mathbf{\nabla}\cdot\mathbf{v} = 0 \qquad (3.5\text{-}8)$$

The continuity equation can be used to derive an interesting special form of the Reynolds transport theorem. If the scalar S is given by,

$$S = \rho\mathcal{S} \qquad (3.5\text{-}9)$$

substitution in Eq. 3.4-18 yields

$$\frac{D}{Dt} \int_{\mathscr{V}_{m(t)}} \rho S \, dV = \int_{\mathscr{V}_{m(t)}} \frac{\partial}{\partial t} (\rho S) \, dV + \int_{\mathscr{A}_{m(t)}} \rho S \mathbf{v} \cdot \mathbf{n} \, dA$$

$$= \int_{\mathscr{V}_{m(t)}} \left[\frac{\partial}{\partial t} (\rho S) + \nabla \cdot (\rho S \mathbf{v}) \right] dV \qquad (3.5\text{-}10)$$

$$= \int_{\mathscr{V}_{m(t)}} \left[\rho \frac{\partial S}{\partial t} + S \frac{\partial \rho}{\partial t} + S \nabla \cdot (\rho \mathbf{v}) + \rho \mathbf{v} \cdot \nabla S \right] dV$$

Here, the divergence theorem has been used to change the area integral to a volume integral, and the products have been differentiated according to the usual rules. Remembering the formula for the material derivative allows us to express this result as

$$\frac{D}{Dt} \int_{\mathscr{V}_{m(t)}} \rho S \, dV = \int_{\mathscr{V}_{m(t)}} \left[\rho \frac{DS}{Dt} + S \left(\frac{\partial \rho}{\partial t} + \nabla \cdot \rho \mathbf{v} \right) \right] dV \qquad (3.5\text{-}11)$$

The continuity equation may be used to show that the term in parentheses is zero, and we obtain

$$\frac{D}{Dt} \int_{\mathscr{V}_{m(t)}} \rho S \, dV = \int_{\mathscr{V}_{m(t)}} \rho \frac{DS}{Dt} \, dV \qquad \begin{array}{l}\text{Special form of the}\\ \text{Reynolds transport theorem}\end{array} \qquad (3.5\text{-}12)$$

This form of the Reynolds transport theorem will be especially useful in deriving the differential momentum and energy equations.

The expanded forms of the continuity equation are presented in Table 3.5-1 for rectangular, cylindrical, and spherical coordinates. Alphabetical subscripts are used to denote the physical components, which are the projections of the velocity vector on the tangents to the coordinate curves. These projections are illustrated for cylindrical coordinates in Fig. 3.5-1.

Table 3.5-1

THE CONTINUITY EQUATION

Rectangular Coordinates (x, y, z)

$$\frac{\partial \rho}{\partial t} + \frac{\partial}{\partial x} (\rho v_x) + \frac{\partial}{\partial y} (\rho v_y) + \frac{\partial}{\partial z} (\rho v_z) = 0 \qquad \text{(a)}$$

Cylindrical Coordinates (r, θ, z)

$$\frac{\partial \rho}{\partial t} + \frac{1}{r} \frac{\partial}{\partial r} (\rho r v_r) + \frac{1}{r} \frac{\partial}{\partial \theta} (\rho v_\theta) + \frac{\partial}{\partial z} (\rho v_z) = 0 \qquad \text{(b)}$$

Spherical Coordinates (r, θ, ϕ)

$$\frac{\partial \rho}{\partial t} + \frac{1}{r^2} \frac{\partial}{\partial r} (\rho r^2 v_r) + \frac{1}{r \sin \theta} \frac{\partial}{\partial \theta} (\rho v_\theta \sin \theta) + \frac{1}{r \sin \theta} \frac{\partial}{\partial \phi} (\rho v_\phi) = 0 \qquad \text{(c)}$$

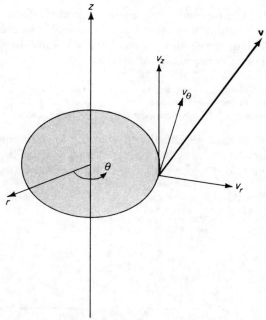

Fig. 3.5-1. Components of the velocity vector in cylindrical coordinates.

The derivation presented in this section has been done in rectangular coordinates; for simplicity, all subsequent developments will be similarly restricted. This procedure allows us to integrate and differentiate vectors in the same way as scalars, without recourse to some more advanced mathematical techniques. The fundamental concepts involved in fluid mechanics present a sufficient challenge to the student so that the complexity of curvilinear coordinates need not be added. However, many problems are much simpler to analyze in either cylindrical or spherical coordinates; for this reason, derived results will always be tabulated in these other coordinate systems. Satisfactory discussions of the problem of transforming vector equations to the different coordinate systems are given elsewhere.[1,3-4]

An alternate derivation of the continuity equation

Another method of deriving the continuity equation exists that does not require the use of the divergence theorem or the transport theorem; it does,

3. A. J. McConnell, *Applications of Tensor Analysis* (New York: Dover Publications Inc., 1957).

4. G. E. Hay, *Vector and Tensor Analysis* (New York: Dover Publications, Inc., 1953).

however, involve a somewhat more lengthy algebraic effort. Nevertheless it is instructive to examine this derivation, for it will give the student some practice in handling "mass flux" terms. For a volume fixed in space, we state the principle of conservation of mass as

$$\begin{Bmatrix} \text{time rate of change} \\ \text{of the mass of the} \\ \text{volume control} \end{Bmatrix} = \begin{Bmatrix} \text{mass flux} \\ \text{into the} \\ \text{volume control} \end{Bmatrix} - \begin{Bmatrix} \text{mass flux} \\ \text{out of the} \\ \text{volume control} \end{Bmatrix} \qquad (3.5\text{-}13)$$

The term "flux" is used repeatedly in reference to mass, momentum, and energy transport and it means "flow per unit time." Thus, the mass flux into the system is the rate at which mass flows into the system (lb_m/sec).

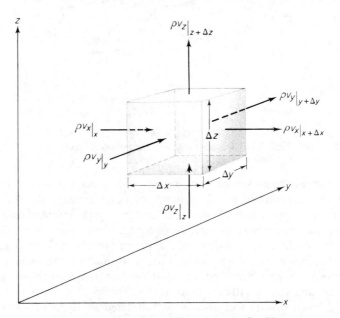

Fig. 3.5-2. Mass balance on a differential cube fixed in space.

Applying Eq. 3.5-13 to the cube illustrated in Fig. 3.5-2, we get

$$\frac{\partial}{\partial t} (\rho \, \Delta x \, \Delta y \, \Delta z) = [\rho v_x|_x - \rho v_x|_{x+\Delta x}] \Delta y \, \Delta z \quad \begin{matrix} \text{Mass flow rate} \\ \text{across } x\text{-surfaces} \end{matrix}$$

$$+ [\rho v_y|_y - \rho v_y|_{y+\Delta y}] \Delta x \, \Delta z \quad \begin{matrix} \text{Mass flow rate} \\ \text{across } y\text{-surfaces} \end{matrix} \qquad (3.5\text{-}14)$$

$$+ [\rho v_z|_z - \rho v_z|_{z+\Delta z}] \Delta x \, \Delta y \quad \begin{matrix} \text{Mass flow rate} \\ \text{across } z\text{-surfaces} \end{matrix}$$

Dividing Eq. 3.5-14 by $\Delta x\, \Delta y\, \Delta z$, and taking the limits $\Delta x \to 0$, $\Delta y \to 0$, $\Delta z \to 0$, we have

$$\frac{\partial \rho}{\partial t} + \lim_{\Delta x \to 0}\left[\frac{\rho v_x|_{x+\Delta x} - \rho v_x|_x}{\Delta x}\right]$$

$$+ \lim_{\Delta y \to 0}\left[\frac{\rho v_y|_{y+\Delta y} - \rho v_y|_y}{\Delta y}\right] \qquad (3.5\text{-}15)$$

$$+ \lim_{\Delta z \to 0}\left[\frac{\rho v_z|_{z+\Delta z} - \rho v_z|_z}{\Delta z}\right] = 0$$

Each limiting process yields a partial derivative, and the result is

$$\frac{\partial \rho}{\partial t} + \frac{\partial}{\partial x}(\rho v_x) + \frac{\partial}{\partial y}(\rho v_y) + \frac{\partial}{\partial z}(\rho v_z) = 0 \qquad (3.5\text{-}16)$$

which is the previously derived Eq. 3.5-5, listed in Table 3.5-1 for rectangular coordinates. The statement given by Eq. 3.5-13 is very different from that given by Eq. 3.5-2, which states that the mass of a material volume is constant. It obviously turns out that both are equivalent statements of the principle of conservation of mass, the latter following intuitively from the former. This easy intuitive deduction results from the fact that the principle of conservation of mass is relatively simple; however, in attacking the momentum and energy equations, we will encounter more complex concepts, and the mathematical tools presented in this chapter will be valuable in obtaining a rational derivation of the differential equations.

*3.6   Streamlines, Path Lines, and Streak Lines

It is of some help in visualizing various flows to have a geometrical representation of the velocity field. A *streamline* is a curve in space drawn so that the velocity vector is everywhere tangent to the curve. The concept of the streamline and the *stream function* (to be defined subsequently) is of considerable importance and will be discussed in detail in this section.

A *path line* is a curve in space that an individual fluid particle would follow. The locus of points on a path line may be expressed by Eq. 3.1-3 as,

$$\mathbf{r} = \mathbf{r}(\mathbf{R}, t), \qquad \mathbf{R} = \text{constant vector}$$

Thus, the path line represents the Lagrangian method of describing the fluid motion.

The *streak line* represents the fluid motion in a way that an observer can see easily, for it is a curve traced out by all particles passing through some

fixed point, r_0. The plume of smoke issuing from a burning cigarette represents a streak line, provided we neglect the lateral diffusion of the smoke
particles.

When the flow is steady, $\partial v/\partial t = 0$, the streamline, path line, and streak
line coincide; however, they generally differ for unsteady flows. The most
lucid discussion of these ideas is contained in the movie entitled "Flow
Visualization."[5]

Returning to our analysis of streamlines, such as those shown in Fig. 3.6-1,
we note that if the flow is steady, they can be visualized by continuously

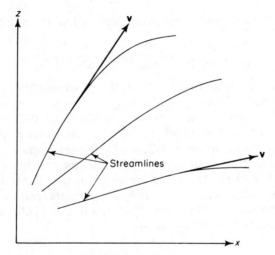

Fig. 3.6-1. Streamlines.

injecting a dye into the fluid at some fixed point. Inasmuch as the streamline is
defined in terms of a tangent vector, we need to define the unit tangent
vector to a curve.

Unit tangent vector

The tangent vector to a curve is defined as the limiting position of the
secant of a curve, such as that illustrated in Fig. 3.6-2 The arclength s along
the curve is a function of the spatial coordinates

$$s = s(x, y, z) \tag{3.6-1}$$

5. Prepared by Professor S. J. Kline of Stanford University and distributed by Educational Services, Inc., 47 Galen St., Watertown, Mass. 02172.

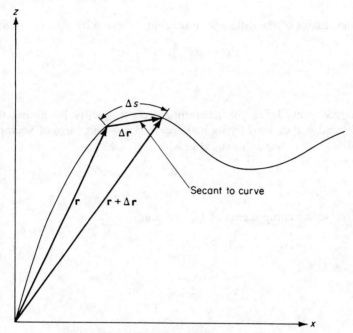

Fig. 3.6-2. Unit tangent vector to a curve.

and the parametric representation of the curve is

$$x = x(s), \qquad y = y(s), \qquad z = z(s) \qquad (3.6\text{-}2)$$

Equation 3.6-2 means that if the arclength is given, the spatial coordinates of that point on the curve are determined; conversely, Eq. 3.6-1 indicates that if the spatial coordinates are given, the arclength to that point (measured from some arbitrary reference) is determined. We may write Eqs. 3.6-1 and 3.6-2 in vector notation as

$$s = s(\mathbf{r}) \qquad (3.6\text{-}3a)$$
$$\mathbf{r} = \mathbf{r}(s) \qquad (3.6\text{-}3b)$$

The unit tangent vector $\boldsymbol{\lambda}$ is given by

$$\boldsymbol{\lambda} = \lim_{\Delta s \to 0} \frac{\Delta \mathbf{r}}{\Delta s} = \frac{d\mathbf{r}}{ds} \qquad (3.6\text{-}4)$$

It is easy to prove that $\boldsymbol{\lambda}$ is a unit vector by forming the scalar product

$$\begin{aligned}
\boldsymbol{\lambda} \cdot \boldsymbol{\lambda} &= \left(\frac{d\mathbf{r}}{ds}\right) \cdot \left(\frac{d\mathbf{r}}{ds}\right) \\
&= \left(\mathbf{i}\frac{dx}{ds} + \mathbf{j}\frac{dy}{ds} + \mathbf{k}\frac{dz}{ds}\right) \cdot \left(\mathbf{i}\frac{dx}{ds} + \mathbf{j}\frac{dy}{ds} + \mathbf{k}\frac{dz}{ds}\right) \\
&= \left(\frac{dx}{ds}\right)^2 + \left(\frac{dy}{ds}\right)^2 + \left(\frac{dz}{ds}\right)^2
\end{aligned} \qquad (3.6\text{-}5)$$

Since the square of the differential arclength is given by

$$ds^2 = dx^2 + dy^2 + dz^2 \qquad (3.6\text{-}6)$$

we see that

$$\boldsymbol{\lambda} \cdot \boldsymbol{\lambda} = 1 \qquad (3.6\text{-}7)$$

We may now define the streamline more explicitly by noting that the velocity vector $\mathbf{v}$ divided by its magnitude v is a unit tangent vector to the streamline, and is therefore equal to $\boldsymbol{\lambda}$.

$$\boldsymbol{\lambda} = \frac{d\mathbf{r}}{ds} = \frac{\mathbf{v}}{v} \qquad (3.6\text{-}8)$$

The three scalar components of Eq. 3.6-8 are

$$\frac{dx}{ds} = \frac{v_x}{v} \qquad (3.6\text{-}9\text{a})$$

$$\frac{dy}{ds} = \frac{v_y}{v} \qquad (3.6\text{-}9\text{b})$$

$$\frac{dz}{ds} = \frac{v_z}{v} \qquad (3.6\text{-}9\text{c})$$

where v_x, v_y, and v_z are the three components of the velocity vector. We may rearrange these three equations to give

$$\frac{dx}{v_x} = \frac{dy}{v_y} = \frac{dz}{v_z} \qquad (3.6\text{-}10)$$

These equations define the streamline, and we shall find that they are a key part of the derivation of Bernoulli's equation† presented in Chap. 7. In addition to being useful in mathematical analysis, streamlines are an aid to obtaining a qualitative understanding of fluid motion. To illustrate this point, we shall define the stream function ψ and indicate how a qualitative sketch of the streamline helps us visualize the flow field.

To keep matters simple,‡ we must restrict our discussion to two-dimensional flows so that Eqs. 3.6-10 take the form

$$\frac{dx}{v_x} = \frac{dy}{v_y} \qquad (3.6\text{-}11)$$

† Bernoulli's equation is a scalar component of the equations of motion in the direction of a tangent vector to the streamline when viscous effects are neglected.

‡ Fully three-dimensional flows give rise to two stream functions. See C. S. Yih, *Houille blanche*, 1957, 12:445.

Figure 3.6-3 illustrates the streamlines for a two-dimensional flow and also indicates an arbitrary closed curve along which an integration will be performed to define the stream function.

The mass flow rate, per unit length in the z-direction, across the surface $A \to B$ is given by

$$\int_{A}^{B} \rho \mathbf{v} \cdot \mathbf{n} \, ds = \begin{Bmatrix} \text{mass flow rate} \\ \text{across the} \\ \text{surface } A \to B \end{Bmatrix} \qquad (3.6\text{-}12)$$

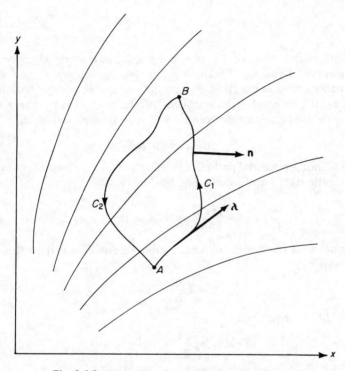

Fig. 3.6-3. Streamlines for a two-dimensional flow.

where s is the arclength measured counterclockwise along the curve. Similarly the mass flow rate across the surface $B \to A$ is given by

$$\int_{B}^{A} \rho \mathbf{v} \cdot \mathbf{n} \, ds = \begin{Bmatrix} \text{mass flow rate} \\ \text{across the} \\ \text{surface } B \to A \end{Bmatrix} \qquad (3.6\text{-}13)$$

Since the mass in the region bounded by the curves C_1 and C_2 is constant if the flow is incompressible, it follows that

$$\int_A^B \mathbf{v} \cdot \mathbf{n} \, ds \bigg|_{\text{along } C_1} + \int_B^A \mathbf{v} \cdot \mathbf{n} \, ds \bigg|_{\text{along } C_2} = 0 \qquad (3.6\text{-}14)$$

where the density has been removed, for it must be constant for this statement to be generally true. Changing the direction of integration along C_2 changes the sign, and Eq. 3.6-14 takes the form

$$\int_A^B \mathbf{v} \cdot \mathbf{n} \, ds \bigg|_{\text{along } C_1} = \int_A^B \mathbf{v} \cdot \mathbf{n} \, ds \bigg|_{\text{along } C_2} \qquad (3.6\text{-}15)$$

For the moment, think of C_2 as some *fixed* curve while C_1 may be any *arbitrary* curve. Thus, Eq. 3.6-15 indicates that the integral of $\mathbf{v} \cdot \mathbf{n} \, ds$ along any arbitrary curve connecting two points, A and B, always has the same value—i.e., the integral is independent of the path. Under these circumstances, $\mathbf{v} \cdot \mathbf{n} \, ds$ is an exact differential and may be represented as

$$d\psi = \mathbf{v} \cdot \mathbf{n} \, ds \qquad (3.6\text{-}16)$$

where ψ is independent of path. Expressing ψ as a function of x and y, and expanding the right-hand side of Eq. 3.6-16, we have

$$\left(\frac{\partial \psi}{\partial x}\right) dx + \left(\frac{\partial \psi}{\partial y}\right) dy = v_x n_x \, ds + v_y n_y \, ds \qquad (3.6\text{-}17)$$

The normal $\mathbf{n}$ to the curves C_1 and C_2 must be orthogonal to the tangent vector given by†

$$\boldsymbol{\lambda} = \mathbf{i} \frac{dx}{ds} + \mathbf{j} \frac{dy}{ds} \qquad (3.6\text{-}18)$$

Equation 3.6-18 requires that

$$\mathbf{n} \cdot \boldsymbol{\lambda} = n_x \frac{dx}{ds} + n_y \frac{dy}{ds} = 0 \qquad (3.6\text{-}19)$$

and either

$$n_x = \frac{dy}{ds}, \qquad n_y = -\frac{dx}{ds} \qquad (3.6\text{-}20a)$$

or

$$n_x = -\frac{dy}{ds}, \qquad n_y = \frac{dx}{ds} \qquad (3.6\text{-}20b)$$

depending on which direction we assign to the unit tangent vector, $\boldsymbol{\lambda}$. If $\boldsymbol{\lambda}$ is taken in the same direction as s, examination of Fig. 3.6-3 will indicate that Eq. 3.6-20a is the desired solution. Substitution of Eq. 3.6-20a into Eq.

† Here $\boldsymbol{\lambda}$ is the unit tangent vector to the curves C_1 and C_2.

3.6-17, and placement of all the terms on the left-hand side, yield

$$\left(\frac{\partial \psi}{\partial x} + v_y\right) dx + \left(\frac{\partial \psi}{\partial y} - v_x\right) dy = 0 \qquad (3.6\text{-}21)$$

Since this result is true for any arbitrary curve, the values of dx and dy are arbitrary and the terms in parentheses must be zero.

$$v_x = \frac{\partial \psi}{\partial y}, \qquad v_y = -\frac{\partial \psi}{\partial x} \qquad (3.6\text{-}22)$$

The derivation presented here proves the existence of a stream function and shows that it must satisfy Eqs. 3.6-22.

While this result is of some interest, it is of more interest to note that the volumetric flow rate (per unit depth) between two points A and B is

$$\psi_B - \psi_A = \begin{Bmatrix} \text{volumetric flow rate per unit depth} \\ \text{between points } A \text{ and } B \end{Bmatrix} \qquad (3.6\text{-}23)$$

Thus, if A and B are any two points *on the same streamline,*

$$\psi_B - \psi_A = 0 \qquad (3.6\text{-}24)$$

and we conclude that the value of ψ is constant along any streamline. This last result may not be obvious, but it is proved readily.

$$\psi_B - \psi_A = \int_A^B d\psi = \int_A^B \mathbf{v} \cdot \mathbf{n}\, ds \qquad (3.6\text{-}25)$$

Because the curve connecting A and B is *arbitrary*, we can choose the streamline that passes through both points. Along this *particular* curve

$$\mathbf{v} = v\boldsymbol{\lambda} \qquad (3.6\text{-}26)$$

by Eq. 3.6-8, and Eq. 3.6-25 becomes

$$\psi_B - \psi_A = \int_A^B v\boldsymbol{\lambda} \cdot \mathbf{n}\, ds \qquad (3.6\text{-}27)$$

Inasmuch as $\boldsymbol{\lambda} \cdot \mathbf{n}$ is always zero, Eq. 3.6-24 is proved.

In Fig. 3.6-4, we consider two points, A and B, chosen such that $\mathbf{n}$ and $\mathbf{v}$ are parallel. For that case,

$$\psi_B - \psi_A = v\,\Delta s$$

or

$$\left(\frac{\psi_B - \psi_A}{\Delta s}\right) = v \qquad (3.6\text{-}28)$$

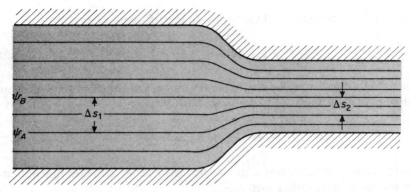

Fig. 3.6-4. Qualitative description of a flow field using streamlines.

From this result, we can express the ratio of velocities as

$$\frac{v_1}{v_2} = \frac{\Delta s_2}{\Delta s_1} \tag{3.6-29}$$

and conclude that when the streamlines are close together the velocity is high, and when the streamlines are far apart the velocity is low. This idea is especially useful if the streamlines are known; however, if they are sketched in on the basis of intuition, we must view the results strictly as a qualitative description of the flow field.

PROBLEMS

3-1. If the density of the air in the atmosphere is given by the formula,

$$\rho = \rho_0[1 + a(x^2 + y^2) + e^{-bz}]$$

where $\rho_0 = 0.075 \, \text{lb}_m/\text{ft}^3$

$a = 1 \times 10^{-5}/\text{ft}^2$

$b = 1 \times 10^{-4}/\text{ft}$

and the velocity of an airplane flying through the atmosphere is given by,

$$\mathbf{w} = \mathbf{i}w_x + \mathbf{j}w_y + \mathbf{k}w_z$$

where $w_x = 300 \, \text{mph}$

$w_y = 20 \, \text{mph}$

$w_z = -20 \, \text{mph}$

how would the air density measured at the airplane change with time if the coordinates of the plane are $x = y = 0$, and $z = 15,000$ ft?

Ans.: $4.9 \times 10^{-5} \, \text{lb}_m/\text{ft}^3$-sec.

3-2. If the fluid velocity $\mathbf{v}$ is given by

$$\mathbf{v} = u_0 e^{-at}[\mathbf{i}bx + \mathbf{j}cy^2]$$

where a has units of sec^{-1}

b has units of ft^{-1}

c has units of ft^{-2}

u_0 has units of ft/sec

obtain an expression for the fluid acceleration $D\mathbf{v}/Dt$ in terms of a, b, c, and u_0.

3-3. If the stream function is given by

$$\psi = U_0 L \left[\cos\left(\frac{x}{L}\right) e^{-y^2/L^2} \right]$$

determine the two components of the velocity, v_x and v_y.

3-4. (a) Sketch the streamlines in the region $0 \leq y \leq \infty$ and $0 \leq x \leq L$ for a two-dimensional velocity field.

$$v_x = y\left(1 - \frac{x}{L}\right)$$

$$v_y = \frac{y^2}{2L}$$

(b) Is the continuity equation for incompressible flow satisfied for this velocity field?

3-5. The Leibnitz rule for differentiating an integral the limits of which are functions of the independent variable is given as follows: If

$$\phi(x) = \int_{a(x)}^{b(x)} f(x, y)\, dy$$

then

$$\frac{d\phi}{dx} = \int_{a(x)}^{b(x)} \left(\frac{\partial f}{\partial x}\right) dy + f[x, b(x)]\frac{db}{dx} - f[x, a(x)]\frac{da}{dx}$$

Derive this result, which is a one-dimensional analogue of the transport theorem. *Hint:* Start with the definition of the derivative; rearrange the limits of integration and apply the mean value theorem for the integrals between $a(x)$ and $a(x + \Delta x)$, and between $b(x)$ and $b(x + \Delta x)$.

3-6. Express the Reynolds transport theorem for a vector quantity in index notation.

3-7. Green's theorem in a plane may be written as

$$\oint_C (R\,dx + S\,dy) = \int_A \left(\frac{\partial S}{\partial x} - \frac{\partial R}{\partial y}\right) dx\,dy$$

where C denotes a closed curve bounding the region A, oriented such that the region is on the left as we advance along the curve in the positive direction. Prove this result using the same approach described in the derivation of the divergence theorem. *Note:* When $R = v_x$ and $S = v_z$, this result is known as Stokes' theorem.

3-8. Express the continuity equation using index notation.

3-9. Considering an arbitrary, fixed volume $\mathscr{V}$, apply the integral method to Eq. 3.5-13 to derive the continuity equation.

3-10. Using Eq. 3.5-13 and the differential volume shown in Fig. 3-10, derive the continuity equation in cylindrical coordinates.

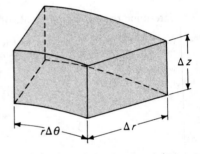

3-11. If v_x, v_y, and v_z are independent of time, is the acceleration Dv/Dt necessarily zero?

3-12. Using Gibbs notation, prove that

$$\nabla \cdot (S\mathbf{v}) = \mathbf{v} \cdot \nabla S + S\nabla \cdot \mathbf{v}$$

Fig. 3-10

3-13. For a compressible, steady, two-dimensional flow, show that a stream function ψ^* can be defined such that

$$\rho v_x = \frac{\partial \psi^*}{\partial y}, \qquad \rho v_y = -\frac{\partial \psi^*}{\partial x}$$

where $\psi_B^* - \psi_A^* = \begin{Bmatrix} \text{mass flow rate per unit depth} \\ \text{between points } A \text{ and } B \end{Bmatrix}$

3-14. Prove that

$$\frac{d}{dt}\int_{\mathscr{V}_a(t)} S\,dV = \int_{\mathscr{V}_a(t)} \frac{dS}{dt}\,dV$$

if $\mathbf{w}$ is independent of x, y, and z.

Stress in a Fluid   4

*4.1   The Stress Vector

In the previous chapter we developed certain ideas about the kinematics
of a continuum. Our purpose was to acquire the tools necessary to treat the
left-hand side of the linear momentum equation.

$$\frac{D}{Dt}\int_{\mathscr{V}_m(t)} \rho\mathbf{v}\,dV = \int_{\mathscr{V}_m(t)} \rho\mathbf{g}\,dV + \int_{\mathscr{A}_m(t)} \mathbf{t}_{(n)}\,dA \qquad (4.1\text{-}1)$$

| Time rate of change of momentum | Body force | Surface force |

We must now turn our attention to the problem of describing the forces
which act upon the fluid. The body force presents no difficulty, but the
surface force requires a good deal of study; therefore, our objective in this
chapter is to investigate the nature of the stress vector, $\mathbf{t}_{(n)}$.

We assume that ρ, $\mathbf{v}$, and $\mathbf{t}_{(n)}$ are continuous functions of the spatial coordinates and time. In addition, $\mathbf{t}_{(n)}$ is assumed to be a continuous function
of the orientation of the surface element under consideration, as designated
by the outwardly directed unit normal $\mathbf{n}$. We shall prove the following in
order.

1. The stress vectors acting upon opposite sides of the same surface at a
   given point are equal in magnitude and opposite in direction—i.e.,
   $t_{(n)} = -t_{(-n)}$.

2. The stress *vector* may be written in terms of the stress *tensor* **T** as
   $t_{(n)} = n \cdot T$.

3. The stress tensor is symmetric, $T_{ij} = T_{ji}$.

In each case, we will be examining a special material volume, and we will
make use of the mean value theorem in applying both the linear and angular
momentum equations to these volumes. The mean value theorem in one
dimension states that

$$f\Big|_{x=\xi} (b-a) = \int_a^b f(x)\,dx, \qquad a \le \xi \le b \qquad (4.1\text{-}2)$$

This result is represented graphically in Fig. 4.1-1, where we see that the area
under the curve of $f(x)$ versus x is given by the integral in Eq. 4.1-2. It is
intuitively obvious that the area can also be represented by the product of
the length $b - a$ and some mean value of the function $f(x)$. The idea is easily

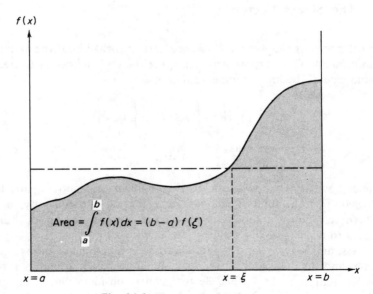

Fig. 4.1-1. The mean-value theorem.

extended to area and volume integrals,[1] which are expressed as

$$\langle f \rangle A = \int_A f \, dA \tag{4.1-3a}$$

$$\langle f \rangle V = \int_V f \, dV \tag{4.1-3b}$$

As we mentioned previously, we shall use angular brackets ($\langle \; \rangle$) to represent the mean or average value of some function. No special notation will be used to indicate whether an area or a volume average is meant, for it is usually obvious.

In proving that $\mathbf{t}_{(n)} = -\mathbf{t}_{(-n)}$, we will make use of the material volume illustrated in Fig. 4.1-2. This volume is formed by two parallel surfaces of

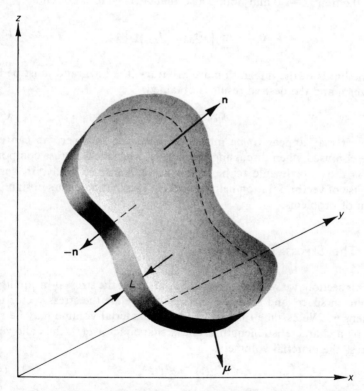

Fig. 4.1-2. Material volume having the form of an arbitrary slab.

1. T. M. Apostal, *Mathematical Analysis* (Reading, Mass.: Addison-Wesley Publishing Company, Inc., 1957), p. 269.

area $A_n(t)$ connected by a strip perpendicular to the two parallel surfaces of width L and area $A_s(t)$. Application of Eq. 4.1-1 to this volume yields

$$\frac{D}{Dt} \int_{\mathscr{V}_m(t)} \rho \mathbf{v} \, dV = \int_{\mathscr{V}_m(t)} \rho \mathbf{g} \, dV + \int_{A_s(t)} \mathbf{t}_{(\mu)} \, dA + \int_{A_n(t)} \mathbf{t}_{(n)} \, dA + \int_{A_n(t)} \mathbf{t}_{(-n)} \, dA \quad (4.1\text{-}4)$$

where the area integral of the stress vector has been split into the three distinct areas forming the slab. Applying the mean value theorem to the first three integrals, and putting the last two under the same integral sign, we get

$$\frac{D}{Dt} [\langle \rho \mathbf{v} \rangle L A_n(t)] = \langle \rho \mathbf{g} \rangle L A_n(t) + \langle \mathbf{t}_{(\mu)} \rangle A_s(t) + \int_{A_n(t)} [\mathbf{t}_{(n)} + \mathbf{t}_{(-n)}] \, dA \quad (4.1\text{-}5)$$

Taking the limit $L \to 0$ and noting also that $A_s(t) \to 0$, we obtain

$$0 = \lim_{L \to 0} \int_{A_n(t)} [\mathbf{t}_{(n)} + \mathbf{t}_{(-n)}] \, dA \quad (4.1\text{-}6)$$

Since the limits of the integration are arbitrary, the integrand must be identically zero, and the desired result is obtained.

$$\mathbf{t}_{(n)} = -\mathbf{t}_{(-n)} \quad (4.1\text{-}7)$$

This result may appear to be intuitively obvious; however, we can easily become confused when discussing the sign of a particular stress component, and it is thus worthwhile to have this result stated formally. In general, careful use of vector notation helps greatly in eliminating errors in sign in the solution of problems.

*4.2   The Stress Tensor

In this section, we wish to demonstrate first that the stress is in equilibrium at a point in space, and then use this result to relate the stress vector to the stress tensor. We assume that any arbitrary material volume may be represented by a characteristic length L and a shape factor $\alpha(t)$, thus allowing us to express the material volume as

$$\mathscr{V}_m(t) = \alpha(t) L^3 \quad (4.2\text{-}1)$$

Applying the mean value theorem to Eq. 4.1-1 in conjunction with Eq. 4.2-1, we obtain

$$\frac{D}{Dt} [\langle \rho \mathbf{v} \rangle \alpha(t) L^3] = \langle \rho \mathbf{g} \rangle \alpha(t) L^3 + \int_{\mathscr{A}_m(t)} \mathbf{t}_{(n)} \, dA \quad (4.2\text{-}2)$$

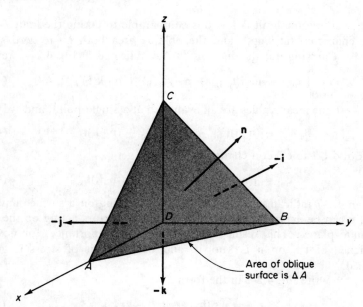

Fig. 4.2-1. A material volume in the form of a tetrahedron.

Dividing by L^2 and taking the limit $L \to 0$, we have the desired result.

$$0 = \lim_{L \to 0} \frac{1}{L^2} \int_{\mathscr{A}_m(t)} \mathbf{t}_{(\mathbf{n})} \, dA \qquad (4.2\text{-}3)$$

In its present form, Eq. 4.2-3 appears to be a rather obtuse result; however, when applied to the tetrahedron illustrated in Fig. 4.2-1, we will obtain some interesting information. Table 4.2-1 indicates the stress vector and areas associated with the four planes of the tetrahedron.

Table 4.2-1

STRESSES ACTING ON A TETRAHEDRON

Plane	Area	Normal	Stress Vector
ABC	ΔA	$\mathbf{n}$	$\mathbf{t}_{(\mathbf{n})}$
BCD	$\mathbf{n} \cdot \mathbf{i} \, \Delta A$	$-\mathbf{i}$	$\mathbf{t}_{(-\mathbf{i})}$
ADC	$\mathbf{n} \cdot \mathbf{j} \, \Delta A$	$-\mathbf{j}$	$\mathbf{t}_{(-\mathbf{j})}$
ABD	$\mathbf{n} \cdot \mathbf{k} \, \Delta A$	$-\mathbf{k}$	$\mathbf{t}_{(-\mathbf{k})}$

In Eq. 4.2-3, we let L^2 equal the oblique area ΔA and apply the mean value theorem to the four plane surfaces making up the area integral.

$$\lim_{\Delta A \to 0} \left\{ \frac{1}{\Delta A} \left[\Delta A \langle \mathbf{t}_{(\mathbf{n})} \rangle + \mathbf{n} \cdot \mathbf{i} \, \Delta A \langle \mathbf{t}_{(-\mathbf{i})} \rangle + \mathbf{n} \cdot \mathbf{j} \, \Delta A \langle \mathbf{t}_{(-\mathbf{j})} \rangle + \mathbf{n} \cdot \mathbf{k} \, \Delta A \langle \mathbf{t}_{(-\mathbf{k})} \rangle \right] \right\} = 0$$

$$(4.2\text{-}4)$$

Note that taking the limit $\Delta A \to 0$ is comparable to taking the limit $L \to 0$, for the characteristic length and the oblique area both go to zero simultaneously. Carrying out the division by ΔA indicated in Eq. 4.2-4, we have

$$\lim_{\Delta A \to 0} [\langle t_{(n)} \rangle + n \cdot i \langle t_{(-i)} \rangle + n \cdot j \langle t_{(-j)} \rangle + n \cdot k \langle t_{(-k)} \rangle] = 0 \qquad (4.2\text{-}5)$$

As $\Delta A \to 0$, the mean values are all evaluated at a single point, and we write

$$t_{(n)} = -[(n \cdot i)t_{(-i)} + (n \cdot j)t_{(-j)} + (n \cdot k)t_{(-k)}] \qquad (4.2\text{-}6)$$

Using Eq. 4.1-7 to effect a change of signs, we get

$$t_{(n)} = [(n \cdot i)t_{(i)} + (n \cdot j)t_{(j)} + (n \cdot k)t_{(k)}] \qquad (4.2\text{-}7)$$

Equation 4.2-7 indicates that the stress vector acting on a surface having a normal n can be expressed in terms of the stress vectors acting on the three coordinate planes. This result is of considerable importance, for now the dependence of $t_{(n)}$ on n is known, and our analysis of stress is greatly simplified.

We now write Eq. 4.2-7 in the form

$$t_{(n)} = n \cdot [it_{(i)} + jt_{(j)} + kt_{(k)}] \qquad (4.2\text{-}8)$$

where the quantity in brackets is *defined* as the stress tensor T, leading us to write

$$t_{(n)} = n \cdot T \qquad (4.2\text{-}9)$$

The stress tensor is composed of terms of the type $it_{(i)}$, which is neither the scalar (dot) product nor the vector (cross) product of two vectors. It is often called a *dyad*[2] and represents a type of multiplication which is generally new to the student and deserves some discussion. In going from Eq. 4.2-7 to Eq. 4.2-8, we have in effect stated that

$$(A \cdot B)C = A \cdot (BC) \qquad (4.2\text{-}10)$$

and the question naturally arises, "Why should this be so?" The answer is that it is so by definition, and the explanation is as follows. The left-hand side of Eq. 4.2-10 consists of the scalar product $A \cdot B$ and a vector C. Multiplication of a vector C by a scalar $A \cdot B$ is a straightforward operation yielding a vector. Obviously, the left-hand side of Eq. 4.2-10 is a well-defined quantity. It follows, then, that Eq. 4.2-10 *defines* the dot product between a vector A and a tensor (BC)—i.e., it is the operation that yields the vector $(A \cdot B)C$.

To view the stress vector in its proper perspective, we might note that a more general description of functions would designate a scalar (a quantity having magnitude only) as a zero order tensor, a vector

2. J. W. Gibbs and E. B. Wilson, *Vector Analysis* (New Haven, Conn.: Yale University Press, 1901).

(having magnitude and direction) as a first-order tensor, and a tensor such as the stress tensor (being a doubly directed quantity) as a second-order tensor. In this text, the word "tensor" will always mean a second-order tensor. A qualitative description of a tensor is a rather elusive item. We can describe a vector nicely from the qualitative point of view by referring to it as a directed line segment, which obviously has meaning consistent with physical reality and mathematical definition. Moreover, we can construct it very nicely with a piece of chalk and a blackboard. However, we cannot draw a tensor on the blackboard, and its meaning must therefore be more closely confined to the realm of mathematical definition. From the physical point of view, it seems best to view the stress tensor as that quantity which, when dotted with the normal $\mathbf{n}$, yields the stress vector acting on a surface having a normal $\mathbf{n}$. The definition given by Eq. 4.2-9 must be expanded considerably before it can be of any use to us.

Since the stress vector acting on any arbitrary surface may be expressed in terms of the stress vectors acting on the coordinate planes by Eq. 4.2-8, we need only know the scalar components of $\mathbf{t}_{(i)}$, $\mathbf{t}_{(j)}$, and $\mathbf{t}_{(k)}$ to determine the surface forces in general. In rectangular coordinates, we write the three stress vectors as

$$\mathbf{t}_{(i)} = \mathbf{i}T_{xx} + \mathbf{j}T_{xy} + \mathbf{k}T_{xz} \qquad \begin{array}{l}\text{Force per unit area} \\ \text{acting on the } x\text{-surface}\end{array} \qquad (4.2\text{-}11a)$$

$$\mathbf{t}_{(j)} = \mathbf{i}T_{yx} + \mathbf{j}T_{yy} + \mathbf{k}T_{yz} \qquad \begin{array}{l}\text{Force per unit area} \\ \text{acting on the } y\text{-surface}\end{array} \qquad (4.2\text{-}11b)$$

$$\mathbf{t}_{(k)} = \mathbf{i}T_{zx} + \mathbf{j}T_{zy} + \mathbf{k}T_{zz} \qquad \begin{array}{l}\text{Force per unit area} \\ \text{acting on the } z\text{-surface}\end{array} \qquad (4.2\text{-}11c)$$

The nine scalar components given here represent the nine components of the stress tensor $\mathbf{T}$. The stress tensor is often represented in matrix form as

$$\mathbf{T} = \begin{pmatrix} T_{xx} & T_{xy} & T_{xz} \\ T_{yx} & T_{yy} & T_{yz} \\ T_{zx} & T_{zy} & T_{zz} \end{pmatrix}$$

The first subscript indicates the plane upon which the stress acts, and the second subscript indicates the direction in which the stress acts. Thus T_{zx} is the stress acting on the z-surface in the x-direction. This notation is illustrated in Fig. 4.2-2 showing the stresses acting on the x-surfaces of a cube. In accordance with Eq. 4.1-7, the stresses acting on the plane having a normal $+\mathbf{i}$ are oppositely directed to the stresses acting on the plane having a normal $-\mathbf{i}$. The sign convention adopted here is that the stress acting on a coordinate plane having a positive outwardly directed normal is positive if the stress itself also acts in the positive direction. A consequence of Eq. 4.1-7 is that the stress is also considered positive if it acts in the negative direction on a surface having a negative outwardly directed normal.

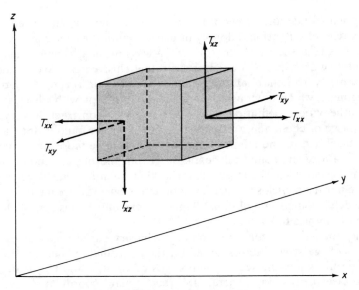

Fig. 4.2-2. Stresses on a cube.

The unit normal may be expressed in terms of its scalar components as

$$\mathbf{n} = \mathbf{i}n_x + \mathbf{j}n_y + \mathbf{k}n_z \qquad (4.2\text{-}12)$$

When substituted into Eq. 4.2-7, Eq. 4.2-12 gives

$$\mathbf{t}_{(n)} = n_x \mathbf{t}_{(i)} + n_y \mathbf{t}_{(j)} + n_z \mathbf{t}_{(k)} \qquad (4.2\text{-}13)$$

If we now substitute Eqs. 4.2-11 into Eq. 4.2-13, we obtain an expression for the stress vector in terms of the three scalar components of the normal and the nine scalar components of the stress tensor.

$$\mathbf{t}_{(n)} = \begin{aligned} &\mathbf{i}[n_x T_{xx} + n_y T_{yx} + n_z T_{zx}] \\ +&\mathbf{j}[n_x T_{xy} + n_y T_{yy} + n_z T_{zy}] \\ +&\mathbf{k}[n_x T_{xz} + n_y T_{yz} + n_z T_{zz}] \end{aligned} \qquad (4.2\text{-}14)$$

In arriving at this result, we have made no use of the stress tensor **T** or the operation of dotting the normal with the stress tensor. Since that is a defined operation, we are simply laying the groundwork for a workable definition. Notice that the subscripts in Eq. 4.2-14 occur in a very ordered fashion. The first subscript on the stress component is always the same as the subscript on the scalar component of the normal, and the second subscript indicates a direction corresponding to the particular base vector multiplying each bracketed term. This correspondence will logically lead us to the use of index notation. Writing the three scalar components of $\mathbf{t}_{(n)}$ as $t_{(n)x}$, $t_{(n)y}$, and $t_{(n)z}$ allows us to express the stress vector as

$$\mathbf{t}_{(n)} = \mathbf{i}t_{(n)x} + \mathbf{j}t_{(n)y} + \mathbf{k}t_{(n)z} \tag{4.2-15}$$

Referring to Eq. 4.2-14, we see that the scalar components become

$$t_{(n)x} = n_x T_{xx} + n_y T_{yx} + n_z T_{zx} \tag{4.2-16a}$$

$$t_{(n)y} = n_x T_{xy} + n_y T_{yy} + n_z T_{zy} \tag{4.2-16b}$$

$$t_{(n)z} = n_x T_{xz} + n_y T_{yz} + n_z T_{zz} \tag{4.2-16c}$$

The verbal description of the scalar $t_{(n)x}$ might be given as "the force per unit area acting on the **n**-surface in the x-direction." Thus, the two subscripts are interpreted in the same manner as the subscripts on a scalar component of the stress tensor.

Replacement of x, y, and z with 1, 2, and 3 yields

$$t_{(n)1} = n_1 T_{11} + n_2 T_{21} + n_3 T_{31} \tag{4.2-17a}$$

$$t_{(n)2} = n_1 T_{12} + n_2 T_{22} + n_3 T_{32} \tag{4.2-17b}$$

$$t_{(n)3} = n_1 T_{13} + n_2 T_{23} + n_3 T_{33} \tag{4.2-17c}$$

The repeated indices are easily expressed in terms of the summation convention, and we write

$$t_{(n)1} = n_j T_{j1} \tag{4.2-18a}$$

$$t_{(n)2} = n_j T_{j2} \tag{4.2-18b}$$

$$t_{(n)3} = n_j T_{j3} \tag{4.2-18c}$$

Note that any letter could be used for the repeated indices and the equations would still have the same meaning. Remembering that a free index takes on the values 1, 2, and 3, we can *represent* Eqs. 4.2-18 by the single equation,

$$t_{(n)i} = n_j T_{ji} \tag{4.2-19}$$

which is the index notation analogue of Eq. 4.2-9. The result obviously conveys a great deal of information once the convention for repeated and free indices is understood. The only drawback to this expression is that it deals with the scalar components of the stress vector, and the directional nature of this quantity is left to the reader's imagination. Equation 4.2-19 may be taken as a general definition of the dot product between a vector and a tensor. If the vector $\mathbf{C}$ is represented as,

$$\mathbf{C} = \mathbf{A} \cdot \mathbf{B} \tag{4.2-20}$$

then the scalar components of $\mathbf{C}$ are given by

$$C_i = A_j B_{ji} \tag{4.2-21}$$

This result could just as well be expressed as

$$C_i = B_{ji}A_j \qquad (4.2\text{-}22)$$

for the summation convention is in no way altered by this rearrangement. Things are not so simple in Gibbs notation, for in general $\mathbf{A} \cdot \mathbf{B}$ and $\mathbf{B} \cdot \mathbf{A}$ are different, and it will be helpful to examine this difference.

Returning to Eqs. 4.2-8 and 4.2-9, we see that the normal vector $\mathbf{n}$ was used as a *prefactor* in forming the dot product with the stress tensor. This means that when the dot product was formed, the scalar multiplication was carried out with the first vector (or the *antecedent*) of each dyad. We now examine the process of using $\mathbf{n}$ as a *postfactor* and write an equation analogous to Eq. 4.2-8.

$$\tilde{\mathbf{t}}_{(n)} = [\mathbf{i}\mathbf{t}_{(i)} + \mathbf{j}\mathbf{t}_{(j)} + \mathbf{k}\mathbf{t}_{(k)}] \cdot \mathbf{n} \qquad (4.2\text{-}23)$$

Carrying out the scalar multiplication in this case, we get

$$\tilde{\mathbf{t}}_{(n)} = \left[\mathbf{i}(\mathbf{t}_{(i)} \cdot \mathbf{n}) + \mathbf{j}(\mathbf{t}_{(j)} \cdot \mathbf{n}) + \mathbf{k}(\mathbf{t}_{(k)} \cdot \mathbf{n}) \right] \qquad (4.2\text{-}24)$$

Substitution of Eqs. 4.2-11 and expansion yield

$$\tilde{\mathbf{t}}_{(n)} = \begin{aligned} &\mathbf{i}[T_{xx}n_x + T_{xy}n_y + T_{xz}n_z] \\ +\, &\mathbf{j}[T_{yx}n_x + T_{yy}n_y + T_{yz}n_z] \\ +\, &\mathbf{k}[T_{zx}n_x + T_{zy}n_y + T_{zz}n_z] \end{aligned} \qquad (4.2\text{-}25)$$

Comparison of this result with Eq. 4.2-14 indicates that the diagonal terms $(n_x T_{xx}, n_y T_{yy}, n_z T_{zz})$ are the same; however, the off-diagonal terms have the subscripts reversed. In index notation, Eq. 4.2-25 becomes

$$\tilde{t}_{(n)i} = T_{ij}n_j \qquad (4.2\text{-}26)$$

and the Gibbs notation analogue of this result is

$$\tilde{\mathbf{t}}_{(n)} = \mathbf{T} \cdot \mathbf{n} \qquad (4.2\text{-}27)$$

In the next section, we will show that the stress tensor is symmetric, leading us to the result

$$\mathbf{n} \cdot \mathbf{T} = \mathbf{T} \cdot \mathbf{n} \qquad (4.2\text{-}28)$$

Although we will not prove it, Eq. 4.2-19 is also valid for curvilinear coordinate systems provided the scalar components of a vector are taken as the projections of the vector on the unit tangent vectors to the three coordinate curves. For a cylindrical system, 1, 2, and 3 represent r, θ and z; in spherical coordinates, these numbers represent r, θ, and ϕ. For example, in cylindrical coordinates, Eq. 4.2-17b would be written

$$t_{(n)\theta} = n_r T_{r\theta} + n_\theta T_{\theta\theta} + n_z T_{z\theta} \qquad (4.2\text{-}29)$$

Most often we will be concerned with forces acting on coordinate surfaces, and the normal vector will have only one nonzero component. For the cylindrical surface illustrated in Fig. 4.2-3, the components of the outwardly directed unit normal vector are

$$n_r = n_1 = 1$$

$$n_2 = n_\theta = 0$$

$$n_3 = n_z = 0$$

and Eq. 4.2-19 yields

$$t_{(n)r} = T_{rr}$$

$$t_{(n)\theta} = T_{r\theta}$$

$$t_{(n)z} = T_{rz}$$

These equations are obviously consistent with the components of the stress vector shown in Fig. 4.2-3.

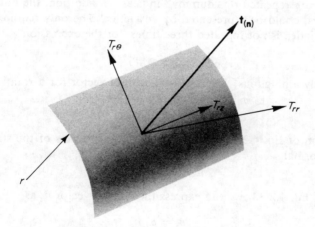

Fig. 4.2-3. Stress on a cylindrical surface.

The subscripts for the components of the stress tensor have the same meaning in cylindrical coordinates as they did in rectangular coordinates. Thus, $T_{r\theta}$ represents the stress acting on the r-surface in the θ-direction. We should remember that the derivation of the relationship between the stress vector and the stress tensor for rectangular coordinates is well within the realm of understanding of any student having the usual background in calculus. However, the results for other coordinate systems are beyond the scope of this text, and Eq. 4.2-19 must be accepted without proof for curvilinear systems.

Transformation of tensors

In Chap. 1, it was shown that a rotation of coordinates from x, y, z to x', y', z' (or x_i to x_i') gave rise to a transformation of the components of a vector expressed as

$$v_l' = v_k \cos \theta_{kl} \qquad (4.2\text{-}30)$$

where θ_{kl} was the angle between the x_k-axis and the x_l'-axis. Thus, θ_{12} is the angle between x_1 and x_2'. For convenience, we will write Eq. 4.2-30 as

$$v_l' = v_k \alpha_{kl} \qquad (4.2\text{-}31)$$

for a coordinate transformation $x_k \rightarrow x_k'$. Similarly, the old components (unprimed) can be related to the new components (primed) by

$$v_i = \alpha_{ij} v_j' \qquad (4.2\text{-}32)$$

Note that the k and j in these two equations could be replaced by any index since they are repeated or "dummy" indices. In addition, the l and i, being free indices, could be represented by any letter. The only requirement here is that an index is not repeated three times, for the expression

$$v_j = \alpha_{jj} v_j' \qquad (4.2\text{-}33)$$

is obviously ambiguous. Expressing the stress vector for a rotation of axes gives

$$t_{(\mathbf{n})i}' = t_{(\mathbf{n})j} \alpha_{ji} \qquad (4.2\text{-}34)$$

Application of Eq. 4.2-19 yields an expression in terms of the stress tensor and the normal

$$n_k' T_{ki}' = (n_l T_{lj}) \alpha_{ji} \qquad (4.2\text{-}35)$$

In light of Eq. 4.2-32, we can express the normal vector n_l as

$$n_l = \alpha_{lk} n_k' \qquad (4.2\text{-}36)$$

Substitution of Eq. 4.2-36 into Eq. 4.2-35, and placement of both terms on the left-hand side of the equation give us

$$n_k' [T_{ki}' - T_{lj} \alpha_{lk} \alpha_{ji}] = 0 \qquad (4.2\text{-}37)$$

Because n_k' is arbitrary and the terms in the bracket are independent of n_k', they must be zero. The transformation law for tensors results.

$$T_{ki}' = T_{lj} \alpha_{lk} \alpha_{ji} \qquad (4.2\text{-}38)$$

In Chap. 1, we pointed out that the mathematical definition of a vector required only that it be a group of three scalar quantities which obeyed a certain transformation law. The definition of a tensor requires that it be a group of nine scalar quantities that obey the law of transformation given by Eq. 4.2-38.

*4.3 Symmetry of the Stress Tensor

So far we have gained considerable knowledge of the nature of stress in a continuum by applying the linear momentum equation to two special material volumes. We can learn still more by applying the angular momentum equation to a third material volume. Following the procedure used in developing the stress tensor, we first prove local equilibrium of torques and then apply this result to the differential cube shown in Fig. 4.3-1. For an arbitrary

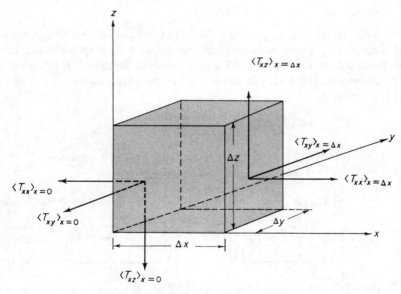

Fig. 4.3-1. Stresses on a differential cube.

material volume, the angular momentum equation is

$$\frac{D}{Dt} \int_{\mathcal{V}_{m}(t)} (\mathbf{r} \times \rho \mathbf{v}) \, dV = \int_{\mathcal{V}_{m}(t)} (\mathbf{r} \times \rho \mathbf{g}) \, dV + \int_{\mathcal{A}_{m}(t)} (\mathbf{r} \times \mathbf{t}_{(n)}) \, dA \qquad (4.3\text{-}1)$$

|Time rate of change of angular momentum|Torque owing to body force|Torque owing to surface force|

provided all torques are the moments of forces—i.e., there are no local stress couples[3] acting on the surface $\mathscr{A}_m(t)$. Once again we represent the material volume as

$$\mathscr{V}_m(t) = \alpha(t)L^3 \qquad (4.3\text{-}2)$$

and apply the mean value theorem to the volume integrals in Eq. 4.3-1.

$$\frac{D}{Dt}[\langle \mathbf{r} \times \rho\mathbf{v}\rangle\alpha(t)L^3] = \langle \mathbf{r} \times \rho\mathbf{g}\rangle\alpha(t)L^3 + \int\limits_{\mathscr{A}_m(t)} (\mathbf{r} \times \mathbf{t}_{(n)}) \, dA \qquad (4.3\text{-}3)$$

For the cube illustrated in Fig. 4.3-1, the characteristic length is taken as $L = \Delta x = \Delta y = \Delta z$. Since the position vector $\mathbf{r}$ is a directed line segment from the origin to any point on the cube, it tends to zero as $L \to 0$. Dividing Eq. 4.3-3 by L^3 and taking the limit $L \to 0$, we reach the result that torques are in local equilibrium.

$$0 = \lim_{L \to 0} \frac{1}{L^3} \int\limits_{\mathscr{A}_m(t)} (\mathbf{r} \times \mathbf{t}_{(n)}) \, dA \qquad (4.3\text{-}4)$$

As in the case when we proved local equilibrium of stress, the significance of this result will not be apparent until we apply it to a special case. If we form the scalar product of Eq. 4.3-4 with the base vector $\mathbf{k}$, an equation for the z-component of the torque will result. Application to the cube shown in Fig. 4.3-1 gives

$$
\begin{aligned}
0 = \lim_{L \to 0} \frac{1}{L^3}\Bigg\{ &\frac{1}{2}\Bigg[\overset{\text{Lever arm}}{\frac{L}{2}}\overset{\text{Force}}{T_{xx}}\Big|_{x=0} L^2\Bigg] - \frac{L}{2}\Big[T_{xx}\Big|_{x=\Delta x} L^2 \Big] + L\Big[T_{xy}\Big|_{x=\Delta x} L^2 \Big] \quad &x\text{-surfaces} \\
+ \ &\frac{L}{2}\Big[T_{yy}\Big|_{y=\Delta y} L^2 \Big] - \frac{L}{2}\Big[T_{yy}\Big|_{y=0} L^2 \Big] - L\Big[T_{yx}\Big|_{y=\Delta y} L^2 \Big] \quad &y\text{-surfaces} \qquad (4.3\text{-}5)\\
+ \ &\frac{L}{2}\Big[T_{zx}\Big|_{z=0} L^2 - T_{zx}\Big|_{z=\Delta z} L^2 \Big] - \frac{L}{2}\Big[T_{zy}\Big|_{z=\Delta z} L^2 - T_{zy}\Big|_{z=0} L^2 \Big]\Bigg\} \quad &z\text{-surfaces}
\end{aligned}
$$

where the averaging brackets ($\langle \ \rangle$) have been dropped to simplify the notation. The two underlined terms are the only ones which do not cancel as $L \to 0$; thus, carrying out the indicated division by L^3 and taking the limit, we get

$$\lim_{L \to 0} [T_{xy}\big|_{x=\Delta x} - T_{yx}\big|_{y=\Delta y}] = 0 \qquad (4.3\text{-}6)$$

or

$$T_{yx} = T_{xy} \qquad (4.3\text{-}7a)$$

3. D. W. Condiff and J. S. Dahler, "Fluid Mechanical Aspects of Antisymmetrical Stress," *Phys. Fluids*, 1964, 7:842:54.

By examining the other two scalar components of Eq. 4.3-4, we can also show

$$T_{zy} = T_{yz} \tag{4.3-7b}$$

$$T_{xz} = T_{zx} \tag{4.3-7c}$$

In index notation, these results are conveniently expressed as

$$T_{ij} = T_{ji} \tag{4.3-8}$$

*4.4   The Stress Equations of Motion

Our objective here is to derive the differential equations of motion for any continuum in terms of the components of the stress tensor. We start with Eq. 4.1-1, and, to keep the mathematics at a familiar level, we form the scalar product of Eq. 4.1-1 with an arbitrary constant vector **b**. Remember that this allows the scalar components, b_x, b_y, and b_z to take on any value provided they are independent of the spatial coordinates and time. For this reason, **b** can be taken inside integral signs and differential operators whenever necessary, and Eq. 4.1-1 may be written as

$$\frac{D}{Dt} \int_{\mathscr{V}_{m}(t)} \rho \mathbf{v} \cdot \mathbf{b} \, dV = \int_{\mathscr{V}_{m}(t)} \rho \mathbf{g} \cdot \mathbf{b} \, dV + \int_{\mathscr{A}_{m}(t)} \mathbf{t}_{(n)} \cdot \mathbf{b} \, dA \tag{4.4-1}$$

Before continuing with this analysis, it should be noted that forming the scalar product with the vector **b** eliminates, for the present, the necessity of dealing with the divergence of a tensor, $\nabla \cdot \mathbf{T}$, or the convective momentum flux tensor, $\rho \mathbf{vv}$. The latter will be treated in Chap. 6, and the former will be defined during the course of this development; however, it seems reasonable to introduce these new ideas as leisurely as possible, and working with Eq. 4.4-1 instead of Eq. 4.1-1 allows us to do this.

We now make use of the special form of the Reynolds transport theorem (see Eq. 3.5-12, Sec. 3.5), taking $\mathbf{v} \cdot \mathbf{b}$ to be the scalar S. We may thus write Eq. 4.4-1 as

$$\int_{\mathscr{V}_{m}(t)} \rho \frac{D}{Dt} (\mathbf{v} \cdot \mathbf{b}) \, dV = \int_{\mathscr{V}_{m}(t)} \rho \mathbf{g} \cdot \mathbf{b} \, dV + \int_{\mathscr{A}_{m}(t)} \mathbf{t}_{(n)} \cdot \mathbf{b} \, dA \tag{4.4-2}$$

Expressing the stress vector in terms of the stress tensor,

$$\mathbf{t}_{(n)} \cdot \mathbf{b} = (\mathbf{n} \cdot \mathbf{T}) \cdot \mathbf{b} = \mathbf{n} \cdot (\mathbf{T} \cdot \mathbf{b}) \tag{4.4-3}$$

yields

$$\int_{\mathscr{V}_{m}(t)} \rho \frac{D}{Dt} (\overset{\text{Scalar}}{\mathbf{v} \cdot \mathbf{b}}) \, dV = \int_{\mathscr{V}_{m}(t)} \rho \mathbf{g} \overset{\text{Scalar}}{\cdot} \mathbf{b} \, dV + \int_{\mathscr{A}_{m}(t)} \mathbf{n} \cdot (\overset{\text{Vector}}{\mathbf{T} \cdot \mathbf{b}}) \, dA \tag{4.4-4}$$

The area integral may now be transformed to a volume integral by the divergence theorem, and all terms can be put under the same integral sign.

$$\int_{\mathcal{V}_{m(t)}} \left\{ \rho \frac{D}{Dt} (\mathbf{v} \cdot \mathbf{b}) - \rho \mathbf{g} \cdot \mathbf{b} - \nabla \cdot (\mathbf{T} \cdot \mathbf{b}) \right\} dV = 0 \qquad (4.4\text{-}5)$$

Since the limits of integration are arbitrary, the integrand must be identically zero and the stress equation of motion for the **b**-direction is obtained.

$$\rho \frac{D}{Dt} (\mathbf{v} \cdot \mathbf{b}) = \rho \mathbf{g} \cdot \mathbf{b} + \nabla \cdot (\mathbf{T} \cdot \mathbf{b}) \qquad (4.4\text{-}6)$$

We now wish to eliminate the vector **b** to obtain the general vector form of the stress equations of motion.

The vector **b** can be removed easily from the first two terms in Eq. 4.4-6; however, removal from the last term gives rise to a new mathematical operation (the divergence of a tensor), and we need to perform this step carefully. Let us *define* a vector **f** by the equation,

$$\nabla \cdot (\mathbf{T} \cdot \mathbf{b}) = \mathbf{f} \cdot \mathbf{b} \qquad (4.4\text{-}7)$$

Note that the operation $\mathbf{T} \cdot \mathbf{b}$ has been previously defined and yields a vector. The divergence of a vector is a familiar operation; thus, the left-hand side of Eq. 4.4-7 is well defined and it follows that the vector **f** is determined. Following the result given by Eq. 4.2-25, we express the term $\mathbf{T} \cdot \mathbf{b}$ as

$$\mathbf{T} \cdot \mathbf{b} = \begin{array}{l} \mathbf{i}(T_{xx}b_x + T_{xy}b_y + T_{xz}b_z) \\ + \mathbf{j}(T_{yx}b_x + T_{yy}b_y + T_{yz}b_z) \\ + \mathbf{k}(T_{zx}b_x + T_{zy}b_y + T_{zz}b_z) \end{array} \qquad (4.4\text{-}8)$$

Taking the divergence of this vector and setting it equal to $\mathbf{f} \cdot \mathbf{b}$, we get

$$\begin{array}{l} \dfrac{\partial}{\partial x} (T_{xx}b_x + T_{xy}b_y + T_{xz}b_z) \\[2mm] + \dfrac{\partial}{\partial y} (T_{yx}b_x + T_{yy}b_y + T_{yz}b_z) = f_x b_x + f_y b_y + f_z b_z \\[2mm] + \dfrac{\partial}{\partial z} (T_{zx}b_x + T_{zy}b_y + T_{zz}b_z) \end{array} \qquad (4.4\text{-}9)$$

Carrying out the differentiation (remembering that b_x, b_y, and b_z are constant) and putting all the terms on the left-hand side, we have

$$\begin{array}{l} \left[\left(\dfrac{\partial T_{xx}}{\partial x} + \dfrac{\partial T_{yx}}{\partial y} + \dfrac{\partial T_{zx}}{\partial z} \right) - f_x \right] b_x \\[3mm] + \left[\left(\dfrac{\partial T_{xy}}{\partial x} + \dfrac{\partial T_{yy}}{\partial y} + \dfrac{\partial T_{zy}}{\partial z} \right) - f_y \right] b_y = 0 \\[3mm] + \left[\left(\dfrac{\partial T_{xz}}{\partial x} + \dfrac{\partial T_{yz}}{\partial y} + \dfrac{\partial T_{zz}}{\partial z} \right) - f_z \right] b_z \end{array} \qquad (4.4\text{-}10)$$

Inasmuch as the scalar components of **b** are arbitrary, each term in brackets must be zero. The scalar components of the vector **f** are therefore defined by Eq. 4.4-10. To convey as much information as possible, we denote the vector **f** by the symbol $\nabla \cdot \mathbf{T}$ and write

$$\mathbf{f} = \nabla \cdot \mathbf{T} = \begin{aligned} & \mathbf{i}\left(\frac{\partial T_{xx}}{\partial x} + \frac{\partial T_{yx}}{\partial y} + \frac{\partial T_{zx}}{\partial z}\right) \\[2mm] & +\mathbf{j}\left(\frac{\partial T_{xy}}{\partial x} + \frac{\partial T_{yy}}{\partial y} + \frac{\partial T_{zy}}{\partial z}\right) \\[2mm] & +\mathbf{k}\left(\frac{\partial T_{xz}}{\partial x} + \frac{\partial T_{yz}}{\partial y} + \frac{\partial T_{zz}}{\partial z}\right) \end{aligned} \qquad (4.4\text{-}11)$$

We may now rearrange Eq. 4.4-6 into the form

$$\left[\rho\,\frac{D\mathbf{v}}{Dt} - \rho\mathbf{g} - \nabla \cdot \mathbf{T}\right] \cdot \mathbf{b} = 0 \qquad (4.4\text{-}12)$$

Once again, the term in brackets must be zero because **b** is arbitrary, and the stress equations of motion are obtained.

$$\underset{\substack{\text{Acceleration}}}{\underset{\big\uparrow}{\rho\,\frac{D\mathbf{v}}{Dt}}} = \underset{\substack{\text{Surface force per}\\\text{unit volume}}}{\underset{\big\uparrow}{\overset{\big\downarrow}{\overset{\substack{\text{Mass per}\quad\text{Body force per}\\\text{unit volume}\ \ \text{unit volume}}}{\rho\mathbf{g} + \nabla \cdot \mathbf{T}}}}} \qquad (4.4\text{-}13)$$

Here we see that our result is nothing more than an expression of the linear momentum principle per unit volume. The result is valid for any continuum, and the student may well have seen the right-hand side of Eq. 4.4-13 in a course on solid mechanics or "strength of materials."

Remember that we started our analysis with the *integral* or *macroscopic* formulation of the linear momentum principle (see Eq. 4.1-1). This equation was valid for any material volume—i.e., any body moving and deforming in space and time. Use of the Reynolds transport theorem allowed us to put the material derivative inside the integral sign, and representing the surface forces in terms of the stress tensor permitted the area integral to be transformed to a volume integral. All terms in the equation could then be put under the same volume integral and the *differential* or *microscopic* equation resulted.

PROBLEMS

4-1. Starting with Eq. 4.4-1, use index notation and the special form of the Reynolds transport theorem given by Eq. 3.5-12 to derive the stress equations of motion. *Note:* Make use of the result that

$$\frac{\partial}{\partial x_j}(T_{ij}b_i) = \frac{\partial T_{ij}}{\partial x_j}\, b_i$$

when b_i is a constant vector.

4-2. (a) How many distinct components are there in a symmetric tensor? A skew symmetric tensor is one for which

$$D_{ij} = -D_{ji}$$

(b) How many distinct components are there in a skew symmetric tensor?

4-3. If the stress distribution in a body is uniform and given by

$$
\begin{aligned}
T_{xx} &= 500 \text{ psia} & T_{xy} &= 0 \\
T_{yy} &= 1000 \text{ psia} & T_{xz} &= 500 \text{ psia} \\
T_{zz} &= 1000 \text{ psia} & T_{yz} &= -500 \text{ psia}
\end{aligned}
$$

what is the normal stress T_{nn} on the plane $ABCD$ of the parallelepiped shown in Fig. 4-3?

Ans: 567 psia

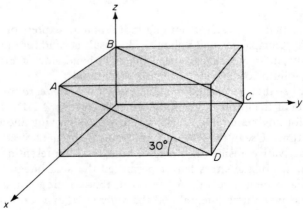

Fig. 4-3

4-4. If the components of stress T_{zz}, T_{zy}, T_{zx}, are zero, the stress distribution is two-dimensional and is called "plane stress." Given the following stresses at a point,

$$T_{xx} = 100 \text{ psia}$$
$$T_{yy} = -50 \text{ psia}$$
$$T_{xy} = T_{yx} = 50 \text{ psia}$$

find the plane (designated by $\mathbf{n}_1$) upon which the normal stress is a maximum

$$(T_{nn})\text{max} = \mathbf{n}_1 \cdot (\mathbf{n}_1 \cdot \mathbf{T})$$

and the plane (designated by $\mathbf{n}_2$) upon which the tangential (or shear) stress is a maximum

$$(T_{ns})\text{max} = \boldsymbol{\lambda} \cdot (\mathbf{n}_2 \cdot \mathbf{T})$$

Note that $\boldsymbol{\lambda} \cdot \mathbf{n}_2 = 0$. *Hint:* Let $n_x = \cos \theta$ and $n_y = \sin \theta$, and use the trigonometric identities

$$\cos^2 \theta = \tfrac{1}{2}(1 + \cos 2\theta)$$
$$\sin^2 \theta = \tfrac{1}{2}(1 - \cos 2\theta)$$
$$\sin 2\theta = 2 \sin \theta \cos \theta$$

Ans: $\theta = 16°51'$ for maximum normal stress
$\theta = 61°51'$ for maximum shear stress

4-5. Label the stresses shown in Fig. 4-5 with alphabetical and numerical subscripts and indicate whether they are positive or negative according to our sign convention.

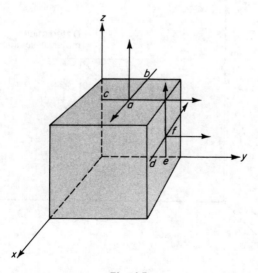

Fig. 4-5

Stress in a Fluid   Chap. 4

4-6. If the x and y axes are rotated counterclockwise 30° about the z-axis, as shown in Fig. 4-6, what are the values of T'_{xx}, T'_{xy}, and T'_{yz} in the rotated coordinate system for the uniform stress distribution described in Prob. 4-3? Use Eq. 4.2-38 to determine the three stress components; then use Eq. 4.2-14 to check your value for T'_{yz}. *Hint:* If $\mathbf{i}'$ is the unit vector directed along the x'-axis, then $T'_{xx} = \mathbf{i}' \cdot \mathbf{t}_{(i')}$.

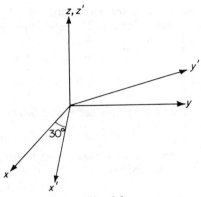

Fig. 4-6

4-7. If $D_{ij} = -D_{ji}$, prove that

$$D_{ij}\lambda_i\lambda_j = 0$$

where λ_i is an arbitrary vector. *Hint:* This may be done either by carrying out the double summation and regrouping the terms, or by relabeling the indices in an appropriate manner.

4-8. Apply the linear momentum principle to the differential, material cube shown in Fig. 4-8, to derive the x-direction stress equation of motion. Note that the time rate of change of momentum of the cube $(D/Dt)(\rho v_x \Delta V)$ may be expressed

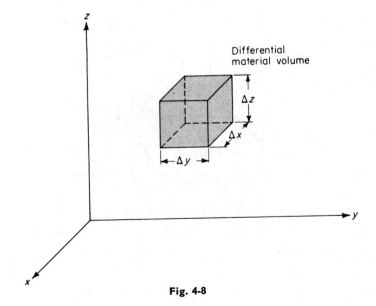

Fig. 4-8

as

$$\frac{D}{Dt}(\rho v_x \, \Delta V) = \rho \, \Delta V \frac{Dv_x}{Dt}$$

because the mass of the cube $\rho \, \Delta V$ is a constant.

4-9. An "inviscid" (or nonviscous) fluid is one that exerts no shear stress; thus, the stress vector is given by

$$t_{(n)} = -np, \text{ for an inviscid fluid}$$

Repeat Prob. 4-8 for this case and generalize the result to three dimensions to obtain

$$\rho \left(\frac{\partial \mathbf{v}}{\partial t} + \mathbf{v} \cdot \nabla \mathbf{v} \right) = -\nabla p + \rho \mathbf{g}$$

4-10. If **r** is the position vector, prove that

$$\frac{D}{Dt}(\mathbf{r} \times \mathbf{v}) = \mathbf{r} \times \frac{D\mathbf{v}}{Dt}$$

4-11. If **g** is a constant vector, what form must the scalar ϕ take so that $\mathbf{g} = -\nabla\phi$?

4-12. If $\mathbf{F} = \nabla S$, prove that $\nabla \times \mathbf{F} = 0$, i.e., the curl of the gradient of a scalar is zero.

4-13. The Kronecker delta δ_{ij} has the property that

$$\delta_{ij} = 0, \quad i \neq j$$
$$\delta_{ij} = 1, \quad i = j$$

Show that

$$\delta_{ij} \frac{\partial v_i}{\partial x_j} = \frac{\partial v_i}{\partial x_i}$$

Hint: Write out the left-hand side in full.

4-14. Show that an arbitrary tensor B_{ij} can be split into a symmetric and a skew symmetric tensor by writing it as

$$B_{ij} = \tfrac{1}{2}(B_{ij} + B_{ji}) + \tfrac{1}{2}(B_{ij} - B_{ji})$$

4-15. Given the divergence theorem for a vector,

$$\int_{\mathcal{V}} \nabla \cdot \mathbf{G} \, dV = \int_{\mathcal{A}} \mathbf{G} \cdot \mathbf{n} \, dA$$

derive the divergence theorem for a tensor,

$$\int_{\mathcal{V}} \nabla \cdot \mathbf{A} \, dV = \int_{\mathcal{A}} \mathbf{n} \cdot \mathbf{A} \, dA$$

by letting $\mathbf{G} = \mathbf{A} \cdot \mathbf{b}$. Use this result to derive the vector form of the stress equations of motion without forming the scalar product of the linear momentum equation with the arbitrary constant vector **b**.

4-16. Rederive Eq. 4.2-14 by first forming separate x-, y-, and z-direction force balances on the tetrahedron shown in Fig. 4.2-1 and then adding the results to obtain an expression for $t_{(n)}$.

The Differential
Equations of Motion

5

In the previous chapter we derived the three stress equations of motion.

$$\rho \frac{D\mathbf{v}}{Dt} = \rho \mathbf{g} + \boldsymbol{\nabla} \cdot \mathbf{T}$$

With the continuity equation

$$\frac{\partial \rho}{\partial t} + \boldsymbol{\nabla} \cdot (\rho \mathbf{v}) = 0$$

we have four equations which govern fluid motion. However, there are six unknown components of stress and three unknown components of velocity; therefore, we have *nine* dependent variables and only *four* equations. We overcome this excess of unknowns by introducing a *constitutive equation* relating the stress to the pressure and the velocity gradients thereby reducing the unknowns to four (pressure and the three components of velocity).

*5.1 The Viscous Stress Tensor

A constitutive equation is an empirical relationship that attempts to relate the stress in a continuum to the manner in which the material is deformed.

The statement "stress is a linear function of strain" yields a constitutive equation for solids obeying Hooke's law. "The stress always acts normal to a surface" is a statement leading to a constitutive equation for inviscid fluids, and "stress is a linear function of the rate of strain" yields a constitutive equation for Newtonian fluids. Constitutive equations, like the four fundamental postulates discussed in Chap. 1, are developed on the basis of experimental observation; however, the use of the word "law" (in Hooke's law and Newton's law of viscosity) to describe these results is unfortunate. The two laws of mechanics and the laws of conservation of energy and mass apply to all continua, while constitutive equations apply only to particular materials under limited circumstances. In a sense, there are as many constitutive equations as there are specific materials.

The first step in formulating a constitutive equation is to make use of some very definite ideas we have regarding the state of stress for any fluid at rest. As we indicated in Chap. 2, fluids at rest experience only a normal stress, which is independent of orientation. We call this stress the pressure, and inasmuch as it acts in a direction opposite to the outwardly directed unit normal, we write

$$
\begin{aligned}
\mathbf{t}_{(n)} &= \mathbf{n} \cdot \mathbf{T} \\
&= -\mathbf{n}p, \quad \text{for fluids at rest}
\end{aligned}
\tag{5.1-1}
$$

We note once again that the minus sign in Eq. 5.1-1 results from our convention that $\mathbf{t}_{(n)}$ represents the force exerted *by* the surroundings *on* the system.

It will be helpful in this development to split the stress tensor into two parts, the first representing the pressure stress and the second representing the stress arising from the deformation of the fluid. To do this, we must define a symmetric unit tensor, $\mathbf{I}$, which has the property

$$
\mathbf{A} \cdot \mathbf{I} = \mathbf{I} \cdot \mathbf{A} = \mathbf{A}
\tag{5.1-2}
$$

where $\mathbf{A}$ is a vector. Given Eq. 5.1-2 as the definition of $\mathbf{I}$, the scalar components can be specified on the basis of the previously derived equation for the dot product between a vector and tensor. The result is

$$
I_{xy} = I_{yx} = I_{yz} = I_{zy} = I_{zx} = I_{xz} = 0
\tag{5.1-3a}
$$

$$
I_{xx} = I_{yy} = I_{zz} = 1
\tag{5.1-3b}
$$

Thus, the off-diagonal components are zero, and the three diagonal components are unity. In matrix form, the unit tensor may be represented as

$$
\mathbf{I} = \begin{pmatrix} 1 & 0 & 0 \\ 0 & 1 & 0 \\ 0 & 0 & 1 \end{pmatrix}
\tag{5.1-4}
$$

Using index notation leads us to the conclusion that the scalar components of the unit tensor are given by the Kronecker delta δ_{ij}, and Eq. 5.1-2 becomes

$$A_i \delta_{ij} = A_j$$

where

$$\begin{aligned} \delta_{ij} &= 0, \quad i \neq j \\ \delta_{ij} &= 1, \quad i = j \end{aligned} \qquad (5.1\text{-}5)$$

We now *define* the viscous stress tensor, $\boldsymbol{\tau}$, by the equation

$$\mathbf{T} = -p\mathbf{I} + \boldsymbol{\tau} \qquad (5.1\text{-}6)$$

where the condition stated by Eq. 5.1-1 requires that

$$\boldsymbol{\tau} = 0, \quad \text{for fluids at rest} \qquad (5.1\text{-}7)$$

Because $\mathbf{T}$ and $\mathbf{I}$ are symmetric tensors, it is necessary that $\boldsymbol{\tau}$ be symmetric, and because all the off-diagonal terms of $p\mathbf{I}$ are zero, the off-diagonal terms of $\mathbf{T}$ and $\boldsymbol{\tau}$ are equal,

$$\begin{aligned} T_{xy} &= \tau_{xy} \\ T_{yz} &= \tau_{yz} \\ T_{zx} &= \tau_{zx} \end{aligned}$$

or, in index notation,

$$T_{ij} = \tau_{ij}, \quad i \neq j \qquad (5.1\text{-}8)$$

Equation 5.1-6 is the first tensor equation encountered in this text and it deserves further comment. A tensor equation is simply a way to convey a great deal of information without recourse to an annoying amount of algebra. Consider a scalar equation of the type

$$A = B \qquad (5.1\text{-}9)$$

What this equation means is obvious: A is equal to B. Consider a vector equation of the type

$$\mathbf{A} = \mathbf{B} \qquad (5.1\text{-}10)$$

which means that the *scalar* components of $\mathbf{A}$ are equal to the *scalar* components of $\mathbf{B}$. For rectangular coordinates we obtain

$$\begin{aligned} A_x &= B_x \\ A_y &= B_y \\ A_z &= B_z \end{aligned}$$

Use of vector notation allows us to express these last three equations as a single equation. Similarly, if $\mathbf{A}$ and $\mathbf{B}$ are tensors, the tensor equation

$$\mathbf{A} = \mathbf{B} \qquad (5.1\text{-}11)$$

represents the nine scalar equations,

$$A_{xx} = B_{xx} \qquad A_{xy} = B_{xy} \qquad A_{xz} = B_{xz}$$
$$A_{yx} = B_{yx} \qquad A_{yy} = B_{yy} \qquad A_{yz} = B_{yz}$$
$$A_{zx} = B_{zx} \qquad A_{zy} = B_{zy} \qquad A_{zz} = B_{zz}$$

In matrix form, we would represent them as

$$\begin{pmatrix} A_{xx} & A_{xy} & A_{xz} \\ A_{yx} & A_{yy} & A_{yz} \\ A_{zx} & A_{zy} & A_{zz} \end{pmatrix} = \begin{pmatrix} B_{xx} & B_{xy} & B_{xz} \\ B_{yx} & B_{yy} & B_{yz} \\ B_{zx} & B_{zy} & B_{zz} \end{pmatrix} \tag{5.1-12}$$

where the elements of the A-matrix are equal to the corresponding elements of the B-matrix. Index notation provides the most informative form of Eq. 5.1-11,

$$A_{ij} = B_{ij} \tag{5.1-13}$$

Returning now to Eq. 5.1-6, we wish to substitute this expression for the total stress tensor into the stress equations of motion to obtain

$$\rho \frac{D\mathbf{v}}{Dt} = \rho \mathbf{g} - \nabla \cdot (p\mathbf{I}) + \nabla \cdot \boldsymbol{\tau} \tag{5.1-14}$$

Following Eq. 4.4-11 to obtain the divergence of the tensor, $p\mathbf{I}$, we write

$$\nabla \cdot (p\mathbf{I}) = \begin{aligned} &\mathbf{i}\left[\frac{\partial}{\partial x}(pI_{xx}) + \frac{\partial}{\partial y}(pI_{yx}) + \frac{\partial}{\partial z}(pI_{zx})\right] \\ +&\mathbf{j}\left[\frac{\partial}{\partial x}(pI_{xy}) + \frac{\partial}{\partial y}(pI_{yy}) + \frac{\partial}{\partial z}(pI_{zy})\right] \\ +&\mathbf{k}\left[\frac{\partial}{\partial x}(pI_{xz}) + \frac{\partial}{\partial y}(pI_{yz}) + \frac{\partial}{\partial z}(pI_{zz})\right] \end{aligned} \tag{5.1-15}$$

Inasmuch as the off-diagonal elements of the unit tensor are zero and the diagonal elements are unity, this equation becomes

$$\nabla \cdot (p\mathbf{I}) = \mathbf{i}\frac{\partial p}{\partial x} + \mathbf{j}\frac{\partial p}{\partial y} + \mathbf{k}\frac{\partial p}{\partial z} = \nabla p \tag{5.1-16}$$

Substitution of Eq. 5.1-16 into Eq. 5.1-14 and expansion of the material derivative give the *viscous stress* equations of motion

$$\rho\left(\frac{\partial \mathbf{v}}{\partial t} + \mathbf{v} \cdot \nabla \mathbf{v}\right) = -\nabla p + \rho \mathbf{g} + \nabla \cdot \boldsymbol{\tau} \tag{5.1-17}$$

These equations are listed in Tables 5.1-1, 5.1-2, and 5.1-3 for rectangular, cylindrical, and spherical coordinates.

Table 5.1-1

VISCOUS STRESS EQUATIONS OF MOTION IN RECTANGULAR
COORDINATES (x, y, z)

x-Direction

$$\rho\left(\frac{\partial v_x}{\partial t} + v_x\frac{\partial v_x}{\partial x} + v_y\frac{\partial v_x}{\partial y} + v_z\frac{\partial v_x}{\partial z}\right) = -\frac{\partial p}{\partial x} + \rho g_x + \left(\frac{\partial \tau_{xx}}{\partial x} + \frac{\partial \tau_{yx}}{\partial y} + \frac{\partial \tau_{zx}}{\partial z}\right) \quad \text{(a)}$$

y-Direction

$$\rho\left(\frac{\partial v_y}{\partial t} + v_x\frac{\partial v_y}{\partial x} + v_y\frac{\partial v_y}{\partial y} + v_z\frac{\partial v_y}{\partial z}\right) = -\frac{\partial p}{\partial y} + \rho g_y + \left(\frac{\partial \tau_{xy}}{\partial x} + \frac{\partial \tau_{yy}}{\partial y} + \frac{\partial \tau_{zy}}{\partial z}\right) \quad \text{(b)}$$

z-Direction

$$\rho\left(\frac{\partial v_z}{\partial t} + v_x\frac{\partial v_z}{\partial x} + v_y\frac{\partial v_z}{\partial y} + v_z\frac{\partial v_z}{\partial z}\right) = -\frac{\partial p}{\partial z} + \rho g_z + \left(\frac{\partial \tau_{xz}}{\partial x} + \frac{\partial \tau_{yz}}{\partial y} + \frac{\partial \tau_{zz}}{\partial z}\right) \quad \text{(c)}$$

Table 5.1-2

VISCOUS STRESS EQUATIONS OF MOTION IN CYLINDRICAL
COORDINATES (r, θ, z)

r-Direction

$$\rho\left(\frac{\partial v_r}{\partial t} + v_r\frac{\partial v_r}{\partial r} + \frac{v_\theta}{r}\frac{\partial v_r}{\partial \theta} - \frac{v_\theta^2}{r} + v_z\frac{\partial v_r}{\partial z}\right) = -\frac{\partial p}{\partial r}$$

$$+ \rho g_r + \left[\frac{1}{r}\frac{\partial}{\partial r}(r\tau_{rr}) + \frac{1}{r}\frac{\partial \tau_{\theta r}}{\partial \theta} - \frac{\tau_{\theta\theta}}{r} + \frac{\partial \tau_{zr}}{\partial z}\right] \quad \text{(a)}$$

θ-Direction

$$\rho\left(\frac{\partial v_\theta}{\partial t} + v_r\frac{\partial v_\theta}{\partial r} + \frac{v_\theta}{r}\frac{\partial v_\theta}{\partial \theta} + \frac{v_r v_\theta}{r} + v_z\frac{\partial v_\theta}{\partial z}\right) = -\frac{1}{r}\frac{\partial p}{\partial \theta}$$

$$+ \rho g_\theta + \left[\frac{1}{r^2}\frac{\partial}{\partial r}(r^2\,\tau_{r\theta}) + \frac{1}{r}\frac{\partial \tau_{\theta\theta}}{\partial \theta} + \frac{\partial \tau_{z\theta}}{\partial z}\right] \quad \text{(b)}$$

z-Direction

$$\rho\left(\frac{\partial v_z}{\partial t} + v_r\frac{\partial v_z}{\partial r} + \frac{v_\theta}{r}\frac{\partial v_z}{\partial \theta} + v_z\frac{\partial v_z}{\partial z}\right) = -\frac{\partial p}{\partial z}$$

$$+ \rho g_z + \left[\frac{1}{r}\frac{\partial}{\partial r}(r\tau_{rz}) + \frac{1}{r}\frac{\partial \tau_{\theta z}}{\partial \theta} + \frac{\partial \tau_{zz}}{\partial z}\right] \quad \text{(c)}$$

Table 5.1-3
VISCOUS STRESS EQUATIONS OF MOTION FOR SPHERICAL
COORDINATES (r, θ, ϕ)

r-Direction

$$\rho\left(\frac{\partial v_r}{\partial t} + v_r \frac{\partial v_r}{\partial r} + \frac{v_\theta}{r} \frac{\partial v_r}{\partial \theta} + \frac{v_\phi}{r \sin \theta} \frac{\partial v_r}{\partial \phi} - \frac{v_\theta^2 + v_\phi^2}{r}\right) = -\frac{\partial p}{\partial r}$$

$$+ \rho g_r + \left[\frac{1}{r^2} \frac{\partial}{\partial r}(r^2 \tau_{rr}) + \frac{1}{r \sin \theta} \frac{\partial}{\partial \theta}(\tau_{\theta r} \sin \theta)\right. \tag{a}$$

$$\left. + \frac{1}{r \sin \theta} \frac{\partial \tau_{\phi r}}{\partial \phi} - \frac{\tau_{\theta\theta} + \tau_{\phi\phi}}{r}\right]$$

θ-Direction

$$\rho\left(\frac{\partial v_\theta}{\partial t} + v_r \frac{\partial v_\theta}{\partial r} + \frac{v_\theta}{r} \frac{\partial v_\theta}{\partial \theta} + \frac{v_\phi}{r \sin \theta} \frac{\partial v_\theta}{\partial \phi} + \frac{v_r v_\theta}{r} - \frac{v_\phi^2 \cot \theta}{r}\right)$$

$$= -\frac{1}{r} \frac{\partial p}{\partial \theta} + \rho g_\theta + \left[\frac{1}{r^2} \frac{\partial}{\partial r}(r^2 \tau_{r\theta}) + \frac{1}{r \sin \theta} \frac{\partial}{\partial \theta}(\tau_{\theta\theta} \sin \theta)\right. \tag{b}$$

$$\left. + \frac{1}{r \sin \theta} \frac{\partial \tau_{\phi\theta}}{\partial \phi} + \frac{\tau_{r\theta}}{r} - \frac{\tau_{\phi\phi} \cot \theta}{r}\right]$$

φ-Direction

$$\rho\left(\frac{\partial v_\phi}{\partial t} + v_r \frac{\partial v_\phi}{\partial r} + \frac{v_\theta}{r} \frac{\partial v_\phi}{\partial \theta} + \frac{v_\phi}{r \sin \theta} \frac{\partial v_\phi}{\partial \phi} + \frac{v_\phi v_r}{r} + \frac{v_\theta v_\phi \cot \theta}{r}\right)$$

$$= -\frac{1}{r \sin \theta} \frac{\partial p}{\partial \phi} + \rho g_\phi + \left[\frac{1}{r^2} \frac{\partial}{\partial r}(r^2 \tau_{r\phi}) + \frac{1}{r} \frac{\partial \tau_{\theta\phi}}{\partial \theta}\right. \tag{c}$$

$$\left. + \frac{1}{r \sin \theta} \frac{\partial \tau_{\phi\phi}}{\partial \phi} + \frac{\tau_{r\phi}}{r} + \frac{2\tau_{\theta\phi} \cot \theta}{r}\right]$$

In the next section, the viscous stress tensor $\boldsymbol{\tau}$ will be represented in terms of the rate of strain tensor $\mathbf{d}$ for a Newtonian fluid. The relationship is given by

$$\boldsymbol{\tau} = 2\mu \mathbf{d} + [(\kappa - \tfrac{2}{3}\mu)\nabla \cdot \mathbf{v}]\mathbf{I} \tag{5.1-18a}$$

or

$$\tau_{ij} = 2\mu \, d_{ij} + \left[\left(\kappa - \frac{2}{3}\mu\right)\left(\frac{\partial v_k}{\partial x_k}\right)\right]\delta_{ij} \tag{5.1-18b}$$

where we refer to μ and κ properly as the *shear coefficient of viscosity* and the *bulk coefficient of viscosity*, respectively. In practice, we refer to μ and κ as the "viscosity" and the "bulk viscosity," respectively. The rate of strain tensor is given in terms of the velocity gradients as[†]

$$d_{ij} = \frac{1}{2}\left(\frac{\partial v_i}{\partial x_j} + \frac{\partial v_j}{\partial x_i}\right) \qquad (5.1\text{-}19)$$

A detailed derivation of this result is presented in Sec. 5.2 followed by a qualitative discussion of the rate of strain in Sec. 5.3. The effort required to understand the development is large compared to the benefits reaped from such study; therefore, many students may wish to skip these sections and go directly on to Sec. 5.4. They may do this without detriment to the study of subsequent material; however, any student with a good background in solid mechanics can cover this material very quickly and should do so.

5.2 Newton's Law of Viscosity

Newton's law of viscosity is based on a linear relationship between the viscous stress and the rate of strain. In Chap. 1, Newton's law of viscosity for a simple one-dimensional flow was introduced in the form of a single component of the stress tensor being equal to the coefficient of shear viscosity times a velocity gradient,

$$T_{yx} = \tau_{yx} = \mu\left(\frac{dv_x}{dy}\right) \qquad (5.2\text{-}1)$$

Although this expression may appeal to the student's intuition, it is not at all obvious that dv_x/dy is a measure of the rate of strain for a fluid in plane shear flow, even though the units (sec^{-1}) are satisfactory. Gaining some understanding of the rate of strain and its relationship to the viscous stress is undoubtedly one of the most difficult problems in fluid mechanics; in fact, more than 100 years elapsed between Newton's statement in 1686 that,

> "The resistance arising from want of lubricity in the parts of a fluid is, other things being equal, proportional to the velocity with which the parts of the fluid are separated from one another."

and the derivation of the Navier-Stokes equations by Navier (1821), Poisson (1831), and Stokes (1845).[1] It is only natural, then, that the ideas discussed

---

[†] This relationship should be reminiscent of that between the strain tensor and gradients of the displacement vector encountered in solid mechanics. The scalar components of d_{ij} in rectangular, cylindrical, and spherical coordinates are listed in Table 5.2-1, and the relationship between the scalar components of the viscous stress tensor and the velocity gradients are given in Tables 5.2-2, 5.2-3, and 5.2-4 for Newtonian fluids.

1. P. F. Neményi, "The Main Concepts and Ideas of Fluid Dynamics in Their Historical Development," *Archive for the History of Exact Sciences*, 1962, 2:52.

in this section will be difficult to understand, requiring extra effort by the student. A mathematical description is presented first, followed by some applications and a qualitative description in Sec. 5.3.

The rate of strain

In order to determine the rate of strain at some point in space, let us consider a material line element of length Δs embedded in the fluid. As illustrated in Fig. 5.2-1, P and Q are material points and Δs is the material line

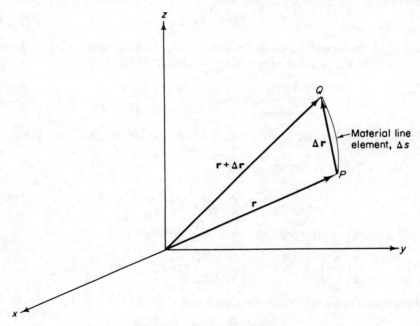

Fig. 5.2-1. Material line element.

element connecting them. If the fluid were moving as a solid body, the line element would be translated and rotated, but the length would never change. However, if the line element were lengthened or shortened, the fluid would be deformed and the rate of change of length of Δs would be a measure of the rate of deformation.

We note that at any point in space, we could visualize an infinite number of line elements, each having a different direction λ_i, where λ_i is the unit tangent vector to the line element

$$\lambda_i = \lim_{\Delta s \to 0} \left(\frac{\Delta r_i}{\Delta s} \right) \qquad (5.2\text{-}2)$$

In solid mechanics, the word "strain" denotes a *change in length per unit length*. We will follow this nomenclature and call the *rate of change in length per unit length* the "rate of strain." We remember that each line element passing through a particular point in space may be undergoing a different rate of strain, depending on its direction; therefore, we define the rate of strain in the following manner:

$$\begin{Bmatrix} \text{the rate of} \\ \text{strain in the} \\ \lambda_j\text{-direction} \end{Bmatrix} = \lim_{\Delta s \to 0} \left\{ \frac{1}{\Delta s} \frac{D}{Dt}(\Delta s) \right\} \tag{5.2-3}$$

Following Fig. 5.2-1, we write

$$\Delta s^2 = \Delta r_i \, \Delta r_i \tag{5.2-4}$$

where we understand that this equation only holds in limit as $\Delta s \to 0$. We may rewrite Eq. 5.2-3 in terms of the square of Δs to obtain

$$\begin{Bmatrix} \text{the rate of} \\ \text{strain in the} \\ \lambda_j\text{-direction} \end{Bmatrix} = \lim_{\Delta s \to 0} \left\{ \left(\frac{1}{2}\right)\left(\frac{1}{\Delta s^2}\right)\frac{D}{Dt}(\Delta s^2) \right\} \tag{5.2-5}$$

In the following steps, it will be understood that we intend to take the limit $\Delta s \to 0$.

By Eq. 5.2-4 we obtain

$$\frac{1}{2}\left(\frac{1}{\Delta s^2}\right)\frac{D}{Dt}(\Delta s^2) = \frac{1}{2}\left(\frac{1}{\Delta s^2}\right)\left\{ \frac{D}{Dt}(\Delta r_i \, \Delta r_i) \right\} \tag{5.2-6}$$

Differentiation of the product yields

$$\frac{1}{2}\left(\frac{1}{\Delta s^2}\right)\frac{D}{Dt}(\Delta s^2) = \frac{1}{2}\left(\frac{1}{\Delta s^2}\right)\left\{ \frac{D}{Dt}(\Delta r_i) \, \Delta r_i + \Delta r_i \frac{D}{Dt}(\Delta r_i) \right\} \tag{5.2-7}$$

By symmetry, we may write the right-hand side as

$$\frac{1}{2}\left(\frac{1}{\Delta s^2}\right)\frac{D}{Dt}(\Delta s^2) = \frac{1}{\Delta s^2}\left\{ \Delta r_i \frac{D}{Dt}(\Delta r_i) \right\} \tag{5.2-8}$$

Noting that

$$\Delta r_i = r_i(Q) - r_i(P) \tag{5.2-9}$$

we write

$$\frac{D}{Dt}(\Delta r_i) = \frac{Dr_i(Q)}{Dt} - \frac{Dr_i(P)}{Dt} = \Delta\left(\frac{Dr_i}{Dt}\right) \tag{5.2-10}$$

and Eq. 5.2-8 takes the form

$$\frac{1}{2}\left(\frac{1}{\Delta s^2}\right)\frac{D}{Dt}(\Delta s^2) = \frac{1}{\Delta s^2}\left\{ \Delta r_i \, \Delta\left(\frac{Dr_i}{Dt}\right) \right\} \tag{5.2-11}$$

Remembering that the material derivative of the position vector is the velocity, we obtain

$$\frac{1}{2}\left(\frac{1}{\Delta s^2}\right)\frac{D}{Dt}(\Delta s^2) = \frac{1}{\Delta s^2}(\Delta r_i\,\Delta v_i) \qquad (5.2\text{-}12)$$

Now, Δv_i represents the change in the velocity vector between Q and P, and a Taylor series expansion of v_i about the point P gives

$$\Delta v_i = \left(\frac{\partial v_i}{\partial x_j}\right)\Delta x_j \qquad (5.2\text{-}13)$$

Here, we have dropped the higher order terms in anticipation of taking the limit $\Delta s \to 0$. Noting that $\Delta x_j = \Delta r_j$, we may rearrange Eq. 5.2-12 in the form

$$\frac{1}{2}\left(\frac{1}{\Delta s^2}\right)\frac{D}{Dt}(\Delta s^2) = \left(\frac{\partial v_i}{\partial x_j}\right)\left(\frac{\Delta r_i}{\Delta s}\right)\left(\frac{\Delta r_j}{\Delta s}\right) \qquad (5.2\text{-}14)$$

Substitution of this result into Eq. 5.2-5 and use of the limit $\Delta s \to 0$ yield†

$$\begin{Bmatrix}\text{the rate of}\\ \text{strain in the}\\ \lambda_j\text{-direction}\end{Bmatrix} = \left(\frac{\partial v_i}{\partial x_j}\right)\lambda_i\lambda_j \qquad (5.2\text{-}15)$$

Note that our result here is very similar to that obtained when we analyzed the stress in a continuum. In that case, the "state of stress" was determined by a tensor T_{ij}, and the stress acting on a plane having a normal n_i in the direction n_j was given by

$$T_{nn} = n_j n_i T_{ij} \qquad (5.2\text{-}16)$$

In this development, we find that the "state of rate of strain" is determined by the tensor $\partial v_i/\partial x_j$, and the rate of strain on a surface having a normal λ_i in the direction λ_j is given by Eq. 5.2-15.

The tensor $\partial v_i/\partial x_j$ may be rearranged by adding and subtracting its conjugate‡ $\partial v_j/\partial x_i$ to obtain

$$\frac{\partial v_i}{\partial x_j} = \frac{1}{2}\left(\frac{\partial v_i}{\partial x_j} + \frac{\partial v_j}{\partial x_i}\right) + \frac{1}{2}\left(\frac{\partial v_i}{\partial x_j} - \frac{\partial v_j}{\partial x_i}\right) \qquad (5.2\text{-}17)$$

† It may be helpful to remember from the small deformation theory of solid mechanics that

$$\begin{Bmatrix}\text{the strain in the}\\ \lambda_j\text{-direction}\end{Bmatrix} = \left(\frac{\partial u_i}{\partial x_j}\right)\lambda_i\lambda_j$$

where u_i is the displacement vector.

‡ The transpose of a matrix is obtained by interchanging the rows and columns. When this operation is applied to a tensor, the result is called the conjugate tensor.

The first term on the right-hand side is called the rate of strain tensor, d_{ij}, and is symmetric.

$$d_{ij} = \frac{1}{2}\left(\frac{\partial v_i}{\partial x_j} + \frac{\partial v_j}{\partial x_i}\right) \qquad (5.2\text{-}18)$$

$$(d_{ij} = d_{ji})$$

The components of d_{ij} for rectangular, cylindrical, and spherical coordinates are listed in Table 5.2-1. The second term in Eq. 5.2-17 is called the vorticity tensor, Ω_{ij}, and is skew symmetric

$$\Omega_{ij} = \frac{1}{2}\left(\frac{\partial v_i}{\partial x_j} - \frac{\partial v_j}{\partial x_i}\right) \qquad (5.2\text{-}19)$$

$$(\Omega_{ij} = -\Omega_{ji})$$

We now wish to show that the vorticity tensor Ω_{ij} makes no contribution to the rate of strain. Later we shall show that the components of this tensor represent the rotational motion of the fluid.

Returning to Eq. 5.2-15 and making use of the definitions given by Eqs. 5.2-18 and 5.2-19, we obtain

$$\left\{\begin{matrix}\text{the rate of} \\ \text{strain in the} \\ \lambda_j\text{-direction}\end{matrix}\right\} = d_{ij}\lambda_i\lambda_j + \Omega_{ij}\lambda_i\lambda_j \qquad (5.2\text{-}20)$$

where the unit tangent vector λ_i is completely arbitrary. We can show the last term on the right-hand side of Eq. 5.2-20 to be *identically* zero by carrying out the double summation and suitably regrouping the terms; however, the proof is somewhat easier if we use the technique of relabeling the repeated or dummy indices. We first split the term into two parts,

$$\Omega_{ij}\lambda_i\lambda_j = \tfrac{1}{2}\Omega_{ij}\lambda_i\lambda_j + \tfrac{1}{2}\Omega_{ij}\lambda_i\lambda_j \qquad (5.2\text{-}21)$$

and in the second term on the right-hand side we relabel i as j and j as i to obtain

$$\Omega_{ij}\lambda_i\lambda_j = \tfrac{1}{2}\Omega_{ij}\lambda_i\lambda_j + \tfrac{1}{2}\Omega_{ji}\lambda_j\lambda_i \qquad (5.2\text{-}22)$$

Changing the order of multiplication by λ_j and λ_i allows us to express this result as

$$\Omega_{ij}\lambda_i\lambda_j = \tfrac{1}{2}(\Omega_{ij} + \Omega_{ji})\lambda_i\lambda_j \qquad (5.2\text{-}23)$$

Because Ω_{ij} is skew symmetric, we know that $(\Omega_{ij} + \Omega_{ji})$ is identically zero and the proof is obtained.

$$\Omega_{ij}\lambda_i\lambda_j = 0 \qquad (5.2\text{-}24)$$

Our expression for the rate of strain is now given entirely in terms of the rate of strain tensor

$$\left\{\begin{matrix}\text{the rate of} \\ \text{strain in the} \\ \lambda_j\text{-direction}\end{matrix}\right\} = d_{ij}\lambda_i\lambda_j \qquad (5.2\text{-}25)$$

Table 5.2-1
SCALAR COMPONENTS OF THE RATE OF STRAIN TENSOR

Rectangular Coordinates (x, y, z)

$$d_{xx} = \frac{\partial v_x}{\partial x}, \qquad d_{xy} = d_{yx} = \frac{1}{2}\left(\frac{\partial v_x}{\partial y} + \frac{\partial v_y}{\partial x}\right)$$

$$d_{yy} = \frac{\partial v_y}{\partial y}, \qquad d_{yz} = d_{zy} = \frac{1}{2}\left(\frac{\partial v_y}{\partial z} + \frac{\partial v_z}{\partial y}\right)$$

$$d_{zz} = \frac{\partial v_z}{\partial z}, \qquad d_{zx} = d_{xz} = \frac{1}{2}\left(\frac{\partial v_z}{\partial x} + \frac{\partial v_x}{\partial z}\right)$$

Cylindrical Coordinates (r, θ, z)

$$d_{rr} = \frac{\partial v_r}{\partial r}, \qquad d_{r\theta} = d_{\theta r} = \frac{1}{2}\left[r\frac{\partial}{\partial r}\left(\frac{v_\theta}{r}\right) + \frac{1}{r}\frac{\partial v_r}{\partial \theta}\right]$$

$$d_{\theta\theta} = \frac{1}{r}\frac{\partial v_\theta}{\partial \theta} + \frac{v_r}{r}, \qquad d_{\theta z} = d_{z\theta} = \frac{1}{2}\left(\frac{\partial v_\theta}{\partial z} + \frac{1}{r}\frac{\partial v_z}{\partial \theta}\right)$$

$$d_{zz} = \frac{\partial v_z}{\partial z}, \qquad d_{zr} = d_{rz} = \frac{1}{2}\left(\frac{\partial v_z}{\partial r} + \frac{\partial v_r}{\partial z}\right)$$

Spherical Coordinates (r, θ, ϕ)

$$d_{rr} = \frac{\partial v_r}{\partial r}, \qquad d_{r\theta} = d_{\theta r} = \frac{1}{2}\left[r\frac{\partial}{\partial r}\left(\frac{v_\theta}{r}\right) + \frac{1}{r}\frac{\partial v_r}{\partial \theta}\right]$$

$$d_{\theta\theta} = \frac{1}{r}\frac{\partial v_\theta}{\partial \theta} + \frac{v_r}{r}, \qquad d_{\theta\phi} = d_{\phi\theta} = \frac{1}{2}\left[\frac{\sin\theta}{r}\frac{\partial}{\partial \theta}\left(\frac{v_\phi}{\sin\theta}\right) + \frac{1}{r\sin\theta}\frac{\partial v_\theta}{\partial \phi}\right]$$

$$d_{\phi\phi} = \left(\frac{1}{r\sin\theta}\frac{\partial v_\phi}{\partial \phi} + \frac{v_r}{r} + \frac{v_\theta \cot\theta}{r}\right), \qquad d_{\phi r} = d_{r\phi} = \frac{1}{2}\left[\frac{1}{r\sin\theta}\frac{\partial v_r}{\partial \phi} + r\frac{\partial}{\partial r}\left(\frac{v_\phi}{r}\right)\right]$$

Newton's law of viscosity

We begin our task of formulating a constitutive equation for fluids by assuming that the viscous stress tensor is a function of the rate of strain tensor. We then restrict ourselves to a linear, isotropic dependence on the rate of strain to obtain Newton's law of viscosity. We generally follow a similar procedure in treating solids—i.e., assume the stress tensor is a function of the strain tensor, and then restrict the analysis to a linear, isotropic dependence on the strain to obtain Hooke's law.

Our starting point is, then,

$$\tau_{ij} = f_{ij}(d_{kl}) \tag{5.2-26}$$

Thus, we have a *tensor function of a tensor* as our first step in formulating a constitutive equation. This idea is undoubtedly new to the student, and it is best to back up a bit to begin at the beginning. We shall consider first a *scalar function of a scalar*,

$$\rho = f(T) \tag{5.2-27}$$

We have indicated here that the density is a function of the temperature. This function is easily plotted as ρ versus T; derivatives are readily identified as the slope of this curve and integrals as the area under this curve.

Next we shall consider a *scalar function of a vector*,

$$\rho = f(x_i) \tag{5.2-28}$$

We have indicated here that the density is a function of the spatial coordinates, x_1, x_2, x_3 (or x, y, z). If ρ were independent of one of the coordinates, we could plot it as a function of x_i to obtain a surface in 3-space. Derivatives are understood as the slopes of tangents to this surface and integrals as volumes under the surface. We might ask, "What of a *vector function of a vector*?"

$$v_i = f_i(x_j) \tag{5.2-29}$$

Certainly this idea is readily acceptable and simply states that each scalar component of the velocity depends on the spatial coordinates.

$$v_1 = f_1(x_1, x_2, x_3) \quad \text{or} \quad v_x = v_x(x, y, z) \tag{5.2-30a}$$

$$v_2 = f_2(x_1, x_2, x_3) \quad \text{or} \quad v_y = v_y(x, y, z) \tag{5.2-30b}$$

$$v_3 = f_3(x_1, x_2, x_3) \quad \text{or} \quad v_z = v_z(x, y, z) \tag{5.2-30c}$$

Although we may feel quite comfortable with such function, we cannot draw a "picture" of it easily, so we must rely on mathematical formalism.

Now let us return to our tensor function of a tensor and state more explicitly what this terminology means. In words, we could say that *each component of τ_{ij} is a function of all the components of d_{ij}*. Symbolically, we may write

$$\tau_{11} = f_{11}(d_{11}, d_{22}, d_{33}, d_{12}, d_{23}, d_{31}) \tag{5.2-31a}$$

$$\tau_{12} = f_{12}(d_{11}, d_{22}, d_{33}, d_{12}, d_{23}, d_{31}) \quad \text{etc.} \tag{5.2-31b}$$

Owing to the symmetry of both τ_{ij} and d_{ij}, we have only six equations representing the dependence of τ_{ij} on the six distinct values of d_{ij}.

Having established what we mean by a tensor function of a tensor, we need only write down the *linear* form of this relationship and require it to be *isotropic* to obtain Newton's law of viscosity. The most general linear form of Eq. 5.2-6 subject to the restriction that†

$$\tau_{ij} = 0 \quad \text{when} \quad d_{ij} = 0 \tag{5.2-32}$$

is given by the following six equations:

$$\tau_{xx} = C_{11}d_{xx} + C_{12}d_{yy} + C_{13}d_{zz} + C_{14}d_{xy} + C_{15}d_{yz} + C_{16}d_{zx} \tag{5.2-33a}$$
$$\tau_{yy} = C_{21}d_{xx} + C_{22}d_{yy} + C_{23}d_{zz} + C_{24}d_{xy} + C_{25}d_{yz} + C_{26}d_{zx} \tag{5.2-33b}$$
$$\tau_{zz} = C_{31}d_{xx} + C_{32}d_{yy} + C_{33}d_{zz} + C_{34}d_{xy} + C_{35}d_{yz} + C_{36}d_{zx} \tag{5.2-33c}$$
$$\tau_{xy} = C_{41}d_{xx} + C_{42}d_{yy} + C_{43}d_{zz} + C_{44}d_{xy} + C_{45}d_{yz} + C_{46}d_{zx} \tag{5.2-33d}$$
$$\tau_{yz} = C_{51}d_{xx} + C_{52}d_{yy} + C_{53}d_{zz} + C_{54}d_{xy} + C_{55}d_{yz} + C_{56}d_{zx} \tag{5.2-33e}$$
$$\tau_{zx} = C_{61}d_{xx} + C_{62}d_{yy} + C_{63}d_{zz} + C_{64}d_{xy} + C_{65}d_{yz} + C_{66}d_{zx} \tag{5.2-33f}$$

We see that the general linear relationship gives rise to 36 unknown constants. Buried in this array is the special form of Newton's law of viscosity discussed in Sec. 1.5 for a simple shearing flow—i.e.,

$$\tau_{yx} = \mu \frac{dv_x}{dy} \tag{5.2-34}$$

which is simply a special form of Eq. 5.2-33d. From experiments of the type described in Sec. 1.5 we can deduce that

$$C_{44} = 2\mu \tag{5.2-35}$$

We can now show that by restricting this linear relationship to be isotropic, only 2 of the 36 coefficients in Eqs. 5.2-33 are distinct. The condition of isotropy for Eq. 5.2-26 is expressed as

$$\tau'_{ij} = f_{ij}(d'_{kl}) \tag{5.2-36}$$

where τ'_{ij} and d'_{ij} are the viscous stress and rate of strain tensors in some rotated coordinate system $x_i \to x'_i$. Equation 5.2-36 states that the functional relationship between τ_{ij} and d_{ij} is independent of the coordinate system. The idea of isotropy is sometimes difficult to grasp, and we should explore it further before we apply this restriction to simplifying Eqs. 5.2-33.

Let us consider two observers located in the x_i and x'_i coordinate systems, respectively. Each observer is going to perform a simple shearing flow experiment on the same body of fluid. Only a single component of the viscous stress tensor and the rate of strain tensor will be nonzero; thus, Eqs. 5.2-33 will reduce to

$$\tau_{xy} = C_{44}d_{xy}, \quad \text{in the } x_i\text{-coordinate system} \tag{5.2-37}$$

and

$$\tau'_{xy} = C'_{44} d'_{xy}, \quad \text{in the } x'_i\text{-coordinate system} \tag{5.2-38}$$

Now, if the fluid is isotropic we expect the observer in the x'_i-coordinate system to obtain the same dependence of stress upon rate of strain as the

† A scalar zero in a tensor equation should be read as the null tensor.

observer in the x_i-coordinate system. Thus, $C'_{44} = C_{44}$, and Eq. 5.2-38 becomes

$$\tau'_{xy} = C_{44}\, d'_{xy} \tag{5.2-39}$$

which is just a special case of Eq. 5.2-36.

We are now in a position to examine Eqs. 5.2-33 for a series of coordinate transformations, for which we will require that the C_{ij} remain constant. The transformed values of τ_{ij} and d_{ij} will be related to the original values by Eqs. 5.2-40

$$\tau'_{ij} = \alpha_{ik}\alpha_{jl}\tau_{kl} \tag{5.2-40a}$$
$$d'_{ij} = \overline{\alpha_{ik}\alpha_{jl}d_{kl}} \tag{5.2-40b}$$

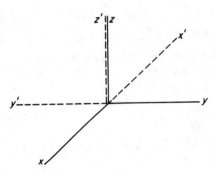

First, let us examine a coordinate transformation consisting of a 180° rotation about the z-axis as shown in Fig. 5.2-2. The direction cosines α_{mn} for this transformation are given by†

$$\alpha_{11} = -1 \qquad \alpha_{12} = 0 \qquad \alpha_{13} = 0$$
$$\alpha_{21} = 0 \qquad \alpha_{22} = -1 \qquad \alpha_{23} = 0$$
$$\alpha_{31} = 0 \qquad \alpha_{32} = 0 \qquad \alpha_{33} = 1$$
$$\tag{5.2-41}$$

Fig. 5.2-2. Coordinate transformation.

We may now apply these results in forming the double sum indicated in Eqs. 5.2-40. For τ'_{11}, we write

$$\tau'_{11} = \alpha_{1k}\alpha_{1l}\tau_{kl}$$

Noting that only α_{11}, α_{22}, and α_{33} are nonzero, we quickly find that

$$\tau'_{11} = \alpha_{11}\alpha_{11}\tau_{11} = (-1)^2\tau_{11} = \tau_{11}$$

The remaining terms for τ'_{ij} and d'_{ij} are calculated readily, and we find

$$\begin{array}{ll} \tau'_{xx} = \tau_{xx} & \tau'_{xy} = \tau_{xy} \\ \tau'_{yy} = \tau_{yy} & \tau'_{yz} = -\tau_{yz} \\ \tau'_{zz} = \tau_{zz} & \tau'_{zx} = -\tau_{zx} \end{array} \tag{5.2-42}$$

and

$$\begin{array}{ll} d'_{xx} = d_{xx} & d'_{xy} = d_{xy} \\ d'_{yy} = d_{yy} & d'_{yz} = -d_{yz} \\ d'_{zz} = d_{zz} & d'_{zx} = -d_{zx} \end{array} \tag{5.2-43}$$

† Remember that according to Eq. 5.2-40, the first index on α refers to the x_i'-coordinate system, and the second index refers to the x_i-coordinate system. Thus, α_{12} is the cosine of the angle between the x'-axis and the y-axis.

We now return to examine the first of Eqs. 5.2-33. We have already decided that the C_{ij} terms are invariant; thus, in the x_i'-coordinate system, Eq. 5.2-33a becomes

$$\tau_{xx}' = C_{11}d_{xx}' + C_{12}d_{yy}' + C_{13}d_{zz}' + C_{14}d_{xy}' + C_{15}d_{yz}' + C_{16}d_{zx}'$$

(5.2-44)

Substitution of the results from Eqs. 5.2-42 and 5.2-43 gives

$$\tau_{xx} = C_{11}d_{xx} + C_{12}d_{yy} + C_{13}d_{zz} + C_{14}d_{xy} - C_{15}d_{yz} - C_{16}d_{zx}$$

(5.2-45)

Comparing this result with Eq. 5.2-33a, we find that

$$C_{15} = C_{16} = 0$$

(5.2-46)

By examining the remaining Eqs. 5.2-33, we find that other coefficients must also be zero, and the array of coefficients takes the form

$$
\begin{array}{cccccc}
C_{11} & C_{12} & C_{13} & C_{14} & 0 & 0 \\
C_{21} & C_{22} & C_{23} & C_{24} & 0 & 0 \\
C_{31} & C_{32} & C_{33} & C_{34} & 0 & 0 \\
C_{41} & C_{42} & C_{43} & C_{44} & 0 & 0 \\
0 & 0 & 0 & 0 & C_{55} & C_{56} \\
0 & 0 & 0 & 0 & C_{65} & C_{66}
\end{array}
$$

(5.2-47)

Finding the other zeros in this array is a straightforward but rather tedious task, and we will only outline briefly the remaining steps. For the rotation shown in Fig. 5.2-3, the array is reduced further to

$$
\begin{array}{cccccc}
C_{11} & C_{12} & C_{13} & 0 & 0 & 0 \\
C_{21} & C_{22} & C_{23} & 0 & 0 & 0 \\
C_{31} & C_{32} & C_{33} & 0 & 0 & 0 \\
0 & 0 & 0 & C_{44} & 0 & 0 \\
0 & 0 & 0 & 0 & C_{55} & 0 \\
0 & 0 & 0 & 0 & 0 & C_{66}
\end{array}
$$

(5.2-48)

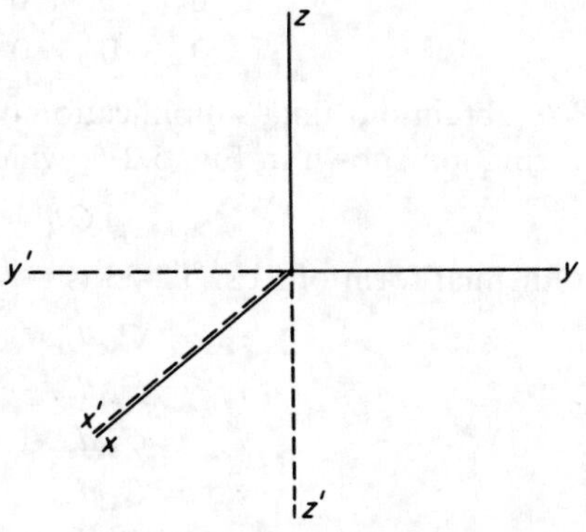

Fig. 5.2-3. Coordinate transformation.

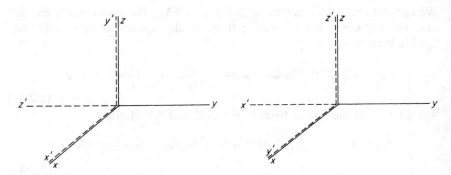

Fig. 5.2-4. Coordinate transformation.   **Fig. 5.2-5.** Coordinate transformation.

Continuing this process, we utilize the rotation shown in Fig. 5.2-4 to obtain

$$
\begin{matrix}
C_{11} & C_{12} & C_{12} & 0 & 0 & 0 \\
C_{21} & C_{22} & C_{23} & 0 & 0 & 0 \\
C_{21} & C_{23} & C_{22} & 0 & 0 & 0 \\
0 & 0 & 0 & C_{44} & 0 & 0 \\
0 & 0 & 0 & 0 & C_{55} & 0 \\
0 & 0 & 0 & 0 & 0 & C_{44}
\end{matrix}
\tag{5.2-49}
$$

Here, we have reduced the array to seven distinct coefficients. For the co-ordinate transformation shown in Fig. 5.2-5, we obtain

$$
\begin{matrix}
C_{11} & C_{12} & C_{12} & 0 & 0 & 0 \\
C_{12} & C_{11} & C_{12} & 0 & 0 & 0 \\
C_{12} & C_{12} & C_{11} & 0 & 0 & 0 \\
0 & 0 & 0 & C_{44} & 0 & 0 \\
0 & 0 & 0 & 0 & C_{44} & 0 \\
0 & 0 & 0 & 0 & 0 & C_{44}
\end{matrix}
\tag{5.2-50}
$$

We obtain our final simplification of the array by using the coordinate transformation shown in Fig. 5.2-6, which allows us to prove that

$$C_{11} = C_{44} + C_{12} \tag{5.2-51}$$

Our final form of Eqs. 5.2-33 is

$$\tau_{xx} = C_{44}d_{xx} + C_{12}(d_{xx} + d_{yy} + d_{zz}) \tag{5.2-52a}$$
$$\tau_{yy} = C_{44}d_{yy} + C_{12}(d_{xx} + d_{yy} + d_{zz}) \tag{5.2-52b}$$
$$\tau_{zz} = C_{44}d_{zz} + C_{12}(d_{xx} + d_{yy} + d_{zz}) \tag{5.2-52c}$$
$$\tau_{xy} = C_{44}d_{xy} \tag{5.2-52d}$$
$$\tau_{yz} = C_{44}d_{yz} \tag{5.2-52e}$$
$$\tau_{zx} = C_{44}d_{zx} \tag{5.2-52f}$$

As we noted previously, in Eq. 5.2-35 the coefficient C_{44} is identified with the coefficient of shear viscosity, and the coefficient C_{12} is traditionally expressed as

$$C_{12} = (\kappa - \tfrac{2}{3}\mu) \quad (5.2\text{-}53)$$

where κ is called the coefficient of bulk viscosity. Expressing Eqs. 5.2-52 in index notation and incorporating the coefficients of viscosity, we get

$$\tau_{ij} = 2\mu d_{ij} + [(\kappa - \tfrac{2}{3}\mu)]d_{kk}\delta_{ij}$$
$$(5.2\text{-}54)$$

In terms of the velocity gradients, this equation reduces to

$$\tau_{ij} = \mu\left(\frac{\partial v_i}{\partial x_j} + \frac{\partial v_j}{\partial x_i}\right)$$
$$+ [(\kappa - \tfrac{2}{3}\mu)]\left(\frac{\partial v_k}{\partial x_k}\right)\delta_{ij}$$
$$(5.2\text{-}55)$$

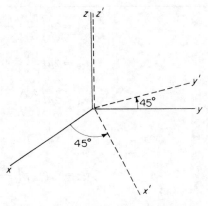

Fig. 5.2-6. Coordinate transformation.

This result is listed in Tables 5.2-2, 3, and 4 for rectangular, cylindrical, and spherical coordinates.

Table 5.2-2
SCALAR COMPONENTS OF THE VISCOUS STRESS
TENSOR FOR NEWTONIAN FLUIDS

Rectangular Coordinates[a] (x, y, z)

$$\tau_{xx} = 2\mu\left(\frac{\partial v_x}{\partial x}\right) + [(\kappa - \tfrac{2}{3}\mu)\nabla \cdot \mathbf{v}] \qquad (a)$$

$$\tau_{yy} = 2\mu\left(\frac{\partial v_y}{\partial y}\right) + [(\kappa - \tfrac{2}{3}\mu)\nabla \cdot \mathbf{v}] \qquad (b)$$

$$\tau_{zz} = 2\mu\left(\frac{\partial v_z}{\partial z}\right) + [(\kappa - \tfrac{2}{3}\mu)\nabla \cdot \mathbf{v}] \qquad (c)$$

$$\tau_{xy} = \tau_{yx} = \mu\left(\frac{\partial v_x}{\partial y} + \frac{\partial v_y}{\partial x}\right) \qquad (d)$$

$$\tau_{yz} = \tau_{zy} = \mu\left(\frac{\partial v_y}{\partial z} + \frac{\partial v_z}{\partial y}\right) \qquad (e)$$

$$\tau_{zx} = \tau_{xz} = \mu\left(\frac{\partial v_z}{\partial x} + \frac{\partial v_x}{\partial z}\right) \qquad (f)$$

[a] In these equations, $\nabla \cdot \mathbf{v} = \dfrac{\partial v_x}{\partial x} + \dfrac{\partial v_y}{\partial y} + \dfrac{\partial v_z}{\partial z}$

Table 5.2-3
SCALAR COMPONENTS OF THE VISCOUS STRESS
TENSOR FOR NEWTONIAN FLUIDS

Cylindrical Coordinates[a] (r, θ, z)

$$\tau_{rr} = 2\mu\left(\frac{\partial v_r}{\partial r}\right) + [(\kappa - \tfrac{2}{3}\mu)\nabla \cdot \mathbf{v}] \tag{a}$$

$$\tau_{\theta\theta} = 2\mu\left(\frac{1}{r}\frac{\partial v_\theta}{\partial \theta} + \frac{v_r}{r}\right) + [(\kappa - \tfrac{2}{3}\mu)\nabla \cdot \mathbf{v}] \tag{b}$$

$$\tau_{zz} = 2\mu\left(\frac{\partial v_z}{\partial z}\right) + [(\kappa - \tfrac{2}{3}\mu)\nabla \cdot \mathbf{v}] \tag{c}$$

$$\tau_{r\theta} = \tau_{\theta r} = \mu\left[r\frac{\partial}{\partial r}\left(\frac{v_\theta}{r}\right) + \frac{1}{r}\frac{\partial v_r}{\partial \theta}\right] \tag{d}$$

$$\tau_{\theta z} = \tau_{z\theta} = \mu\left(\frac{\partial v_\theta}{\partial z} + \frac{1}{r}\frac{\partial v_z}{\partial \theta}\right) \tag{e}$$

$$\tau_{zr} = \tau_{rz} = \mu\left(\frac{\partial v_z}{\partial r} + \frac{\partial v_r}{\partial z}\right) \tag{f}$$

[a] In these equations, $\nabla \cdot \mathbf{v} = \frac{1}{r}\frac{\partial}{\partial r}(rv_r) + \frac{1}{r}\frac{\partial v_\theta}{\partial \theta} + \frac{\partial v_z}{\partial z}$

Table 5.2-4
SCALAR COMPONENTS OF THE VISCOUS STRESS
TENSOR FOR NEWTONIAN FLUIDS

Spherical Coordinates[a] (r, θ, ϕ)

$$\tau_{rr} = 2\mu\left(\frac{\partial v_r}{\partial r}\right) + [(\kappa - \tfrac{2}{3}\mu)\nabla \cdot \mathbf{v}] \tag{a}$$

$$\tau_{\theta\theta} = 2\mu\left(\frac{1}{r}\frac{\partial v_\theta}{\partial \theta} + \frac{v_r}{r}\right) + [(\kappa - \tfrac{2}{3}\mu)\nabla \cdot \mathbf{v}] \tag{b}$$

$$\tau_{\phi\phi} = 2\mu\left(\frac{1}{r\sin\theta}\frac{\partial v_\phi}{\partial \phi} + \frac{v_r}{r} + \frac{v_\theta\cot\theta}{r}\right) + [(\kappa - \tfrac{2}{3}\mu)\nabla \cdot \mathbf{v}] \tag{c}$$

$$\tau_{r\theta} = \tau_{\theta r} = \mu\left[r\frac{\partial}{\partial r}\left(\frac{v_\theta}{r}\right) + \frac{1}{r}\frac{\partial v_r}{\partial \theta}\right] \tag{d}$$

$$\tau_{\theta\phi} = \tau_{\phi\theta} = \mu\left[\frac{\sin\theta}{r}\frac{\partial}{\partial \theta}\left(\frac{v_\phi}{\sin\theta}\right) + \frac{1}{r\sin\theta}\frac{\partial v_\theta}{\partial \phi}\right] \tag{e}$$

$$\tau_{\phi r} = \tau_{r\phi} = \mu\left[\frac{1}{r\sin\theta}\frac{\partial v_r}{\partial \phi} + r\frac{\partial}{\partial r}\left(\frac{v_\phi}{r}\right)\right] \tag{f}$$

[a] In these equations, $\nabla \cdot \mathbf{v} = \frac{1}{r^2}\frac{\partial}{\partial r}(r^2 v_r) + \frac{1}{r\sin\theta}\frac{\partial}{\partial \theta}(v_\theta\sin\theta) + \frac{1}{r\sin\theta}\frac{\partial v_\phi}{\partial \phi}$

5.3 Qualitative Description of the Rate of Strain

While our treatment of Newton's law of viscosity is essentially complete, the analysis presented in the previous section has been rather abstract, and it will be worthwhile to discuss the subject further. Let us now examine the

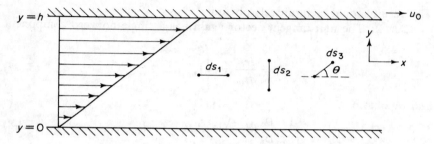

Fig. 5.3-1. Rates of deformation for plane Couette flow.

rate of strain for the three line elements illustrated in Fig. 5.3-1. The scalar components of the velocity vector for this flow are

$$v_x = u_0\left(\frac{y}{h}\right) \tag{5.3-1a}$$

$$v_y = v_z = 0 \tag{5.3-1b}$$

For each of the three cases, we wish to compute the rate of strain using the equation,

$$\begin{Bmatrix} \text{rate of strain} \\ \text{in the} \\ \lambda\text{-direction} \end{Bmatrix} = \frac{1}{ds_{(\lambda)}} \frac{D}{Dt}(ds_{(\lambda)}) = (\mathbf{d} \cdot \boldsymbol{\lambda}) \cdot \boldsymbol{\lambda} \tag{5.3-2}$$

where the unit tangent vector $\boldsymbol{\lambda}$ is given by

$$\lambda_i = \frac{dr_i}{ds_{(\lambda)}} \tag{5.3-3}$$

Case 1: The unit tangent vector has only one nonzero component

$$\lambda_i = \frac{dr_i}{ds_{(1)}} = \begin{cases} 1, & i = 1 \\ 0, & i = 2 \\ 0, & i = 3 \end{cases} \tag{5.3-4}$$

and Eq. 5.3-2 reduces to

$$\frac{1}{ds_{(1)}} \frac{D}{Dt}(ds_{(1)}) = d_{ij}\lambda_i\lambda_j = d_{11} \tag{5.3-5}$$

From Table 5.2-1 we may obtain an expression for d_{11} (listed as d_{xx}), and the rate of strain becomes

$$\frac{1}{ds_{(1)}} \frac{D}{Dt}(ds_{(1)}) = \frac{\partial v_x}{\partial x} = 0 \tag{5.3-6}$$

This result should be intuitively obvious.

CASE 2: The unit tangent vector again has a single nonzero component

$$\lambda_i = \frac{dr_i}{ds_{(2)}} = \begin{cases} 0, & i = 1 \\ 1, & i = 2 \\ 0, & i = 3 \end{cases} \tag{5.3-7}$$

and we obtain

$$\frac{1}{ds_{(2)}} \frac{D}{Dt}(ds_{(2)}) = d_{ij}\lambda_i\lambda_j = d_{22} \tag{5.3-8}$$

From the results in Table 5.2-1, Eq. 5.3-8 becomes

$$\frac{1}{ds_{(2)}} \frac{D}{Dt}(ds_{(2)}) = \frac{\partial v_y}{\partial y} = 0 \tag{5.3-9}$$

Once again, the result should be intuitively obvious, for although the line element $ds_{(2)}$ is rotating, it is certainly not deforming.

CASE 3: The components of the unit tangent vector for this case are

$$\lambda_i = \frac{dr_i}{ds_{(3)}} = \begin{cases} \cos\theta, & i = 1 \\ \sin\theta, & i = 2 \\ 0, & i = 3 \end{cases} \tag{5.3-10}$$

and the rate of strain is given by

$$\frac{1}{ds_{(3)}} \frac{D}{Dt}(ds_{(3)}) = \begin{aligned} &d_{11}\cos^2\theta + d_{12}\cos\theta\sin\theta \\ &+ d_{21}\sin\theta\cos\theta + d_{22}\sin^2\theta \end{aligned} \tag{5.3-11}$$

Noting that d_{ij} is symmetric and using the results of Table 5.2-1, we get

$$\frac{1}{ds_{(3)}} \frac{D}{Dt}(ds_{(3)}) = \left(\frac{\partial v_x}{\partial x}\right)\cos^2\theta + \left(\frac{\partial v_x}{\partial y} + \frac{\partial v_y}{\partial x}\right)\cos\theta\sin\theta + \left(\frac{\partial v_y}{\partial y}\right)\sin^2\theta \tag{5.3-12}$$

which immediately reduces to

$$\frac{1}{ds_{(3)}} \frac{D}{Dt}(ds_{(3)}) = \left(\frac{dv_x}{dy}\right)\cos\theta\sin\theta \tag{5.3-13}$$

Letting $\theta = 0, \pi/2$ gives the rate of strain (i.e., zero) for cases 1 and 2, respectively. The maximum rate of strain occurs for a line element situated at an angle of 45°; thus,

$$\frac{1}{ds_{(3)}}\frac{D}{Dt}(ds_{(3)})\Big|_{\theta=\pi/4} = \frac{1}{2}\left(\frac{dv_x}{dy}\right) \tag{5.3-14}$$

If we compare this result with Eq. 5.2-1 or Eq. 1.5-7, we find that the stress acting on the y-surface in the x-direction is directly proportional to the rate of strain of a line element inclined at a 45° angle between the x- and y-axes. This situation is rather curious, and requires further explanation. The following discussion is rather qualitative in nature and must be accepted on that basis.

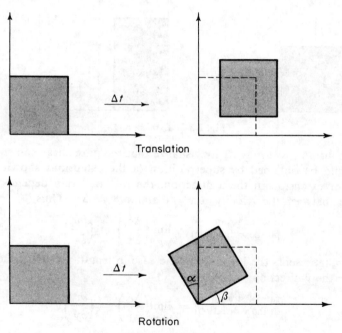

Fig. 5.3-2. Solid-body motion.

Let us consider, now, the two-dimensional motion, illustrated in Fig. 5.3-2, of a small fluid element which *does not undergo* deformation. These motions consist of pure translation and rotation, and may be referred to as solid body motion. The element may undergo extension (or compression), as shown in Fig. 5.3-3, or it may be subjected to what is known as *pure shear*, illustrated in Fig. 5.3-4. Note that these illustrations indicate deformation for an incompressible flow by requiring the volume of the fluid element to

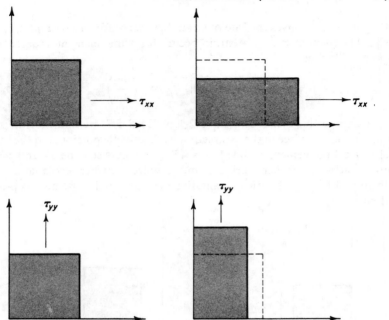

Fig. 5.3-3. Extension.

remain constant. We may easily visualize that the pure shear shown in Fig. 5.3-4 could be obtained by superposition of the extensions shown in Fig. 5.3-3. For extension in the x-direction, the rate of strain depends on the difference between the velocity at $x = 0$ and at $x = \Delta x$. Thus,

$$\begin{Bmatrix}\text{rate of strain} \\ \text{in the } x\text{-direction}\end{Bmatrix} = \lim_{\Delta x \to 0}\left(\frac{\Delta v_x}{\Delta x}\right) = \left(\frac{\partial v_x}{\partial x}\right) \tag{5.3-15}$$

where Δv_x represents the incremental increase in length per unit time. Similarly, for the y-direction, we obtain

$$\begin{Bmatrix}\text{rate of strain} \\ \text{in the } y\text{-direction}\end{Bmatrix} = \lim_{\Delta y \to 0}\left(\frac{\Delta v_y}{\Delta y}\right) = \left(\frac{\partial v_y}{\partial y}\right) \tag{5.3-16}$$

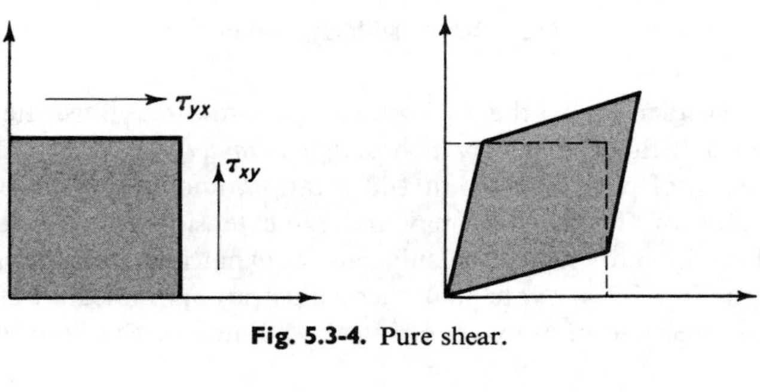

Fig. 5.3-4. Pure shear.

We cannot visualize the rate of strain in pure shear in this simple manner; we are therefore forced either to examine Eq. 5.3-15 or Eq. 5.3-16 under a coordinate transformation (rotation through 45°), or return to the use of Eq. 5.3-2. *Plane shear* is illustrated in Fig. 5.3-5, which shows (graphically, not analytically) that it is actually composed of pure shear plus solid body

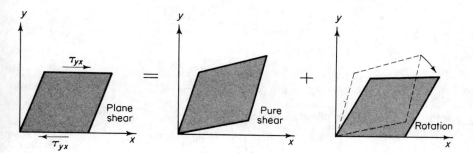

Fig. 5.3-5. Plane shear.

rotation. If we remember that viscous stresses result only from the *deformation* of the fluid and not from any solid body motion, it should appear reasonable that the shear stress τ_{yx} for plane Couette flow (plane shear) is directly proportional to the rate of strain along the 45° line (pure shear).

Rotation

We can learn something about the rotational motion of fluids by examining the time rate of change of the angles α and β shown in Fig. 5.3-6. We define an *average* rotation in the counterclockwise direction by

$$\Delta\theta = \tfrac{1}{2}(\beta - \alpha) \qquad (5.3\text{-}17)$$

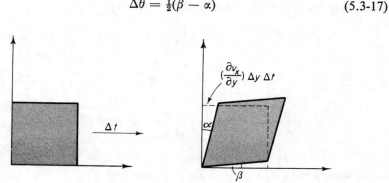

Fig. 5.3-6. An arbitrary deformation.

and the *average* rate of rotation around the z-axis as

$$\Omega_z = \lim_{\Delta\theta \to 0} \left(\frac{\Delta\theta}{\Delta t}\right)$$

For small angles (i.e., $\Delta t \to 0$), α and β are given by

$$\alpha = \tan \alpha = \left[\frac{\left(\dfrac{\partial v_x}{\partial y}\right) \Delta y \, \Delta t}{\Delta y}\right] \tag{5.3-18a}$$

$$\beta = \tan \beta = \left[\frac{\left(\dfrac{\partial v_y}{\partial x}\right) \Delta x \, \Delta t}{\Delta x}\right] \tag{5.3-18b}$$

and the average rate of rotation becomes

$$\Omega_z = \frac{1}{2}\left(\frac{\partial v_y}{\partial x} - \frac{\partial v_x}{\partial y}\right) \tag{5.3-19a}$$

In a similar manner, we can show that

$$\Omega_y = \frac{1}{2}\left(\frac{\partial v_x}{\partial z} - \frac{\partial v_z}{\partial x}\right) \tag{5.3-19b}$$

and

$$\Omega_x = \frac{1}{2}\left(\frac{\partial v_z}{\partial y} - \frac{\partial v_y}{\partial z}\right) \tag{5.3-19c}$$

These three terms may be recognized as one-half the three scalar components of the vorticity vector $\boldsymbol{\omega}$, which is the curl of the velocity vector.

$$\boldsymbol{\omega} = \nabla \times \mathbf{v} = \mathbf{i}\left(\frac{\partial v_z}{\partial y} - \frac{\partial v_y}{\partial z}\right) + \mathbf{j}\left(\frac{\partial v_x}{\partial z} - \frac{\partial v_z}{\partial x}\right) + \mathbf{k}\left(\frac{\partial v_y}{\partial x} - \frac{\partial v_x}{\partial y}\right) \tag{5.3-20}$$

Examining the scalar components of the vorticity tensor,

$$\Omega = \begin{bmatrix} 0 & -\dfrac{1}{2}\left(\dfrac{\partial v_y}{\partial x} - \dfrac{\partial v_x}{\partial y}\right) & \dfrac{1}{2}\left(\dfrac{\partial v_x}{\partial z} - \dfrac{\partial v_z}{\partial x}\right) \\[3ex] \dfrac{1}{2}\left(\dfrac{\partial v_y}{\partial x} - \dfrac{\partial v_x}{\partial y}\right) & 0 & -\dfrac{1}{2}\left(\dfrac{\partial v_z}{\partial y} - \dfrac{\partial v_y}{\partial z}\right) \\[3ex] -\dfrac{1}{2}\left(\dfrac{\partial v_x}{\partial z} - \dfrac{\partial v_z}{\partial x}\right) & \dfrac{1}{2}\left(\dfrac{\partial v_z}{\partial y} - \dfrac{\partial v_y}{\partial z}\right) & 0 \end{bmatrix} \tag{5.3-21}$$

we note that the diagonal elements are zero and only three of the six off-diagonal elements are distinct. Except for the factor $\frac{1}{2}$, these three distinct components are the same as those making up the vorticity vector. We can construct a vector from the components of a skew-symmetric tensor, called the "axial vector" of that tensor. In this case, twice the axial vector of the vorticity tensor yields the vorticity vector $\boldsymbol{\omega}$; thus, the skew-symmetric part of the tensor $\partial v_i/\partial x_j$ is a measure of the rotational motion of the fluid.

*5.4 The Equations of Motion

Our objective in this section is to apply the constitutive equation for a Newtonian fluid to the viscous stress equations of motion. Our final result will be valid only for incompressible flows and constant viscosity fluids. Starting with Eq. 5.1-17,

$$\rho\left(\frac{\partial \mathbf{v}}{\partial t} + \mathbf{v} \cdot \nabla\mathbf{v}\right) = -\nabla p + \rho\mathbf{g} + \nabla \cdot \boldsymbol{\tau} \tag{5.4-1}$$

we make use of the constitutive equation for a Newtonian fluid to obtain

$$\rho\left(\frac{\partial \mathbf{v}}{\partial t} + \mathbf{v} \cdot \nabla\mathbf{v}\right) = -\nabla p + \rho\mathbf{g} + \nabla \cdot [2\mu\mathbf{d} + (\kappa - \tfrac{2}{3}\mu)\,(\nabla \cdot \mathbf{v})\,\mathbf{I}] \tag{5.4-2}$$

At this point, the analysis is restricted to constant viscosity, yielding, in index notation,

$$\rho\left(\frac{\partial v_i}{\partial t} + v_j\frac{\partial v_i}{\partial x_j}\right) = -\frac{\partial p}{\partial x_i} + \rho g_i + 2\mu\frac{\partial d_{ij}}{\partial x_j} + \left(\kappa - \frac{2}{3}\mu\right)\frac{\partial}{\partial x_i}\left(\frac{\partial v_k}{\partial x_k}\right) \tag{5.4-3}$$

Considering only the divergence of the rate of strain tensor, we substitute Eq. 5.2-18 for d_{ij} and write

$$2\mu\frac{\partial d_{ij}}{\partial x_j} = 2\mu\frac{\partial}{\partial x_j}\left[\frac{1}{2}\left(\frac{\partial v_i}{\partial x_j} + \frac{\partial v_j}{\partial x_i}\right)\right] = \left[\mu\left(\frac{\partial^2 v_i}{\partial x_j\,\partial x_j} + \frac{\partial^2 v_j}{\partial x_j\,\partial x_i}\right)\right] \tag{5.4-4}$$

Here, we restrict the analysis to incompressible flows and write

$$\frac{\partial^2 v_j}{\partial x_j\,\partial x_i} = \frac{\partial}{\partial x_i}\left(\frac{\partial v_j}{\partial x_j}\right) = 0 \tag{5.4-5}$$

We obtain this result by changing the order of differentiation and noting that the continuity equation for incompressible flows reduces to

$$\nabla \cdot \mathbf{v} = \frac{\partial v_j}{\partial x_j} = 0 \tag{5.4-6}$$

Applying Eq. 5.4-5 and substituting Eq. 5.4-4 into Eq. 5.4-3, we have the differential equations of motion for the incompressible flow of a constant viscosity, Newtonian fluid

$$\rho\left(\frac{\partial v_i}{\partial t} + v_j \frac{\partial v_i}{\partial x_j}\right) = -\frac{\partial p}{\partial x_i} + \rho g_i + \mu \frac{\partial^2 v_i}{\partial x_j \, \partial x_j} \qquad (5.4\text{-}7)$$

If we carry out the double summation for the term $\partial^2/\partial x_j \, \partial x_j$, we obtain

$$\frac{\partial^2}{\partial x_j \, \partial x_j} = \frac{\partial^2}{\partial x_1^2} + \frac{\partial^2}{\partial x_2^2} + \frac{\partial^2}{\partial x_3^2} \qquad (5.4\text{-}8)$$

This scalar operator is known as the Laplacian and designated in Gibbs notation by ∇^2 where

$$\nabla^2 = \nabla \cdot \nabla = \frac{\partial^2}{\partial x^2} + \frac{\partial^2}{\partial y^2} + \frac{\partial^2}{\partial z^2} \qquad (5.4\text{-}9)$$

In Gibbs notation, Eq. 5.4-7 becomes

$$
\underset{\substack{\uparrow \\ \text{Convective} \\ \text{acceleration}}}{\overset{\substack{\text{Local} \\ \text{acceleration} \\ \downarrow}}{\rho\left(\frac{\partial \mathbf{v}}{\partial t} + \mathbf{v}\cdot\nabla\mathbf{v}\right)}} = \underset{\substack{\uparrow \\ \text{Body force} \\ \text{per unit volume}}}{-\nabla p + \rho \mathbf{g}} + \overset{\substack{\text{Viscous force} \\ \text{per unit volume} \\ \downarrow}}{\mu\,\nabla^2 \mathbf{v}} \qquad (5.4\text{-}10)
$$

We should note that this result is nothing more than a differential form of the linear momentum principle—i.e., the time rate of change of momentum (represented in terms of local and convective acceleration) is equal to the body force and the surface force (represented in terms of both the pressure and viscous forces). Equation 5.4-10 is often known as the Navier-Stokes equation in honor of the two scientists who first developed this final form. It will serve as a starting point for many of the subsequent developments and applications. These equations are tabulated in Tables 5.4-1, 5.4-2, and 5.4-3 for rectangular cylindrical and spherical coordinates.

Moving reference frames

Inherent in the development of the equations of continuity and motion was the idea of a fixed reference frame (or coordinate system) with respect to which distances and velocities were measured. In the analysis of some problems, it is convenient to view the system as if one were an observer

Table 5.4-1
THE EQUATIONS OF MOTION FOR CONSTANT μ AND ρ IN
RECTANGULAR COORDINATES (x, y, z)

x-Direction

$$\rho\left(\frac{\partial v_x}{\partial t} + v_x \frac{\partial v_x}{\partial x} + v_y \frac{\partial v_x}{\partial y} + v_z \frac{\partial v_x}{\partial z}\right) = -\frac{\partial p}{\partial x} + \rho g_x + \mu\left(\frac{\partial^2 v_x}{\partial x^2} + \frac{\partial^2 v_x}{\partial y^2} + \frac{\partial^2 v_x}{\partial z^2}\right) \quad (a)$$

y-Direction

$$\rho\left(\frac{\partial v_y}{\partial t} + v_x \frac{\partial v_y}{\partial x} + v_y \frac{\partial v_y}{\partial y} + v_z \frac{\partial v_y}{\partial z}\right) = -\frac{\partial p}{\partial y} + \rho g_y + \mu\left(\frac{\partial^2 v_y}{\partial x^2} + \frac{\partial^2 v_y}{\partial y^2} + \frac{\partial^2 v_y}{\partial z^2}\right) \quad (b)$$

z-Direction

$$\rho\left(\frac{\partial v_z}{\partial t} + v_x \frac{\partial v_z}{\partial x} + v_y \frac{\partial v_z}{\partial y} + v_z \frac{\partial v_z}{\partial z}\right) = -\frac{\partial p}{\partial z} + \rho g_z + \mu\left(\frac{\partial^2 v_z}{\partial x^2} + \frac{\partial^2 v_z}{\partial y^2} + \frac{\partial^2 v_z}{\partial z^2}\right) \quad (c)$$

Table 5.4-2
THE EQUATIONS OF MOTION FOR CONSTANT μ AND ρ IN
CYLINDRICAL COORDINATES (r, θ, z)

r-Direction

$$\rho\left(\frac{\partial v_r}{\partial t} + v_r \frac{\partial v_r}{\partial r} + \frac{v_\theta}{r}\frac{\partial v_r}{\partial \theta} - \frac{v_\theta^2}{r} + v_z \frac{\partial v_r}{\partial z}\right)$$

$$= -\frac{\partial p}{\partial r} + \rho g_r + \mu\left[\frac{\partial}{\partial r}\left(\frac{1}{r}\frac{\partial}{\partial r}(rv_r)\right) + \frac{1}{r^2}\frac{\partial^2 v_r}{\partial \theta^2} - \frac{2}{r^2}\frac{\partial v_\theta}{\partial \theta} + \frac{\partial^2 v_r}{\partial z^2}\right] \quad (a)$$

θ-Direction

$$\rho\left(\frac{\partial v_\theta}{\partial t} + v_r \frac{\partial v_\theta}{\partial r} + \frac{v_\theta}{r}\frac{\partial v_\theta}{\partial \theta} + \frac{v_r v_\theta}{r} + v_z \frac{\partial v_\theta}{\partial z}\right)$$

$$= -\frac{1}{r}\frac{\partial p}{\partial \theta} + \rho g_\theta + \mu\left[\frac{\partial}{\partial r}\left(\frac{1}{r}\frac{\partial}{\partial r}(rv_\theta)\right) + \frac{1}{r^2}\frac{\partial^2 v_\theta}{\partial \theta^2} + \frac{2}{r^2}\frac{\partial v_r}{\partial \theta} + \frac{\partial^2 v_\theta}{\partial z^2}\right] \quad (b)$$

z-Direction

$$\rho\left(\frac{\partial v_z}{\partial t} + v_r \frac{\partial v_z}{\partial r} + \frac{v_\theta}{r}\frac{\partial v_z}{\partial \theta} + v_z \frac{\partial v_z}{\partial z}\right)$$

$$= -\frac{\partial p}{\partial z} + \rho g_z + \mu\left[\frac{1}{r}\frac{\partial}{\partial r}\left(r\frac{\partial v_z}{\partial r}\right) + \frac{1}{r^2}\frac{\partial^2 v_z}{\partial \theta^2} + \frac{\partial^2 v_z}{\partial z^2}\right] \quad (c)$$

Table 5.4-3

THE EQUATIONS OF MOTION CONSTANT μ AND ρ IN
SPHERICAL COORDINATES (r, θ, ϕ)†

r-Direction

$$\rho\left(\frac{\partial v_r}{\partial t} + v_r\frac{\partial v_r}{\partial r} + \frac{v_\theta}{r}\frac{\partial v_r}{\partial \theta} + \frac{v_\phi}{r\sin\theta}\frac{\partial v_r}{\partial \phi} - \frac{v_\theta^2 + v_\phi^2}{r}\right)$$

$$= -\frac{\partial p}{\partial r} + \rho g_r + \mu\left(\nabla^2 v_r - \frac{2v_r}{r^2} - \frac{2}{r^2}\frac{\partial v_\theta}{\partial \theta} - \frac{2\,v_\theta\cot\theta}{r^2} - \frac{2}{r^2\sin\theta}\frac{\partial v_\phi}{\partial \phi}\right) \quad \text{(a)}$$

θ-Direction

$$\rho\left(\frac{\partial v_\theta}{\partial t} + v_r\frac{\partial v_\theta}{\partial r} + \frac{v_\theta}{r}\frac{\partial v_\theta}{\partial \theta} + \frac{v_\phi}{r\sin\theta}\frac{\partial v_\theta}{\partial \phi} + \frac{v_r v_\theta}{r} - \frac{v_\phi^2\cot\theta}{r}\right)$$

$$= -\frac{1}{r}\frac{\partial p}{\partial \theta} + \rho g_\theta + \mu\left(\nabla^2 v_\theta + \frac{2}{r^2}\frac{\partial v_r}{\partial \theta} - \frac{v_\theta}{r^2\sin^2\theta} - \frac{2\cos\theta}{r^2\sin^2\theta}\frac{\partial v_\phi}{\partial \phi}\right) \quad \text{(b)}$$

ϕ-Direction

$$\rho\left(\frac{\partial v_\phi}{\partial t} + v_r\frac{\partial v_\phi}{\partial r} + \frac{v_\theta}{r}\frac{\partial v_\phi}{\partial \theta} + \frac{v_\phi}{r\sin\theta}\frac{\partial v_\phi}{\partial \phi} + \frac{v_\phi v_r}{r} + \frac{v_\theta v_\phi}{r}\cot\theta\right)$$

$$= -\frac{1}{r\sin\theta}\frac{\partial p}{\partial \phi} + \rho g_\phi + \mu\left(\nabla^2 v_\phi - \frac{v_\phi}{r^2\sin^2\theta} + \frac{2}{r^2\sin\theta}\frac{\partial v_r}{\partial \phi} + \frac{2\cos\theta}{r^2\sin^2\theta}\frac{\partial v_\theta}{\partial \phi}\right) \quad \text{(c)}$$

† For spherical coordinates the Laplacian is,

$$\nabla^2 = \frac{1}{r^2}\frac{\partial}{\partial r}\left(r^2\frac{\partial}{\partial r}\right) + \frac{1}{r^2\sin\theta}\frac{\partial}{\partial \theta}\left(\sin\theta\frac{\partial}{\partial \theta}\right) + \frac{1}{r^2\sin^2\theta}\left(\frac{\partial^2}{\partial \phi^2}\right)$$

moving with a constant velocity $\mathbf{w}$ rather than fixed in space. If an observer is moving with a velocity $\mathbf{w}$, then the relative fluid velocity $\mathbf{v}_r$ that he measures is

$$\mathbf{v}_r = \mathbf{v} - \mathbf{w} \qquad (5.4\text{-}11)$$

As an example, consider an observer situated on a ship moving through a quiescent ocean. The fluid velocity $\mathbf{v}$ is zero and the relative velocity is just equal and opposite to the velocity of the observer.

$$\mathbf{v}_r = -\mathbf{w} \qquad (5.4\text{-}12)$$

If we substitute $\mathbf{v}_r + \mathbf{w}$ for the fluid velocity in the continuity equation, we obtain

$$\frac{\partial \rho}{\partial t} + \nabla \cdot (\rho\mathbf{v}) = \frac{\partial \rho}{\partial t} + \nabla \cdot (\rho\mathbf{v}_r) + \nabla \cdot (\rho\mathbf{w}) = 0 \qquad (5.4\text{-}13)$$

Inasmuch as **w** is a constant vector, we may write this equation as

$$\frac{\partial \rho}{\partial t} + \mathbf{w} \cdot \nabla \rho + \nabla \cdot (\rho \mathbf{v}_r) = 0 \qquad (5.4\text{-}14)$$

Referring to Eq. 3.2-20, we note that the first two terms of Eq. 5.4-14 are the total derivative; thus,

$$\frac{d\rho}{dt} + \nabla \cdot (\rho \mathbf{v}_r) = 0 \qquad (5.4\text{-}15)$$

and we see that the continuity equation for a moving reference frame has the same form as that for a fixed reference frame. In changing reference frames, we require only that the fluid velocity **v** be replaced by the relative fluid velocity $\mathbf{v}_r$ and the time derivative holding the spatial coordinates constant $\partial/\partial t$ be replaced with the time derivative holding the coordinates in the moving frame constant d/dt. For an observer fixed in space, $d\rho/dt$ represents the time rate of change of the density at a point moving with a velocity **w**; however, for an observer moving at a velocity **w** the time rate of change of the density at a fixed point is given by $d\rho/dt$. In general, Eq. 5.4-15 is not used to describe the continuity equation for a moving observer. We simply state that Eq. 5.4-16

$$\frac{\partial \rho}{\partial t} + \nabla \cdot (\rho \mathbf{v}) = 0 \qquad (5.4\text{-}16)$$

applies to both fixed reference frames, and reference frames which move at a constant velocity. For moving frames, velocities and time derivatives are evaluated in terms of an observer moving with the frame.

If we replace **v** by $\mathbf{v}_r + \mathbf{w}$ in the Navier-Stokes equations, we obtain

$$\rho \left[\frac{\partial}{\partial t}(\mathbf{v}_r + \mathbf{w}) + (\mathbf{v}_r + \mathbf{w}) \cdot \nabla(\mathbf{v}_r + \mathbf{w}) \right] = -\nabla p + \rho \mathbf{g} + \mu \nabla^2(\mathbf{v}_r + \mathbf{w})$$

$$(5.4\text{-}17)$$

Since **w** is constant, this equation reduces to

$$\rho \left(\frac{\partial \mathbf{v}_r}{\partial t} + \mathbf{w} \cdot \nabla \mathbf{v}_r + \mathbf{v}_r \cdot \nabla \mathbf{v}_r \right) = -\nabla p + \rho \mathbf{g} + \mu \nabla^2 \mathbf{v}_r \qquad (5.4\text{-}18)$$

Once again the first two terms on the left-hand side of Eq. 5.4-18 represent the total derivative, and we write

$$\rho \left(\frac{d\mathbf{v}_r}{dt} + \mathbf{v}_r \cdot \nabla \mathbf{v}_r \right) = -\nabla p + \rho \mathbf{g} + \mu \nabla^2 \mathbf{v}_r \qquad (5.4\text{-}19)$$

This result indicates that the equations of motion take the same form for an observer moving at a constant velocity as they do for an observer fixed in space. The situation clearly becomes more complex for accelerating reference frames, and that case is left for more advanced study.

*5.5 Dimensional Analysis

Before going on to the solution of the equations of motion for uniformly accelerated flows and one-dimensional laminar flows, we shall investigate the dimensionless form of these equations. Each term in Eq. 5.4-10 has units of either force per unit volume or time rate of change of momentum per unit volume, both being equivalent by definition. By dividing each term in Eq. 5.4-10 by a constant having these same dimensions, we will obtain the dimensionless equations that will give rise to two important dimensionless numbers—the Reynolds number, N_{Re}, and the Froude number, N_{Fr}. In forming the dimensionless equations we shall make use of some characteristic length, L, and some characteristic time, L/u_0, where u_0 is the characteristic velocity. In a sense, we can look upon this process as one of choosing a special set of fundamental units (L instead of 1 cm and L/u_0 instead of 1 sec) for each particular problem. Such a choice leads to the scale factors, N_{Re} and N_{Fr}.

The main purpose of dimensional analysis is to aid us in interpreting the experiments often performed to gain information about flows not susceptible to analysis. For incompressible flows, the velocity and pressure are determined by:

1. the equations of motion;
2. the continuity equation;
3. the boundary conditions.

From these requirements follows the guiding principle behind dimensional analysis, which states that the *dependent* variables (**v** and p) are functions of:

1. the *independent* variables (x, y, z, and t);
2. the parameters that occur in the differential equations (ρ, μ, and **g**);
3. any parameters that occur in the boundary conditions.

By putting the equations in dimensionless form, we can reduce the number of parameters in the differential equations from three to one, and show that the Froude number is important only for two-phase flows or free-surface flows.

In analyzing Eq. 5.4-10, we first represent the gravity vector as the gradient of a scalar, ϕ

$$\mathbf{g} = -\boldsymbol{\nabla}\phi \qquad (5.5\text{-}1)$$

where $\phi = -(g_x x + g_y y + g_z z)$

The first two terms on the right-hand side of Eq. 5.4-10 may now be expressed as

$$
\begin{aligned}
-\nabla p + \rho \mathbf{g} &= -\nabla p - \rho \, \nabla \phi \\
&= -\nabla(p + \rho\phi) \\
&= -\nabla[(p - p_0) + \rho\phi]
\end{aligned}
\tag{5.5-2}
$$

where p_0 is a constant generally taken to be atmospheric pressure. This rearrangement is possible only if the density is constant—i.e., for incompressible flows. Substitution of Eq. 5.5-2 into Eq. 5.4-10 gives

$$
\rho\left(\frac{\partial \mathbf{v}}{\partial t} + \mathbf{v} \cdot \nabla \mathbf{v}\right) = -\nabla[(p - p_0) + \rho\phi] + \mu \nabla^2 \mathbf{v}
\tag{5.5-3}
$$

For any given flow there may be several possible choices for the characteristic length and velocity. In closed-conduit flow, the characteristic length is traditionally chosen to be four times the hydraulic radius, R_h, and the characteristic velocity is taken to be the average velocity, $\langle v_z \rangle$. The hydraulic radius is defined as the cross-sectional area divided by the wetted perimeter.

$$
R_h = \frac{\text{cross-sectional area}}{\text{wetted perimeter}}
\tag{5.5-4}
$$

For a pipe, the hydraulic radius is equal to one-fourth the diameter,

$$
\begin{aligned}
R_h &= \frac{\left(\dfrac{\pi D^2}{4}\right)}{\pi D} \\
&= \frac{D}{4}
\end{aligned}
\tag{5.5-5}
$$

For the present we will simply designate the characteristic length and velocity by L and u_0, and multiply every term in Eq. 5.5-3 by $L/\rho u_0^2$ to obtain

$$
\frac{\partial\left(\dfrac{\mathbf{v}}{u_0}\right)}{\partial\left(\dfrac{t u_0}{L}\right)} + \left(\frac{\mathbf{v}}{u_0}\right) \cdot (L\nabla)\left(\frac{\mathbf{v}}{u_0}\right) = -(L\nabla)\left(\frac{p - p_0}{\rho u_0^2} + \frac{\phi}{u_0^2}\right) + \left(\frac{\mu}{\rho u_0 L}\right)(L^2 \nabla^2)\left(\frac{\mathbf{v}}{u_0}\right)
$$

$$
\tag{5.5-6}
$$

Each term in parentheses in Eq. 5.5-6 is dimensionless; to work with a less cumbersome equation, we need to define some dimensionless variables. In defining these variables, it is helpful to choose symbols which clearly represent the quantity in question. Insofar as it is possible, we shall try to do so by using the capital letter or script letter associated with the particular dimensional quantity. Often, such a choice would lead to confusion, as it would if

V were used to represent the dimensionless velocity, or if T were used to represent the dimensionless time. Under these circumstances, some other variable is chosen to represent the dimensionless variable. The dimensionless variables in Eq. 5.5-6 are defined as

$$\mathbf{U} = \left(\frac{\mathbf{v}}{u_0}\right) \quad \{\text{dimensionless velocity}\}$$

$$\Theta = \left(\frac{tu_0}{L}\right) \quad \{\text{dimensionless time}\}$$

$$\boldsymbol{\nabla} = L\boldsymbol{\nabla} \quad \{\text{dimensionless vector operator}\}\dagger$$

$$P = \left(\frac{p - p_0}{\rho u_0^2}\right) \quad \{\text{dimensionless pressure}\}$$

$$N_{\mathrm{Re}} = \frac{\rho u_0 L}{\mu} \quad \left\{\begin{matrix}\text{dimensionless parameter called the}\\ \text{Reynolds number}\end{matrix}\right\}$$

$$\mathscr{P} = P + \frac{\phi}{u_0^2} \quad \left\{\begin{matrix}\text{dimensionless pressure which includes}\\ \text{the body force term}\end{matrix}\right\}$$

Use of these dimensionless variables allows us to write Eq. 5.5-6 as

$$\frac{\partial \mathbf{U}}{\partial \Theta} + \mathbf{U} \cdot \boldsymbol{\nabla}\mathbf{U} = -\boldsymbol{\nabla}\mathscr{P} + \frac{1}{N_{\mathrm{Re}}}\, \nabla^2\mathbf{U} \qquad (5.5\text{-}7)$$

For incompressible flows, the dimensionless continuity equation takes the form

$$\boldsymbol{\nabla} \cdot \mathbf{U} = 0 \qquad (5.5\text{-}8)$$

So far we have reduced the number of parameters in the differential equations from three (μ, ρ, **g**) to one (N_{Re}); however, both **U** and $\mathscr{P}$ will depend on the parameters that appear in the boundary conditions, and we need to examine two specific cases to indicate how the boundary conditions are treated in dimensional analysis. From these two examples, we shall see that the Froude number enters the solution as a parameter in the normal stress condition at a fluid-fluid interface. For confined flows, the dimensionless velocity and pressure, **U** and $\mathscr{P}$, are independent of the Froude number.

Sudden contraction in a pipeline

As an example of flow in a closed conduit, we consider the sudden contraction in a pipeline such as that illustrated in Fig. 5.5-1. We assume that the Reynolds number is less than 2100; the flow is therefore laminar, and the velocity profile is essentially parabolic at some distance from the

† Lack of a suitable symbol for the dimensionless "del" operator compels us to use the same symbol for both the dimensionless and the dimensional form.

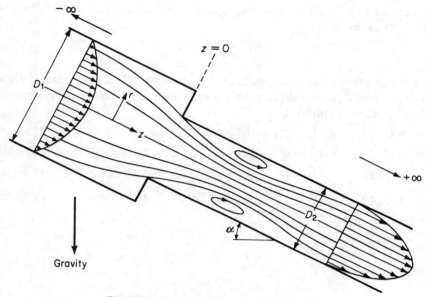

Fig. 5.5-1. Sudden contraction in a pipeline.

sudden contraction. For practical purposes this distance is finite, but from the mathematical point of view we simply state that the velocity profile is parabolic at $z = \pm\infty$.

While it is possible to solve the equations of motion for this flow† and thus determine the pressure variation along the z-axis, it may be less expensive to investigate this effect experimentally and develop a correlation for this pressure variation. To obtain the maximum amount of information from the minimum amount of experimental effort, we must examine the problem in dimensionless form. The differential equations are already available in dimensionless form and we must now put the boundary conditions in this form. The boundary conditions are

B.C. 1: $\qquad v_z = 2\langle v_z\rangle_1\left[1 - 4\left(\dfrac{r}{D_1}\right)^2\right], \qquad z = -\infty$ $\qquad$ (5.5-9a)

B.C. 2: $\qquad v_z = 0, \qquad r = r_1, \qquad 0 > z \geq -\infty$ $\qquad$ (5.5-9b)

B.C. 3: $\qquad v_z = 0, \qquad r = r_2, \qquad +\infty \geq z \geq 0$ $\qquad$ (5.5-9c)

B.C. 4: $\qquad v_z = 2\langle v_z\rangle_1\left(\dfrac{D_1}{D_2}\right)^2\left[1 - 4\left(\dfrac{r}{D_2}\right)^2\right], \qquad z = +\infty$ $\qquad$ (5.5-9d)

† Numerical methods have been used with success on such problems. Details may be found in J. E. Fromm, "A Method for Computing Nonsteady, Incompressible, Viscous Flows" (Los Alamos, Calif.: Los Alamos Scientific Laboratory, 1963), LA-2910.

where we have made use of conservation of mass (or volume in this case of incompressible flow)

$$\frac{\pi D_1^2}{4} \langle v_z \rangle_1 = \frac{\pi D_2^2}{4} \langle v_z \rangle_2 \tag{5.5-10}$$

in formulating boundary condition 4. Choosing $\langle v_z \rangle_1$ as the characteristic velocity and D_1 as the characteristic length leads to the following dimensionless boundary conditions,

B.C. 1': $U_z = 2(1 - 4R^2),$ $Z = -\infty$ (5.5-11a)

B.C. 2': $U_z = 0,$ $R = \frac{1}{2},$ $0 > Z \geq -\infty$ (5.5-11b)

B.C. 3': $U_z = 0,$ $R = \frac{1}{2}\mathscr{R}_D,$ $\infty \geq Z \geq 0$ (5.5-11c)

B.C. 4': $U_z = 2\mathscr{R}_D^{-2}(1 - 4\mathscr{R}_D^{-2}R^2),$ $Z = +\infty$ (5.5-11d)

where

$$R = \frac{r}{D_1}$$

$$Z = \frac{z}{D_1}$$

$$\mathscr{R}_D = \frac{D_2}{D_1} \dagger$$

On the basis of Eqs. 5.5-7, 5.5-8, and 5.5-11, we may express the functional dependence of $\mathbf{U}$ and $\mathscr{P}$ as

$$\mathbf{U} = \mathbf{U}(R, \theta, Z, \Theta, N_{\mathrm{Re}}, \mathscr{R}_D) \tag{5.5-12}$$

$$\mathscr{P} = \mathscr{P}(R, \theta, Z, \Theta, N_{\mathrm{Re}}, \mathscr{R}_D) \tag{5.5-13}$$

Confining our attention to the pressure term, we express the time average and area average as‡

$$\langle \overline{\mathscr{P}} \rangle = f(Z, N_{\mathrm{Re}}, \mathscr{R}_D) \tag{5.5-14}$$

where the dependence on R, θ, and Θ is removed by the averaging process. This result indicates that the dimensionless pressure depends on Z and the two parameters, N_{Re} and $\mathscr{R}_D$. Note that one of these parameters came from the differential equation, while the second entered the solution via a boundary condition.

Actual experiments will be concerned with the dimensional pressure p, which may be expressed as

$$\langle \bar{p} \rangle = \rho \langle \bar{v}_z \rangle_1^2 f(Z, N_{\mathrm{Re}}, \mathscr{R}_D) - \rho \langle \phi \rangle + p_0 \tag{5.5-15}$$

† A script $\mathscr{R}$ with an appropriate subscript will be used throughout the text to denote a dimensionless ratio of two like quantities.

‡ Time averages will be discussed in Chap. 6 and will always be denoted with overbar ($\frown$).

For the configuration shown in Fig. 5.5-1, the scalar $\langle\phi\rangle$ is given by

$$\langle\phi\rangle = -gz\,\sin\alpha \qquad (5.5\text{-}16)$$

and the pressure becomes

$$\langle\bar{p}\rangle = \rho\langle\bar{v}_z\rangle_1^2 f(Z, N_{\mathrm{Re}}, \mathscr{R}_D) + \rho gz\,\sin\alpha + p_0 \qquad (5.5\text{-}17)$$

Here we see that gravity simply gives rise to an additive hydrostatic pressure term, $\rho gz \cos\alpha$, and does not influence the velocity $\mathbf{U}$. An experimental study would seek only to determine the function $f(Z, N_{\mathrm{Re}}, \mathscr{R}_D)$.

Racing sloop hull design

To illustrate how the Froude number enters into free surface problems, let us assume that we are assigned the job of determining the best possible hull shape for an America's Cup defender. The design of a hull for a racing sloop is a subtle and complex task generally undertaken by wise and venerable sailor-designers; however, some useful information about hull design can be obtained by towing models through a testing tank, such as that illustrated in Fig. 5.5-2. The model is a scaled-down version of a proposed hull, and every dimension—such as the length, beam, etc.—is related to the dimensions of the

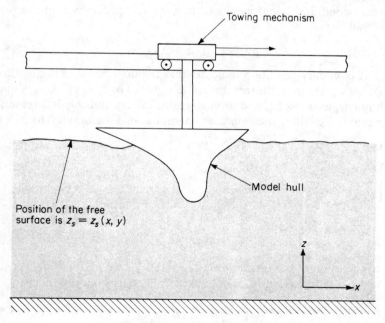

Fig. 5.5-2. Model towing tank.

actual hull by

$$L_{\text{model}} = \mathcal{R}_L L_{\text{actual}} \qquad (5.5\text{-}18)$$

where $\mathcal{R}_L < 1$. Thus, the model is geometrically similar to the actual hull.

Our experiment might consist of towing several models, all having the same scale factor $\mathcal{R}_L$, through the tank to determine which produces the least drag at a given speed. Presumably we know approximately at what speed the actual hull will be moving, and we know the physical properties of the fluid (salt water) through which it will move. The question to be answered is: What should be the conditions in the tank so that the tests are dynamically similar to the actual motion? The answer is that the Reynolds number and Froude number must be the same; our objective is to prove it.

It is easiest to view this problem as if the hull were fixed in space and the fluid were flowing past it with a uniform velocity. Under these conditions the boundary conditions are

B.C. 1: $\qquad\qquad \mathbf{v} = -\mathbf{i}u_0, \qquad x, y, z \to \pm\infty \qquad (5.5\text{-}19a)$

(i.e., the flow is undisturbed far from the hull, the origin of the coordinate system being on the hull), and

B.C. 2: $\qquad\qquad \mathbf{v} = 0, \qquad a(x, y, z) = 0 \qquad (5.5\text{-}19b)$

Here, $a(x, y, z)$ is a function which describes the surface of the hull; thus, boundary condition 2 indicates that the fluid velocity is zero on the surface of the hull.

B.C. 3: $\qquad\qquad p = p_0, \qquad z = z_s(x, y) \qquad (5.5\text{-}19c)$

This last boundary condition indicates that the fluid pressure is equal to the atmospheric pressure at the free surface, designated by $z_s(x, y)$. This boundary condition neglects viscous and surface tension effects, but this is a reasonable assumption. Rewriting the boundary conditions in dimensionless form, we get

B.C. 1': $\qquad\qquad \mathbf{U} = -\mathbf{i}, \qquad X, Y, Z \to \pm\infty \qquad (5.5\text{-}20a)$

B.C. 2': $\qquad\qquad \mathbf{U} = 0, \qquad A(X, Y, Z) = 0 \qquad (5.5\text{-}20b)$

B.C. 3': $\qquad\qquad \mathscr{P} = \dfrac{\phi}{u_0^2}\bigg|_{z=z_s(x,y)}, \qquad Z = Z_s(X, Y) \qquad (5.5\text{-}20c)$

The function ϕ is given by

$$\phi = gz \qquad (5.5\text{-}21)$$

and to incorporate the dimensionless variable Z, we multiply and divide ϕ by the characteristic length L, and rewrite boundary condition 3' as

B.C. 3'': $\qquad\qquad \mathscr{P} = \left(\dfrac{gL}{u_0^2}\right)Z, \qquad Z = Z_s(X, Y) \qquad (5.5\text{-}22)$

The Froude number is defined as†

$$N_{\mathrm{Fr}} = \frac{u_0^2}{gL} \qquad (5.5\text{-}23)$$

thus yielding the final form of boundary condition 3,

B.C. 3″: $\qquad\qquad \mathscr{P} = \dfrac{Z}{N_{\mathrm{Fr}}}, \qquad Z = Z_s(X, Y) \qquad (5.5\text{-}24)$

On the basis of Eqs. 5.5-7 and 5.5-8 and the boundary conditions given by Eqs. 5.5-20a and b and Eq. 5.5-24, the functional dependence of **U** and $\mathscr{P}$ is represented by

$$\mathbf{U} = \mathbf{U}[X, Y, Z, \Theta, A(X, Y, Z), N_{\mathrm{Re}}, N_{\mathrm{Fr}}] \qquad (5.5\text{-}25)$$

$$\mathscr{P} = \mathscr{P}[X, Y, Z, \Theta, A(X, Y, Z), N_{\mathrm{Re}}, N_{\mathrm{Fr}}] \qquad (5.5\text{-}26)$$

Since the models are geometrically similar to the proposed actual hull, the function $A(X, Y, Z)$ is identical for both. For the actual flow and the model flow to be dynamically similar, we require that the Reynolds number and the Froude number be the same; thus,

$$N_{\mathrm{Re}} = \left(\frac{u_0 L}{\nu}\right)_{\mathrm{actual}} = \left(\frac{u_0 L}{\nu}\right)_{\mathrm{model}} \qquad (5.5\text{-}27)$$

and

$$N_{\mathrm{Fr}} = \left(\frac{u_0^2}{gL}\right)_{\mathrm{actual}} = \left(\frac{u_0^2}{gL}\right)_{\mathrm{model}} \qquad (5.5\text{-}28)$$

When these conditions are subjected to the restriction given by Eq. 5.5-18, we find

$$(u_0)_{\mathrm{model}} = \mathscr{R}_L^{1/2}(u_0)_{\mathrm{actual}} \qquad (5.5\text{-}29)$$

and

$$\nu_{\mathrm{model}} = \mathscr{R}_L^{3/2}\nu_{\mathrm{actual}} \qquad (5.5\text{-}30)$$

The condition on the velocity is easily met; however, the condition on the kinematic viscosity is difficult if not impossible to meet for most practical cases. Since $\mathscr{R}_L$ is necessarily much smaller than one, the kinematic viscosity of the fluid in the towing tank must be one to two orders of magnitude less than the kinematic viscosity of water. Such a fluid is rather difficult to find, and in practice we can maintain either the Reynolds number or the Froude number constant but not both. Under such conditions considerable skill and intuition are required to determine the effect of a free surface on the performance of a hull.

† Most often the Froude number is defined as $u_0/\sqrt{gL}$; however, the form given by Eq. 5.5-23 arises naturally from the dimensionless form of the equations of motion and will be used throughout this text.

The treatment of dimensional analysis given here is brief in comparison to the usefulness of the method. A more thorough discussion is available elsewhere.[2-3]

*5.6 Applications of the Differential Equations of Motion

There are only four classes of problems for which we may easily obtain analytic solutions of the equations of motion: fluids at rest or moving at a constant velocity; uniformly accelerated flows; one-dimensional laminar flow; and irrotational flow. With the aid of advanced analytical or numerical methods, practically all laminar flows are susceptible to analysis; however, these four types of flow represent the limits of the undergraduate at this time.

Although irrotational flow theory is a key tool in the analysis of flow around immersed bodies, and wave propagation in open channel flow, it will not be treated in this text. A readable account of this particular area of fluid mechanics is given by Temple,[4] although the classic in the field is still the detailed treatment of Milne-Thomson.[5]

If the fluid velocity is constant,

$$\mathbf{v} = \mathbf{b} \tag{5.6-1}$$

where the constant vector $\mathbf{b}$ is zero if the fluid is at rest. Substitution of Eq. 5.6-1 into Eq. 5.4-10 yields the previously derived result,

$$0 = -\nabla p + \rho\mathbf{g} \tag{5.6-2}$$

The solution of this equation was treated in detail in Chap. 2; we shall not discuss it further here.

Uniformly accelerated flow

Uniform acceleration means that each element of the fluid experiences the same acceleration; thus, $\mathbf{v}$ is a function of time but not position. Making use of the material derivative, we may write Eq. 5.4-10 as

$$\rho\frac{D\mathbf{v}}{Dt} = -\nabla p + \rho\mathbf{g} + \mu\nabla^2\mathbf{v} \tag{5.6-3}$$

2. G. Birkhoff, *Hydrodynamics, A Study in Logic, Fact and Similitude* (Princeton, N.J.: Princeton University Press, 1960).

3. P. W. Bridgman, *Dimensional Analysis*, (New Haven, Conn.: Yale University Press, 1931).

4. G. Temple, *An Introduction to Fluid Dynamics* (New York: Oxford Press, 1958).

5. L. M. Milne-Thomson, *Theoretical Hydrodynamics*, 4th ed. (New York: The Macmillan Company, 1960).

For uniform acceleration,

$$\frac{D\mathbf{v}}{Dt} = \mathbf{a}, \qquad \text{a constant vector} \tag{5.6-4}$$

and

$$\nabla^2 \mathbf{v} = 0 \tag{5.6-5}$$

In light of Eqs. 5.6-4 and 5.6-5, Eq. 5.6-3 reduces to

$$0 = -\nabla p + \rho(\mathbf{g} - \mathbf{a}) \tag{5.6-6}$$

for uniform acceleration. Equation 5.6-6 has the same form as Eq. 5.6-2, except that the gravity vector has been replaced by $(\mathbf{g} - \mathbf{a})$. We obtain the three scalar forms of Eq. 5.6-6 by taking the scalar product with $\mathbf{i}$, $\mathbf{j}$, and $\mathbf{k}$, respectively,

$$\frac{\partial p}{\partial x} = \rho \mathbf{i} \cdot (\mathbf{g} - \mathbf{a}) \tag{5.6-7a}$$

$$\frac{\partial p}{\partial y} = \rho \mathbf{j} \cdot (\mathbf{g} - \mathbf{a}) \tag{5.6-7b}$$

$$\frac{\partial p}{\partial z} = \rho \mathbf{k} \cdot (\mathbf{g} - \mathbf{a}) \tag{5.6-7c}$$

Noting that the total differential of the pressure is

$$dp = \frac{\partial p}{\partial x} dx + \frac{\partial p}{\partial y} dy + \frac{\partial p}{\partial z} dz \tag{5.6-8}$$

we may use Eqs. 5.6-7 to obtain

$$dp = \rho[\mathbf{i} \cdot (\mathbf{g} - \mathbf{a}) \, dx + \mathbf{j} \cdot (\mathbf{g} - \mathbf{a}) \, dy + \mathbf{k} \cdot (\mathbf{g} - \mathbf{a}) \, dz] \tag{5.6-9}$$

Integration of Eq. 5.6-9 between x_0, y_0, z_0 and any arbitrary point x, y, z gives the general expression for the pressure in a uniformly accelerated fluid.

$$p = p_0 + \rho \left[A_x(x - x_0) + A_y(y - y_0) + A_z(z - z_0) \right] \tag{5.6-10}$$

where $p = p(x, y, z)$

$p_0 = p(x_0, y_0, z_0)$

$A_x = \mathbf{i} \cdot (\mathbf{g} - \mathbf{a})$

$A_y = \mathbf{j} \cdot (\mathbf{g} - \mathbf{a})$

$A_z = \mathbf{k} \cdot (\mathbf{g} - \mathbf{a})$

If the pressure p_0 is known or specified, Eq. 5.6-10 defines the pressure everywhere in the system. If the system contains a free surface at which the pressure is constant, Eq. 5.6-10 may be used to determine the position of the surface.

For example, let us specify that x_0, y_0, z_0 is a point on the free surface where the pressure is p_0. Now let $z = z_s(x, y)$ represent the position of the free surface. Then

$$p[x, y, z_s(x, y)] = p_0 \tag{5.6-11}$$

and Eq. 5.6-10 reduces to

$$A_x(x - x_0) + A_y(y - y_0) + A_z(z_s - z_0) = 0 \tag{5.6-12}$$

Consider the problem of a rectangular tank, illustrated in Fig. 5.6-1, which is accelerated in the x-direction. Initially the fluid in the tank would not

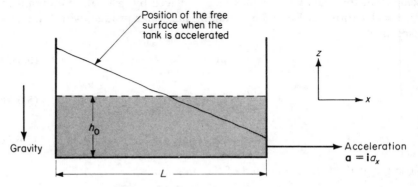

Fig. 5.6-I. An accelerated rectangular tank.

be uniformly accelerated, for it would slosh back and forth and the surface would be wavy. However, after a period of time this secondary motion would die out and movement would be uniform. For this system,

$$A_x = \mathbf{i} \cdot (-\mathbf{k}g - \mathbf{i}a_x) = -a_x \tag{5.6-13a}$$

$$A_y = \mathbf{j} \cdot (-\mathbf{k}g - \mathbf{i}a_x) = 0 \tag{5.6-13b}$$

$$A_z = \mathbf{k} \cdot (-\mathbf{k}g - \mathbf{i}a_x) = -g \tag{5.6-13c}$$

and Eq. 5.6-12 becomes

$$-a_x(x - x_0) - g(z_s - z_0) = 0 \tag{5.6-14}$$

Solving Eq. 5.6-14 for z_s gives

$$z_s = z_0 - \frac{a_x}{g}(x - x_0) \tag{5.6-15}$$

We see that the liquid depth is a linear function of x but the exact position of the interface is not yet determined. To locate the interface, we must make use of the principle of conservation of mass—i.e., the mass of the fluid in the tank remains constant. Since the flow is incompressible, we require that

$$h_0 L = \int_0^L z_s \, dx = \int_0^L \left[z_0 - \frac{a_x}{g}(x - x_0) \right] dx$$

$$= z_0 L - \frac{a_x}{g}\left(\frac{L^2}{2} - x_0 L \right) \tag{5.6-16}$$

Solving for z_0 gives

$$z_0 = h_0 + \frac{a_x}{g}\left(\frac{L}{2} - x_0 \right) \tag{5.6-17}$$

and substitution of Eq. 5.6-17 into Eq. 5.6-15 yields the final result

$$z_s = h_0 + \frac{a_x}{g}\left(\frac{L}{2} - x \right) \tag{5.6-18}$$

One-dimensional laminar flow

As the first example of one-dimensional laminar flow, we shall examine in detail laminar flow in a pipe. We have treated this problem previously in Sec. 2.8, where we applied the linear momentum principle to a differential volume to yield the equation of motion applicable to the particular flow under investigation. That method of analysis has the advantage of providing a solution with a minimum of effort, tending to focus student attention on the shear stress distribution and the shear stress-rate of strain relationship. Its disadvantage is its tendency to gloss over some important assumptions that must be made.

In this example, we shall start with the complete form of the Navier-Stokes equations in cylindrical form and demonstrate under what conditions we may simplify them to obtain the previously derived Hagen-Poiseuille law. In starting with the complete form of the equations, we are forced to state clearly the assumptions that go into the solution. This, then, is the advantage of this method of analysis. We wish to apply the listed equations to the flow illustrated in Fig. 5.6-2.

1. r-direction:

$$\rho\left(\frac{\partial v_r}{\partial t} + v_r \frac{\partial v_r}{\partial r} + \frac{v_\theta}{r}\frac{\partial v_r}{\partial \theta} - \frac{v_\theta^2}{r} + v_z \frac{\partial v_r}{\partial z} \right) = -\frac{\partial p}{\partial r}$$

$$+ \rho g_r + \mu\left[\frac{\partial}{\partial r}\left(\frac{1}{r}\frac{\partial}{\partial r}(rv_r) \right) + \frac{1}{r^2}\frac{\partial^2 v_r}{\partial \theta^2} - \frac{2}{r^2}\frac{\partial v_\theta}{\partial \theta} + \frac{\partial^2 v_r}{\partial z^2} \right] \tag{5.6-19}$$

2. θ-direction:

$$\rho\left(\frac{\partial v_\theta}{\partial t} + v_r \frac{\partial v_\theta}{\partial r} + \frac{v_\theta}{r}\frac{\partial v_\theta}{\partial \theta} + \frac{v_r v_\theta}{r} + v_z \frac{\partial v_\theta}{\partial z} \right) = -\frac{1}{r}\frac{\partial p}{\partial \theta}$$

$$+ \rho g_\theta + \mu\left[\frac{\partial}{\partial r}\left(\frac{1}{r}\frac{\partial}{\partial r}(rv_\theta) \right) + \frac{1}{r^2}\frac{\partial^2 v_\theta}{\partial \theta^2} + \frac{2}{r^2}\frac{\partial v_r}{\partial \theta} + \frac{\partial^2 v_\theta}{\partial z^2} \right] \tag{5.6-20}$$

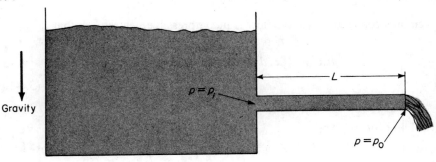

Gravity

$p = p_i$

L

$p = p_0$

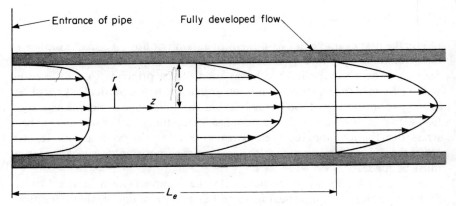

Entrance of pipe   Fully developed flow

r

z

r_0

L_e

Fig. 5.6-2. Laminar flow through a pipe.

3. *z*-direction:

$$\rho\left(\frac{\partial v_z}{\partial t} + v_r\frac{\partial v_z}{\partial r} + \frac{v_\theta}{r}\frac{\partial v_z}{\partial \theta} + v_z\frac{\partial v_z}{\partial z}\right) = -\frac{\partial p}{\partial z} + \rho g_z$$

$$+ \mu\left[\frac{1}{r}\frac{\partial}{\partial r}\left(r\frac{\partial v_z}{\partial r}\right) + \frac{1}{r^2}\frac{\partial^2 v_z}{\partial \theta^2} + \frac{\partial^2 v_z}{\partial z^2}\right] \quad (5.6\text{-}21)$$

4. continuity equation:

$$\frac{1}{r}\frac{\partial}{\partial r}(rv_r) + \frac{1}{r}\frac{\partial v_\theta}{\partial \theta} + \frac{\partial v_z}{\partial z} = 0 \quad (5.6\text{-}22)$$

In attacking this problem, we make four assumptions.

1. The density and viscosity are constant. This assumption is, of course, reflected in the form of the equations of motion and the continuity equation.

2. The flow is steady. This would not be true if the entrance or exit conditions were changing with time.

3. The flow is laminar. For this assumption to hold, we require that the Reynolds number be less than 2100; at higher Reynolds numbers, the flow becomes turbulent. (The transition from laminar to turbulent flow is discussed in Chap. 6.)

4. The velocity components, v_θ and v_r, are zero. This condition need not be true at the entrance of the pipe; however, even if v_θ and v_r are non-zero at the entrance, they will tend toward zero as z increases. A precise treatment of the flow in the entrance region is beyond the scope of this text; nevertheless, we may draw upon other mathematical and experimental studies which indicate that the entrance length L_e is given by

$$L_e \approx 0.058 \, DN_{\text{Re}} \tag{5.6-23}$$

The entrance length is generally defined as the distance at which the centerline velocity is within 1 per cent of its final value.

If we restrict our analysis to values of z greater than L_e, assumption 4 is valid. Imposing assumptions 3 and 4 on Eqs. 5.6-19 through 5.6-22 yields

1. r-direction:

$$0 = -\frac{\partial p}{\partial r} + \rho g_r \tag{5.6-24}$$

2. θ-direction:

$$0 = -\frac{1}{r}\frac{\partial p}{\partial \theta} + \rho g_\theta \tag{5.6-25}$$

3. z-direction:

$$\rho\left(v_z \frac{\partial v_z}{\partial z}\right) = -\frac{\partial p}{\partial z} + \rho g_z + \mu\left[\frac{1}{r}\frac{\partial}{\partial r}\left(r\frac{\partial v_z}{\partial r}\right) + \frac{1}{r^2}\frac{\partial^2 v_z}{\partial \theta^2} + \frac{\partial^2 v_z}{\partial z^2}\right] \tag{5.6-26}$$

4. continuity equation:

$$\frac{\partial v_z}{\partial z} = 0 \tag{5.6-27}$$

Equation 5.6-27 indicates that v_z is independent of z. If we also assume that the flow is axisymmetric—i.e., v_z is independent of θ—and note that $g_z = 0$, the problem is reduced to solving Eqs. 5.6-24, 5.6-25, and 5.6-28.

$$\frac{\partial p}{\partial z} = \mu\left[\frac{1}{r}\frac{\partial}{\partial r}\left(r\frac{\partial v_z}{\partial r}\right)\right] \tag{5.6-28}$$

Equations 5.6-24 and 5.6-25 may be integrated to give

$$p = \rho r \int g_\theta \, d\theta + C_1(r, z) \qquad (5.6\text{-}29)$$

$$p = \rho \int g_r \, dr + C_2(\theta, z) \qquad (5.6\text{-}30)$$

where C_1 and C_2 are the constants of integration and may be functions of r and z, and θ and z, respectively. Differentiating Eqs. 5.6-29 and 5.6-30 with respect to z and equating the results, we have

$$\frac{\partial C_1(r, z)}{\partial z} = \frac{\partial C_2(\theta, z)}{\partial z} \qquad (5.6\text{-}31)$$

Inasmuch as the right-hand side of Eq. 5.6-31 is not a function of r, the left-hand side cannot be a function of r. Similar reasoning with regard to the θ dependence leads us to the conclusion that the derivatives of C_1 and C_2 may only be functions of z. Thus,

$$\frac{\partial p}{\partial z} = \frac{\partial C_1(z)}{\partial z} = \frac{\partial C_2(z)}{\partial z} \qquad (5.6\text{-}32)$$

Referring now to Eq. 5.6-28, we conclude that the left-hand side may only be a function of z, while the right-hand side may only be a function of r. There is only one possible solution to this situation—i.e., both sides are equal. to a constant—and we write

$$-\frac{\Delta p}{L} = \mu \frac{1}{r} \frac{d}{dr}\left(r \frac{dv_z}{dr}\right) \qquad (5.6\text{-}33)$$

where the partial derivatives have been replaced with total derivatives, because v_z is only a function of r. In writing Eq. 5.6-33, we have assumed that dp/dz is a constant (equal to $-\Delta p/L$) over the entire region $0 \le z \le L$; actually, it is not. If the entrance length L_e is much smaller than the total length L, the error in Eq. 5.6-33 is negligible. We solved this equation in Chap. 2 to yield

$$v_z = \left(\frac{\Delta p}{L}\right)\frac{r_0^2}{4\mu}\left[1 - \left(\frac{r}{r_0}\right)^2\right] \qquad (5.6\text{-}34)$$

and

$$Q = \frac{\pi r_0^4}{8\mu}\left(\frac{\Delta p}{L}\right)$$

Very often it is beneficial to put derived results in dimensionless form to indicate clearly what dimensionless parameters must be considered. If we define the dimensionless velocity U_z as

$$U_z = \frac{v_z}{\langle v_z \rangle} \qquad (5.6\text{-}35)$$

and the dimensionless pressure gradient f as

$$f = \frac{\Delta p}{\frac{1}{2}\rho \langle v_z \rangle^2} \left(\frac{D}{L}\right) \tag{5.6-36}$$

we obtain

$$U_z = 2(1 - 4R^2) \tag{5.6-37}$$

and

$$f = \frac{64}{N_{Re}} \tag{5.6-38}$$

where $R = r/D$. In this particular case, there is not much to be gained by putting the results in dimensionless form; however, in treating the more complex problem of turbulent flow in a pipe, it will be helpful to have Eq. 5.6-38 for reference. The term f is known as the friction factor, and we will consider its dependence on the Reynolds number for turbulent flow in Chap. 8.

Flow of two immiscible fluids between parallel plates

Analyzing the flow of two immiscible fluids will help to answer any questions the student might have regarding the application of the principles of continuity of velocity and stress in formulating boundary conditions. The flow illustrated in Fig. 5.6-3 consists of two fluids flowing under the action of a pressure gradient in a channel of height $h_I + h_{II}$. For the purpose of this analysis, we will assume that the channel is infinite in the z-direction; thus, the pressure and velocity can be taken as independent of z.

At this point we need to say something of the common engineering practice of reducing a three-dimensional problem to a two-dimensional problem

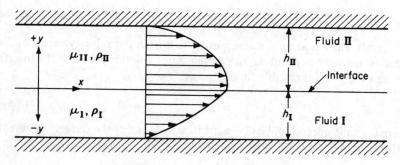

Fig. 5.6-3. Flow of two immiscible fluids.

by assuming that the system is infinite in extent in one direction. Since no real system extends infinitely in any direction, we would like to be able to answer the question, "When will this technique provide a reasonable description of the real system?" There is, in fact, no set answer to this question; each case must be considered individually. For the problem under consideration, reasonable results are obtained with a two-dimensional analysis, provided the width of the channel is at least an order of magnitude (factor of ten) larger than the channel depth, $h_I + h_{II}$. We might press the issue and ask, "Why is this so?" The answer lies in examining the complete three-dimensional solution and comparing it with the two-dimensional result. Because the mathematical techniques required to solve the three-dimensional case are beyond the scope of this text, we must limit ourselves to the simpler case. This restriction is satisfactory, for our purpose is to examine the boundary conditions for two-phase flow rather than to obtain an exact solution.

Assuming steady, one-dimensional flow of incompressible, constant-viscosity fluids allows us to simplify the equations of motion in rectangular coordinates to

$$0 = -\left(\frac{\partial p_I}{\partial x}\right) + \mu_I\left(\frac{\partial^2 v_x^I}{\partial y^2}\right) \tag{5.6-39}$$

$$\left. \vphantom{0}\right\} \text{ Fluid I}$$

$$0 = -\left(\frac{\partial p_I}{\partial y}\right) - \rho_I g \tag{5.6-40}$$

$$0 = -\left(\frac{\partial p_{II}}{\partial x}\right) + \mu_{II}\left(\frac{\partial^2 v_x^{II}}{\partial y^2}\right) \tag{5.6-41}$$

$$\left. \vphantom{0}\right\} \text{ Fluid II}$$

$$0 = -\left(\frac{\partial p_{II}}{\partial y}\right) - \rho_{II} g \tag{5.6-42}$$

Before solving these equations, we must re-examine the behavior of the stress vector at a phase interface. In Sec. 4.1, it was shown that

$$\mathbf{t}_{(+n)} = -\mathbf{t}_{(-n)} \tag{5.6-43}$$

This result was based on the assumption that both the velocity vector and the stress vector were continuous functions. Applying this result to the interface between the two immiscible fluids, we write

$$\mathbf{t}_{(+n)}^I = -\mathbf{t}_{(-n)}^{II} \quad , \quad y = 0 \tag{5.6-44}$$

where the unit normal, $\mathbf{n}$, has been arbitrarily taken as the outwardly directed unit normal for fluid I. At *any* point in fluid II,

$$\mathbf{t}_{(+n)}^{II} = -\mathbf{t}_{(-n)}^{II} \quad , \quad 0 \le y \le h_{II} \tag{5.6-45}$$

and Eq. 5.6-44 may be written as

$$\mathbf{t}_{(n)}^{I} = \mathbf{t}_{(n)}^{II} \qquad y = 0 \qquad (5.6\text{-}46)$$

An implied assumption in this treatment is that the interface is simply a mathematical surface separating the two fluids. In actual fact, the interface itself may be treated as a two-dimensional fluid and the equation of motion for the interface can be incorporated into the analysis.[6] The effect of surface tension, for example, may be treated rationally by this method. However, such a treatment is beyond the scope of this text, and we will limit ourselves to interfaces acting only as mathematical surfaces separating two fluids.

Returning now to the solution of Eqs. 5.6-39 through 5.6-42, we first integrate Eqs. 5.6-40 and 5.6-42 to obtain

$$p_I = -\rho_I g y + C_I(x) \qquad (5.6\text{-}47)$$

$$p_{II} = -\rho_{II} g y + C_{II}(x) \qquad (5.6\text{-}48)$$

Equation 5.6-46 may be expressed as

B.C. 1: $\qquad\qquad \mathbf{t}_{(i)}^{I} = \mathbf{t}_{(i)}^{II} \qquad y = 0 \qquad (5.6\text{-}49)$

or, in component form,

B.C. 1a: $\qquad\qquad T_{yx}^{I} = T_{yx}^{II} \qquad\qquad\qquad (5.6\text{-}50\text{a})$

B.C. 1b: $\qquad\qquad T_{yy}^{I} = T_{yy}^{II} \;\Big\} \quad y = 0 \qquad (5.6\text{-}50\text{b})$

B.C. 1c: $\qquad\qquad T_{yz}^{I} = T_{yz}^{II} \qquad\qquad\qquad (5.6\text{-}50\text{c})$

Referring to Eq. 5.1-6 we see that the component of the stress tensor, T_{yy}, is given by

$$T_{yy} = -p I_{yy} + \tau_{yy} \qquad (5.6\text{-}51)$$

Making use of Eq. 5.1-3 and the results given in Table 5.2-2, we express Eq. 5.6-51 as

$$T_{yy} = -p + 2\mu\left(\frac{\partial v_y}{\partial y}\right) \qquad (5.6\text{-}52)$$

We may now write boundary condition 1b as

$$-p_I + 2\mu_I\left(\frac{\partial v_y^{I}}{\partial y}\right) = -p_{II} + 2\mu_{II}\left(\frac{\partial v_y^{II}}{\partial y}\right), \quad y = 0 \qquad (5.6\text{-}53)$$

Noting that

$$v_y^{I} = v_y^{II} = 0 \qquad (5.6\text{-}54)$$

we may substitute Eqs. 5.6-47 and 5.6-48 into Eq. 5.6-53 to obtain

$$C_I(x) = C_{II}(x) \qquad (5.6\text{-}55)$$

6. R. Aris, *Vectors, Tensors, and the Basic Equations of Fluid Mechanics* (Englewood Cliffs, N.J.: Prentice-Hall, Inc., 1962), Chap. 10.

Equations 5.6-47 and 5.6-48 indicate that the pressure gradients, $\partial p_{\rm I}/\partial x$ and $\partial p_{\rm II}/\partial x$, are not functions of y. Because $v_x^{\rm I}$ and $v_x^{\rm II}$ are not functions of x, Eqs. 5.6-39 and 5.6-41 indicate that the pressure gradients must be constant, and the solutions of these two equations are

$$v_x^{\rm I} = -\left(\frac{\Delta p}{L}\right)\frac{y^2}{2\mu_{\rm I}} + A_{\rm I}y + B_{\rm I} \tag{5.6-56}$$

$$v_x^{\rm II} = -\left(\frac{\Delta p}{L}\right)\frac{y^2}{2\mu_{\rm II}} + A_{\rm II}y + B_{\rm II} \tag{5.6-57}$$

where

$$\left(\frac{\partial p_{\rm I}}{\partial x}\right) = \left(\frac{\partial p_{\rm II}}{\partial x}\right) = -\left(\frac{\Delta p}{L}\right)$$

The principle of continuity of velocity yields the following boundary conditions:

B.C. 2: $v_x^{\rm I} = 0, \qquad y = -h_{\rm I}$ (5.6-58a)

B.C. 3: $v_x^{\rm I} = v_x^{\rm II}, \qquad y = 0$ (5.6-58b)

B.C. 4: $v_x^{\rm II} = 0, \qquad y = h_{\rm II}$ (5.6-58c)

For a Newtonian fluid, boundary condition 1a becomes

B.C. 1a: $\mu_{\rm I}\left(\dfrac{\partial v_x^{\rm I}}{\partial y} + \dfrac{\partial v_y^{\rm I}}{\partial x}\right) = \mu_{\rm II}\left(\dfrac{\partial v_x^{\rm II}}{\partial y} + \dfrac{\partial v_y^{\rm II}}{\partial x}\right), \qquad y = 0$ (5.6-58d)

The four boundary conditions expressed by Eqs. 5.6-58 are used to determine the constants of integration as follows:

B.C. 2: $-\left(\dfrac{\Delta p}{L}\right)\dfrac{h_{\rm I}^2}{2\mu_{\rm I}} - A_{\rm I}h_{\rm I} + B_{\rm I} = 0$ (5.6-59)

B.C. 3: $B_{\rm I} = B_{\rm II}$ (5.6-60)

B.C. 4: $-\left(\dfrac{\Delta p}{L}\right)\dfrac{h_{\rm II}^2}{2\mu_{\rm II}} + A_{\rm II}h_{\rm II} + B_{\rm II} = 0$ (5.6-61)

B.C. 1a: $\mu_{\rm I}A_{\rm I} = \mu_{\rm II}A_{\rm II}$ (5.6-62)

Use of these four equations to evaluate the four constants of integration gives the velocity profiles for the two phases:

$$v_x^{\rm I} = \left(\frac{\Delta p}{L}\right)\frac{h_{\rm II}^2}{2\mu_{\rm I}}\left[\left(\frac{\mu_{\rm I}}{\mu_{\rm II}}\right) - \left(\frac{y}{h_{\rm II}}\right)^2\right] + \Omega\left[\left(\frac{y}{h_{\rm I}}\right) - \left(\frac{h_{\rm II}}{h_{\rm I}}\right)\left(\frac{\mu_{\rm I}}{\mu_{\rm II}}\right)\right] \tag{5.6-63}$$

$$v_x^{\rm II} = \left(\frac{\Delta p}{L}\right)\frac{h_{\rm II}^2}{2\mu_{\rm II}}\left[1 - \left(\frac{y}{h_{\rm II}}\right)^2\right] - \left(\frac{h_{\rm II}}{h_{\rm I}}\right)\left(\frac{\mu_{\rm I}}{\mu_{\rm II}}\right)\Omega\left[1 - \left(\frac{y}{h_{\rm II}}\right)\right] \tag{5.6-64}$$

where

$$\Omega = \frac{\left(\dfrac{\Delta p}{L}\right)\left(\dfrac{1}{2\mu_I}\right)\left(\dfrac{h_{II}^2}{\mu_{II}} - \dfrac{h_I^2}{\mu_I}\right)h_I}{\left(\dfrac{h_I}{\mu_I} + \dfrac{h_{II}}{\mu_{II}}\right)}$$

If the pressure drop Δp, length L, viscosities μ_I and μ_{II}, and fluid depths, h_I and h_{II} are given, Eqs. 5.6-63 and 5.6-64 may be used to calculate the velocity profiles and the flow rates. In practice, we are more likely to be supplied with the volumetric flow rates for fluids I and II and be asked to compute the pressure drop for a given system. This problem would require a trial and error solution where we assume values of h_I and h_{II}, allowing the pressure drop to be calculated by both Eq. 5.6-65 and 5.6-66.

$$q_I = \left(\frac{\Delta p}{L}\right)\frac{h_{II}^2}{2\mu_I}\left[\left(\frac{\mu_I}{\mu_{II}}\right) - \frac{1}{3}\left(\frac{h_I}{h_{II}}\right)^2\right]h_I + \Omega h_I\left[\frac{1}{2} + \frac{h_{II}}{h_I}\left(\frac{\mu_I}{\mu_{II}}\right)\right] \quad (5.6\text{-}65)$$

$$q_{II} = \left(\frac{\Delta p}{L}\right)\frac{h_{II}^2}{2\mu_{II}}\left(\frac{2h_{II}}{3}\right) - \frac{1}{2}\left(\frac{h_{II}}{h_I}\right)\left(\frac{\mu_I}{\mu_{II}}\right)\Omega h_{II} \quad (5.6\text{-}66)$$

Here, q_I and q_{II} are the volumetric flow rates per unit width of the channel. In general, the pressure drops will not be the same and new values of h_I and h_{II} must be assumed until the computed pressure drops are equal.

Flow in a Couette viscometer

In this example, we wish to determine the velocity distribution in the annular region and the torque acting on the inner cylinder for the system shown in Fig. 5.6-4. We start with the Navier-Stokes equations in cylindrical coordinates. If the flow is steady, and the annular region is considered to be infinite in the z-direction, the velocity components v_r and v_z are zero and the Navier-Stokes equations reduce to

1. r-direction:

$$-\rho\frac{v_\theta^2}{r} = -\left(\frac{\partial p}{\partial r}\right) \quad (5.6\text{-}67)$$

2. θ-direction:

$$0 = -\frac{1}{r}\left(\frac{\partial p}{\partial \theta}\right) + \mu\left[\frac{\partial}{\partial r}\left(\frac{1}{r}\frac{\partial}{\partial r}(rv_\theta)\right)\right] \quad (5.6\text{-}68)$$

3. z-direction:

$$0 = -\left(\frac{\partial p}{\partial z}\right) - \rho g \quad (5.6\text{-}69)$$

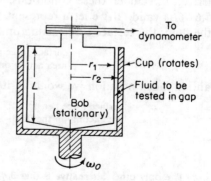

Fig. 5.6-4. Couette viscometer.

Inasmuch as

$$\int_{\theta}^{\theta+2\pi} \left(\frac{\partial p}{\partial \theta}\right) d\theta = 0 \qquad (5.6\text{-}70)$$

the pressure gradient in the θ-direction must be zero,† and Eq. 5.6-68 may be written as

$$\frac{d}{dr}\left(\frac{1}{r}\frac{d}{dr}(rv_\theta)\right) = 0 \qquad (5.6\text{-}71)$$

Integration gives

$$\frac{1}{r}\frac{d}{dr}(rv_\theta) = C_1 \qquad (5.6\text{-}72)$$

Multiplying by $r\,dr$ and integrating again, we get

$$v_\theta = \frac{C_1 r}{2} + \frac{C_2}{r} \qquad (5.6\text{-}73)$$

which is subject to the boundary conditions

B.C. 1: $\qquad\qquad v_\theta = 0, \qquad r = r_1 \qquad (5.6\text{-}74)$

B.C. 2: $\qquad\qquad v_\theta = r_2\omega_0, \qquad r = r_2 \qquad (5.6\text{-}75)$

Application of these boundary conditions yields the velocity distribution,

$$v_\theta = r\omega_0 \frac{\left[1 - \left(\frac{r_1}{r}\right)^2\right]}{\left[1 - \left(\frac{r_1}{r_2}\right)^2\right]} \qquad (5.6\text{-}76)$$

Although we have assumed that the annular region extends to infinity in the z-direction, it is, of course, not the case for any real Couette viscometer. In general, the viscometer is made such that $r_2 - r_1$ is much smaller than the length, L. Under these conditions, the end effects are negligible and Eq. 5.6-76 is valid. If we let **n** represent the outwardly directed unit normal for the fluid, the surface force acting on the fluid is given by

$$\begin{Bmatrix}\text{surface force per unit}\\ \text{area acting on the fluid}\end{Bmatrix} = \mathbf{t}_{(\mathbf{n})} \qquad (5.6\text{-}77)$$

and in index notation we would write

$$\begin{aligned}\begin{Bmatrix}\text{surface force per unit}\\ \text{area acting on the fluid}\end{Bmatrix} &= t_{(\mathbf{n})i} \\ &= n_j T_{ji} \qquad (5.6\text{-}78)\\ &= n_1 T_{1i} + n_2 T_{2i} + n_3 T_{3i}\end{aligned}$$

† The only other alternative is that $\partial p/\partial \theta$ takes on both positive and negative values in the region $0 \le \theta \le 2\pi$.

Remembering now that the expression $t_{(n)i} = n_j T_{ji}$ applies to curvilinear coordinates, provided we interpret the scalar components of vectors as projections on the tangent vectors to the coordinate curves, we may write

$$\begin{Bmatrix} \text{surface force per unit} \\ \text{area in the } \theta\text{-direction} \\ \text{acting on the fluid} \end{Bmatrix} = t_{(n)\theta} = n_r T_{r\theta} + n_\theta T_{\theta\theta} + n_z T_{z\theta} \qquad (5.6\text{-}79)$$

The components of the unit outwardly directed normal $\mathbf{n}$ at the surface of the inner cylinder are given by

$$n_r = -1, \qquad n_\theta = 0, \qquad n_z = 0 \qquad (5.6\text{-}80)$$

and we obtain

$$\begin{Bmatrix} \text{surface force per unit area} \\ \text{exerted by the inner cylinder} \\ \text{on the fluid in the } \theta\text{-direction} \end{Bmatrix} = -T_{r\theta} = -\tau_{r\theta}, \qquad r = r_1 \qquad (5.6\text{-}81)$$

The torque that the inner cylinder exerts on the fluid is

$$\mathscr{T}_z = \underbrace{-\tau_{r\theta}|_{r=r_1}}_{\text{Force/unit area}} \overbrace{(2\pi r_1 L)}^{\text{Area}} \underbrace{r_1}_{\text{Lever arm}} \qquad (5.6\text{-}82)$$

From Eq. (d) in Table 5.2-3, we obtain

$$\tau_{r\theta} = \mu \left[r \frac{\partial}{\partial r}\left(\frac{v_\theta}{r}\right) + \frac{1}{r}\frac{\partial v_r}{\partial \theta} \right] \qquad (5.6\text{-}83)$$

Thus,

$$\tau_{r\theta}\Big|_{r=r_1} = \mu \left[r \frac{d}{dr}\left(\frac{v_\theta}{r}\right) \right]_{r=r_1} = \frac{2\mu\omega_0}{\left[1 - \left(\dfrac{r_1}{r_2}\right)^2 \right]} \qquad (5.6\text{-}84)$$

and the torque is

$$\mathscr{T}_z = -\frac{4\pi\mu L r_1^2 \omega_0}{\left[1 - \left(\dfrac{r_1}{r_2}\right)^2 \right]} \qquad (5.6\text{-}85)$$

In this example, we treat the torque as a scalar. A rigorous treatment would formulate Eq. 5.6-82 as,

$$\mathscr{T} = \int_A \mathbf{r} \times \mathbf{t}_{(n)} \, dA \qquad (5.6\text{-}86)$$

but inasmuch as it requires taking the cross product of two vectors in cylindrical coordinates, it was not done.

PROBLEMS

5-1. (a) Show that $\delta_{ii} = 3$.
     (b) Show that $\delta_{ij}A_j = A_i$.

5-2. If $B_{11} = B_{22} = B_{33} = \frac{1}{2}$, $B_{12} = B_{21} = \frac{3}{2}$, $B_{31} = B_{13} = 1$, and $B_{32} = B_{23} = 0$, write out the nine components of the tensor A_{ij}, given that

$$A_{ij} = B_{ij} + \delta_{ij}$$

5-3. Prove, using Gibbs notation, that

$$(\mathbf{n} \cdot \mathbf{T}) \cdot \mathbf{b} = (\mathbf{b} \cdot \mathbf{T}) \cdot \mathbf{n}$$

provided **T** is symmetric. Expand both sides and show that they are equivalent.

5-4. Prove
$$\nabla \cdot (p\mathbf{I}) = \nabla p$$
using index notation.

5-5. A metal rod, shown in Fig. 5-5, is being stretched and compressed sinusoidally. The displacement Δx of the end of the rod is given by

$$\Delta x = -\tfrac{1}{2} \, \Delta L \, (\cos \omega t)$$

where

$$\Delta L \ll L$$

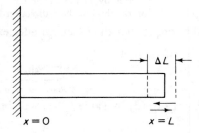

Fig. 5-5

If the displacement is a linear function of x, what is the rate of strain as a function of x and t?

5-6. Is the tensor $\nabla \mathbf{v}$ symmetric?

5-7. If $\boldsymbol{\lambda}$ is a tangent vector to a free surface, what is the value of $\boldsymbol{\lambda} \cdot \nabla p$ at the free surface?

5-8. A stirred tank such as that shown in Fig. 5-8 is a common device for blending or mixing two fluid streams. The rate of mixing depends on the propeller geometry and the size and number of baffles. In designing a mixer, one must weigh the cost of the original equipment versus the operating cost (i.e., power input). To do this, experiments must be performed to determine the power input as a function of propeller geometry and the baffling arrangement. What dimensionless groups

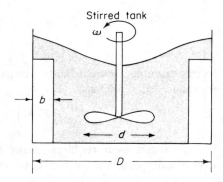

Stirred tank

Fig. 5-8

will the power input depend upon? *Assume:* (a) The propellers to be used in the experiments are all geometrically similar. (b) The number of baffles is fixed, but the size may vary. (c) A number of tank diameters are to be tested. (d) The height of the baffles remains constant; only the width b is varied.

5-9. Determine the Reynolds number and Froude number for the falling liquid film shown in Fig. 5-9; show that they cannot be specified independently.

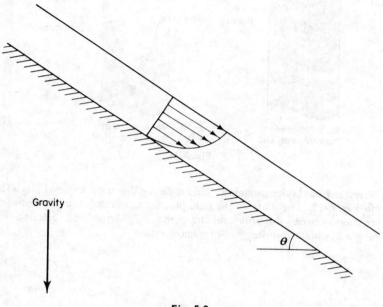

Gravity

θ

Fig. 5-9

Obtain the functional relationship between N_{Re} and N_{Fr}. Assume the flow is laminar and one-dimensional, and that q is given.

Ans: $N_{Fr} = N_{Re} \sin \theta / 3$

5-10. When two immiscible fluids, such as oil and water or water and air, are simultaneously pumped through a pipe, a variety of flow patterns may occur depending on the relative flow rates and the physical properties of the two fluids. Indicate what parameters you would fix in order to maintain dynamic similarity between a model system and an actual system. Surface tension effects are to be neglected, although this may be the most important effect for some systems.

5-11. A problem of some practical importance is the replacement of one fluid by another in a pipe. Such a situation is illustrated in Fig. 5-11, which shows the replacement taking place from the action of gravity. If viscous forces predominate (i.e., the left-hand side of the equations of motion is negligible), what parameters must be held constant to model this system? Neglect surface tension.

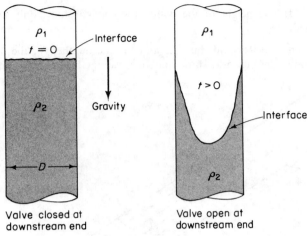

Fig. 5-11

5-12. A rectangular tank containing a fluid is sliding down the inclined plane shown
in Fig. 5-12. The mass of the fluid plus the tank is M, and the coefficient of
friction between the tank and the plane is ξ. Derive an expression for the
angle β, obtained during uniform acceleration.

Ans: $\beta = \tan^{-1} \xi$

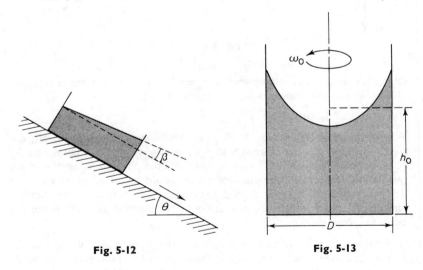

Fig. 5-12   **Fig. 5-13**

5-13. If a cylindrical tank of liquid is rotated at a constant angular velocity ω_0,
the free surface will assume some shape, such as that illustrated in Fig. 5-13.
Use the equations of motion in cylindrical coordinates to determine the
position of the surface. The fluid depth at rest is h_0.

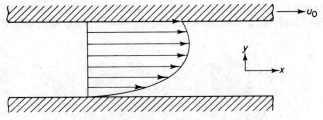

Fig. 5-14

5-14. Determine the velocity profile and the volumetric flow rate per unit width for the plane Couette flow illustrated in Fig. 5-14. The system consists of two parallel plates, the lower fixed and the upper moving at a velocity u_0. The applied pressure gradient $\partial p/\partial x$ is a constant. Determine the value of $\partial p/\partial x$ required to reduce the volumetric flow rate to zero, and sketch the velocity profile for this condition.

5-15. A film of water is flowing down a vertical wall as illustrated in Fig. 5-15. Specify how large the air gap h_{II} must be so that the effect of the air on the water velocity profile can be neglected.

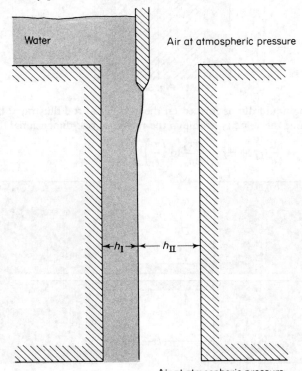

Fig. 5-15

5-16. Determine the magnitude and direction of the maximum normal viscous stress in Prob. 5-14—i.e., maximize τ_{nn} for the case of zero flow rate.

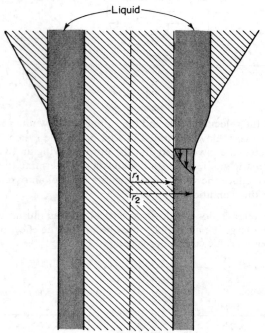

Fig. 5-17

5-17. A falling liquid film is formed on the cylindrical rod illustrated in Fig. 5-17. Determine the velocity profile in the region of one-dimensional flow.

$$Ans: v_z = \frac{\rho g}{4\mu}(r_1^2 - r^2) + \frac{\rho g r_2^2}{2\mu}\ln\left(\frac{r}{r_1}\right)$$

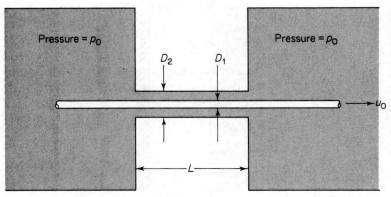

Fig. 5-18

5-18. A wire is pulled through a circular cylinder which connects two large chambers as shown in Fig. 5-18. The two chambers are maintained at a constant pressure, p_0. Derive an expression for the volumetric flow rate between the two chambers, and an expression for the force required to pull the wire through the cylinder.

5-19. If inertial effects can be neglected and the flow is two-dimensional, show that the stream function ψ defined in Sec. 3.6 must satisfy the biharmonic equation,

$$\frac{\partial^4 \psi}{\partial x^4} + 2 \frac{\partial^4 \psi}{\partial x^2 \, \partial y^2} + \frac{\partial^4 \psi}{\partial y^4} = 0$$

5-20. Given a tensor

$$A_{ij} = \begin{pmatrix} 5 & 3 & 1 \\ 3 & 7 & 2 \\ 3 & 4 & 3 \end{pmatrix}$$

write out in matrix form the components of the symmetric and skew symmetric tensors into which A_{ij} can be decomposed.

5-21. A long circular cylinder of radius r_0 rotates with an angular velocity ω_0 in an infinite fluid. Determine the velocity profile.

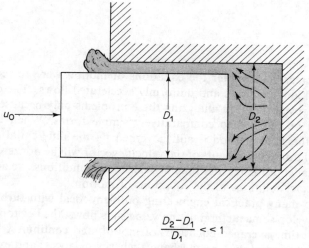

$$\frac{D_2 - D_1}{D_1} << 1$$

Fig. 5-22

5-22. If the velocity of the cylindrical ram shown in Fig. 5-22 is a constant u_0, determine the force which must be applied to the ram as a function of time. Assume that viscous effects predominate and the flow in the annular region may be approximated by steady, one-dimensional flow. In computing the force, remember to include both viscous and pressure forces, keeping in mind that you cannot obtain an exact solution.

Turbulent Flow 6

In the preceding chapter the equations of motion were solved for one-dimensional laminar flows and uniformly accelerated flows. The differential equations proved useful in analyzing these problems only because the equations could be reduced to comparatively simple forms. When the flow is turbulent, the fluid motion is still governed by the differential equations; however, all three components of the velocity vector will be nonzero functions of the spatial coordinates and time. Under these conditions, we are not able to obtain exact solutions to the equations of motion.

Since so many practical engineering problems deal with turbulent flow, we must develop some method of analyzing such flows, the key tools of which will be: the time-averaged equations of motion and continuity; the macroscopic mass, momentum, and mechanical energy balances; and experimental or empirical friction factors and drag coefficients. We will first deal with the time-averaged equations of motion and then present a qualitative description of turbulent flow. Chapter 7 is devoted to the formulation of the macroscopic balances and their application to problems where viscous effects may be neglected. Chapter 8 deals with the definition of friction factors and drag coefficients and the application of the macroscopic balances to problems where viscous effects are important.

*6.1   Time Averages

We *define* the time average of some function S at a time t as

$$\bar{S} = \frac{1}{2\,\Delta t} \int_{t-\Delta t}^{t+\Delta t} S\,dt \tag{6.1-1}$$

The time interval Δt is *arbitrary*, but in general we would hope that Δt could be made large enough so that $\bar{S}$ is independent of Δt. The dependence of $\bar{S}$ on Δt is illustrated in Fig. 6.1-1, where Δt^* depends on the nature of the

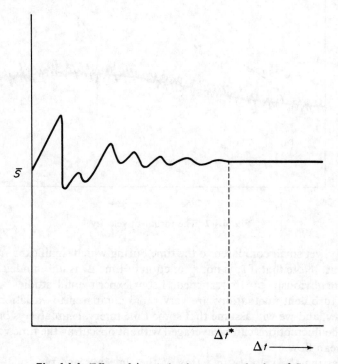

Fig. 6.1-1. Effect of Δt on the time-averaged value of S.

function S. Not all quantities have meaningful time averages in that $\bar{S}$ is independent of Δt; however, the components of velocity and pressure do possess meaningful averages for turbulent flows in closed conduits and around immersed bodies. For other cases, such as atmospheric turbulence, it may not hold true, and the analysis presented in this section would not be valid.

If we measured one component of the velocity in a slowly changing turbulent stream, the result might look like the curve in Fig. 6.1-2, where the average velocity $\bar{v}_z$ changes only slowly with time compared to the fluctuating component v_z'. To separate the velocity into an average value and a fluctuating value, we require that Δt be large enough for us to average the fluctuations

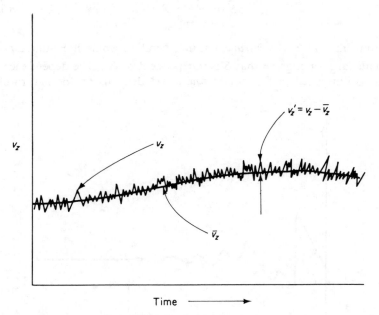

Fig. 6.1-2. The turbulent velocity.

effectively, yet small compared to the time during which significant variations in $\bar{v}_z$ occur. Note that if $\bar{v}_z$ is not a function of time Δt is unbounded and this condition obviously can be satisfied. From experimental studies we know that the turbulent fluctuations are very rapid compared to variations in the mean flow, and we will assume that some time interval can always be chosen so that the fluctuations can be averaged without obscuring the time variations of the mean flow.

Expressing the velocity in terms of the time average plus a fluctuating component,

$$v_z = \bar{v}_z + v_z' \tag{6.1-2}$$

and substituting into Eq. 6.1-1, we have

$$\bar{v}_z = \frac{1}{2\,\Delta t} \int_{t-\Delta t}^{t+\Delta t} v_z\, dt = \frac{1}{2\,\Delta t} \int_{t-\Delta t}^{t+\Delta t} (\bar{v}_z + v_z')\, dt \tag{6.1-3}$$

In the time interval $2 \Delta t$, the time-averaged velocity may be considered constant, and Eq. 6.1-3 reduces to

$$\bar{v}_z = \bar{v}_z + \frac{1}{2 \Delta t} \int_{t-\Delta t}^{t+\Delta t} v_z' \, dt \qquad (6.1\text{-}4)$$

We thus see that the time average of the fluctuation is zero.

$$\overline{v_z'} = 0 \qquad (6.1\text{-}5)$$

However, the average of the square of the fluctuation is not zero, and the quantity

$$\frac{\sqrt{\overline{(v_z')^2}}}{\bar{v}_z}$$

is used as a convenient measure of the magnitude of the turbulent fluctuations. It is known as the "intensity of turbulence" and ranges from approximately 0.01 to 0.10 for most turbulent flows. The percentage turbulence is defined by

$$\text{percentage turbulence} = 100 \times \frac{\sqrt{\overline{(v_z')^2}}}{\bar{v}_z} \qquad (6.1\text{-}6)$$

and is therefore in the neighborhood of 1 to 10 per cent.

*6.2 Time-Averaged Equations of Continuity and Motion

Continuity equation

Restricting ourselves to incompressible flows, we write the continuity equation as

$$\boldsymbol{\nabla} \cdot \mathbf{v} = 0 \qquad (6.2\text{-}1)$$

Writing the velocity vector in terms of the time average and fluctuating components,

$$\mathbf{v} = \bar{\mathbf{v}} + \mathbf{v}' \qquad (6.2\text{-}2)$$

allows us to write Eq. 6.2-1 as

$$\boldsymbol{\nabla} \cdot \bar{\mathbf{v}} + \boldsymbol{\nabla} \cdot \mathbf{v}' = 0 \qquad (6.2\text{-}3)$$

Taking the time average yields

$$\frac{1}{2 \Delta t} \int_{t-\Delta t}^{t+\Delta t} \boldsymbol{\nabla} \cdot \bar{\mathbf{v}} \, dt + \frac{1}{2 \Delta t} \int_{t-\Delta t}^{t+\Delta t} \boldsymbol{\nabla} \cdot \mathbf{v}' \, dt = 0 \qquad (6.2\text{-}4)$$

We may change the order of differentiation and integration to obtain

$$\boldsymbol{\nabla}\cdot\left[\frac{1}{2\,\Delta t}\int_{t-\Delta t}^{t+\Delta t}\bar{\mathbf{v}}\,dt\right]+\boldsymbol{\nabla}\cdot\left[\frac{1}{2\,\Delta t}\int_{t-\Delta t}^{t+\Delta t}\mathbf{v}'\,dt\right]=0 \qquad (6.2\text{-}5)$$

Since the second integral is zero by definition and the first integral yields the time-averaged velocity vector, the time-averaged continuity equation is

$$\boldsymbol{\nabla}\cdot\bar{\mathbf{v}}=0 \qquad (6.2\text{-}6)$$

and from Eq. 6.2-3 we note that

$$\boldsymbol{\nabla}\cdot\mathbf{v}'=0 \qquad (6.2\text{-}7)$$

Following the discussion in Sec. 3.6, we may use the time-averaged velocity vector to define a time-averaged streamline given by

$$\frac{dx}{\bar{v}_x}=\frac{dy}{\bar{v}_y}=\frac{dz}{\bar{v}_z} \qquad (6.2\text{-}8)$$

Equations of motion

Starting with the Navier-Stokes equations

$$\rho\left(\frac{\partial\mathbf{v}}{\partial t}+\mathbf{v}\cdot\boldsymbol{\nabla}\mathbf{v}\right)=-\boldsymbol{\nabla}p+\rho\mathbf{g}+\mu\,\nabla^2\mathbf{v} \qquad (6.2\text{-}9)$$

we form the time average to obtain

$$\rho\left(\frac{1}{2\,\Delta t}\int_{t-\Delta t}^{t+\Delta t}\left(\frac{\partial\mathbf{v}}{\partial t}\right)dt+\frac{1}{2\,\Delta t}\int_{t-\Delta t}^{t+\Delta t}(\mathbf{v}\cdot\boldsymbol{\nabla}\mathbf{v})\,dt\right)$$
$$=-\frac{1}{2\,\Delta t}\int_{t-\Delta t}^{t+\Delta t}\boldsymbol{\nabla}p\,dt+\rho\mathbf{g}+\frac{1}{2\,\Delta t}\int_{t-\Delta t}^{t+\Delta t}\mu\,\nabla^2\mathbf{v}\,dt \qquad (6.2\text{-}10)$$

In analyzing Eq. 6.2-10, we shall start with the term farthest to the right and work steadily to the left, thereby dealing with the easiest terms first. Starting with the viscous term, we change the order of differentiation and integration to obtain

$$\frac{1}{2\,\Delta t}\int_{t-\Delta t}^{t+\Delta t}\mu\,\nabla^2\mathbf{v}\,dt=\mu\,\nabla^2\left[\frac{1}{2\,\Delta t}\int_{t-\Delta t}^{t+\Delta t}\mathbf{v}\,dt\right]=\mu\,\nabla^2\bar{\mathbf{v}} \qquad (6.2\text{-}11)$$

Similarly, the pressure term reduces to

$$\frac{1}{2\,\Delta t} \int\limits_{t-\Delta t}^{t+\Delta t} \nabla p \, dt = \nabla \bar{p} \tag{6.2-12}$$

In treating the nonlinear, convective acceleration term, we must express the velocity in terms of $\bar{\mathbf{v}}$ and $\mathbf{v}'$

$$\frac{1}{2\,\Delta t} \int\limits_{t-\Delta t}^{t+\Delta t} \mathbf{v} \cdot \nabla \mathbf{v} \, dt = \frac{1}{2\,\Delta t} \int\limits_{t-\Delta t}^{t+\Delta t} (\bar{\mathbf{v}} + \mathbf{v}') \cdot \nabla(\bar{\mathbf{v}} + \mathbf{v}') \, dt \tag{6.2-13a}$$

and expand the result to obtain

$$\frac{1}{2\,\Delta t} \int\limits_{t-\Delta t}^{t+\Delta t} \mathbf{v} \cdot \nabla \mathbf{v} \, dt = \frac{1}{2\,\Delta t} \int\limits_{t-\Delta t}^{t+\Delta t} \bar{\mathbf{v}} \cdot \nabla \bar{\mathbf{v}} \, dt \qquad \text{(a)}$$

$$+ \frac{1}{2\,\Delta t} \int\limits_{t-\Delta t}^{t+\Delta t} \mathbf{v}' \cdot \nabla \bar{\mathbf{v}} \, dt \quad \text{(b)}$$

$$\tag{6.2-13b}$$

$$+ \frac{1}{2\,\Delta t} \int\limits_{t-\Delta t}^{t+\Delta t} \bar{\mathbf{v}} \cdot \nabla \mathbf{v}' \, dt \quad \text{(c)}$$

$$+ \frac{1}{2\,\Delta t} \int\limits_{t-\Delta t}^{t+\Delta t} \mathbf{v}' \cdot \nabla \mathbf{v}' \, dt \quad \text{(d)}$$

Starting with term (a) on the right-hand side of Eq. 6.2-13b, we need only comment that time-average terms are essentially constant in the period $2\,\Delta t$; thus,

$$\frac{1}{2\,\Delta t} \int\limits_{t-\Delta t}^{t+\Delta t} \bar{\mathbf{v}} \cdot \nabla \bar{\mathbf{v}} \, dt = \bar{\mathbf{v}} \cdot \nabla \bar{\mathbf{v}} \tag{6.2-14a}$$

Term (b) can be handled by removing the *tensor* $\nabla \bar{\mathbf{v}}$ from the integral to obtain

$$\frac{1}{2\,\Delta t} \int\limits_{t-\Delta t}^{t+\Delta t} \mathbf{v}' \cdot \nabla \bar{\mathbf{v}} \, dt = \left[\frac{1}{2\,\Delta t} \int\limits_{t-\Delta t}^{t+\Delta t} \mathbf{v}' \, dt \right] \cdot \nabla \bar{\mathbf{v}} = 0 \tag{6.2-14b}$$

since the time average of the fluctuating component is zero. Term (c) is treated in a similar manner by removing the *scalar operator* $\bar{\mathbf{v}} \cdot \nabla$ from the integral.

$$\frac{1}{2\,\Delta t} \int_{t-\Delta t}^{t+\Delta t} \bar{\mathbf{v}} \cdot \nabla \mathbf{v}'\, dt = \bar{\mathbf{v}} \cdot \nabla \left[\frac{1}{2\,\Delta t} \int_{t-\Delta t}^{t+\Delta t} \mathbf{v}'\, dt \right] = 0 \qquad (6.2\text{-}14c)$$

Term (d) represents the turbulent convective transport, and for the present we simply express this term as

$$\frac{1}{2\,\Delta t} \int_{t-\Delta t}^{t+\Delta t} \mathbf{v}' \cdot \nabla \mathbf{v}'\, dt = \overline{\mathbf{v}' \cdot \nabla \mathbf{v}'} \qquad (6.2\text{-}14d)$$

In treating the remaining term in Eq. 6.2-10, we must proceed carefully, paying proper attention to the use of dummy variables of integration. What we wish to prove here is that the *average of the derivative is equal to the derivative of the average*. This statement has a great deal of intuitive appeal, and, because the proof is a bit laborious, the student may simply wish to scan the development quickly and move directly to Eq. 6.2-23. Expressing the integral properly in terms of a dummy variable of integration, we find

$$\frac{1}{2\,\Delta t} \int_{t-\Delta t}^{t+\Delta t} \frac{\partial \mathbf{v}}{\partial t}\, dt = \frac{1}{2\,\Delta t} \int_{\eta=t-\Delta t}^{\eta=t+\Delta t} \frac{\partial \mathbf{v}}{\partial \eta}\, d\eta \qquad (6.2\text{-}15)$$

Carrying out the integration yields an expression for the average of the derivative,

$$\frac{1}{2\,\Delta t} \int_{t-\Delta t}^{t+\Delta t} \left(\frac{\partial \mathbf{v}}{\partial t} \right) dt = \frac{1}{2\,\Delta t} \left(\mathbf{v}|_{t+\Delta t} - \mathbf{v}|_{t-\Delta t} \right) \qquad \begin{array}{l}\text{The average}\\ \text{of the}\\ \text{derivative}\end{array} \qquad (6.2\text{-}16)$$

We now turn our attention to the derivative of the average.

$$\frac{\partial \bar{\mathbf{v}}}{\partial t} = \frac{\partial}{\partial t} \left\{ \frac{1}{2\,\Delta t} \int_{\eta=t-\Delta t}^{\eta=t+\Delta t} \mathbf{v}\, d\eta \right\} \qquad \begin{array}{l}\text{The derivative}\\ \text{of the average}\end{array} \qquad (6.2\text{-}17)$$

In this part of the analysis, we must remember that Δt is a *parameter* and not a variable. Expressing the derivative in terms of its definition yields

$$\frac{\partial \bar{\mathbf{v}}}{\partial t} = \lim_{\delta t \to 0} \frac{\displaystyle\int_{\eta=t-\Delta t+\delta t}^{\eta=t+\Delta t+\delta t} \mathbf{v}\, d\eta - \int_{\eta=t-\Delta t-\delta t}^{\eta=t+\Delta t-\delta t} \mathbf{v}\, d\eta}{(2\delta t)\,(2\,\Delta t)} \qquad (6.2\text{-}18)$$

We must keep in mind that we are simply expressing the derivative of some function $f(t)$ as

$$\frac{\partial f}{\partial t} = \lim_{\delta t \to 0} \left[\frac{f(t + \delta t) - f(t - \delta t)}{2\delta t} \right] \qquad (6.2\text{-}19)$$

The limits of integration in Eq. 6.2-18 may be rearranged by a series of steps to yield

$$\frac{\partial \bar{\mathbf{v}}}{\partial t} = \lim_{\delta t \to 0} \frac{\displaystyle\int_{\eta = t + \Delta t - \delta t}^{\eta = t + \Delta t + \delta t} \mathbf{v}\, d\eta \;-\; \int_{\eta = t - \Delta t - \delta t}^{\eta = t - \Delta t + \delta t} \mathbf{v}\, d\eta}{(2\delta t)\,(2\,\Delta t)} \qquad (6.2\text{-}20)$$

Applying the mean value theorem to these two integrals gives

$$\frac{\partial \bar{\mathbf{v}}}{\partial t} = \lim_{\delta t \to 0} \left\{ \frac{(2\delta t)\mathbf{v}\big|_{t + \Delta t + \alpha \delta t} - (2\delta t)\mathbf{v}\big|_{t - \Delta t + \beta \delta t}}{(2\delta t)\,(2\,\Delta t)} \right\} \qquad (6.2\text{-}21)$$

where α and β lie between ± 1. Cancelling the factor of $2\delta t$ and taking the limit, we get

$$\frac{\partial \bar{\mathbf{v}}}{\partial t} = \frac{1}{2\,\Delta t}\left(\mathbf{v}\big|_{t + \Delta t} - \mathbf{v}\big|_{t - \Delta t} \right) \qquad \begin{array}{l}\text{The derivative}\\ \text{of the average}\end{array} \qquad (6.2\text{-}22)$$

Comparison of Eqs. 6.2-16 and 6.2-22 indicates that the average of the derivative is equal to the derivative of the average, and we write

$$\frac{1}{2\,\Delta t} \int_{t - \Delta t}^{t + \Delta t} \frac{\partial \mathbf{v}}{\partial t}\, dt = \frac{\partial \bar{\mathbf{v}}}{\partial t} \qquad (6.2\text{-}23)$$

Collection of all the terms contained in Eqs. 6.2-11 through Eq. 6.2-23 yields the time-averaged equations of motion.

$$\rho\left(\frac{\partial \bar{\mathbf{v}}}{\partial t} + \bar{\mathbf{v}} \cdot \nabla \bar{\mathbf{v}} \right) = -\nabla \bar{p} + \rho \mathbf{g} + \mu \nabla^2 \bar{\mathbf{v}} - \rho \overline{\mathbf{v}' \cdot \nabla \mathbf{v}'} \qquad (6.2\text{-}24)$$

We see that this result has precisely the same form as the Navier-Stokes equation with the exception of the term $\rho \overline{\mathbf{v}' \cdot \nabla \mathbf{v}'}$. Our next task is to show that this term can be represented as the divergence of a tensor, i.e.,

$$\rho \overline{\mathbf{v}' \cdot \nabla \mathbf{v}'} = \nabla \cdot (\rho \overline{\mathbf{v}'\, \mathbf{v}'}) \qquad (6.2\text{-}25)$$

We can prove Eq. 6.2-25 by expanding both sides and showing that they are equivalent; however, the proof can be obtained easily using index notation. To do so, we first express Eq. 6.2-7 in index notation

$$\frac{\partial v_i'}{\partial x_i} = 0 \qquad (6.2\text{-}26)$$

and then analyze the right-hand side of Eq. 6.2-25 using index notation and disregarding the time-averaging.

$$\frac{\partial}{\partial x_i}(\rho v_i' v_j') = \rho v_i' \frac{\partial v_j'}{\partial x_i} + v_j' \frac{\partial}{\partial x_i}(\rho v_i') \qquad (6.2\text{-}27)$$

Here, we have simply used the rule for differentiating a product of two functions. Since we are only treating incompressible flows, the second term on the right-hand side of Eq. 6.2-27 is zero by Eq. 6.2-26

$$v_j' \frac{\partial}{\partial x_i}(\rho v_i') = \rho v_j' \left(\frac{\partial v_i'}{\partial x_i}\right) = 0 \qquad (6.2\text{-}28)$$

and our proof is complete.

Index notation
$$\frac{\partial}{\partial x_i}(\rho v_i' v_j') = \rho v_i' \left(\frac{\partial v_j'}{\partial x_i}\right)$$

$$\qquad (6.2\text{-}29)$$

Gibbs notation
$$\boldsymbol{\nabla} \cdot (\rho \mathbf{v}' \, \mathbf{v}') = \rho \mathbf{v}' \cdot \boldsymbol{\nabla} \mathbf{v}'$$

We now define the turbulent stress tensor

$$\bar{\boldsymbol{\tau}}^{(t)} = -\rho \overline{\mathbf{v}' \, \mathbf{v}'} \qquad (6.2\text{-}30)$$

and write the time-averaged equations of motion as

$$\rho \left(\frac{\partial \bar{\mathbf{v}}}{\partial t} + \bar{\mathbf{v}} \cdot \boldsymbol{\nabla} \bar{\mathbf{v}}\right) = -\boldsymbol{\nabla} \bar{p} + \rho \mathbf{g} + \mu \nabla^2 \bar{\mathbf{v}} + \boldsymbol{\nabla} \cdot \bar{\boldsymbol{\tau}}^{(t)} \qquad (6.2\text{-}31)$$

The terms represented by $\rho \overline{\mathbf{v}' \, \mathbf{v}'}$ are often called the Reynolds stresses,[1] for it was Reynolds who first applied the Navier-Stokes in deriving the general equations of motion for turbulent flow.

Returning to Chap. 5, we note from Eqs. 5.4-1 and 5.4-10 that the viscous term may be written

$$\mu \nabla^2 \mathbf{v} = \boldsymbol{\nabla} \cdot \boldsymbol{\tau} \qquad (6.2\text{-}32)$$

and the time-averaged form is

$$\mu \nabla^2 \bar{\mathbf{v}} = \boldsymbol{\nabla} \cdot \bar{\boldsymbol{\tau}} \qquad (6.2\text{-}33)$$

Substitution of Eq. 6.2-33 into Eq. 6.2-31 yields the time-averaged stress equations of motion

$$\rho \left(\frac{\partial \bar{\mathbf{v}}}{\partial t} + \bar{\mathbf{v}} \cdot \boldsymbol{\nabla} \bar{\mathbf{v}}\right) = -\boldsymbol{\nabla} \bar{p} + \rho \mathbf{g} + \boldsymbol{\nabla} \cdot \bar{\boldsymbol{\tau}}^{(T)} \qquad (6.2\text{-}34)$$

where the total time-averaged stress tensor $\bar{\boldsymbol{\tau}}^{(T)}$ is simply the sum of the time-averaged molecular stress tensor and the turbulent stress tensor,

$$\bar{\boldsymbol{\tau}}^{(T)} = \bar{\boldsymbol{\tau}} + \bar{\boldsymbol{\tau}}^{(t)} \qquad (6.2\text{-}35)$$

1. O. Reynolds, "On the Dynamical Theory of Incompressible Viscous Fluids and the Determination of the Criterion," *Phil. Trans. Roy. Soc.* (*London*) *Ser. A*1, 1895, 186:123.

This result indicates that we may treat time-averaged turbulent flows in the same way that we treat laminar flows, provided the pressure and velocity are replaced by the time-averaged quantities, and the viscous stress tensor with the total time-averaged stress tensor. If we could specify $\bar{\tau}^{(t)}$ in terms of gradients of $\bar{v}$ in a manner analogous to Newton's law of viscosity, we could calculate turbulent velocity profiles in just the same manner as we did laminar flow. It would require a constitutive equation for turbulent flow; however, we now have at our disposal only empirical expressions for $\bar{\tau}^{(t)}$, which must be used in conjunction with experimental data to determine velocity profiles. Even though we do not know how to evaluate $\bar{\tau}^{(t)}$ a priori, it is extremely important to know that the time-averaged equations take the form indicated by Eqs. 6.2-6 and 6.2-34. These will be key points to keep in mind when we derive and apply the macroscopic balances.

*6.3   A Qualitative Description of Turbulent Flow

As we illustrated in Chap. 1 with a burning cigarette, most flows can be classified as either laminar or turbulent. The onset of turbulence, or the transition from laminar to turbulent flow, is an active area of current research and rather difficult to discuss in a quantitative manner. The transition is closely related to the Reynolds number, which may be considered the ratio of inertial forces, ρu_0^2, to viscous forces, $\mu u_0 / L$.

$$N_{\text{Re}} = \frac{\rho u_0 L}{\mu} = \frac{\rho u_0^2}{\dfrac{\mu u_0}{L}} = \frac{\text{inertial force per unit area}}{\text{viscous force per unit area}} \qquad (6.3\text{-}1)$$

At Reynolds numbers greater than about 2×10^3, most flows in closed conduits become unstable, which means that any small disturbance in the flow will tend to become larger and the laminar velocity profile is destroyed by the growth of turbulent eddies. When the flow becomes turbulent, the drag force that the fluid exerts on solid surfaces increases sharply, and a larger pressure drop is required to maintain a given flow rate. The Reynolds number is not the sole criterion for predicting the onset of turbulence. Accelerating flows (i.e., flows in a converging section of conduit) are more stable than decelerating flows. Indeed, a transition to turbulent flow can take place in a diverging section of conduit at Reynolds numbers far below the value of 2×10^3. This fact should not be particularly surprising, because we know that the velocity is a function of the independent variables (x, y, z, and t), the parameters appearing in the equations of motion (N_{Re}), and the parameters appearing in the boundary conditions. In a diverging or converging conduit, a parameter indicating the rate of change of cross-sectional area will appear in the boundary conditions; thus, we should expect the transition to turbulence to be affected by this parameter.

Turbulent flow in a tube

When the flow is laminar and the fluid is Newtonian, the velocity profile in a tube is

$$v_z = v_{z,\max}\left[1 - \left(\frac{r}{r_0}\right)^2\right] \tag{6.3-2}$$

Although we cannot compute the velocity profile directly for turbulent flow, we can obtain experimental measurements of the time-averaged velocity and the fluctuating components. A representative curve for the velocity is shown in Fig. 6.3-1 based on the approximate expression

$$\bar{v}_z = \bar{v}_{z,\max}\left(1 - \frac{r}{r_0}\right)^{1/7} \tag{6.3-3}$$

Equation 6.3-3 could not be used to predict the shear stress at the tube wall, because the derivative of $\bar{v}_z$ with respect to r tends to infinity as $r \to r_0$.

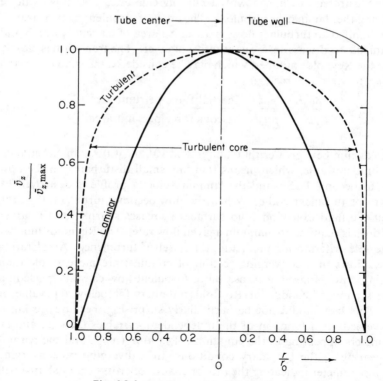

Fig. 6.3-1. Laminar and turbulent velocity profiles.

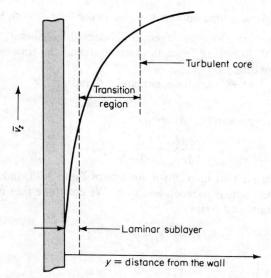

Fig. 6.3-2. Laminar sublayer and transition region in a tube.

Nevertheless, it is a reasonably accurate expression of the turbulent velocity profile.

In the central region of the tube, the velocity fluctuations are large and the turbulent stress far exceeds the viscous stress—i.e.,

$$\bar{\tau}^{(t)} \gg \bar{\tau} \quad \text{In the core} \tag{6.3-4}$$

Since the velocity fluctuations are zero at the wall,

$$-\overline{\rho \mathbf{v}' \, \mathbf{v}'} = \bar{\tau}^{(t)} = 0 \quad \text{At the wall} \tag{6.3-5}$$

there must be a transition region where turbulent and viscous stresses are comparable. The region outside the core can be arbitrarily divided into two regions, as shown in Fig. 6.3-2.

Stresses in turbulent tube flow

If we examine the time-averaged stress equation of motion in the z-direction for cylindrical coordinates, we obtain, from Table 5.1-2,

$$\rho\left(\frac{\partial \bar{v}_z}{\partial t} + \bar{v}_r \frac{\partial \bar{v}_z}{\partial r} + \frac{\bar{v}_\theta}{r}\frac{\partial \bar{v}_z}{\partial \theta} + \bar{v}_z \frac{\partial \bar{v}_z}{\partial z}\right)$$

$$= -\left(\frac{\partial \bar{p}}{\partial z}\right) + \rho g_z + \left[\frac{1}{r}\frac{\partial}{\partial r}(r\bar{\tau}_{rz}^{(T)}) + \frac{1}{r}\frac{\partial \bar{\tau}_{\theta z}^{(T)}}{\partial \theta} + \frac{\partial \bar{\tau}_{zz}^{(T)}}{\partial z}\right] \tag{6.3-6}$$

Following the analysis for laminar flow, we make four assumptions:

1. $\bar{v}_r = \bar{v}_\theta = 0$, the time-averaged flow is one-dimensional;
2. $\partial \bar{v}_z / \partial z = 0$, following from assumption 1 and the time-averaged continuity equation;
3. $\bar{\tau}_{\theta z}^{(T)}$, $\bar{\tau}_{zz}^{(T)}$, and $\bar{\tau}_{zr}^{(T)}$ are independent of θ and z;
4. $g_z = 0$.

Equation 6.3-5 immediately reduces to

$$\left(\frac{\partial \bar{p}}{\partial z}\right) = \frac{1}{r}\frac{\partial}{\partial r}(r\bar{\tau}_{rz}^{(T)}) \qquad (6.3\text{-}7)$$

Once again we argue that the right-hand side of Eq. 6.3-7 is independent of z while the left-hand side is independent of r. We conclude that both sides are equal to a constant and write

$$-\frac{\Delta \bar{p}}{L} = \frac{1}{r}\frac{d}{dr}(r\bar{\tau}_{rz}^{(T)}) \qquad (6.3\text{-}8)$$

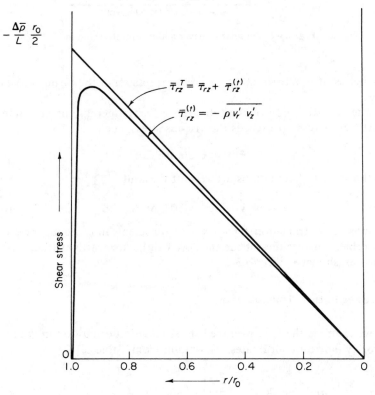

Fig. 6.3-3. Total shear stress and turbulent shear stress for flow in a tube.

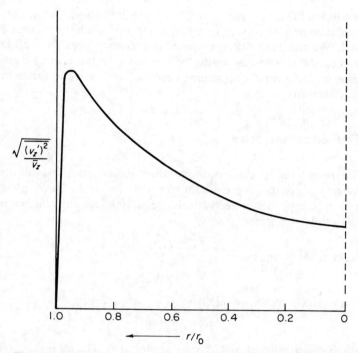

Fig. 6.3-4. Variation of intensity of turbulence with radial position.

where $\Delta\bar{p}$ is the time-average pressure difference and L is the length of the tube. We have again neglected entrance and end effects in obtaining this result. Integration and application of the boundary condition

$$\text{B.C. 1:}\quad \bar{\tau}_{rz}^{(T)} \text{ is finite for } 0 \leq r \leq r_0 \qquad (6.3\text{-}9)$$

yields an equation for the total time-average shear stress

$$\bar{\tau}_{rz}^{(T)} = \bar{\tau}_{rz} + \bar{\tau}_{rz}^{(t)} = -\left(\frac{\Delta\bar{p}}{L}\right)\frac{r}{2} \qquad (6.3\text{-}10)$$

Thus, the total shear stress distribution is determined by measurement of the pressure drop.

Experimental studies of the turbulent shear stress,

$$\bar{\tau}_{rz}^{(t)} = -\rho\overline{v_r' v_z'} \qquad (6.3\text{-}11)$$

have been made by a number of investigators, and illustrative results are shown in Fig. 6.3-3. The variation of intensity of turbulence is illustrated in Fig. 6.3-4. We find from these two figures that the turbulent shear stress predominates in the core region and falls to zero at the wall. We also discover that the maximum intensity of turbulence and turbulent shear stress is near $r/r_0 = 0.9$. We conclude that turbulence is generated near the wall and the intensity falls off toward the center of the tube. In the central region, the generating force (shear deformation) decreases and viscous forces tend to reduce the intensity.

6.4   The Eddy Viscosity

An interesting intuitive description of the turbulent stress may be obtained by proposing a constitutive equation for $\bar{\tau}^{(t)}$ similar to Newton's law of viscosity. In Chap. 5 the constitutive equation for an incompressible Newtonian fluid was stated as

$$\tau = 2\mu \mathbf{d} \tag{6.4-1}$$

The time-average form is

$$\bar{\tau} = 2\mu \bar{\mathbf{d}} \tag{6.4-2}$$

By analogy (albeit poor), we might write

$$\bar{\tau}^{(t)} = 2\mu^{(t)} \bar{\mathbf{d}} \tag{6.4-3}$$

thus defining the turbulent or "eddy" viscosity, $\mu^{(t)}$. The total time-averaged stress tensor is now given by

$$\bar{\tau}^{(T)} = \bar{\tau} + \bar{\tau}^{(t)} = 2(\mu + \mu^{(t)}) \bar{\mathbf{d}} \tag{6.4-4}$$

The eddy viscosity is not a very useful quantity for analysis, but it helps to develop a qualitative feel for the nature of turbulent flow. The constitutive equation, Eq. 6.4-1, is a postulated relationship between the stress and the rate of deformation, and experiments show that μ is indeed a constant for a large class of fluids. On the other hand, $\mu^{(t)}$ is not a constant but depends on position and on the intensity of turbulence. In this section, we shall make use of an empirical expression for $\mu^{(t)}$ to analyze the turbulent velocity profile in a tube.

Prandtl's mixing length theory

Prandtl's mixing length theory[2] was one of the first attempts at a semi-theoretical analysis of turbulent flow. The arguments leading to its development are not very precise, but they are useful in developing a qualitative understanding of the mechanism of turbulent momentum transfer. We now

2. L. Prandtl, "Investigations on Turbulent Flow," *Zamm*, 1925, 5:136.

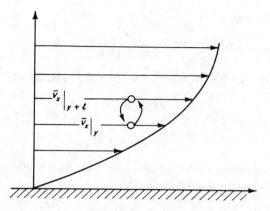

Fig. 6.4-1. Turbulent momentum transfer.

consider the steady (on the average), one-dimensional flow illustrated in Fig. 6.4-1. If we assume that discrete "lumps" or particles of fluid can move from one position to another and still retain their momenta during this motion, then the net rate of momentum transfer for the process shown in the figure is

$$\begin{Bmatrix} x\text{-momentum transferred} \\ \text{across a } y\text{-surface} \end{Bmatrix} = M\bar{v}_x\Big|_{y+\ell} - M\bar{v}_x\Big|_y \tag{6.4-5}$$

where the mass M of the two fluid particles must be the same if the flow is incompressible. The turbulent shear stress, $\bar{\tau}_{yx}^{(t)}$, will depend on the rate at which this transfer takes place, and the y-surface area over which the transfer occurs. Thus†,

$$\begin{Bmatrix} \text{force per} \\ \text{unit area} \end{Bmatrix} = \begin{Bmatrix} \text{momentum transferred per} \\ \text{unit time per unit area} \end{Bmatrix}. \tag{6.4-6}$$

and we write

$$\bar{\tau}_{yx}^{(t)} = \frac{M}{\Delta t\,\Delta A}\left(\bar{v}_x\Big|_{y+\ell} - \bar{v}_x\Big|_y\right) \tag{6.4-7}$$

where Δt is the average time required for the process to take place and ΔA is the average area associated with the transfer. It is easy to imagine that Δt and ΔA are dependent on the structure of the turbulence, i.e., on the magnitude and frequency of the velocity fluctuations. Making use of the first term of a Taylor series expansion for $\bar{v}_x$ gives,

$$\bar{v}_x\Big|_{y+\ell} \approx \bar{v}_x\Big|_y + \ell\left(\frac{d\bar{v}_x}{dy}\right) \tag{6.4-8}$$

† This expression follows from the linear momentum principle; however, the connection is not obvious, and the student must wait until the macroscopic momentum balance is derived in Chap. 7 before he can understand this result clearly.

and Eq. 6.4-7 becomes

$$\bar{\tau}_{yx}^{(t)} = \frac{M\ell}{\Delta t\,\Delta A}\left(\frac{d\bar{v}_x}{dy}\right) \tag{6.4-9}$$

We can carry the analysis further by writing the mass M as

$$M = \rho\,\Delta V \tag{6.4-10}$$

and the volume ΔV as

$$\Delta V = c\ell\,\Delta A \tag{6.4-11}$$

where c is an unknown dimensionless constant. Substitution of Eqs. 6.4-10 and 6.4-11 into Eq. 6.4-9 gives

$$\bar{\tau}_{yx}^{(t)} = \left(\frac{c}{\Delta t}\right)\rho\ell^2\left(\frac{d\bar{v}_x}{dy}\right) \tag{6.4-12}$$

We can go no further, for there is no a priori knowledge of the constant c or the time interval over which the transfer takes place. However, we do know from experimental data that the turbulent shear stress tends to be large when the velocity gradient is large, and small when the velocity gradient is small. This fact, of course, does not hold at the wall where the velocity gradient is a maximum and the turbulent shear stress is zero; yet the Prandtl mixing length theory in effect states

$$\left(\frac{c}{\Delta t}\right) = \left|\frac{d\bar{v}_x}{dy}\right| \tag{6.4-13}$$

and Eq. 6.4-12 takes the form

$$\bar{\tau}_{yx}^{(t)} = \rho\ell^2\left|\frac{d\bar{v}_x}{dy}\right|\left(\frac{d\bar{v}_x}{dy}\right) \tag{6.4-14}$$

This equation defines the mixing length ℓ in terms of experimentally determined values of $\bar{\tau}_{yx}^{(t)}$ and $\left(\frac{d\bar{v}_x}{dy}\right)$. The general tensor form of Eq. 6.4-14 is

$$\bar{\tau}^{(t)} = \left\{2\rho\ell^2\sqrt{2\bar{\mathbf{d}}:2\bar{\mathbf{d}}}\right\}\bar{\mathbf{d}} \tag{6.4-15}$$

which leads to an eddy viscosity given by

$$\mu^{(t)} = \rho\ell^2\sqrt{2\bar{\mathbf{d}}:\bar{\mathbf{d}}} \tag{6.4-16}$$

If ℓ were a constant, or depended upon $\bar{\mathbf{d}}$ in a simple manner, this result would be very useful. However, neither is true, and the Prandtl mixing length theory is of limited value.

6.5 Turbulent Flow in a Tube

In this section, we will apply the Prandtl mixing length theory to the problem of turbulent flow in a tube. If the time-averaged flow is steady and gravity is neglected, the stress equation of motion integrates to†

$$\bar{\tau}_{rz}^{(T)} = -\left(\frac{\Delta \bar{p}}{L}\right)\frac{r}{2} \tag{6.5-1}$$

Use of Eq. 6.4-4 to determine $\bar{\tau}_{rz}^{(T)}$ yields

$$2(\mu + \mu^{(t)})\,\bar{d}_{rz} = -\left(\frac{\Delta \bar{p}}{L}\right)\frac{r}{2} \tag{6.5-2}$$

If we examine the time-averaged rate of strain tensor in cylindrical coordinates (see Table 5.2-1) we find only two nonzero components

$$\bar{d}_{rz} = \bar{d}_{zr} = \frac{1}{2}\left(\frac{d\bar{v}_z}{dr}\right) \tag{6.5-3}$$

and the eddy viscosity given by Eq. 6.4-16 is

$$\mu^{(t)} = \rho \ell^2 \sqrt{\left(\frac{d\bar{v}_z}{dr}\right)^2} \tag{6.5-4}$$

Substitution of Eqs. 6.5-3 and 6.5-4 into Eq. 6.5-2 yields

$$\left[\mu + \rho \ell^2 \sqrt{\left(\frac{d\bar{v}_z}{dr}\right)^2}\,\right]\frac{d\bar{v}_z}{dr} = -\left(\frac{\Delta \bar{p}}{L}\right)\frac{r}{2} \tag{6.5-5}$$

Following Prandtl, we let y be the distance measured from the wall,

$$y = r_0 - r \tag{6.5-6}$$

and let the mixing length be a linear function of y,

$$\ell = \alpha y \tag{6.5-7}$$

where α will be chosen to give the best agreement between the analysis and experimental data. The form chosen for the mixing length is purely intuitive; however, it does satisfy the requirement that the turbulent shear stress become zero at the wall. Noting that

$$r = r_0 - y \quad \text{and} \quad \frac{d}{dr} = -\frac{d}{dy}$$

† See Eqs. 6.3-6 through 6.3-10.

we may write Eq. 6.5-5

$$\mu\left(\frac{d\bar{v}_z}{dy}\right) + \rho\alpha^2 y^2 \left(\frac{d\bar{v}_z}{dy}\right)^2 = \frac{\Delta\bar{p}}{L}\left(\frac{r_0 - y}{2}\right) \tag{6.5-8}$$

which is a rather difficult, first-order, ordinary differential equation to solve, requiring the use of either an analogue or a digital computer. However, we may obtain a reasonably satisfactory solution by recognizing that the laminar sublayer and turbulent core are two fairly distinct regions where the viscous and turbulent stresses predominate, respectively. In what follows, we in effect "shrink" the transition region to a cylindrical surface located at $y = y^*$.

We assume that there is a region close to the wall such that

$$\mu \gg \mu^{(t)} \quad \text{for} \quad 0 \leq y \leq y^* \tag{6.5-9}$$

where $y^* \ll r_0$. In this region, Eq. 6.5-8 becomes, approximately,

$$\mu\left(\frac{d\bar{v}_z}{dy}\right) = \frac{\Delta\bar{p}}{L}\frac{r_0}{2}, \qquad r_0 - y \approx r_0 \tag{6.5-10}$$

Integration and application of the boundary condition

B.C. 1: $\bar{v}_z = 0, \qquad y = 0 \tag{6.5-11}$

yields the solution for the velocity profile near the wall.

$$\bar{v}_z = \left(\frac{\Delta\bar{p}}{L}\right)\frac{r_0 y}{2\mu}, \qquad 0 \leq y \leq y^* \tag{6.5-12}$$

We now assume that

$$\mu \ll \mu^{(t)}, \qquad \text{for } y^* \leq y \leq r_0 \tag{6.5-13}$$

which, of course, implies a discontinuity in the eddy viscosity at $y = y^*$. Such a discontinuity is not allowed on physical principles; however, $\mu^{(t)}$ does change very rapidly in the transition region, and it is not too unsatisfactory to approximate this change by a discontinuity.

In the second region we write Eq. 6.5-8 as

$$\rho\alpha^2 y^2 \left(\frac{d\bar{v}_z}{dy}\right)^2 = \left(\frac{\Delta\bar{p}}{L}\right)\left(\frac{r_0 - y}{2}\right), \qquad y^* \leq y \leq r_0 \tag{6.5-14a}$$

or

$$\frac{d\bar{v}_z}{dy} = \left[\frac{\Delta\bar{p}}{2L\rho\alpha^2}\left(\frac{r_0 - y}{y^2}\right)\right]^{1/2}, \qquad y^* \leq y \leq r_0 \tag{6.5-14b}$$

Integration gives

$$\bar{v}_z = \left(\frac{\Delta\bar{p}}{2L\rho\alpha^2}\right)^{1/2} \int_{\eta=y^*}^{\eta=y} \frac{(r_0 - \eta)^{1/2}}{\eta}\, d\eta + C_1, \qquad y^* \leq y \leq r_0 \tag{6.5-15}$$

where η is a dummy variable of integration. To determine the constant of integration C_1, we require that the velocity be a continuous function over the entire region, $0 \leq y \leq r_0$. Equating Eqs. 6.5-12 and 6.5-15 at $y = y^*$ allows us to evaluate the constant C_1, and the velocity profile is then given by Eq. 6.5-12 and

$$\bar{v}_z = \left(\frac{\Delta\bar{p}}{2L\rho\alpha^2}\right)^{1/2} \int_{\eta=v^*}^{\eta=v} \frac{(r_0 - \eta)^{1/2}}{\eta}\, d\eta + \left(\frac{\Delta\bar{p}}{L}\right)\frac{r_0 y^*}{2\mu}, \qquad y^* \leq y \leq r_0$$

$$(6.5\text{-}16)$$

Let us review briefly our attack on this problem. We started with the stress equations of motion, which for this case reduce to Eq. 6.3-8. We introduced a constitutive equation, Eq. 6.4-4, and a semitheoretical equation, Eq. 6.4-16, for the eddy viscosity. We obtained a differential equation, Eq. 6.5-8, for the velocity $\bar{v}_z$, which contained a single undetermined parameter α, and the undetermined distance, y^*.

A comparison of the solution to this differential equation with experimental data perhaps could be used to test the Prandtl mixing length theory and to specify the parameters α and y^*; however, with two adjustable parameters it is quite likely that even an unsatisfactory theory could be made to fit experimental data reasonably well.

To obtain a solution to this equation without expending a great deal of effort, we need to evaluate the integral in Eq. 6.5-16. We can do so numerically or graphically for any value of y; however, by assuming

$$(r_0 - \eta)^{1/2} \approx r_0^{1/2} \qquad (6.5\text{-}17)$$

we can obtain an algebraic solution for the velocity and compare it with experimental data. This approximation cannot be valid near the center of the tube, but it is not a bad approximation over a limited portion of the turbulent core. For example, if $\eta = 0.3r_0$, then

$$(r_0 - \eta)^{1/2} = r_0^{1/2}(0.7)^{1/2} = 0.84 r_0^{1/2} \approx r_0^{1/2} \qquad (6.5\text{-}18)$$

Since this value of η takes us well into the turbulent core, we can expect the solution to predict satisfactorily the velocity profile from the wall into the turbulent core. On the basis of Eq. 6.5-17, the velocity is given by

$$\bar{v}_z = \left(\frac{\Delta\bar{p}}{L}\right)\frac{r_0 y}{2\mu}, \qquad 0 \leq y \leq y^* \qquad (6.5\text{-}19\text{a})$$

$$\bar{v}_z = \left(\frac{\Delta\bar{p}\, r_0}{2L\rho\alpha^2}\right)^{1/2} \ln\left(\frac{y}{y^*}\right) + \left(\frac{\Delta\bar{p}}{L}\right)\frac{r_0 y^*}{2\mu}, \qquad y^* \leq y \leq 0.3r_0 \quad (6.5\text{-}19\text{b})$$

We now define the wall shear stress as,

$$\tau_0 = \frac{\Delta\bar{p}}{L}\frac{r_0}{2} = -\bar{\tau}_{rz}^{(T)}\Big|_{r=r_0} \qquad (6.5\text{-}20)$$

Thus, τ_0 is the shear stress that the fluid exerts *on* the wall. Noting that $\sqrt{\tau_0/\rho}$ has the units of velocity, and that v, the kinematic viscosity, has the units of length times velocity, we may define a dimensionless velocity, v^+, as

$$v^+ = \frac{\bar{v}_z}{\sqrt{\dfrac{\tau_0}{\rho}}} \tag{6.5-21}$$

and a dimensionless distance, y^+, as

$$y^+ = \frac{y\sqrt{\dfrac{\tau_0}{\rho}}}{v} \tag{6.5-22}$$

Equations 6.5-19a and b are now written in dimensionless form as

$$v^+ = y^+, \qquad 0 \le y^+ \le y_0^+ \tag{6.5-23a}$$

$$v^+ = \frac{1}{\alpha}\ln\left(\frac{y^+}{y_0^+}\right) + y_0^+, \qquad y_0^+ \le y^+ \le \frac{0.3r_0\sqrt{\dfrac{\tau_0}{\rho}}}{v} \tag{6.5-23b}$$

where

$$y_0^+ = \frac{y^*\sqrt{\dfrac{\tau_0}{\rho}}}{v}$$

These results may be compared with the experimental work of Deissler[3] and Laufer[4] for turbulent velocity distributions in tubes. The results are shown in Fig. 6.5-1 for $\alpha = 0.36$ and $y_0^+ = 10.0$. We see that for $y^+ < 5.0$, Eq. 6.5-23a represents the data quite well. This region is that of the laminar sublayer where $\mu \gg \mu^{(t)}$. The analysis also agrees well with the data for $y^+ > 25$. We may assume, therefore, that the transition zone occupies the region $5 < y^+ < 25$, and we did not expect to get good agreement in this region.

More extensive and detailed treatments of this problem are available elsewhere.[5-6] Most important is that at present there exists no theoretical treatment of turbulent flow which would provide a generally valid constitutive equation relating the turbulent shear stress, $\bar{\tau}^{(t)}$, to the time-average rate of strain tensor, $\bar{\mathbf{d}}$. For this reason, we must always make use of some experimental information to solve turbulent flow problems.

3. R. G. Deissler, *NACA Tech. Note* 3016, 1953.
4. J. Laufer, *NACA Tech. Note* 2954, 1953.
5. R. B. Bird, W. E. Stewart, and E. N. Lightfoot, *Transport Phenomena* (New York: John Wiley and Sons, Inc., 1960), Chap. 5.
6. H. Schlichting, *Boundary Layer Theory*, 4th ed. (New York: McGraw-Hill Book Company, Inc., 1960), Chap. 20.

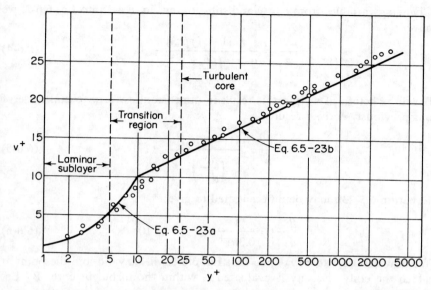

Fig. 6.5-1. Comparison of Prandtl mixing length theory with experimental data.

6.6 Relative Magnitude of Molecular and Eddy Viscosity

We may gain some insight into the relative magnitude of turbulent momentum transport by examining the ratio $\mu^{(t)}/\mu$ for flow in a tube. This is best done by starting with

$$\bar{\tau}_{rz}^{(T)} = \bar{\tau}_{rz} + \bar{\tau}_{rz}^{(t)} = [\mu + \mu^{(t)}]\frac{d\bar{v}_z}{dr} \qquad (6.6\text{-}1)$$

and rearranging to obtain

$$\frac{\mu^{(t)}}{\mu} = \frac{1}{\mu}\frac{[\bar{\tau}_{rz} + \bar{\tau}_{rz}^{(t)}]}{\left(\dfrac{d\bar{v}_z}{dr}\right)} - 1 \qquad (6.6\text{-}2)$$

By Eqs. 6.3-10 and 6.5-20, the stress may be written as

$$[\bar{\tau}_{rz} + \bar{\tau}_{rz}^{(t)}] = -\frac{\Delta\bar{p}}{L}\frac{r}{2} = -\tau_0\left(\frac{r}{r_0}\right) \qquad (6.6\text{-}3)$$

Changing variables from r to y and substituting Eq. 6.6-3 into Eq. 6.6-2, we have

$$\frac{\mu^{(t)}}{\mu} = \frac{1}{\mu} \frac{\tau_0 \left[1 - (y/r_0)\right]}{\left(\dfrac{d\bar{v}_z}{dy}\right)} - 1 \tag{6.6-4}$$

It will be helpful if we put this result in dimensionless form to make use of our previously derived results.

$$\frac{\mu^{(t)}}{\mu} = \frac{\left[1 - (y/r_0)\right]}{\left(\dfrac{dv^+}{dy^+}\right)} - 1 \tag{6.6-5}$$

Equation 6.5-23b may be differentiated to give

$$\frac{dv^+}{dy^+} = \frac{1}{0.36 y^+}, \qquad y^+ \geq 10 \tag{6.6-6}$$

We now choose y to be $r_0/4$, so that Eq. 6.6-6 will be valid and the point at which the eddy viscosity is evaluated is within the turbulent core. By Eq. 6.5-22,

$$y^+ = \left(\frac{r_0}{4}\right) \frac{\sqrt{\dfrac{\tau_0}{\rho}}}{\nu} \tag{6.6-7}$$

and we may write Eq. 6.6-5 as

$$\frac{\mu^{(t)}}{\mu} = \left(\frac{3}{4}\right)(0.36)\left(\frac{r_0}{4}\right) \frac{\sqrt{\dfrac{\tau_0}{\rho}}}{\nu} - 1 \tag{6.6-8}$$

To examine this result for a particular case, we must make use of some information discussed more thoroughly in Chap. 8. There we find that the shear stress at the wall is given approximately by

$$\tau_0 = \frac{0.039 \rho \langle \bar{v}_z \rangle^2}{N_{\text{Re}}^{1/3}} \quad \text{for} \quad 2.1 \times 10^3 \leq N_{\text{Re}} \leq 10^5 \tag{6.6-9}$$

Substituting Eq. 6.6-9 into Eq. 6.6-8 and carrying out the arithmetic, we find

$$\frac{\mu^{(t)}}{\mu} \approx N_{\text{Re}}^{7/8} \times 10^{-2} \tag{6.6-10}$$

For Reynolds numbers in the range from 10^3 to 10^5, the ratio of eddy viscosity to molecular viscosity ranges from 10 to 10^3. From this example, we learn that molecular momentum transport is generally negligible compared to the turbulent momentum transport in the core region.

PROBLEMS

6-1. Given a velocity

$$v_z = u_0(1 + bt + ct^2)$$

where b and c are constants having units of $\sec^{-1}$ and $\sec^{-2}$ respectively, compute the time-average velocity by means of Eq. 6.1-1. Indicate what range of values Δt may take (in terms of b and c) so that it is permissible to make the statement that $\bar{v}_z$ is "essentially constant in the period 2 Δt." Do this by comparing the average of the average $\bar{\bar{v}}_z$ with the average $\bar{v}_z$ and requiring that they be within 1 per cent of each other.

Ans: $\Delta t \leq [0.03(1 + bt + ct^2)/c]^{1/2}$

6-2. Prove that

$$\frac{1}{2\,\Delta t} \int_{t-\Delta t}^{t+\Delta t} \mathbf{v}' \cdot \nabla \bar{\mathbf{v}}\, dt = 0$$

by expanding the integrand into the scalar components and integrating.

6-3. Prove that

$$\mathbf{v} \cdot \nabla \mathbf{v} = \nabla \cdot (\mathbf{vv})$$

for incompressible flows by expanding both sides and showing that they are equal. The expression for the divergence of a tensor is given by Eq. 4.4-11. Note that the scalar components of the tensor $\mathbf{vv}$ are $v_x v_x$, $v_x v_y$, etc.

6-4. Put Eq. 6.2-24 in dimensionless form in order to determine what parameter (exclusive of those occurring in the boundary conditions) $\bar{\mathbf{v}}$ should depend upon.

6-5. Apply dimensional analysis to the flow in the diverging circular conduit shown in Fig. 6-5. Show that the velocity depends upon both N_{Re} and the angle α. Thus one can expect the transition from laminar to turbulent flow to depend upon both N_{Re} and α.

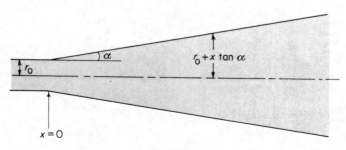

Fig. 6-5

6-6. Put Eq. 6.5-8 in dimensionless form in terms of v^+ and y^+ and integrate numerically for values of α ranging from 0.3 to 0.5. Compare the results with the approximate solution given in the text.
Note: This problem requires some careful analysis, in addition to the use of a digital computer.

6-7. Using the approximation

$$\bar{v}_z = \bar{v}_{z,\max}\left(1 - \frac{r}{r_0}\right)^{1/7}$$

for water at 70°F flowing in a smooth 2-in. diameter tube at an average velocity of 6 ft/sec, compute
(a) The total shear stress at $r/r_0 = 0.9$
(b) The fraction of this shear stress due to the turbulent stress.
Note: Use Eq. 6.6-9 to compute the wall shear stress, τ_0.

6-8. Water at 70°F is flowing in a 6-in. diameter pipe with an average velocity of 48 ft/sec. Find the thickness of the laminar sublayer.

6-9. Assuming Eq. 6.5-23b can be used to determine the velocity from the laminar sublayer to the center of the tube,

$$v^+ = \frac{1}{\alpha}\ln\left(\frac{y^+}{y_0^+}\right) + y_0^+, \qquad y_0^+ \le y^+ \le \frac{r_0\sqrt{\tau_0/\rho}}{\nu}$$

derive a relationship between the friction factor f and the Reynolds number N_{Re}. Neglect the flow in the region $0 \le y^+ \le y_0^+$ in carrying out this calculation, and simplify your result for large values of $r_0\sqrt{\tau_0/\rho}/\nu$. Express the friction factor as

$$f = 4\tau_0/\tfrac{1}{2}\rho\langle\bar{v}_z\rangle^2$$

6-10. Derive the time-averaged form of the continuity equation for compressible flow. Keep in mind that the density may be a function of both time and the spatial coordinates.

Macroscopic Balances: Inertial Effects

7

In Chap. 5, we formulated the differential equations of motion and applied them to some simple laminar flows. In Chap. 6, we investigated turbulent flow, and it became apparent that we could not obtain exact solutions of the time-averaged equations of motion for even the simplest turbulent flows. In this chapter, we will formulate the macroscopic (or integral) mass, momentum, and mechanical energy balances. An exact solution of these macroscopic equations will provide us with results which are correct "on the average." Thus, we will be able to compute total forces and total flow rates while the pressure distribution and velocity profile—i.e., the details of the flow topology—will remain undetermined by the analysis. We shall also derive Bernoulli's equation giving us another useful equation for obtaining approximate solutions to complex flow problems.

After deriving these equations, we shall apply them to a variety of flows where inertial effects predominate but cannot completely explain observed results. The application of the macroscopic balances to flows where viscous effects must be considered will be covered in Chap. 8. It may seem unreasonable to split up our study of the macroscopic balances in this way; however, we encounter two distinct problems in applying these balances: determination of fluxes of mass, momentum, and energy at the entrances and exits of the control volume; determination of the forces which act upon the surfaces of the control volume. In Chap. 7, we deal with the first problem in addition to treating pressure forces, while the detailed discussion of the second is left until Chap. 8.

The student should be forewarned that the methods to be studied in this chapter, and subsequent ones, are approximate; in general, there will be no "right" answers. There will often, however, be a "best" answer, and as often as possible we shall try to determine the best answer by comparing our results with experiments. In attacking this chapter, we should remember that the macroscopic balances are perhaps the most powerful tool the engineer possesses for solving the often ill-defined problems of everyday practice. Judicious application of these equations comes only with experience and practice. At best, the student can hope to understand the development of the equations and gain some insight regarding the difficulties that may be encountered in their application.

*7.1   The Macroscopic Mass Balance

To develop a completely general form of the macroscopic mass balance, we will apply the principle of conservation of mass to the arbitrary volume $\mathscr{V}_a(t)$ illustrated in Fig. 7.1-1. Remember that points on the surface of this volume move with a velocity $\mathbf{w}$ which may be a function of the spatial coordinates and time. The continuity equation,

$$\frac{\partial \rho}{\partial t} + \nabla \cdot (\rho \mathbf{v}) = 0 \tag{7.1-1}$$

holds at every point in space; thus, we may integrate Eq. 7.1-1 over the volume $\mathscr{V}_a(t)$ to obtain

$$\int_{\mathscr{V}_a(t)} \left[\frac{\partial \rho}{\partial t} + \nabla \cdot (\rho \mathbf{v})\right] dV = 0 \tag{7.1-2}$$

This equation, in effect, represents the macroscopic mass balance, but it is of little use to us in this form. The following steps are not aimless mathematical manipulation but necessary steps in the development of an equation useful in solving problems.

Application of the divergence theorem allows us to write the second term under the integral as an area integral to obtain

$$\int_{\mathscr{V}_a(t)} \left(\frac{\partial \rho}{\partial t}\right) dV + \int_{\mathscr{A}_a(t)} \rho \mathbf{v} \cdot \mathbf{n} \, dA = 0 \tag{7.1-3}$$

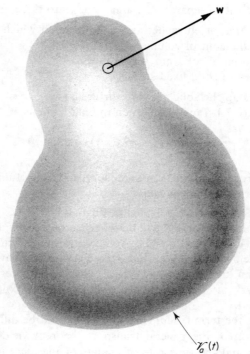

Fig. 7.1-1. Arbitrary moving control volume.

We now make use of the general transport theorem by letting the scalar S in Eq. 3.4-16 be the density, ρ, which gives

$$\frac{d}{dt} \int_{\mathscr{V}_a(t)} \rho \, dV = \int_{\mathscr{V}_a(t)} \left(\frac{\partial \rho}{\partial t}\right) dV + \int_{\mathscr{A}_a(t)} \rho \mathbf{w} \cdot \mathbf{n} \, dA \qquad (7.1\text{-}4)$$

It should be clearly understood that Eq. 7.1-4 is a mathematical relationship and is not related to the physical principle of conservation of mass. The volume integral of $(\partial \rho/\partial t)$ in Eq. 7.1-3 may now be substituted into Eq. 7.1-4 to give

$$\frac{d}{dt} \int_{\mathscr{V}_a(t)} \rho \, dV = - \int_{\mathscr{A}_a(t)} \rho \mathbf{v} \cdot \mathbf{n} \, dA + \int_{\mathscr{A}_a(t)} \rho \mathbf{w} \cdot \mathbf{n} \, dA \qquad (7.1\text{-}5)$$

Putting the two terms on the right-hand side under the same integral sign, and rearranging the equation, we get

$$\frac{d}{dt} \int_{\mathscr{V}_a(t)} \rho \, dV + \int_{\mathscr{A}_a(t)} \rho(\mathbf{v} - \mathbf{w}) \cdot \mathbf{n} \, dA = 0 \qquad (7.1\text{-}6)$$

It will be convenient to separate the area $\mathscr{A}_a(t)$ into three areas:

1. $A_e(t)$, the area of entrances and exits through which fluid may enter and leave the control volume;
2. $A_s(t)$, the area of solid moving surfaces;
3. A_s, the area of solid fixed surfaces.

Since $\mathbf{v} - \mathbf{w} = 0$ on the solid moving surfaces, and $\mathbf{v} = \mathbf{w} = 0$ on the solid fixed surfaces, Eq. 7.1-6 may be written in final form as

$$\frac{d}{dt}\int_{\mathscr{V}_a(t)} \rho \, dV + \int_{A_e(t)} \rho(\mathbf{v} - \mathbf{w}) \cdot \mathbf{n} \, dA = 0 \qquad (7.1\text{-}7)$$

Although this process has been relatively simple, it is helpful in understanding the development to review the steps.

1. The physical principle is stated in Eq. 7.1-1.
2. Integration is performed to obtain a macroscopic equation, Eq. 7.1-2.
3. The term $\nabla \cdot (\rho\mathbf{v})$ in Eq. 7.1-2 would be rather difficult to evaluate for the problems we have in mind, so we applied the divergence theorem to yield an area integral of $\rho\mathbf{v} \cdot \mathbf{n}$. This term represents a mass flux and is very often precisely the quantity that is known or must be determined.
4. Similarly, the term $(\partial\rho/\partial t)$ in Eq. 7.1-2 would be difficult to evaluate. Application of the general transport theorem yielded another mass flux term and the time rate of change of the *mass in control volume*, which is often the quantity to be calculated or is specified by the nature of the problem.

The point is that practical reasons exist for arranging the macroscopic balance in the form indicated by Eq. 7.1-7.

In words, Eq. 7.1-7 may be written as

$$\begin{Bmatrix} \text{time rate of change} \\ \text{of the mass of the} \\ \text{control volume} \end{Bmatrix} - \begin{Bmatrix} \text{mass flux} \\ \text{into the} \\ \text{control volume} \end{Bmatrix} + \begin{Bmatrix} \text{mass flux} \\ \text{out of the} \\ \text{control volume} \end{Bmatrix} = 0 \qquad (7.1\text{-}8)$$

which is the same statement used in Sec. 3.5 for the alternate derivation of the continuity equation. Equation 7.1-8 is valid for any arbitrary volume; thus, it naturally applies to the differential cube illustrated in Fig. 3.5-2.

Special forms

Very often we will want to apply the macroscopic mass balance to a control volume fixed in space. Under this condition, $\mathbf{w} = 0$ and we write

$$\frac{d}{dt}\int_{\mathscr{V}} \rho \, dV + \int_{A_e} \rho\mathbf{v} \cdot \mathbf{n} \, dA = 0 \qquad \begin{matrix} \text{Control volume} \\ \text{fixed in space} \end{matrix} \qquad (7.1\text{-}9)$$

where $A_e(t)$ has been replaced by A_e and $\mathscr{V}_a(t)$ by $\mathscr{V}$ to indicate that the volume is fixed in space. Because the spatial coordinates are held constant in this case, the total derivative may be written as a partial derivative and the order of differentiation and integration changed to give

$$\int_{\mathscr{V}} \left(\frac{\partial \rho}{\partial t}\right) dV + \int_{A_e} \rho \mathbf{v} \cdot \mathbf{n} \, dA = 0 \qquad (7.1\text{-}10)$$

For incompressible flows, $(\partial \rho / \partial t) = 0$, and Eq. 7.1-10 reduces to

$$\int_{A_e} \rho \mathbf{v} \cdot \mathbf{n} \, dA = 0 \qquad \begin{array}{l}\text{Incompressible flow,}\\ \text{control volume} \\ \text{fixed in space}\end{array} \qquad (7.1\text{-}11)$$

The velocity $\mathbf{w}$ is arbitrary and we may set it equal to the fluid velocity, $\mathbf{v}$. The area integral in Eq. 7.1-7 is then zero, and we obtain

$$\frac{d}{dt} \int_{\mathscr{V}_a(t)} \rho \, dV = 0 \quad \text{for} \quad \mathbf{w} = \mathbf{v} \qquad (7.1\text{-}12)$$

However, the arbitrary volume $\mathscr{V}_a(t)$ is now a material volume $\mathscr{V}_m(t)$, and Eq. 7.1-12 should be written

$$\frac{D}{Dt} \int_{\mathscr{V}_m(t)} \rho \, dV = 0 \qquad (7.1\text{-}13)$$

which is our original statement of the principle of conservation of mass.

Removal of liquid from a cylindrical hole

As an illustration of the application of Eq. 7.1-7 we will analyze the system shown in Fig. 7.1-2. A rod of diameter D_0 is being forced into a cylindrical hole of diameter D_1 and length L. The velocity of the rod is constant at u_0 and the flow is to be treated as incompressible. We wish to derive an expression for the average velocity in the annular region. Since the density is constant, Eq. 7.1-7 may be written as

$$\frac{d\mathscr{V}_a(t)}{dt} + \int_{A_e(t)} (\mathbf{v} - \mathbf{w}) \cdot \mathbf{n} \, dA = 0 \qquad (7.1\text{-}14)$$

The only entrance or exit is the cross-sectional area of the annulus at $z = 0$. At that surface, the outwardly directed unit normal to the control volume is

$$\mathbf{n} = -\mathbf{k} \qquad (7.1\text{-}15)$$

and since $\mathbf{w} = 0$, we write

$$(\mathbf{v} - \mathbf{w}) \cdot \mathbf{n} = \mathbf{v} \cdot (-\mathbf{k}) = -v_z \quad \text{at} \quad z = 0 \qquad (7.1\text{-}16)$$

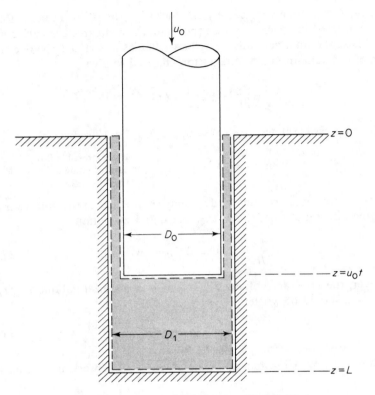

Fig. 7.1-2. Removal of fluid from a cylindrical hole.

Substitution of Eq. 7.1-16 into Eq. 7.1-14 and expression of the area integral in terms of the average velocity times the area give

$$\frac{d\mathscr{V}_a(t)}{dt} - \langle v_z \rangle \left[\frac{\pi}{4} (D_1^2 - D_0^2) \right] = 0 \qquad (7.1\text{-}17)$$

Substitution of the expression for $\mathscr{V}_a(t)$,

$$\mathscr{V}_a(t) = \tfrac{1}{4}(\pi D_1^2 L - \pi D_0^2 u_0 t) \qquad (7.1\text{-}18)$$

into Eq. 7.1-17 and rearrangement yield the average velocity in the annular region,

$$\langle v_z \rangle = - \frac{u_0}{\left[\left(\dfrac{D_1}{D_0} \right)^2 - 1 \right]} \qquad (7.1\text{-}19)$$

*7.2   The Macroscopic Momentum Balance

In deriving the macroscopic momentum balance, it is convenient to begin with the general statement of the linear momentum principle:

$$\frac{D}{Dt} \int_{\mathscr{V}_m(t)} \rho \mathbf{v} \, dV = \int_{\mathscr{V}_m(t)} \rho \mathbf{g} \, dV + \int_{\mathscr{A}_m(t)} \mathbf{t}_{(\mathbf{n})} \, dA \qquad (7.2\text{-}1)$$

Representing the stress vector in terms of the stress tensor and applying the Reynolds transport theorem (see Eq. 3.4-18) gives

$$\int_{\mathscr{V}_m(t)} \frac{\partial}{\partial t} (\rho \mathbf{v}) \, dV + \int_{\mathscr{A}_m(t)} \rho \mathbf{v} \mathbf{v} \cdot \mathbf{n} \, dA = \int_{\mathscr{V}_m(t)} \rho \mathbf{g} \, dV + \int_{\mathscr{A}_m(t)} \mathbf{T} \cdot \mathbf{n} \, dA \qquad (7.2\text{-}2)$$

Note that the term $\mathbf{v} \mathbf{v} \cdot \mathbf{n}$ can be looked upon as either a tensor $\mathbf{v} \mathbf{v}$ dotted with a vector $\mathbf{n}$, or a vector $\mathbf{v}$ multiplied by a scalar $\mathbf{v} \cdot \mathbf{n}$; both interpretations are equivalent. From a physical point of view, it is best to interpret the term $\rho \mathbf{v} \mathbf{v} \cdot \mathbf{n} \, dA$ as the momentum per unit volume, $\rho \mathbf{v}$, times the volumetric flow rate, $\mathbf{v} \cdot \mathbf{n} \, dA$; thus, this term represents a momentum flux (momentum per unit volume times volume per unit time), and $\rho \mathbf{v} \mathbf{v}$ is often called the *momentum flux tensor*.

Application of the divergence theorem† to the two area integrals in Eq. 7.2-2 allows us to put all the terms under the same integral sign, and we readily obtain the stress equations of motion.

$$\frac{\partial}{\partial t} (\rho \mathbf{v}) + \boldsymbol{\nabla} \cdot (\rho \mathbf{v} \mathbf{v}) = \rho \mathbf{g} + \boldsymbol{\nabla} \cdot \mathbf{T} \qquad (7.2\text{-}3)$$

Formation of the integral of Eq. 7.2-3 over the volume $\mathscr{V}_a(t)$ yields the macroscopic momentum balance

$$\int_{\mathscr{V}_a(t)} \frac{\partial}{\partial t} (\rho \mathbf{v}) \, dV + \int_{\mathscr{V}_a(t)} \boldsymbol{\nabla} \cdot (\rho \mathbf{v} \mathbf{v}) \, dV = \int_{\mathscr{V}_a(t)} \rho \mathbf{g} \, dV + \int_{\mathscr{V}_a(t)} \boldsymbol{\nabla} \cdot \mathbf{T} \, dV \qquad (7.2\text{-}4)$$

As with the first step in the macroscopic mass balance, the terms in this equation are difficult to analyze from a practical point of view. In attacking this problem, we will use the divergence theorem to obtain area integrals of the momentum flux tensor and the stress vector, and the general transport theorem to replace the first term in Eq. 7.2-4 with something more susceptible to analysis.

Application of the divergence theorem to the second and fourth integrals gives

$$\int_{\mathscr{V}_a(t)} \frac{\partial}{\partial t} (\rho \mathbf{v}) \, dV + \int_{\mathscr{A}_a(t)} \rho \mathbf{v} \mathbf{v} \cdot \mathbf{n} \, dA = \int_{\mathscr{V}_a(t)} \rho \mathbf{g} \, dV + \int_{\mathscr{A}_a(t)} \mathbf{T} \cdot \mathbf{n} \, dA \qquad (7.2\text{-}5)$$

† See Prob. 4-15 for the derivation of the divergence theorem for a tensor.

We now employ the general transport theorem (see Eq. 3.4-16) to provide the *mathematical* relationship

$$\frac{d}{dt}\int_{\mathcal{V}_a(t)} \rho\mathbf{v}\, dV = \int_{\mathcal{V}_a(t)} \frac{\partial}{\partial t}(\rho\mathbf{v})\, dV + \int_{\mathcal{A}_a(t)} \rho\mathbf{v}\mathbf{w}\cdot\mathbf{n}\, dA \qquad (7.2\text{-}6)$$

which we may use in conjunction with Eq. 7.2-5 to obtain

$$\frac{d}{dt}\int_{\mathcal{V}_a(t)} \rho\mathbf{v}\, dV + \int_{\mathcal{A}_a(t)} \rho\mathbf{v}(\mathbf{v}-\mathbf{w})\cdot\mathbf{n}\, dA = \int_{\mathcal{V}_a(t)} \rho\mathbf{g}\, dV + \int_{\mathcal{A}_a(t)} \mathbf{t}_{(\mathbf{n})}\, dA \qquad (7.2\text{-}7)$$

Here, we have made use of

$$\mathbf{T}\cdot\mathbf{n} = \mathbf{t}_{(\mathbf{n})} \qquad (7.2\text{-}8)$$

We may write the area integral of the momentum flux as

$$\int_{\mathcal{A}_a(t)} \rho\mathbf{v}(\mathbf{v}-\mathbf{w})\cdot\mathbf{n}\, dA = \int_{A_e(t)} \rho\mathbf{v}(\mathbf{v}-\mathbf{w})\cdot\mathbf{n}\, dA \qquad (7.2\text{-}9)$$

and the final form of the macroscopic momentum balance results.†

Time rate of change of the momentum of the control volume   Net flux of momentum leaving the control volume

$$\frac{d}{dt}\int_{\mathcal{V}_a(t)} \rho\mathbf{v}\, dV + \int_{A_e(t)} \rho\mathbf{v}(\mathbf{v}-\mathbf{w})\cdot\mathbf{n}\, dA$$

$$= \int_{\mathcal{V}_a(t)} \rho\mathbf{g}\, dV + \int_{\mathcal{A}_a(t)} \mathbf{t}_{(\mathbf{n})}\, dA \qquad (7.2\text{-}10)$$

Body force   Surface force

An especially useful form of Eq. 7.2-10 is that for steady flow in a control volume fixed in space. Under these conditions, we have

$$\int_{A_e} (\rho\mathbf{v})\mathbf{v}\cdot\mathbf{n}\, dA = \int_{\mathcal{V}} \rho\mathbf{g}\, dV + \int_{\mathcal{A}} \mathbf{t}_{(\mathbf{n})}\, dA \qquad \text{Steady flow, control volume fixed in space} \quad (7.2\text{-}11)$$

For turbulent flows, we simply carry out the preceding analysis using the time-averaged stress equations of motion. The final result is obtained by replacing $\mathbf{v}$ and $\mathbf{t}_{(\mathbf{n})}$ by the time-averaged quantities, $\bar{\mathbf{v}}$ and $\bar{\mathbf{t}}_{(\mathbf{n})}$, where

$$\bar{\mathbf{t}}_{(\mathbf{n})} = -\mathbf{n}\bar{p} + \mathbf{n}\cdot[\bar{\boldsymbol{\tau}} + \bar{\boldsymbol{\tau}}^{(t)}] \qquad (7.2\text{-}12)$$

The body force term in Eq. 7.2-10 is easily evaluated, and the two integrals on the left-hand side can usually be represented with a fair degree of accuracy by means of average velocities, volumes, and cross-sectional areas.

† Note that the phrase *momentum of the control volume* should properly be interpreted as *momentum of the fluid within the control volume*.

When viscous effects are important, the area integral of the stress vector must be determined on the basis of experimental or empirical friction factors or drag coefficients. However, a number of problems exist for which we may reasonably neglect viscous effects. Such problems arise when there are large changes of velocity in the direction of flow and the inertial terms in the equations of motion predominate. Flow through a sudden expansion or contraction in a pipeline, or the impinging of a liquid jet on a flat plate are cases where viscous effects may be neglected and reasonable results still obtained. For such problems the stress vector is written as

$$\mathbf{t}_{(\mathbf{n})} = -\mathbf{n}p \qquad (7.2\text{-}13)$$

and the macroscopic mass and momentum balances are solved in terms of average velocities and pressures.

The differential stress equations of motion

As an application of Eq. 7.2-10, we will rederive the x-direction differential stress equation of motion given previously in Chap. 4. This example may seem to be overly repetitious inasmuch as we have just integrated the differential equation to obtain the macroscopic balance. However, the derivation of the differential equation by application of Eq. 7.2-10 to a differential cube fixed in space provides an excellent opportunity to compute some momentum fluxes. Past experience has shown that this particular example provides a fine test of the students' understanding of Eq. 7.2-10.

We consider a differential cube, fixed in space, such as those shown in Figs. 7.2-1a and b. For a control volume fixed in space, $\mathbf{w} = 0$ and the x-component of Eq. 7.2-10 reduces to

$$\frac{\partial}{\partial t}\int_{\mathscr{V}} \rho v_x \, dV + \int_{A_e} \rho v_x \mathbf{v} \cdot \mathbf{n} \, dA$$
$$= \int_{\mathscr{V}} \rho g_x \, dV + \int_{\mathscr{A}} t_{(\mathbf{n})x} \, dA \qquad (7.2\text{-}14)$$

In Fig. 7.2-1a, the surface stresses are all drawn in the x-direction, and are all shown as positive stresses. In Fig. 7.2-1b, the momentum flux terms are represented by arrows the direction of which indicates the direction of mass flow, presuming v_x, v_y, and v_z are all positive. An arrow pointing into the cube represents the convection of x-direction momentum into the cube and an arrow pointing out of the cube represents convection of x-direction momentum out of the cube.

Returning to Fig. 3.5-2, which indicates the mass convected into and out of a cube, we see that the momentum balance involves the convection of x-direction momentum per unit volume ρv_x in the same way that the mass balance involves the convection of mass per unit volume, ρ. We shall now

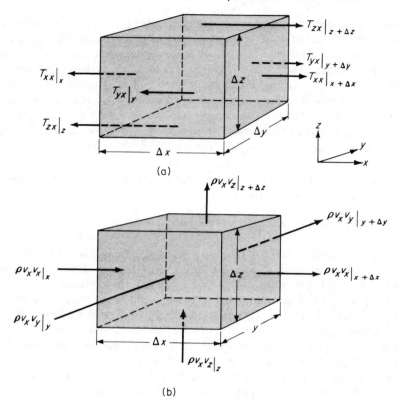

Fig. 7.2-1. x-direction surface forces.

analyze Eq. 7.2-14 term by term, starting with the first term on the left-hand side.

$$\frac{\partial}{\partial t} \int_{\mathscr{V}} \rho v_x \, dV = \frac{\partial}{\partial t} (\rho v_x \, \Delta x \, \Delta y \, \Delta z) \tag{7.2-15a}$$

$$\int_{\mathscr{A}} \rho v_x \mathbf{v} \cdot \mathbf{n} \, dA = \begin{cases} -\rho v_x v_x|_x \, \Delta y \, \Delta z + \rho v_x v_x|_{x+\Delta x} \, \Delta y \, \Delta z & \text{Momentum flux across x-surfaces} \\[4pt] -\rho v_x v_y|_y \, \Delta x \, \Delta z + \rho v_x v_y|_{y+\Delta y} \, \Delta x \, \Delta z & \text{Momentum flux across y-surfaces} \\[4pt] -\rho v_x v_z|_z \, \Delta x \, \Delta y + \rho v_x v_z|_{z+\Delta z} \, \Delta x \, \Delta y & \text{Momentum flux across z-surfaces} \end{cases} \tag{7.2-15b}$$

$$\int_{\mathscr{V}} \rho g_x \, dV = \rho g_x \, \Delta x \, \Delta y \, \Delta z \tag{7.2-15c}$$

$$\int_{\mathscr{A}} t_{(\mathbf{n})x} \, dA = \begin{cases} -T_{xx}|_x \, \Delta y \, \Delta z + T_{xx}|_{x+\Delta x} \, \Delta y \, \Delta z & \text{Forces on the x-surfaces} \\[4pt] -T_{yx}|_y \, \Delta x \, \Delta z + T_{yx}|_{y+\Delta y} \, \Delta x \, \Delta z & \text{Forces on the y-surfaces} \\[4pt] -T_{zx}|_z \, \Delta x \, \Delta y + T_{zx}|_{z+\Delta z} \, \Delta x \, \Delta y & \text{Forces on the z-surfaces} \end{cases} \tag{7.2-15d}$$

If we substitute Eqs. 7.2-15 into Eq. 7.2-14 and divide by $\Delta x \, \Delta y \, \Delta z$, we obtain

$$
\frac{\partial}{\partial t}(\rho v_x) + \left(\frac{\rho v_x v_x|_{x+\Delta x} - \rho v_x v_x|_x}{\Delta x} \right)
$$

$$
+ \left(\frac{\rho v_x v_y|_{y+\Delta y} - \rho v_x v_y|_y}{\Delta y} \right)
$$

$$
+ \left(\frac{\rho v_x v_z|_{z+\Delta z} - \rho v_x v_z|_z}{\Delta z} \right)
$$

$$
= \rho g_x + \left(\frac{T_{xx}|_{x+\Delta x} - T_{xx}|_x}{\Delta x} \right) \tag{7.2-16}
$$

$$
+ \left(\frac{T_{yx}|_{y+\Delta y} - T_{yx}|_y}{\Delta y} \right)
$$

$$
+ \left(\frac{T_{zx}|_{z+\Delta z} - T_{zx}|_z}{\Delta z} \right)
$$

Taking the limits $\Delta x \to 0$, $\Delta y \to 0$, $\Delta z \to 0$ yields the stress equation of motion in the x-direction,

$$
\frac{\partial}{\partial t}(\rho v_x) + \frac{\partial}{\partial x}(\rho v_x v_x) + \frac{\partial}{\partial y}(\rho v_x v_y) + \frac{\partial}{\partial z}(\rho v_x v_z)
$$

$$
= \rho g_x + \left[\frac{\partial T_{xx}}{\partial x} + \frac{\partial T_{yx}}{\partial y} + \frac{\partial T_{zx}}{\partial z} \right] \tag{7.2-17}
$$

which we can obtain readily from Eq. 7.2-3 by forming the dot product with **i**. In applying Eq. 7.2-10 to more complex control volumes, we must be very careful in evaluating the surface integrals of the surface force and momentum flux. The majority of errors that occur in the application of the macroscopic momentum balance are caused by neglecting the momentum flux or the surface force acting on some portion of the control surface.

*7.3 The Macroscopic Mechanical Energy Balance

Before we apply the macroscopic momentum balance to some simple flows, it will be advantageous to derive the macroscopic mechanical energy balance so that we may compare the results from these two approximate methods. We should keep in mind that no new physical principles are involved in this derivation. It is simply a mathematical development providing us with an extremely useful equation based on the linear momentum principle. The development is somewhat longer than those presented in the previous two sections, for we must first derive the differential mechanical energy equation. The development will be restricted to incompressible flows.

Starting with the stress equations of motion,

$$\rho\left(\frac{\partial \mathbf{v}}{\partial t} + \mathbf{v} \cdot \nabla \mathbf{v}\right) = \rho\mathbf{g} + \nabla \cdot \mathbf{T} \qquad (7.3\text{-}1)$$

we make use of the material derivative to obtain

$$\rho\frac{D\mathbf{v}}{Dt} = \rho\mathbf{g} + \nabla \cdot \mathbf{T} \qquad (7.3\text{-}2)$$

Forming the scalar product of Eq. 7.3-2 with the velocity vector $\mathbf{v}$ gives

$$\rho\mathbf{v} \cdot \frac{D\mathbf{v}}{Dt} = \mathbf{v} \cdot \rho\mathbf{g} + \mathbf{v} \cdot (\nabla \cdot \mathbf{T}) \qquad (7.3\text{-}3)$$

There is no easy way of treating the left-hand side of Eq. 7.3-3, so we must expand the scalar product and regroup the terms as follows:

$$
\begin{aligned}
\rho\mathbf{v} \cdot \frac{D\mathbf{v}}{Dt} &= \rho(\mathbf{i}v_x + \mathbf{j}v_y + \mathbf{k}v_z) \cdot \left(\mathbf{i}\frac{Dv_x}{Dt} + \mathbf{j}\frac{Dv_y}{Dt} + \mathbf{k}\frac{Dv_z}{Dt}\right) \\[6pt]
&= \rho v_x\frac{Dv_x}{Dt} + \rho v_y\frac{Dv_y}{Dt} + \rho v_z\frac{Dv_z}{Dt} \\[6pt]
&= \frac{D}{Dt}\left(\tfrac{1}{2}\rho v_x^2\right) + \frac{D}{Dt}\left(\tfrac{1}{2}\rho v_y^2\right) + \frac{D}{Dt}\left(\tfrac{1}{2}\rho v_z^2\right) \\[6pt]
&= \frac{D}{Dt}\left(\tfrac{1}{2}\rho v^2\right)
\end{aligned}
\qquad (7.3\text{-}4)
$$

where $v^2 = v_x^2 + v_y^2 + v_z^2$. The density has been treated as a constant in accordance with the restriction to incompressible flows. In treating the gravitational term, we note that any constant vector may be written as the gradient of a scalar. For example, if we represent $\mathbf{g}$ as

$$\mathbf{g} = \mathbf{i}g_x + \mathbf{j}g_y + \mathbf{k}g_z \qquad (7.3\text{-}5)$$

where g_x, g_y, and g_z are constant, we may define a scalar ϕ as

$$\phi = -(xg_x + yg_y + zg_z) \qquad (7.3\text{-}6)$$

so that

$$\mathbf{g} = -\nabla\phi \qquad (7.3\text{-}7)$$

We may now write the first term on the right-hand side of Eq. 7.3-3 as

$$\mathbf{v} \cdot \rho\mathbf{g} = -\mathbf{v} \cdot \nabla(\rho\phi) = -\nabla \cdot (\rho\phi\mathbf{v}) \qquad (7.3\text{-}8)$$

where the restriction to incompressible flow has been imposed so that $\nabla \rho = 0$ and $\nabla \cdot \mathbf{v} = 0$. Analysis of the last term is best done in index notation. We first note that

$$\mathbf{v} \cdot (\nabla \cdot \mathbf{T}) = v_i \left(\frac{\partial T_{ji}}{\partial x_j} \right) \qquad (7.3\text{-}9)$$

and then examine the term $(\partial / \partial x_j)\,(v_i T_{ji})$ to obtain

$$\frac{\partial}{\partial x_j}\,(v_i T_{ji}) = v_i \frac{\partial T_{ji}}{\partial x_j} + \left(\frac{\partial v_i}{\partial x_j} \right) T_{ji} \qquad (7.3\text{-}10)$$

In Gibbs notation, the tensor $(\partial v_i / \partial x_j)$ is represented by $\nabla \mathbf{v}$, and Eq. 7.3-10 takes the form

$$\nabla \cdot (\mathbf{v} \cdot \mathbf{T}) = \mathbf{v} \cdot (\nabla \cdot \mathbf{T}) + \nabla \mathbf{v} : \mathbf{T} \qquad (7.3\text{-}11)$$

The double dot (or scalar) product between two tensors is clearly defined by index notation. For example,

$$\mathbf{A} : \mathbf{B} = A_{ij} B_{ij} = \begin{array}{l} A_{11}B_{11} + A_{12}B_{12} + A_{13}B_{13} \\ +\ A_{21}B_{21} + A_{22}B_{22} + A_{23}B_{23} \\ +\ A_{31}B_{31} + A_{32}B_{32} + A_{33}B_{33} \end{array}$$

If both of the tensors $\mathbf{A}$ and $\mathbf{B}$ were skew symmetric, we would have to be more careful in defining the double-dot product. However, in our case the stress tensor $\mathbf{T}$ is symmetric and we need not worry about this problem.

By Eq. 7.3-11, the second term on the right-hand side of Eq. 7.3-3 may be written

$$\mathbf{v} \cdot (\nabla \cdot \mathbf{T}) = \nabla \cdot (\mathbf{v} \cdot \mathbf{T}) - \nabla \mathbf{v} : \mathbf{T} \qquad (7.3\text{-}12)$$

which we may simplify by further analysis. The last term on the right-hand side may be expressed in terms of the pressure and the viscous stress tensor.

$$\nabla \mathbf{v} : \mathbf{T} = \nabla \mathbf{v} : (-\mathbf{I}p + \boldsymbol{\tau}) \qquad (7.3\text{-}13)$$

Switching to index notation,

$$\left(\frac{\partial v_i}{\partial x_j} \right) T_{ji} = \frac{\partial v_i}{\partial x_j}\,(-\delta_{ji}p + \tau_{ji}) \qquad (7.3\text{-}14)$$

we note that

$$\left(\frac{\partial v_i}{\partial x_j} \right) \delta_{ji}p = \left(\frac{\partial v_i}{\partial x_i} \right) p = 0 \qquad (7.3\text{-}15)$$

for incompressible flows. Incorporating this simplification in Eq. 7.3-12 and defining the *dissipation function*, Φ, as

$$\Phi = \nabla \mathbf{v} : \boldsymbol{\tau} \qquad (7.3\text{-}16)$$

allows us to write

$$\mathbf{v} \cdot (\nabla \cdot \mathbf{T}) = \nabla \cdot (\mathbf{v} \cdot \mathbf{T}) - \Phi \qquad (7.3\text{-}17)$$

It may not be apparent now (but it will be in Chap. 10) that Φ represents the rate at which mechanical energy is converted to thermal energy via viscous forces. We can understand this concept clearly only when the principle of conservation of energy is analyzed in detail.† Substitution of Eqs. 7.3-4, 7.3-8, and 7.3-17 into Eq. 7.3-3 yields the differential mechanical energy equation for incompressible flows.

Time rate of change
of kinetic energy
per unit volume

Rate of work done
by surface forces
per unit volume

$$\frac{D}{Dt}(\tfrac{1}{2}\rho v^2) = -\nabla\cdot(\rho\phi\mathbf{v}) + \nabla\cdot(\mathbf{v}\cdot\mathbf{T}) - \Phi \qquad (7.3\text{-}18)$$

Rate of work done
by gravity per unit
volume

Rate of conversion
to thermal energy
per unit volume

This derivation has been somewhat more abstract than our previous efforts and it may be helpful to discuss this result before going on to the derivation of the macroscopic balance.

We started with the stress equations of motion, which represent a balance between the time rate of change of momentum per unit volume and the forces per unit volume. Forming the scalar product of the velocity and the time rate of change of momentum gives rise to the time rate of change of kinetic energy, while the scalar product between the velocity and a force (force times distance per unit time) naturally gives rise to the *rate of work*. The body force, $\rho\mathbf{g}$, gave rise to a term representing the rate of work done by gravity, while the surface force $\nabla\cdot\mathbf{T}$ gave rise to *two* rate of work terms. The second term represents the *irreversible* rate of surface work, which is converted to thermal energy.

If the rate of surface work is negligible, Eq. 7.3-18 indicates a balance between kinetic energy and potential energy. The student may recall experiments in beginning physics courses designed to demonstrate that kinetic and potential energy were conserved provided "frictional" effects were small. Expressions for Φ in rectangular, cylindrical, and spherical coordinates are given in Table 7.3-1 for Newtonian fluids. There, we note that Φ is composed entirely of squared terms and is therefore always positive.

Forming the integral of Eq. 7.3-18 over the volume $\mathscr{V}_a(t)$ yields the macroscopic balance,

$$\int_{\mathscr{V}_a(t)}\frac{\partial}{\partial t}(\tfrac{1}{2}\rho v^2)\,dV + \int_{\mathscr{V}_a(t)}\nabla\cdot(\tfrac{1}{2}\rho v^2\mathbf{v})\,dV = -\int_{\mathscr{V}_a(t)}\nabla\cdot(\rho\phi\mathbf{v})\,dV$$
$$+ \int_{\mathscr{V}_a(t)}\nabla\cdot(\mathbf{v}\cdot\mathbf{T})\,dV - \int_{\mathscr{V}_a(t)}\Phi\,dV \qquad (7.3\text{-}19)$$

† This analysis is given in Secs. 10.1 and 10.2.

Here, we have made use of

$$\frac{D}{Dt}\left(\tfrac{1}{2}\,\rho v^2\right) = \frac{\partial}{\partial t}\left(\tfrac{1}{2}\,\rho v^2\right) + \mathbf{v}\cdot\boldsymbol{\nabla}\left(\tfrac{1}{2}\,\rho v^2\right)$$

$$= \frac{\partial}{\partial t}\left(\tfrac{1}{2}\,\rho v^2\right) + \boldsymbol{\nabla}\cdot\left(\tfrac{1}{2}\,\rho v^2\mathbf{v}\right) \tag{7.3-20}$$

since $\boldsymbol{\nabla}\cdot\mathbf{v} = 0$. Application of the general transport theorem to the first integral in Eq. 7.3-19, and of the divergence theorem to the second, third,

Table 7.3-1

THE DISSIPATION FUNCTION Φ FOR NEWTONIAN FLUIDS

Rectangular coordinates x, y, z

$$\Phi = 2\mu\left[\left(\frac{\partial v_x}{\partial x}\right)^2 + \left(\frac{\partial v_y}{\partial y}\right)^2 + \left(\frac{\partial v_z}{\partial z}\right)^2\right]$$

$$+ \mu\left[\left(\frac{\partial v_y}{\partial x} + \frac{\partial v_x}{\partial y}\right)^2 + \left(\frac{\partial v_z}{\partial y} + \frac{\partial v_y}{\partial z}\right)^2 + \left(\frac{\partial v_z}{\partial x} + \frac{\partial v_x}{\partial z}\right)^2\right]$$

Cylindrical Coordinates r, θ, z

$$\Phi = 2\mu\left[\left(\frac{\partial v_r}{\partial r}\right)^2 + \left(\frac{1}{r}\frac{\partial v_\theta}{\partial \theta} + \frac{v_r}{r}\right)^2 + \left(\frac{\partial v_z}{\partial z}\right)^2\right]$$

$$+ \mu\left[r\frac{\partial}{\partial r}\left(\frac{v_\theta}{r}\right) + \frac{1}{r}\left(\frac{\partial v_r}{\partial \theta}\right)\right]^2 + \mu\left[\frac{1}{r}\left(\frac{\partial v_z}{\partial \theta}\right) + \left(\frac{\partial v_\theta}{\partial z}\right)\right]^2$$

$$+ \mu\left(\frac{\partial v_r}{\partial z} + \frac{\partial v_z}{\partial r}\right)^2$$

Spherical Coordinates r, θ, ϕ

$$\Phi = 2\mu\left[\left(\frac{\partial v_r}{\partial r}\right)^2 + \left(\frac{1}{r}\frac{\partial v_\theta}{\partial \theta} + \frac{v_r}{r}\right)^2 + \left(\frac{1}{r\sin\theta}\frac{\partial v_\phi}{\partial \phi} + \frac{v_r}{r} + \frac{v_\theta\cot\theta}{r}\right)^2\right]$$

$$+ \mu\left[r\frac{\partial}{\partial r}\left(\frac{v_\theta}{r}\right) + \frac{1}{r}\frac{\partial v_r}{\partial \theta}\right]^2 + \mu\left[\frac{1}{r\sin\theta}\frac{\partial v_r}{\partial \phi} + r\frac{\partial}{\partial r}\left(\frac{v_\phi}{r}\right)\right]^2$$

$$+ \mu\left[\frac{\sin\theta}{r}\frac{\partial}{\partial \theta}\left(\frac{v_\phi}{\sin\theta}\right) + \frac{1}{r\sin\theta}\frac{\partial v_\theta}{\partial \phi}\right]^2$$

and fourth integrals, gives

$$\frac{d}{dt} \int_{\mathscr{V}_a(t)} (\tfrac{1}{2}\, \rho v^2)\, dV + \int_{\mathscr{A}_a(t)} (\tfrac{1}{2}\, \rho v^2)\, (\mathbf{v} - \mathbf{w}) \cdot \mathbf{n}\, dA$$

$$= \int_{\mathscr{A}_a(t)} (\mathbf{v} \cdot \mathbf{T}) \cdot \mathbf{n}\, dA - \int_{\mathscr{A}_a(t)} \rho \phi \mathbf{v} \cdot \mathbf{n}\, dA - \int_{\mathscr{V}_a(t)} \Phi\, dV \qquad (7.3\text{-}21)$$

Once again, there are some very definite reasons for transforming the volume integrals to area integrals. For example, if the gravitation term were left as it first appeared in Eq. 7.3-3, the macroscopic balance would contain an integral of the type

$$\int_{\mathscr{V}_a(t)} \mathbf{v} \cdot \rho \mathbf{g}\, dV$$

Evaluation of this integral would require knowledge of $\mathbf{v}$ everywhere in the system. However, expressing the gravity vector as the divergence of a scalar and applying the divergence theorem yield the area integral in Eq. 7.3-21, which we may evaluate with reasonable accuracy in terms of distance above a reference plane and average velocities.†

Following our development of the macroscopic mass and momentum balances, we again wish to separate the total area $\mathscr{A}_a(t)$ into the area of entrances and exits, fixed solid surfaces, and moving solid surfaces. Thus,

$$\mathscr{A}_a(t) = \begin{array}{ll} A_e(t) & \text{Area of entrances and exits} \\ + A_s(t) & \text{Area of solid moving surfaces} \\ + A_s & \text{Area of solid fixed surfaces} \end{array} \qquad (7.3\text{-}22)$$

An illustrative control volume $\mathscr{V}_a(t)$ is shown in Fig. 7.3-1, and we now wish to examine each term in Eq. 7.3-21 to see what kind of simplifications or special interpretations we can make in terms of the three different areas. The first term (from left to right) remains unchanged. In the second term, we note that

$$\mathbf{v} = \mathbf{w} = 0 \quad \text{on} \quad A_s$$
$$\mathbf{v} - \mathbf{w} = 0 \quad \text{on} \quad A_s(t)$$

and we write

$$\int_{\mathscr{A}_a(t)} (\tfrac{1}{2}\rho v^2)(\mathbf{v} - \mathbf{w}) \cdot \mathbf{n}\, dA = \int_{A_e(t)} (\tfrac{1}{2}\rho v^2)(\mathbf{v} - \mathbf{w}) \cdot \mathbf{n}\, dA \qquad (7.3\text{-}23)$$

† If we sought an exact solution, we would have to know $\mathbf{v}$ everywhere, in which case there would be no point in using the macroscopic balance and no advantage in using the area integral. However, we seek approximate solutions to a great many problems, and in those cases the area integral has great preference.

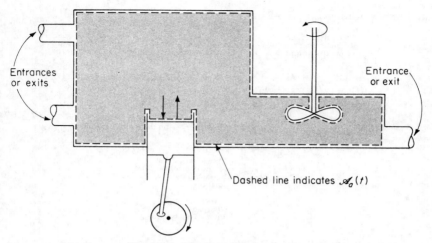

Fig. 7.3-1. Moving control volume,

In attacking the first term on the right-hand side of Eq. 7.3-21, we must remember that $\mathbf{t}_{(n)}$ is the force per unit area that the surroundings exert on the system. Thus, the term

$$(\mathbf{v} \cdot \mathbf{T}) \cdot \mathbf{n} = \mathbf{v} \cdot (\mathbf{T} \cdot \mathbf{n}) = \mathbf{v} \cdot \mathbf{t}_{(n)} \qquad (7.3\text{-}24)$$

represents the rate at which the surroundings do work on the control volume. If we define $\dot{W}$ as the rate at which the solid moving surfaces are doing work on the control volume,† then

$$\dot{W} = \int\limits_{A_s(t)} \mathbf{v} \cdot \mathbf{t}_{(n)} \, dA \qquad (7.3\text{-}25)$$

and the total area integral takes the form

$$\int\limits_{\mathscr{A}_a(t)} (\mathbf{v} \cdot \mathbf{T}) \cdot \mathbf{n} \, dA = \int\limits_{A_e(t)} \mathbf{v} \cdot \mathbf{t}_{(n)} \, dA + \dot{W} \qquad (7.3\text{-}26)$$

Here, we have made use of the fact that $\mathbf{v} = 0$ on A_s. Defining the total rate of viscous dissipation to internal energy as

$$\dot{E}_v = \int\limits_{\mathscr{V}_a(t)} \Phi \, dV$$

† The dot over this term is used as a reminder that the units are foot pounds force *per second* or some equivalent.

and incorporating Eqs. 7.3-23 and 7.3-26, we can write Eq. 7.3-21

$$\frac{d}{dt}\int_{\mathscr{V}_a(t)} (\tfrac{1}{2}\,\rho v^2)\,dV + \int_{A_e(t)} \tfrac{1}{2}\rho v^2(\mathbf{v}-\mathbf{w})\cdot\mathbf{n}\,dA = \int_{A_e(t)} \mathbf{v}\cdot\mathbf{t}_{(n)}\,dA$$

Time rate of change of kinetic energy of the control volume	Net flux of kinetic energy leaving the control volume
	Rate of work done on control volume at entrances and exits

$$-\int_{\mathscr{A}_a(t)} \rho\phi\mathbf{v}\cdot\mathbf{n}\,dA \qquad \text{Rate of work done on the control volume by gravity} \qquad (7.3\text{-}27)$$

$$+\;\dot{W} \qquad\qquad \text{Rate of work done on the control volume by solid moving surfaces}$$

$$-\;\dot{E}_v \qquad\qquad \text{Rate of viscous dissipation to internal energy}$$

Turbulent flows

In treating turbulent flows, we wish to obtain a form of Eq. 7.3-27 containing the appropriate time-averaged terms. This task is most easily done by examining the time-averaged differential mechanical energy equation and then reinterpreting the terms in Eq. 7.3-27. We may express each term as the sum of time-averaged and fluctuating components as follows:

$$\mathbf{v} = \bar{\mathbf{v}} + \mathbf{v}'$$
$$v^2 = \mathbf{v}\cdot\mathbf{v} = \bar{v}^2 + 2\bar{\mathbf{v}}\cdot\mathbf{v}' + (v')^2$$
$$\mathbf{T} = \overline{\mathbf{T}} + \mathbf{T}'$$

Substitution of these quantities into Eqs. 7.3-18 and 7.3-16, and taking the time average, yield†

$$\frac{\partial}{\partial t}\,[\tfrac{1}{2}\rho\bar{v}^2 + \tfrac{1}{2}\rho\overline{(v')^2}] + \bar{\mathbf{v}}\cdot\boldsymbol{\nabla}[\tfrac{1}{2}\rho\bar{v}^2 + \tfrac{1}{2}\rho\overline{(v')^2}]$$
$$= -\boldsymbol{\nabla}\cdot(\rho\phi\bar{\mathbf{v}}) + \boldsymbol{\nabla}\cdot(\bar{\mathbf{v}}\cdot\overline{\mathbf{T}}^{(T)}) - (\overline{\Phi} + \overline{\Phi}') + \boldsymbol{\nabla}\cdot\overline{(\mathbf{v}'\cdot\mathbf{T}')} \quad (7.3\text{-}28)$$

where $\overline{\mathbf{T}}^{(T)} = -\mathbf{I}\bar{p} + \bar{\boldsymbol{\tau}} + \bar{\boldsymbol{\tau}}^{(t)}$

$$\mathbf{T}' = -\mathbf{I}p' + \boldsymbol{\tau}'$$

and we obtain Φ' by substituting v_x', v_y', and v_z' into the formulas for Φ. If we define the total viscous dissipation function as

$$\overline{\Phi}^{(T)} = \overline{\Phi} + \overline{\Phi}' \qquad\qquad\qquad (7.3\text{-}29)$$

† The route to Eq. 7.3-28 follows the development in Chap. 6 and is straightforward, although lengthy. Here, again, we have expanded the material derivative as indicated by Eq. 7.3-20.

and invoke the order of magnitude arguments

$$\overline{(v')^2} \ll \bar{v}^2$$

$$\overline{\mathbf{v}' \cdot \mathbf{T}'} \ll \bar{\mathbf{v}} \cdot \mathbf{T}^{(T)}$$

Eq. 7.3-28 reduces to the same form as Eq. 7.3-18

$$\frac{\partial}{\partial t}(\tfrac{1}{2}\rho\bar{v}^2) + \bar{\mathbf{v}} \cdot \mathbf{\nabla}(\tfrac{1}{2}\rho\bar{v}^2) = -\mathbf{\nabla} \cdot (\rho\phi\bar{\mathbf{v}}) + \mathbf{\nabla} \cdot (\bar{\mathbf{v}} \cdot \overline{\mathbf{T}^{(T)}}) - \overline{\Phi^{(T)}} \qquad (7.3\text{-}30)$$

Thus, the macroscopic mechanical energy balance may be applied to turbulent flows provided the terms are interpreted as follows:

Laminar flow	Turbulent flow
v	$\bar{v}$
$\mathbf{v}$	$\bar{\mathbf{v}}$
$\mathbf{t}_{(n)}$	$\bar{\mathbf{t}}_{(n)} = \mathbf{n} \cdot \overline{\mathbf{T}}^{(T)}$
$\dot{W}$	$\displaystyle\int_{A_s(t)} \bar{\mathbf{v}} \cdot \bar{\mathbf{t}}_{(n)}\, dA$
$\dot{E}_v$	$\displaystyle\int_{\mathscr{V}_a(t)} [\overline{\Phi} + \overline{\Phi'}]\, dV$

An important special case of Eq. 7.3-27 is for steady flow and a fixed control volume. Under these conditions, we obtain

$$\int_{A_e} \tfrac{1}{2}\rho v^2 \mathbf{v} \cdot \mathbf{n}\, dA = \int_{A_e} \mathbf{v} \cdot \mathbf{t}_{(n)}\, dA - \int_{A_e} \rho\phi\mathbf{v} \cdot \mathbf{n}\, dA - \dot{E}_v \quad \begin{array}{l}\text{For a fixed control}\\ \text{volume and}\\ \text{steady flow}\end{array} \quad (7.3\text{-}31)$$

If we compare this result with the macroscopic momentum balance for the same conditions (see Eq. 7.2-11), we see that by forming the scalar product with the velocity vector the necessity of evaluating terms at solid boundaries has been eliminated. However, it does give rise to the viscous dissipation term $\dot{E}_v$, which must be evaluated experimentally. The momentum and mechanical energy balances, derived from the *same physical principle*, present two fairly distinct approaches to obtaining approximate solutions.

In general, we make use of the momentum balance when forces on solid surfaces are required, and of the mechanical energy balance when pressures and velocities are required at entrances and exits. Many problems can be solved by both balances; they are interesting cases to study, for the comparison between the two solutions and experimental data gives an indication of the validity of the assumptions made.

In setting up macroscopic balance problems, the placement or choice of
control volume deserves considerable attention. Often the same result will
be obtained for two different control volumes simply because the approximations made to solve the problem hide the errors of the solution. Proper
placement of the control volume may not change the result, but it should alert
the engineer to the assumptions so often made tacitly. Two rules generally
should be followed.

1. The control volume, whether it is fixed in space or moving, should be
   set up so that surface forces are easily calculated.
2. The surface of the control volume should be placed where the flow is
   one-dimensional, thus allowing the flux terms to be calculated easily.

*7.4 Bernoulli's Equation

Before studying the application of the macroscopic balances, we will
derive Bernoulli's equation along a streamline. We do so by forming the
scalar product of the unit tangent vector to a streamline and the equations of
motion, thus yielding the scalar component of the equations of motion in
the direction of the streamline. We are already familiar with the scalar
components in the coordinate directions (listed in Tables 5.1-1, 5.1-2, 5.1-3),
and the important aspect of the scalar component along a streamline is that
the inertial terms take a particularly simply form.

The principal value of Bernoulli's equation is that it provides an extremely
simple relationship between velocity, pressure, and height above some reference plane for steady flow when viscous effects may be neglected. Under
these conditions, the equations of motion reduce to

$$\rho \mathbf{v} \cdot \nabla \mathbf{v} = -\nabla p + \rho \mathbf{g} \qquad (7.4-1)$$

The unit tangent vector $\boldsymbol{\lambda}$ may be expressed as

$$\boldsymbol{\lambda} = \frac{d\mathbf{r}}{ds} = \frac{\mathbf{v}}{v} \qquad (7.4-2)$$

In forming the scalar product of $\boldsymbol{\lambda}$ with Eq. 7.4-1, we write

$$\frac{d\mathbf{r}}{ds} \cdot (\rho \mathbf{v} \cdot \nabla \mathbf{v}) = -\frac{d\mathbf{r}}{ds} \cdot \nabla(p + \rho \phi) \qquad (7.4-3)$$

where the flow is taken to be incompressible and the gravity vector has been
replaced by $-\nabla \phi$. In treating the left-hand side of Eq. 7.4-3, we must
expand this term, form the scalar product, and regroup the individual terms

in a suitable fashion. The scalar product is given by

$$\frac{d\mathbf{r}}{ds} \cdot (\rho\mathbf{v} \cdot \nabla\mathbf{v}) = \rho\left(v_x\frac{\partial\mathbf{v}}{\partial x} + v_y\frac{\partial\mathbf{v}}{\partial y} + v_z\frac{\partial\mathbf{v}}{\partial z}\right) \cdot \left(\frac{d\mathbf{r}}{ds}\right)$$

$$= \rho\left(v_x\frac{\partial v_x}{\partial x} + v_y\frac{\partial v_x}{\partial y} + v_z\frac{\partial v_x}{\partial z}\right)\left(\frac{dx}{ds}\right)$$

$$+ \rho\left(v_x\frac{\partial v_y}{\partial x} + v_y\frac{\partial v_y}{\partial y} + v_z\frac{\partial v_y}{\partial z}\right)\left(\frac{dy}{ds}\right) \qquad (7.4\text{-}4)$$

$$+ \rho\left(v_x\frac{\partial v_z}{\partial x} + v_y\frac{\partial v_z}{\partial y} + v_z\frac{\partial v_z}{\partial z}\right)\left(\frac{dz}{ds}\right)$$

Making use of Eq. 3.6-10 in Chap. 3, we obtain

$$v_y\,dz = v_z\,dy \qquad \text{along a streamline} \qquad (7.4\text{-}5a)$$

$$v_z\,dx = v_x\,dz \qquad \text{along a streamline} \qquad (7.4\text{-}5b)$$

$$v_x\,dy = v_y\,dx \qquad \text{along a streamline} \qquad (7.4\text{-}5c)$$

which we may use to arrange Eq. 7.4-4 in the form

$$\frac{d\mathbf{r}}{ds} \cdot (\rho\mathbf{v} \cdot \nabla\mathbf{v}) = \rho\left[v_x\left(\frac{\partial v_x}{\partial x}\right)\frac{dx}{ds} + v_x\left(\frac{\partial v_x}{\partial y}\right)\frac{dy}{ds} + v_x\left(\frac{\partial v_x}{\partial z}\right)\frac{dz}{ds}\right]$$

$$+ \rho\left[v_y\left(\frac{\partial v_y}{\partial x}\right)\frac{dx}{ds} + v_y\left(\frac{\partial v_y}{\partial y}\right)\frac{dy}{ds} + v_y\left(\frac{\partial v_y}{\partial z}\right)\frac{dz}{ds}\right] \qquad (7.4\text{-}6)$$

$$+ \rho\left[v_z\left(\frac{\partial v_z}{\partial x}\right)\frac{dx}{ds} + v_z\left(\frac{\partial v_z}{\partial y}\right)\frac{dy}{ds} + v_z\left(\frac{\partial v_z}{\partial z}\right)\frac{dz}{ds}\right]$$

We have contrived to arrange the individual terms so that we may write them as derivatives of the square of the velocity component—i.e.,

$$v_x\left(\frac{\partial v_x}{\partial x}\right) = \frac{1}{2}\frac{\partial}{\partial x}(v_x^2) \qquad (7.4\text{-}7)$$

Making this change in each term and summing the columns in Eq. 7.4-6, we get

$$\frac{d\mathbf{r}}{ds} \cdot (\rho\mathbf{v} \cdot \nabla\mathbf{v}) = \rho\left[\frac{1}{2}\frac{\partial}{\partial x}(v_x^2 + v_y^2 + v_z^2)\frac{dx}{ds}\right]$$

$$+ \rho\left[\frac{1}{2}\frac{\partial}{\partial y}(v_x^2 + v_y^2 + v_z^2)\frac{dy}{ds}\right] \qquad (7.4\text{-}8)$$

$$+ \rho\left[\frac{1}{2}\frac{\partial}{\partial z}(v_x^2 + v_y^2 + v_z^2)\frac{dz}{ds}\right]$$

Noting that the differential operator d/ds can be expanded in the form

$$\frac{d}{ds} = \frac{dx}{ds}\frac{\partial}{\partial x} + \frac{dy}{ds}\frac{\partial}{\partial y} + \frac{dz}{ds}\frac{\partial}{\partial z} \qquad (7.4\text{-}9)$$

and that

$$v^2 = v_x^2 + v_y^2 + v_z^2 \qquad (7.4\text{-}10)$$

we can write Eq. 7.4-8

$$\left(\frac{d\mathbf{r}}{ds}\right) \cdot (\rho \mathbf{v} \cdot \nabla \mathbf{v}) = \rho \frac{1}{2}\frac{dv^2}{ds} = \frac{d}{ds}(\tfrac{1}{2}\rho v^2) \qquad (7.4\text{-}11)$$

provided the variations in the density are negligible. The right-hand side of Eq. 7.4-3 is treated in an analogous manner to yield

$$\left(\frac{d\mathbf{r}}{ds}\right) \cdot \nabla(p + \rho\phi) = \frac{d}{ds}(p + \rho\phi) \qquad (7.4\text{-}12)$$

Note that the quantity $\boldsymbol{\lambda} \cdot \nabla$ is often called the "directional derivative," for it is a measure of the gradient in the $\boldsymbol{\lambda}$-direction by the formula

$$\boldsymbol{\lambda} \cdot \nabla = \left(\frac{d\mathbf{r}}{ds}\right) \cdot \nabla = \frac{dx}{ds}\frac{\partial}{\partial x} + \frac{dy}{ds}\frac{\partial}{\partial y} + \frac{dz}{ds}\frac{\partial}{\partial z} = \frac{d}{ds} \qquad (7.4\text{-}13)$$

Substitution of Eqs. 7.4-11 and 7.4-12 into Eq. 7.4-3 yields

$$\frac{d}{ds}(\tfrac{1}{2}\rho v^2 + p + \rho\phi) = 0 \qquad (7.4\text{-}14)$$

which may be integrated to give

$$\tfrac{1}{2}\rho v^2 + p + \rho\phi = C_s \qquad (7.4\text{-}15)$$

where C_s is the constant of integration. The subscript s has been used to indicate that the value of the constant may be a function of the streamline. The assumptions for Eq. 7.4-15 should be kept in mind—i.e., steady, incompressible flow and negligible viscous effects. The simplicity of this result makes it especially valuable for rapid qualitative evaluation of many flows.

In general, the coordinate system is taken so that the positive z-axis is oppositely directed to the gravity vector; thus,

$$\phi = gz \qquad (7.4\text{-}16)$$

and Bernoulli's equation takes the form

$$\tfrac{1}{2}\rho v^2 + p + \rho g z = C_s \qquad (7.4\text{-}17)$$

If the fluid is at rest, $v = 0$ and the result derived in Sec. 2.2 for static fluids is obtained. In order to evaluate C_s, we need to know the pressure and the magnitude of the velocity vector at some point in space. If we designate this point as 0 and any other arbitrary point as 1, Eq. 7.4-17 reduces to

$$\tfrac{1}{2}\rho(v_1^2 - v_0^2) + (p_1 - p_0) + \rho g(z_1 - z_0) = 0 \qquad (7.4\text{-}18)$$

Another variation of this development is useful in the qualitative analysis of many flows. We may obtain it by forming the scalar product of Eq. 7.4-1 with the unit normal to the streamline to determine pressure variations normal to the streamline. The analysis is a good deal more complicated than obtaining the tangent scalar component of the equations of motion, and we will resort to an intuitive construction of the final result. Figure 7.4-1 indicates a streamline for steady flow using two tangent circles to describe the

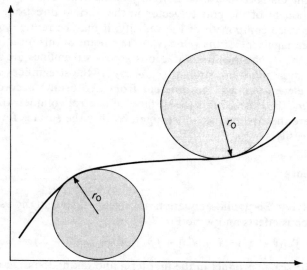

Fig. 7.4-I. Streamline for steady flow.

curvature at two points. At each of those points, the scalar component of the equations of motion normal to the streamline would be the r-component equation of motion in cylindrical coordinates, provided the origin of the coordinate system were located as in Fig. 7.4-1. The key assumption in this development is that for each point on the streamline we can construct a cylindrical coordinate system having one of its coordinate curves tangent to the streamline. Referring now to Table 5.4-2, we write the normal or r-component equation of motion

$$\rho\left(v_r \frac{\partial v_r}{\partial r} + \frac{v_\theta}{r}\frac{\partial v_r}{\partial \theta} - \frac{v_\theta^2}{r} + v_z \frac{\partial v_r}{\partial z}\right) = -\frac{\partial p}{\partial r}$$

$$+ \rho g_r + \mu\left[\frac{\partial}{\partial r}\left(\frac{1}{r}\frac{\partial}{\partial r}(rv_r)\right) + \frac{1}{r^2}\frac{\partial^2 v_r}{\partial \theta^2} - \frac{2}{r^2}\frac{\partial v_\theta}{\partial \theta} + \frac{\partial^2 v_r}{\partial z^2}\right] \qquad (7.4\text{-}19)$$

For the special coordinate systems under consideration, $v_r = v_z = 0$ at $r = r_0$, where r_0 is the radius of curvature of the streamline. Once again we neglect viscous effects, and Eq. 7.4-19 reduces to

$$-\rho \frac{v_\theta^2}{r_0} = -\frac{\partial p}{\partial r} + \rho g_r \qquad (7.4\text{-}20)$$

Most often, this result is expressed

$$-\rho \frac{v^2}{r_0} = -\frac{\partial p}{\partial n} + \rho g_n \qquad (7.4\text{-}21)$$

where n is the distance measured normally to the curve and g_n represents the scalar component of the gravity vector in the normal direction. Since v_θ is the only nonzero component of the velocity, it may be represented at every point as the magnitude of the velocity, v. The point of this intuitive development is to show that pressure variations across streamlines are hydrostatic only if the streamlines are straight ($r_0 \to \infty$). If the streamlines are curved, the pressure variation will be different from hydrostatic according to the term $-\rho v^2/r_0$. Because of this the surfaces of control volumes will always be placed where the streamlines are straight, so that the surface forces may be calculated easily.

Turbulence

In applying Bernoulli's equation to steady turbulent flows, we again neglect viscous effects and write Eq. 7.4-17 as[†]

$$\tfrac{1}{2}\rho[(\bar{\mathbf{v}} + \mathbf{v}') \cdot (\bar{\mathbf{v}} + \mathbf{v}')] + (\bar{p} + p') + \rho g(\bar{z} + z') = C_s \qquad (7.4\text{-}22)$$

Forming the scalar product in the first term and taking the time average, we find

$$\tfrac{1}{2}\rho\bar{v}^2 + \tfrac{1}{2}\rho(\overline{v'})^2 + \bar{p} + \rho g\bar{z} = C_s \qquad (7.4\text{-}23)$$

Once, again, we invoke the order of magnitude argument that

$$(\overline{v'})^2 \ll \bar{v}^2 \qquad (7.4\text{-}24)$$

and the time-averaged form of Bernoulli's equation becomes

$$\tfrac{1}{2}\rho\bar{v}^2 + \bar{p} + \rho g\bar{z} = C_s \qquad (7.4\text{-}25)$$

Viscous effects

Before applying Bernoulli's equation, we need to consider under what conditions we might expect the viscous terms in the equations of motion to be

[†] Here we are making use of the fact that the time average of $\partial v'/\partial t$ is zero.

negligible. We can gain some insight into this problem by examining the dimensionless form of the equations of motion derived in Sec. 5.5.

$$\frac{\partial \mathbf{U}}{\partial \Theta} + \mathbf{U} \cdot \nabla \mathbf{U} = -\nabla \mathscr{P} + \frac{1}{N_{\text{Re}}} \nabla^2 \mathbf{U} \qquad (7.4\text{-}26)$$

When the Reynolds number becomes very large, it might seem that the viscous terms would be negligible, but this is not necessarily so. As an example, Eq. 7.4-26 for steady flow in a pipe reduces to

$$0 = -\nabla \mathscr{P} + \frac{1}{N_{\text{Re}}} \nabla^2 \mathbf{U} \qquad (7.4\text{-}27)$$

and the viscous terms are equal to the pressure terms regardless of what the Reynolds number might be. Thus, a high Reynolds number does not necessarily mean negligible viscous effects. In general, we will find that viscous effects can be neglected when

$$\mathbf{U} \cdot \nabla \mathbf{U} \gg \frac{1}{N_{\text{Re}}} \nabla^2 \mathbf{U} \qquad (7.4\text{-}28)$$

If the Reynolds number is large and

$$\mathbf{U} \cdot \nabla \mathbf{U} = 0(\nabla^2 \mathbf{U}) \qquad (7.4\text{-}29)$$

the inequality will be satisfied. This latter condition requires that the rate of change of velocity in the direction of flow is comparable to the rate of change of velocity perpendicular to the flow. The best way to gain some insight regarding the importance of viscous effects is to solve some problems and compare the results with experiment, for there are no hard and fast rules to guide us in making these approximations.

PART II—APPLICATIONS

7.5 Sudden Expansion in a Pipeline

In this example, we wish to calculate the pressure change caused by a sudden expansion in a pipeline, such as that shown in Fig. 7.5-1. The dashed line indicates the surface of the control volume to which we wish to apply the macroscopic mass, momentum, and mechanical energy balances. The points a and b indicate the segment of the center streamline to which we will apply Bernoulli's equation. The flow is steady, turbulent and incompressible.

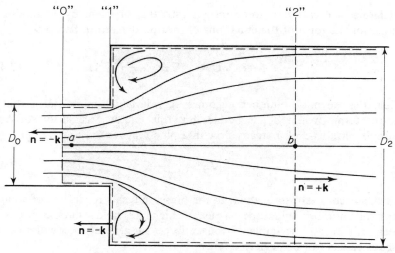

Fig. 7.5-1. Sudden expansion in a pipeline.

Mass balance

For a fixed control volume and steady, incompressible flow, we start with Eq. 7.1-11

$$\int_{A_e} \rho \mathbf{v} \cdot \mathbf{n} \, dA = 0 \tag{7.5-1}$$

which quickly reduces to

$$\rho \langle v_z \rangle_2 \frac{\pi D_2^2}{4} = \rho \langle v_z \rangle_0 \frac{\pi D_0^2}{4} \tag{7.5-2}$$

or

$$\langle v_z \rangle_2 = \langle v_z \rangle_0 \left(\frac{D_0}{D_2} \right)^2$$

Momentum balance

We start with Eq. 7.2-11

$$\int_{A_e} (\rho \mathbf{v}) \mathbf{v} \cdot \mathbf{n} \, dA = \int_{\mathscr{V}} \rho \mathbf{g} \, dV + \int_{\mathscr{A}} \mathbf{t}_{(n)} \, dA \tag{7.5-3}$$

and assume that viscous and turbulent stresses are small,† so that the stress

---

† The assumption of negligible viscous effects is to be made throughout this chapter. Turbulent stresses are identically zero at solid surfaces and are generally considered to be small compared to the pressure at entrances and exits.

vector is given by

$$\mathbf{t}_{(n)} = -\mathbf{n}p \tag{7.5-4}$$

In all these examples, we will dispense with the time-average symbol, which should be used with turbulent flows, and require the student to remember the adjustments necessary to account properly for the time averaging. Substitution of Eq. 7.5-4 into Eq. 7.5-3, and formation of the scalar product with the unit vector $\mathbf{k}$, yield

$$\int_{A_e} \rho v_z \mathbf{v} \cdot \mathbf{n} \, dA = -\int_{\mathscr{A}} p\mathbf{k} \cdot \mathbf{n} \, dA \tag{7.5-5}$$

where we have made use of the fact that $\mathbf{k} \cdot \mathbf{g} = 0$. The planes at 0 and 2 are placed far enough upstream and downstream so that the flow is one-dimensional at these points; however, the answer obtained in this example will be independent of the placement of 0 and 2. The purpose in placing them in a correct location is in some respects a device for forcing the questions: "Does the disturbance propagate upstream at all?" "How far downstream must one go before the flow is one-dimensional?" or, in the language of Sec. 1.3, "What is the flow topology?" Asking these questions helps to emphasize the assumptions made in solving the problem, for if the distance between 1 and 2 is very large,† the assumption of negligible viscous forces is unsatisfactory.

The area integral on the left-hand side of Eq. 7.5-5 is to be evaluated only at the entrance and exit of the control volume, while the area integral on the right-hand side must be evaluated over the entire surface. Noting that $\mathbf{n} \cdot \mathbf{k} = 0$ along the walls of the pipe, and expressing the integrals in terms of area averages yields

$$-\rho\langle v_z^2\rangle_0 \frac{\pi D_0^2}{4} + \rho\langle v_z^2\rangle_2 \frac{\pi D_2^2}{4}$$

$$= \langle p\rangle_0 \frac{\pi D_0^2}{4} + \langle p\rangle_1 \frac{\pi}{4}(D_2^2 - D_0^2) - \langle p\rangle_2 \frac{\pi D_2^2}{4} \tag{7.5-6}$$

There is a very important point to be made regarding the term $\langle p\rangle_1$ $(\pi/4)(D_2^2 - D_0^0)$, for experience has shown that students will often neglect this term. The reason appears to be associated with a general error made in the analysis of macroscopic balance problems—i.e., focusing attention on entrances and exits and completely forgetting about other surfaces. Whenever the symbol $\mathscr{A}$ appears on an integral, the student is urged to examine each and every portion of the control surface, especially those which are not entrances or exits.

---

† The distance between 0 and 1 is negligible except for flows where $N_{\mathrm{Re}} < 1$.

If we wish to develop an expression for the pressure difference†

$$\Delta p = \langle p \rangle_0 - \langle p \rangle_2 \qquad (7.5\text{-}7)$$

we must eliminate $\langle p \rangle_1$ from Eq. 7.5-6. If the distance between 0 and 1 is negligible and the pressure variation over the annular region is hydrostatic, it is reasonable to make the approximation

$$\langle p \rangle_1 = \langle p \rangle_0 \qquad (7.5\text{-}8)$$

and Eq. 7.5-6 can be rearranged in the form

$$\Delta p = \rho \langle v_z^2 \rangle_2 - \rho \langle v_z^2 \rangle_0 \left(\frac{D_0}{D_2} \right)^2 \qquad (7.5\text{-}9)$$

For turbulent flows, the velocity profile is nearly flat; thus, the average of the square may be approximated by the square of the average. We shall investigate this approximation in more detail later; for now, we simply write,

$$\langle v_z^2 \rangle = \langle v_z \rangle^2 \qquad (7.5\text{-}10)$$

and make use of the macroscopic mass balance to arrange Eq. 7.5-9 in the form

$$\Delta p = \rho \langle v_z \rangle_0^2 \left[\left(\frac{D_0}{D_2} \right)^2 - 1 \right] \left(\frac{D_0}{D_2} \right)^2 \qquad (7.5\text{-}11)$$

We note that

$$\left(\frac{D_0}{D_2} \right)^2 - 1 \le 0$$

and the pressure therefore rises from 0 to 2. It often seems incongruous that the pressure would rise in the direction of flow. An intuitive explanation may be helpful. As a particle of fluid moves from 0 to 2, its velocity, and hence its momentum, must decrease. For the momentum of a fluid particle to decrease, a force must be applied in the direction opposite to the flow. In the sudden expansion this force is the pressure rise.

In comparing this result with experimental data, it is convenient to define a dimensionless pressure difference as

$$\Delta P = \frac{\Delta p}{\frac{1}{2}\rho \langle v_z \rangle_0^2} \qquad (7.5\text{-}12)$$

where the factor of $\frac{1}{2}$ in the denominator is simply a matter of tradition. The dimensionless pressure difference given by the momentum equation now takes the form

$$\Delta P = 2 \left[\left(\frac{D_0}{D_2} \right)^2 - 1 \right] \left(\frac{D_0}{D_2} \right)^2 \qquad (7.5\text{-}13)$$

† The symbol Δp will always be used to denote upstream pressure minus downstream pressure.

The assumptions for this result follow.

1. Viscous effects were neglected—i.e., viscous surface forces were considered negligible.
2. The average pressure on the annular surface was taken to be equal to the average pressure at point 0.
3. The velocity profiles were assumed to be flat at 0 and 2.

Next, we will attack this problem using the mechanical energy balance, which will allow us to obtain a solution for ΔP while making simplifying assumptions different from those listed above.

Mechanical energy balance

We start this analysis with the steady flow, fixed control volume form of the mechanical energy balance

$$\int_{A_e} \tfrac{1}{2}\rho v^2 \mathbf{v} \cdot \mathbf{n}\, dA = \int_{A_e} \mathbf{v} \cdot \mathbf{t}_{(\mathbf{n})}\, dA - \int_{A_e} \rho \phi \mathbf{v} \cdot \mathbf{n}\, dA - \dot{E}_v \qquad (7.5\text{-}14)$$

In this case, neglecting viscous effects requires that we assume

$$\dot{E}_v = 0 \qquad (7.5\text{-}15)$$

Since the flow is one-dimensional at the entrance and exit, we may write

$$\mathbf{v} \cdot \mathbf{t}_{(\mathbf{n})} = \pm(k v_z) \cdot \mathbf{t}_{(\mathbf{n})} = \pm v_z\left(\mp p \pm 2\mu \frac{\partial v_z}{\partial z}\right) \qquad (7.5\text{-}16)$$

But $\partial v_z/\partial z$ is zero for one-dimensional flows and Eq. 7.5-16 becomes

$$\mathbf{v} \cdot \mathbf{t}_{(\mathbf{n})} = \pm v_z p \qquad (7.5\text{-}17)$$

indicating that the viscous effects at the entrance and exit are identically zero. The potential energy flux term may be written as

$$\int_{A_e} \rho \phi \mathbf{v} \cdot \mathbf{n}\, dA = -\rho\langle \phi v_z \rangle_0 \frac{\pi D_0^2}{4} + \rho\langle \phi v_z \rangle_2 \frac{\pi D_2^2}{4} \qquad (7.5\text{-}18)$$

Since the velocity profiles are taken to be flat, and $\phi = gy$, this term is zero,

$$\int_{A_e} \rho \phi \mathbf{v} \cdot \mathbf{n}\, dA = -\rho\langle v_z \rangle_0 \frac{\pi D_0^2}{4} [\langle gy \rangle_0 - \langle gy \rangle_2] = 0 \qquad (7.5\text{-}19)$$

Incorporating this result into Eq. 7.5-14 along with Eqs. 7.5-15 and 7.5-17, and expressing the integrals in terms of averages and areas, we get

$$-\tfrac{1}{2}\rho\langle v_z^3\rangle_0 \frac{\pi D_0^2}{4} + \tfrac{1}{2}\rho\langle v_z^3\rangle_2 \frac{\pi D_2^2}{4}$$

$$= -\langle pv_z\rangle_2 \frac{\pi D_2^2}{4} + \langle pv_z\rangle_0 \frac{\pi D_0^2}{4}$$

(7.5-20)

We again assume that the velocity profiles are flat in order to write

$$\langle v_z^3\rangle = \langle v_z\rangle^3 \quad \text{and} \quad \langle pv_z\rangle = \langle p\rangle\langle v_z\rangle \qquad (7.5\text{-}21)$$

and apply the mass balance to Eq. 7.5-20 to obtain the dimensionless pressure difference

$$\Delta P = \left[\left(\frac{D_0}{D_2}\right)^4 - 1 \right] \qquad (7.5\text{-}22)$$

The assumptions for this result follow.

1. Viscous effects were neglected—i.e., viscous dissipation was considered negligible.
2. The velocity profiles were assumed to be flat at 0 and 2.

Aside from the flat velocity profiles, the assumptions made to obtain a solution with the mechanical energy balance were very different from those made in applying the momentum balance. That the results differ simply indicates some of the assumptions must be in error. In using the mechanical energy balance, no assumption regarding the pressure acting on the annular region was necessary. The assumption of negligible viscous effects leads to two different assumptions when applied to the momentum and mechanical energy balances. In the former case, it leads to the neglect of viscous surface forces

$$\mathbf{n}\cdot\boldsymbol{\tau} \approx 0 \qquad \begin{array}{l}\text{over the } surface \text{ of} \\ \text{the control volume}\end{array} \qquad (7.5\text{-}23)$$

while in the latter case it leads to the neglect of viscous dissipation

$$\nabla \mathbf{v} : \boldsymbol{\tau} \approx 0 \qquad \begin{array}{l}\text{over the } volume \text{ of} \\ \text{the control volume}\end{array} \qquad (7.5\text{-}24)$$

Before comparing these two solutions with experimental data, let us apply Bernoulli's equation to this problem. Although Bernoulli's equation is not particularly suited for analyzing problems of this type, it will help us gain some practice in its application.

Bernoulli's equation along a streamline

We assume the flow to be steady and neglect viscous effects. Under these conditions, we may apply Bernoulli's equation along the streamline between points a and b to obtain

$$\tfrac{1}{2}\rho v_b^2 + p_b + \rho \phi_b = \tfrac{1}{2}\rho v_a^2 + p_a + \rho \phi_a \qquad (7.5\text{-}25)$$

Since $\phi_b = \phi_a$, the pressure difference between points a and b is

$$p_b - p_a = \tfrac{1}{2}\rho(v_a^2 - v_b^2) \qquad (7.5\text{-}26)$$

To proceed with the analysis and make use of the macroscopic mass balance, we must assume that the velocity profiles are flat at 0 and 2. We may then write

$$v_a = \langle v_z \rangle_0 \qquad (7.5\text{-}27a)$$

$$v_b = \langle v_z \rangle_2 \qquad (7.5\text{-}27b)$$

Because the pressure variation is linear across the pipe, we may also write

$$p_a = \langle p \rangle_0 \qquad (7.5\text{-}28a)$$

$$p_b = \langle p \rangle_2 \qquad (7.5\text{-}28b)$$

Substitution of Eqs. 7.5-27 and 7.5-28 into Eq. 7.5-26 gives

$$\langle p \rangle_2 - \langle p \rangle_0 = \tfrac{1}{2}\rho[\langle v_z \rangle_0^2 - \langle v_z \rangle_2^2] \qquad (7.5\text{-}29)$$

Use of the macroscopic mass balance and the definition of the dimensionless pressure difference give

$$\Delta P = \left[\left(\frac{D_0}{D_2} \right)^4 - 1 \right] \qquad (7.5\text{-}30)$$

which is the same result obtained with the mechanical energy balance. Because the two equations were derived in nearly the same manner and the assumptions made in solving this problem were the same, we should expect the result to be similar if not identical.

Very often the final result can be obtained with less effort by using Bernoulli's equation instead of the mechanical energy balance; however, the mechanical energy balance is derived for the express purpose of solving macroscopic (or integral) problems, and it is best to use it whenever possible. Later, we shall encounter some problems best treated with Bernoulli's equation; thus, it is necessary to become skillful in applying both methods.

The results obtained from the momentum balance and the mechanical energy balance are compared with experiments in Table 7.5-1.

From this comparison, we learn that the agreement between the momentum balance and experiment is reasonably good, while the agreement with the mechanical energy balance becomes progressively worse as $(D_0/D_2) \to 0$. In this particular instance, the viscous surface forces are justifiably neglected in the momentum balance, whereas the viscous dissipation term in the mechanical energy balance may not be neglected. If the dissipation term is

Table 7.5-1

COMPARISON OF CALCULATED AND MEASURED PRESSURE
RISE AT A SUDDEN EXPANSION IN A PIPELINE[a]

Ratio of Diameters D_0/D_2	Experimental Value ΔP_{exp}	Momentum Balance, Eq. 7.5-13 ΔP_{mom}	Mechanical Energy Balance, Eq. 7.5-22 $\Delta P_{mech\ eng}$
0.843	−0.33	−0.41	−0.49
0.695	−0.42	−0.50	−0.77
0.590	−0.45	−0.45	−0.88
0.394	−0.24	−0.26	−0.98
0.328	−0.18	−0.19	−0.99

[a] Data obtained from W. H. Archer. *Trans. ASCE.* 1913. 76: 999.

included in the analysis, Eq. 7.5-22 becomes

$$\Delta P = \left[\left(\frac{D_0}{D_2} \right)^4 - 1 \right] + \frac{8\dot{E}_v}{\pi D_0^2 \rho \langle v_z \rangle_0^3} \qquad (7.5\text{-}31)$$

Inasmuch as the dissipation term is always positive, Eq. 7.5-31 indicates that the pressure difference determined by the mechanical energy balance would be smaller (and therefore in better agreement with the experimental data) if the viscous dissipation term were included.

We should make an important point regarding these results. Namely, the momentum and mechanical energy balance may give results which are not very satisfactory. If they both give essentially the same result, there is a good chance that the result is satisfactory. However, if they give appreciably different results, the engineer must beware. Another point to be made is that it is not at all obvious, a priori, that it was reasonable to neglect viscous surface forces and unreasonable to neglect viscous dissipation. It takes more experience than a student can possibly gain in one or two courses in fluid mechanics to make sound judgments regarding such assumptions.

Velocity profiles

For future reference, we wish to investigate the validity of the approximations

$$\langle v_z^2 \rangle = \langle v_z \rangle^2 \qquad (7.5\text{-}32a)$$

$$\langle v_z^3 \rangle = \langle v_z \rangle^3 \qquad (7.5\text{-}32b)$$

Experimental measurements of the time-averaged velocity for turbulent flow in a pipe indicate that the velocity profile is given approximately by

$$v_z = v_{z,\max} \left(1 - \frac{r}{r_0} \right)^{1/n} \qquad (7.5\text{-}33)$$

where n is given as a function of the Reynolds number in Table 7.5-2.

Table 7.5-2
DEPENDENCE OF THE COEFFICIENT, n, ON
THE REYNOLDS NUMBER, N_{Re}

$n =$	6	7	10
$N_{Re} =$	4×10^3	1×10^5	3×10^6

The average velocity in a pipe is given by

$$\langle v_z \rangle = \frac{\int_0^{2\pi} \int_0^{r_0} v_{z,\max}\left(1 - \frac{r}{r_0}\right)^{1/n} r\, dr\, d\theta}{\int_0^{2\pi} \int_0^{r} r\, dr\, d\theta} = v_{z,\max} \frac{2n^2}{(1 + n)(1 + 2n)}$$

(7.5-34a)

Similarly, we can determine the average of the square and cube of the velocity.

$$\langle v_z^2 \rangle = v_{z,\max}^2 \frac{n^2}{(1 + n)(2 + n)}$$

(7.5-34b)

$$\langle v_z^3 \rangle = v_{z,\max}^3 \frac{2n^2}{(3 + n)(3 + 2n)}$$

(7.5-34c)

Using these results, we can test the approximations indicated by Eqs. 7.5-32 for various values of n. The results appear in Table 7.5-3 and indicate that even though the velocity profile is certainly not flat, for which case $\langle v_z \rangle / v_{z,\max} = 1.0$, the approximations given by Eqs. 7.5-32 are very reasonable. The values for the parabolic profile which occurs when the flow is laminar are

Table 7.5-3
DEVIATIONS FROM THE FLAT VELOCITY PROFILE

	Turbulent					Laminar
n	6	7	8	9	10	Parabolic Profile
$\dfrac{\langle v_z \rangle}{v_{z,\max}}$	0.79	0.82	0.84	0.85	0.87	0.5
$\dfrac{\langle v_z^2 \rangle}{\langle v_z \rangle^2}$	1.03	1.02	1.02	1.01	1.01	1.33
$\dfrac{\langle v_z^3 \rangle}{\langle v_z \rangle^3}$	1.08	1.06	1.05	1.04	1.03	2.0

also given for comparison, and we see that the terms in the macroscopic balances must be treated with caution if the flow is laminar.

7.6 Sudden Contraction in a Pipeline

In this example, we again wish to apply the momentum and mechanical energy balances to a particular system and then compare the results with experimental data. We will not apply Bernoulli's equation inasmuch as it

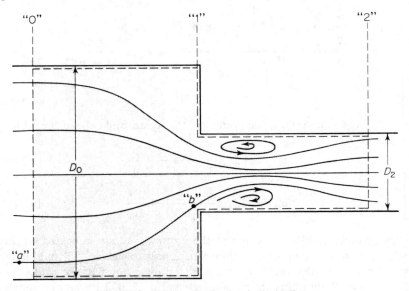

Fig. 7.6-1. Sudden contraction in a pipeline.

obviously gives the same result as the mechanical energy balance. The sudden contraction and the control volume to be used are illustrated in Fig. 7.6-1.

Momentum balance

Starting with Eq. 7.2-11, we neglect the viscous stresses and apply it to this system to obtain

$$
\begin{aligned}
-\rho \langle v_z^2 \rangle_0 \frac{\pi D_0^2}{4} + \rho \langle v_z^2 \rangle_2 \frac{\pi D_2^2}{4} \\
= \langle p \rangle_0 \frac{\pi D_0^2}{4} - \langle p \rangle_1 \frac{\pi}{4} (D_0^2 - D_2^2) - \langle p \rangle_2 \frac{\pi D_2^2}{4}
\end{aligned}
\tag{7.6-1}
$$

In this case, our intuition does not encourage us to set $\langle p \rangle_1$ equal to $\langle p \rangle_0$, nor does it seem reasonable to equate $\langle p \rangle_1$ and $\langle p \rangle_2$. However, to derive an expression for the pressure difference between points 0 and 2, the pressure at 1 must be eliminated from Eq. 7.6-1. For this reason we will set $\langle p \rangle_1$ equal to $\langle p \rangle_0$ and assume the velocity profiles are flat at 0 and 2. We obtain

$$\langle p \rangle_0 - \langle p \rangle_2 = \rho \langle v_z \rangle_2^2 - \rho \langle v_z \rangle_0^2 \left(\frac{D_0}{D_2}\right)^2 \tag{7.6-2}$$

In this case, we define the dimensionless pressure difference as

$$\Delta P = \frac{\langle p \rangle_0 - \langle p \rangle_2}{\frac{1}{2}\rho \langle v_z \rangle_2^2} \tag{7.6-3}$$

the denominator of which differs from that used for the sudden expansion. The macroscopic mass balance may be used in conjunction with Eqs. 7.6-2 and 7.6-3 to yield

$$\Delta P = 2\left[1 - \left(\frac{D_2}{D_0}\right)^2\right] \tag{7.6-4}$$

Because $(D_2/D_0)^2$ is always less than unity, Eq. 7.6-4 predicts a pressure drop in the direction of flow. Since the momentum of the fluid increases from 0 to 2, a force in that direction must be applied to the fluid and this force is supplied by the pressure drop.

Mechanical energy equation

Starting with Eq. 7.3-31, we assume that the rate of viscous dissipation is negligible and note from the previous example that the potential energy term is zero. We obtain

$$\int_{A_e} (\tfrac{1}{2}\rho v^2)\mathbf{v} \cdot \mathbf{n} \, dA = -\int_{A_e} p\mathbf{v} \cdot \mathbf{n} \, dA \tag{7.6-5}$$

Application of this equation to the sudden contraction is straightforward, and the result is

$$\Delta P = \left[1 - \left(\frac{D_2}{D_0}\right)^4\right] \tag{7.6-6}$$

Once again, the results from the two macroscopic balances are very different. The comparison with experiments is given in Table 7.6-1. The momentum balance predicts a pressure drop that is too large and the mechanical energy balance predicts a pressure drop that is too small.

Table 7.6-1

COMPARISON OF CALCULATED AND MEASURED PRESSURE DIFFERENCES
AT A SUDDEN CONTRACTION IN A PIPELINE[a]

D_2/D_0	Experimental Value ΔP_{exp}	Momentum Balance, Eq. 7.6-4 ΔP_{mom}	Mechanical Energy Balance, Eq. 7.6-6 $\Delta P_{mech\ eng}$
0.91	0.35	0.34	0.31
0.71	0.98	0.99	0.75
0.50	1.30	1.50	0.94
0.33	1.41	1.78	0.99
0.20	1.45	1.92	1.00
0.10	1.46	1.98	1.00
0.0	1.47	2.00	1.00

[a] Data are taken from H. W. King and E. F. Brater, *Handbook of Hydraulics* (New York: McGraw-Hill Book Company, Inc., 1963), pp. 6-21. Experimental values are for Reynolds numbers on the order of 10^5.

The error in the momentum balance must arise either from the assumption that $\langle p \rangle_1$ is equal to $\langle p \rangle_0$, or from the neglect of viscous surface forces. Let us return to Eq. 7.6-1 and modify it to include a viscous surface force, F_v, which must act in the direction opposite to the flow and also express the average pressure at point 1 as

$$\langle p \rangle_1 = \langle p \rangle_0 + \delta p \qquad (7.6\text{-}7)$$

Equation 7.6-1 now becomes

$$-\rho \langle v_z^2 \rangle_0 \frac{\pi D_0^2}{4} + \rho \langle v_z^2 \rangle_2 \frac{\pi D_2^2}{4} = \langle p \rangle_0 \frac{\pi D_0^2}{4}$$

$$-[\langle p \rangle_0 + \delta p] \frac{\pi}{4}(D_0^2 - D_2^2) - \langle p \rangle_2 \frac{\pi D_2^2}{4} - F_v \qquad (7.6\text{-}8)$$

Assuming the velocity profiles to be flat, and making use of the macroscopic mass balance, we can write the dimensionless pressure drop,

$$\Delta P = 2\left[1 - \left(\frac{D_2}{D_0}\right)^2\right] - \delta P\left[1 - \left(\frac{D_0}{D_2}\right)^2\right] + \frac{8F_v}{\rho \langle v_z \rangle_2^2 \pi D_2^2} \qquad (7.6\text{-}9)$$

where

$$\delta P = \frac{\delta p}{\frac{1}{2}\rho \langle v_z \rangle_2^2}$$

We see from this result that the inclusion of viscous forces would make ΔP even larger, thus increasing the disagreement between calculation and experiment. Inasmuch as the term

$$\left[1 - \left(\frac{D_0}{D_2}\right)^2\right]$$

is always negative, δP must be negative for Eq. 7.6-9 to agree with the experimental data. Thus, the pressure at 1 must be less than the pressure at 0. We may make an attempt to calculate the pressure at 1 by applying Bernoulli's equation along a streamline from a to b. From the results of the mechanical energy balance, we already know that viscous dissipation is not negligible; however, it is probable that most of the dissipation takes place in the region between 1 and 2. Neglecting viscous dissipation and gravitational effects, we find that Bernoulli's equation gives us

$$p_b - p_a = \tfrac{1}{2}\rho(v_a^2 - v_b^2) \tag{7.6-10}$$

If we assume

$$\delta p = p_b - p_a$$
$$\langle v_z \rangle_0^2 = v_a^2$$

we may write Eq. 7.6-10 as

$$\delta P = \frac{\langle v_z \rangle_0^2 - v_b^2}{\langle v_z \rangle_2^2} \tag{7.6-11}$$

Since we do not know the flow field at 1, we can carry this analysis no further; however, it seems logical that $v_b > \langle v_z \rangle_0$ and Bernoulli's equation confirms our previous deduction that δP must be negative.

In comparing the mechanical energy balance with the experimental data, we can conclude easily that the neglect of viscous dissipation is the cause of disagreement between the calculated and experimental values. If this term is included in the analysis, Eq. 7.6-6 takes the form

$$\Delta P = \left[1 - \left(\frac{D_2}{D_0} \right)^4 \right] + \frac{8\dot{E}_v}{\rho \langle v_z \rangle_2^3 \pi D_2^2} \tag{7.6-12}$$

Because $\dot{E}_v$ is positive, inclusion of viscous dissipation in the analysis would necessarily improve the result.

Once again, the momentum and mechanical energy balances and Bernoulli's equation provide only approximate answers. In the case of the sudden expansion in a pipeline, the momentum balance gave reasonably good agreement with experiment while the mechanical energy balance gave rather poor results. For the sudden contraction, both balances showed considerable error as $(D_2/D_0) \to 0$. If nothing else, these two examples should encourage the student to view approximate solutions with skepticism. In the next section, we shall continue this comparison between the three approximate solutions and experimental data for the nozzle and the Borda mouthpiece.

7.7 The Nozzle and the Borda Mouthpiece

Figure 7.7-1 illustrates a large tank with a smooth rounded nozzle near the bottom. If the nozzle is properly shaped, the streamlines will be nearly parallel as the fluid issues into the surrounding atmosphere and the pressure

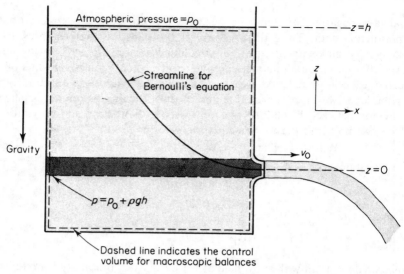

Fig. 7.7-1. Nozzle in a large tank.

in the jet will be atmospheric. Since the top surface, at $z = h$, is moving, we must be cautious when applying the macroscopic balances.

Momentum balance

We start with the complete momentum balance given previously as Eq. 7.2-10.

$$\frac{d}{dt} \int_{\mathscr{V}_a(t)} \rho \mathbf{v} \, dV + \int_{A_e(t)} \rho \mathbf{v}(\mathbf{v} - \mathbf{w}) \cdot \mathbf{n} \, dA = \int_{\mathscr{V}_a(t)} \rho \mathbf{g} \, dV + \int_{\mathscr{A}_a(t)} \mathbf{t}_{(n)} \, dA \qquad (7.7\text{-}1)$$

We assume first that the level in the tank is changed slowly, and we make the approximation

$$\frac{d}{dt} \int_{\mathscr{V}_a(t)} \rho \mathbf{v} \, dV \approx 0 \qquad (7.7\text{-}2)$$

This type of assumption classifies the analysis as "quasi-steady," for we are treating an inherently transient system with the steady-state form of the momentum balance. This kind of approximation is a common tool of engineering analysis, and it should always be accompanied by the question, "Is this a reasonable approximation?" This question is rather difficult to answer; however, it would appear to be a reasonable approximation if the tank were large and the drainage rate small.†

† After the solution for the flow rate is obtained one may use it to estimate the acceleration term, and thus determine the validity of Eq. 7.7-2.

We also assume that viscous effects are negligible and take the scalar product of Eq. 7.7-1 with the unit vector $\mathbf{i}$ to obtain

$$\int_{A_e(t)} \rho v_x (\mathbf{v} - \mathbf{w}) \cdot \mathbf{n} \, dA = -\int_{\mathscr{A}_a(t)} p\mathbf{n} \cdot \mathbf{i} \, dA \qquad (7.7\text{-}3)$$

The momentum flux integral is zero everywhere, except at the nozzle where it takes on the value

$$\int_{A_e(t)} \rho v_x (\mathbf{v} - \mathbf{w}) \cdot \mathbf{n} \, dA = \rho v_0^2 A_0 \qquad (7.7\text{-}4)$$

where A_0 equals the nozzle area. In obtaining this result, we have assumed that the velocity profile at the exit of the nozzle is flat. If we take the pressure everywhere in the tank to be hydrostatic, the right-hand side of Eq. 7.7-3 becomes

$$-\int_{\mathscr{A}_a(t)} p\mathbf{n} \cdot \mathbf{i} \, dA = \underset{\substack{\text{Opposite the nozzle}}}{(p_0 + \rho gh)A_0} - \underset{\substack{\text{At the} \\ \text{nozzle exit}}}{p_0 A_0} \qquad (7.7\text{-}5)$$

Substituting Eqs. 7.7-4 and 7.7-5 into Eq. 7.7-3, and solving for the velocity and volumetric flow rate, yield

$$v_0 = \sqrt{gh} \qquad (7.7\text{-}6a)$$

$$Q = A_0\sqrt{gh} \qquad (7.7\text{-}6b)$$

The following assumptions contributed to this result.

1. The flow is quasi-steady.
2. Viscous forces are negligible.
3. The velocity profile at the nozzle is flat (very nearly accomplished by proper nozzle design).
4. The pressure everywhere in the tank is the hydrostatic pressure.

Mechanical energy balance

We start with the complete mechanical energy balance given by Eq. 7.3-27. Noting that $\dot{W} = 0$ for this control volume, and assuming that $\dot{E}_v = 0$, we obtain

$$\frac{d}{dt} \int_{\mathscr{V}_a(t)} (\tfrac{1}{2}\rho v^2) \, dV + \int_{A_e(t)} (\tfrac{1}{2}\rho v^2)(\mathbf{v} - \mathbf{w}) \cdot \mathbf{n} \, dA$$

$$= \int_{A_e(t)} \mathbf{v} \cdot \mathbf{t}_{(\mathbf{n})} \, dA - \int_{\mathscr{A}_a(t)} \rho \phi \mathbf{v} \cdot \mathbf{n} \, dA \qquad (7.7\text{-}7)$$

Once again we restrict ourselves to quasi-steady flows and neglect viscous forces to obtain

$$\int_{A_e(t)} (\tfrac{1}{2}\rho v^2)(\mathbf{v} - \mathbf{w}) \cdot \mathbf{n}\, dA = -\int_{A_e(t)} p\mathbf{v} \cdot \mathbf{n}\, dA - \int_{\mathscr{A}_a(t)} \rho gz\mathbf{v} \cdot \mathbf{n}\, dA \qquad (7.7\text{-}8)$$

where we have written

$$\mathbf{t}_{(n)} = -\mathbf{n}p$$
$$\phi = gz$$

The kinetic energy flux term is zero everywhere except at the nozzle where it has the value

$$\int_{A_e(t)} (\tfrac{1}{2}\rho v^2)(\mathbf{v} - \mathbf{w}) \cdot \mathbf{n}\, dA = \tfrac{1}{2}\rho v_0^3 A_0 \qquad (7.7\text{-}9)$$

The first area integral on the right-hand side of Eq. 7.7-8 is finite only at the nozzle and at the free surface where $\mathbf{v} = \mathbf{w}$. The velocity at the free surface, v_s, may be obtained by making a mass balance on the system, which gives

$$v_s A_T = v_0 A_0 \qquad (7.7\text{-}10)$$

where A_T is the cross-sectional area of the tank. Evaluation of the area integral indicates that it is identically zero.

$$-\int_{A_e(t)} p\mathbf{v} \cdot \mathbf{n}\, dA = p_0 v_s A_T - p_0 v_0 A_0 \qquad (7.7\text{-}11)$$

The second integral on the right-hand side of Eq. 7.7-8 is given by

$$\int_{\mathscr{A}_a(t)} \rho gz\mathbf{v} \cdot \mathbf{n}\, dA = -\rho g h v_s A_T + g\langle z \rangle_0 v_0 A_0 = -\rho g h v_s A_T \qquad (7.7\text{-}12)$$

because

$$\langle z \rangle_0 = 0 \qquad (7.7\text{-}13)$$

Substitution of Eqs. 7.7-9 and 7.7-12 into Eq. 7.7-8, and solving for the velocity and volumetric flow rate, yield

$$v_0 = \sqrt{2gh} \qquad (7.7\text{-}14a)$$

$$Q = A_0\sqrt{2gh} \qquad (7.7\text{-}14b)$$

The following assumptions contributed to this result.

1. The flow is quasi-steady.
2. Viscous dissipation is negligible.
3. The velocity profile at the nozzle is flat.

We note that the assumption of quasi-steady flow led us to neglect the time rate of change of the kinetic energy in the control volume, but we did not assume that the free surface velocity, v_s, was zero. If we had, the integral given by Eq. 7.7-11 would not be zero, and a rather different answer for the velocity and volumetric flow rate would have been obtained. In the next section, we will apply Bernoulli's equation along the streamline indicated in Figure 7.6-1 and take v_s to be negligible to obtain the same result given by the mechanical energy balance.

Bernoulli's equation

Assuming quasi-steady flow and neglecting viscous effects, we apply Eq. 7.4-18 to a streamline between the free surface and the nozzle, which gives us

$$\tfrac{1}{2}\rho(v_0^2 - v_s^2) + (p_0 - p_0) + \rho g(0 - h) = 0 \tag{7.7-15}$$

The assumption that the cross-sectional area of the tank is much larger than the cross-sectional area of the nozzle gives

$$\frac{A_0}{A_T} = \frac{v_s}{v_0} \ll 1, \qquad \text{or} \quad v_s \ll v_0$$

and we may solve for the velocity and volumetric flow rate to obtain

$$v_0 = \sqrt{2gh} \tag{7.7-16a}$$

$$Q = A_0\sqrt{2gh} \tag{7.7-16b}$$

which is the same result obtained with the mechanical energy balance. Use of Bernoulli's equation leads us to the final result in just a few steps, whereas the mechanical energy balance requires a somewhat more careful analysis. Note that in Bernoulli's equation the surface velocity v_s is dropped because it is small compared to the nozzle velocity v_0, while in the mechanical energy balance, the term involving the surface velocity very definitely cannot be neglected. While the derivation of the two differential equations that led to the mechanical energy balance and Bernoulli's equation were very similar (in the first, we formed the scalar product with **v** and in the second, with **v**/v), one equation was integrated over a volume while the other was integrated along a streamline; therefore, we may expect the results to be somewhat different.

The results obtained by the momentum balance and the mechanical energy balance (and Bernoulli's equation) differ by a factor of $\sqrt{2}$. Experiments[1]

1. H. W. King and E. F. Brater, *Handbook of Hydraulics* (New York: McGraw-Hill Book Company, 1963), p. 4–20.

for water under conditions such that inertial effects predominate indicate

$$v_0 \approx 0.98\sqrt{2gh} \qquad (7.7\text{-}17\text{a})$$

$$Q \approx 0.98\,A_0\sqrt{2gh} \qquad (7.7\text{-}17\text{b})$$

The excellent agreement between the mechanical energy balance and experiments leads us to believe that either the assumptions were valid, or there are compensating errors in the solution. This latter possibility is not considered as often as it should be; in this case, however, assumptions 1 and 3 are satisfactory, and we conclude that viscous dissipation is indeed negligible for the reported experiments.

A question naturally arises from this example: "Why is the momentum equation in error by approximately 40 per cent?" The answer is that the pressure in the tank is not everywhere hydrostatic, and an analysis of the Borda mouthpiece should help illustrate this point.

The Borda mouthpiece

The nozzle in the tank illustrated in Fig. 7.7-1 may be replaced with a Borda mouthpiece shown in Fig. 7.7-2. The momentum and mechanical energy balances are applied to the Borda mouthpiece in exactly the same manner as for the nozzle, and the results are

$$v_0 = \left(\frac{A_0}{A_c}\right)^{1/2} \sqrt{gh} \qquad \text{momentum balance} \qquad (7.7\text{-}18)$$

$$v_0 = \sqrt{2gh} \qquad \text{mechanical energy balance} \qquad (7.7\text{-}19)$$

On the basis of the excellent result obtained with the mechanical energy balance for the velocity v_0 at the nozzle, we expect the velocity at the Borda mouthpiece to be given accurately by Eq. 7.7-19. Note that we choose the control volume for the Borda mouthpiece to cut the jet at a place where the streamlines are parallel, thus assuring us that the flow is one-dimensional at that point and the pressure in the jet is atmospheric. Although the velocity is determined by Eq. 7.7-19, we cannot compute the volumetric flow rate because the area of the jet where the flow becomes parallel, A_c, is unknown.

If the momentum balance, contrary to the result for the nozzle, provides a satisfactory result for the Borda mouthpiece, we may use Eqs. 7.7-18 and 7.7-19 to calculate A_c and thus the volumetric flow rate. We obtain

$$\left(\frac{A_c}{A_0}\right) = 0.50 \qquad (7.7\text{-}20\text{a})$$

and

$$Q = 0.50A_0\sqrt{2gh} \qquad (7.7\text{-}20\text{b})$$

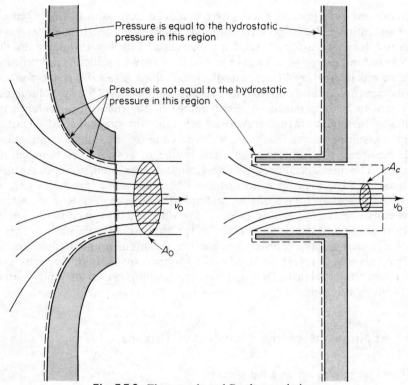

Fig. 7.7-2. Flow nozzle and Borda mouthpiece.

Experimental results† indicate that

$$\frac{A_c}{A_0} = 0.52$$

The good agreement between calculated and experimental values of A_c indicates that the assumptions used in obtaining a solution to the momentum balance are satisfactory for the Borda mouthpiece. The reason must surely be that the region over which the pressure is *not* hydrostatic is made much smaller by the Borda mouthpiece, thus reducing the error caused by this assumption.

In Sec. 7.5, 7.6, and 7.7 we have used the momentum and mechanical energy balances, along with Bernoulli's equation, to analyze four different flow configurations. As expected, the mechanical energy balance and Bernoulli's equation gave the same result for each case and the comparison of interest was made among the momentum balance, the mechanical energy

† See Ref. 1, p. 4–19.

balance, and experimental data. For the sudden expansion in the pipeline, the momentum balance gave the superior result, while both balances gave unsatisfactory results for the sudden contraction. For flow through a nozzle the mechanical energy balance gave an excellent answer, while the momentum balance was in error by 40 per cent. Both equations gave valid results for the Borda mouthpiece, and both had to be used simultaneously for the volumetric flow rate to be determined. A disadvantage of the momentum balance in analysing these flows is the necessity of specifying the stress at solid surfaces, and the assumptions made regarding the pressure for the sudden contraction and the nozzle appear to be the main source of error in the momentum balance. The mechanical energy balance, on the other hand, does not require evaluation of the stress at solid surfaces where the scalar product $\mathbf{v} \cdot \mathbf{t}_{(n)}$ is zero. A further advantage of the mechanical energy balance is that neglect of viscous effects produces an error of known sign; thus, we usually know a priori the sign of the error involved in the approximate analysis.

We cannot always choose to use either the momentum or mechanical energy balance; if forces on fixed solid surfaces are desired, we must use the momentum balance. In the following section, we shall study some problems of this type.

7.8 Applications of the Momentum Balance

Plane jet impinging on a flat plate

Figure 7.8-1 illustrates a two-dimensional plane jet impinging on a flat plate of width b. We would like to determine the force that the liquid exerts on the plate. For steady, incompressible flow and a fixed control volume, we make use of Eq. 7.2-11, forming the scalar product with the unit vector $\mathbf{i}$, to obtain

$$\int_{A_e} \rho v_x \mathbf{v} \cdot \mathbf{n} \, dA = \int_{\mathscr{A}} \mathbf{i} \cdot \mathbf{t}_{(n)} \, dA \qquad (7.8\text{-}1)$$

The stress vector is represented as

$$\mathbf{t}_{(n)} = -\mathbf{n}p + \mathbf{n} \cdot \boldsymbol{\tau} \qquad (7.8\text{-}2)$$

and if the streamlines are straight and the velocity profiles flat wherever the jets are cut by the control surface, the stress vector becomes

$$\mathbf{t}_{(n)} = -\mathbf{n}p_0 \qquad (7.8\text{-}3)$$

everywhere except on the plate. In examining the stress vector at the surface of the plate in contact with the fluid, we must refer to Eq. 4.2-14 in Chap. 4.

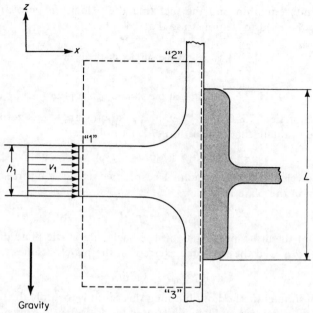

Fig. 7.8-1. Plane jet impinging on a flat plate.

We see from that equation that the term $\mathbf{n} \cdot \boldsymbol{\tau}$ may be expanded as follows:

$$\mathbf{n} \cdot \boldsymbol{\tau} = \mathbf{i}[n_x\tau_{xx} + n_y\tau_{yx} + n_z\tau_{zx}]$$
$$+\mathbf{j}[n_x\tau_{xy} + n_y\tau_{yy} + n_z\tau_{zy}] \qquad (7.8\text{-}4)$$
$$+\mathbf{k}[n_x\tau_{xz} + n_y\tau_{yz} + n_z\tau_{zz}]$$

At the surface of the plate,

$$n_x = 1$$
$$n_y = 0$$
$$n_z = 0$$

and the stress vector becomes

$$\mathbf{t}_{(n)} = -\mathbf{n}p + \mathbf{i}\tau_{xx} + \mathbf{j}\tau_{xy} + \mathbf{k}\tau_{xz} \quad \text{at the surface of the plate,} \quad (7.8\text{-}5)$$

or

$$\mathbf{i} \cdot \mathbf{t}_{(n)} = -p + \tau_{xx} \quad \text{at the surface of the plate} \quad (7.8\text{-}6)$$

For a Newtonian fluid this component of the viscous stress tensor is given by

$$\tau_{xx} = 2\mu\left(\frac{\partial v_x}{\partial x}\right) \qquad (7.8\text{-}7)$$

The continuity equation and the fact that the velocity is zero at the solid surface may be used to demonstrate that

$$\left(\frac{\partial v_x}{\partial x}\right) = 0 \quad \text{at the surface of the plate} \qquad (7.8\text{-}8)$$

and

$$\mathbf{i} \cdot \mathbf{t}_{(\hat{n})} = -p, \quad \text{at the surface of the plate} \qquad (7.8\text{-}9)$$

Making use of Eqs. 7.8-3 and 7.8-9, and assuming that v_x is zero at points 2 and 3, we evaluate the terms in Eq. 7.8-1 to obtain

$$-\rho\langle v_x\rangle_1^2 b h_1 = p_0 b L - \langle p\rangle_{\text{plate}} b L \qquad (7.8\text{-}10)$$

Because the velocity profile at point 1 is specified as flat, the force F_x that the fluid exerts on the plate is

$$F_x = \langle p\rangle_{\text{plate}} b L = p_0 b L + \rho v_1^2 b h_1 \qquad (7.8\text{-}11)$$

We note that the atmosphere acts on the back side of the plate producing a force of $-p_0 b L$, and the net force exerted on the plate becomes

$$F_{x,\text{net}} = \rho v_1^2 b h_1 \qquad (7.8\text{-}12)$$

A much simpler method of obtaining this result is to apply the momentum balance to the control volume illustrated in Fig. 7.8-2. For that control

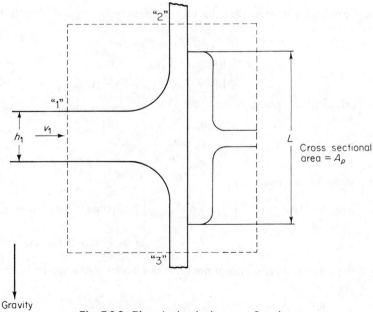

Fig. 7.8-2. Plane jet impinging on a flat plate.

volume, the stress vector becomes

$$t_{(n)} = -np_0, \quad \begin{matrix} \text{everywhere except at} \\ \text{the solid surface} \end{matrix} \qquad (7.8\text{-}13a)$$

$$t_{(n)} = -np_0 + t^*_{(n)} \quad \text{at the solid surface} \qquad (7.8\text{-}13b)$$

where $t^*_{(n)}$ is the stress in the solid in *excess* of that arising from the constant ambient pressure.

The stress produced by atmospheric pressure will contribute nothing to the area integral on the right-hand side of Eq. 7.8-1, and the momentum balance yields

$$-\rho v_1^2 b h_1 = i \cdot t^*_{(n)} A_p \qquad (7.8\text{-}14)$$

where A_p is the cross-sectional area of the solid section supporting the plate. Since $t^*_{(n)} A_p$ is the force exerted on the plate by the solid support, it is equal and opposite to the force exerted on the plate by the impinging jet of liquid, and Eq. 7.8-14 is equivalent to Eq. 7.8-12. The point of this analysis is that the proper choice of a control volume can greatly simplify the computation, for in this case viscous effects need never be considered.

The effect of ambient pressure

We saw in the last example that the ambient pressure, being a constant, made no contribution to the area integral of the stress vector in the momentum balance. Since we will encounter this problem in subsequent applications, it is worthwhile now to draw some general conclusions. If the ambient pressure is a constant p_0, the stress vector may be written as

$$t_{(n)} = -np_0 + t^*_{(n)} \qquad (7.8\text{-}15)$$

where $t^*_{(n)}$ will be referred to as the *net stress vector*. The stress vector may be written in terms of the total pressure p and the viscous stress tensor, τ.

$$t_{(n)} = -np + n \cdot \tau \qquad (7.8\text{-}16)$$

and the net stress vector is then given by

$$t^*_{(n)} = -n(p - p_0) + n \cdot \tau \qquad (7.8\text{-}17)$$

where

$$p - p_0 = p_g$$

the gauge pressure. In the absence of viscous stresses, the net stress is given in terms of the gauge pressure

$$t^*_{(n)} = -np_g \qquad (7.8\text{-}18)$$

The area integral of the stress vector in Eq. 7.2-10 may be written in terms of Eq. 7.8-15 to give

$$\int_{\mathscr{A}_a(t)} t_{(n)} \, dA = -\int_{\mathscr{A}_a(t)} np_0 \, dA + \int_{\mathscr{A}_a(t)} t^*_{(n)} \, dA \qquad (7.8\text{-}19)$$

We may use the divergence theorem for a scalar to show that the integral
containing the ambient pressure is identically zero. Thus,

$$\int_{\mathscr{A}_a(t)} \mathbf{n} p_0 \, dA = \int_{\mathscr{V}_a(t)} \nabla p_0 \, dV \equiv 0 \qquad (7.8\text{-}20)$$

On the basis of this result, we may replace $\mathbf{t}_{(n)}$ by $\mathbf{t}^*_{(n)}$ in Eqs. 7.2-10 and 7.2-11,
and we will neglect the constant ambient pressure in further discussions of the
area integral of the stress vector.

Force exerted by a liquid jet on a curved vane

The use of jets of liquid to move turbine blades is of considerable importance in the theory of turbomachinery. In this example, we will examine the
forces exerted on a curved vane by a jet of liquid, as illustrated in Fig. 7.8-3.

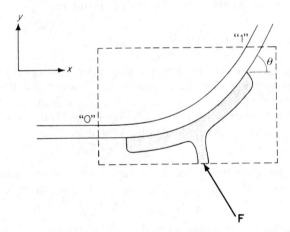

Fig. 7.8-3. Jet impinging on a curved vane.

Making the usual assumptions of steady, incompressible flow and flat
velocity profiles, the momentum equation is

$$\int_{A_e} (\rho \mathbf{v}) \mathbf{v} \cdot \mathbf{n} \, dA = \int_{\mathscr{A}} \mathbf{t}^*_{(n)} \, dA \qquad (7.8\text{-}21)$$

The area integral of the net stress vector gives

$$\int_{\mathscr{A}} \mathbf{t}^*_{(n)} \, dA = \mathbf{F} \qquad (7.8\text{-}22)$$

Substituting Eq. 7.8-22 into Eq. 7.8-21 and taking the scalar product with **i** and **j**, respectively, we get

$$-\rho v_0^2 A_0 + \rho v_1^2 A_1 \cos \theta = F_x \tag{7.8-23}$$

$$\rho v_1^2 A_1 \sin \theta = F_y \tag{7.8-24}$$

The macroscopic mass balance gives

$$\rho v_0 A_0 = \rho v_1 A_1 \tag{7.8-25}$$

If we assume that the angle θ and the density, velocity, and area ρ, v_0, and A_0 of the impinging jet are given, we are left with four unknowns,

$$v_1, A_1, F_x, \quad \text{and} \quad F_y$$

Since we have only the two momentum equations and the mass balance, we need one more equation if the problem is to be solved. Sometimes, but not always, the mechanical energy equation will supply the needed information. If we neglect viscous dissipation and gravitational effects, Eq. 7.3-31 becomes

$$\int_{A_e} (\tfrac{1}{2}\rho v^2)\mathbf{v} \cdot \mathbf{n} \, dA = -\int_{A_e} p\mathbf{v} \cdot \mathbf{n} \, dA \tag{7.8-26}$$

Evaluating the individual terms gives

$$-\tfrac{1}{2}\rho v_0^3 A_0 + \tfrac{1}{2}\rho v_1^3 A_1 = p_0 v_0 A_0 - p_0 v_1 A_1 \tag{7.8-27}$$

Because the fluid is incompressible, the right-hand side of Eq. 7.8-27 is zero by the mass balance. Application of Eq. 7.8-25 to the left-hand side gives

$$v_0 = v_1 \tag{7.8-28}$$

Thus, we have our fourth equation and the final result is

$$F_x = -\rho v_0^2 A_0 (1 - \cos \theta) \tag{7.8-29}$$

$$F_y = \rho v_0^2 A_0 \sin \theta \tag{7.8-30}$$

Plane jet impinging on an inclined plate

An analysis of the flow illustrated in Fig. 7.8-4 will provide an interesting example of the use of Bernoulli's equation and how nicely it fits in with our intuitive knowledge of the flow field. We wish to determine the forces that the jet exerts on the plate and the amount of fluid that flows in each direction on the plate. We start with the momentum balance given by Eq. 7.2-11, neglect gravitational effects, and form the scalar product with the unit normal

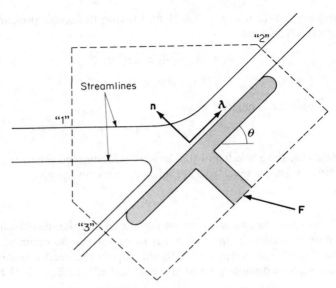

Fig. 7.8-4. Plane jet impinging on an inclined plane.

and tangential vectors **n** and **λ** to obtain

$$\rho v_1^2 A_1 \sin \theta = F_n \tag{7.8-31}$$

$$-\rho v_1^2 A_1 \cos \theta + \rho v_2^2 A_2 - \rho v_3^2 A_3 = F_t \tag{7.8-32}$$

where A_1, A_2, and A_3 are the cross-sectional areas of the liquid streams at points 1, 2, and 3, respectively. We may assume that the density, velocity, and area (ρ, v_1, A_1) of the impinging jet are given; thus, the normal force F_n is immediately determined by Eq. 7.8-31.

In keeping with the context of this chapter, we set $F_t = 0$, for tangential forces can only result from viscous effects. We are left with four unknowns— v_2, v_3, A_2 and A_3—and only one equation (Eq. 7.8-32). The macroscopic mass balance yields one more relationship,

$$v_1 A_1 = v_2 A_2 + v_3 A_3 \tag{7.8-33}$$

and the mechanical energy balance may be applied to give

$$-\tfrac{1}{2}\rho v_1^3 A_1 + \tfrac{1}{2}\rho v_2^3 A_2 + \tfrac{1}{2}\rho v_3^3 A_3 \tag{7.8-34}$$

$$= (v_1 A_1 - v_2 A_2 - v_3 A_3) p_0$$

The right-hand side of Eq. 7.8-34 is zero by the mass balance, and we rearrange this equation to obtain

$$v_1^3 A_1 = v_2^3 A_2 + v_3^3 A_3 \tag{7.8-35}$$

We still require one more equation if we are to solve the problem; yet we have exhausted the tools at our disposal. In previous examples, Bernoulli's equation always gave the same result as the mechanical energy balance; however, in this case the difference between these two equations comes to our aid. If we apply Bernoulli's equation along the top and bottom streamlines indicated in Fig. 7.8-4, we obtain

$$\tfrac{1}{2}\rho(v_2^2 - v_1^2) + (p_2 - p_1) + \rho g(z_2 - z_1) = 0 \qquad (7.8\text{-}36a)$$

$$\tfrac{1}{2}\rho(v_3^2 - v_1^2) + (p_3 - p_1) + \rho g(z_3 - z_1) = 0 \qquad (7.8\text{-}36b)$$

If we neglect gravitational effects and note that the pressure in the free jets is atmospheric, Eqs. 7.8-36 yield

$$v_1 = v_2 = v_3 \qquad (7.8\text{-}37)$$

This result is consistent with Eq. 7.8-35, and we have obtained additional information by using Bernoulli's equation. The velocity is now specified everywhere, and Eqs. 7.8-32 and 7.8-33 will be simplified to

$$\rho v_1^2 (A_2 - A_1 \cos \theta - A_3) = 0 \qquad (7.8\text{-}38)$$

$$A_1 = A_2 + A_3 \qquad (7.8\text{-}39)$$

The areas and volumetric flow rates at points 2 and 3 may now be determined by Eqs. 7.8-38 and 7.8-39,

$$A_2 = \frac{A_1}{2}(1 + \cos \theta), \qquad Q_2 = \frac{Q_1}{2}(1 + \cos \theta) \qquad (7.8\text{-}40a)$$

$$A_3 = \frac{A_1}{2}(1 - \cos \theta), \qquad Q_3 = \frac{Q_1}{2}(1 - \cos \theta) \qquad (7.8\text{-}40b)$$

We see that the smaller the angle θ, the less fluid flows backwards on the plate, and $Q_3 \to 0$ as $\theta \to 0$.

Our treatment of this problem has not been altogether honest, for there is a way in which the mechanical energy balance can be used to obtain the result given by Eq. 7.8-37. It involves a rather subtle choice of control volumes, based on the fact that there is a streamline separating the two streams of fluid. The student is encouraged to give this problem further thought, for it will provide valuable knowledge in the art of choosing control volumes and will illustrate the necessity of having a qualitative understanding of the streamlines for any system to be analyzed.

7.9 Moving Control Volumes and Unsteady Flow Problems

Some of the aspects of moving control volumes were encountered in the analysis of flow through the nozzle and the Borda mouthpiece in Sec. 7.7.

In this section, we shall investigate this type of problem more thoroughly. Before analyzing some specific problems, it will be helpful to examine the macroscopic balances in terms of a coordinate frame moving at a constant velocity, for it is often convenient to view a system as if we were an observer moving with a velocity **w** rather than someone fixed in space.

In Sec. 5.4 we saw that the continuity equation and the equations of motion took the form

$$\frac{d\rho}{dt} + \boldsymbol{\nabla} \cdot (\rho \mathbf{v}_r) = 0 \tag{7.9-1}$$

$$\rho\left(\frac{d\mathbf{v}_r}{dt} + \mathbf{v}_r \cdot \boldsymbol{\nabla}\mathbf{v}_r\right) = -\boldsymbol{\nabla}p + \rho\mathbf{g} + \mu\nabla^2\mathbf{v}_r \tag{7.9-2}$$

where
$$\mathbf{v}_r = \mathbf{v} - \mathbf{w} \tag{7.9-3}$$

for an observer moving at a constant velocity **w**. In a manner similar to that discussed in Sec. 3.6, we may define streamlines in terms of the moving coordinate frame. They are lines viewed by a moving observer that are always tangent to $\mathbf{v}_r$. The unit tangent vector to such a streamline is given by

$$\boldsymbol{\lambda}_r = \frac{\mathbf{v}_r}{v_r} = \frac{d\mathbf{r}_r}{ds_r} \tag{7.9-4}$$

where $\mathbf{r}_r$ is the position vector and s_r is the distance along the streamline. If the flow is steady, *as viewed by an observer moving at constant velocity*, and if viscous effects are neglected, the scalar product between $\boldsymbol{\lambda}_r$ and Eq. 7.9-2 may be formed to yield Bernoulli's equation for a moving observer.

$$(\tfrac{1}{2}\rho v_r^2 + p + \rho gz) = C_s \tag{7.9-5}$$

The macroscopic balances

The macroscopic mass, momentum, and mechanical energy balances were formulated for arbitrary moving control volumes; they therefore provide a rather general attack on macroscopic problems. When the *velocity of the control volume is a constant*, these balances take on especially simple forms. For the mass balance, we start with Eq. 7.1-7 and substitute Eq. 7.9-3 to obtain

$$\frac{d}{dt}\int_{\mathscr{V}_a(t)} \rho\, dV + \int_{A_e(t)} \rho\mathbf{v}_r \cdot \mathbf{n}\, dA = 0 \tag{7.9-6}$$

Substitution of Eq. 7.9-3 into the momentum balance given by Eq. 7.2-10 yields

$$\frac{d}{dt}\int_{\mathscr{V}_a(t)} \rho\mathbf{v}_r\, dV + \mathbf{w}\frac{d}{dt}\int_{\mathscr{V}_a(t)} \rho\, dV + \int_{A_e(t)} (\rho\mathbf{v}_r)\mathbf{v}_r \cdot \mathbf{n}\, dA$$

$$+ \mathbf{w}\int_{A_e(t)} \rho\mathbf{v}_r \cdot \mathbf{n}\, dA = \int_{\mathscr{V}_a(t)} \rho\mathbf{g}\, dV + \int_{\mathscr{A}_a(t)} \mathbf{t}_{(\mathbf{n})}\, dA \tag{7.9-7}$$

where we have removed $\mathbf{w}$ from the differential and integral signs because it is constant. We simplify this result by noting that the second and fourth integrals on the left-hand side sum to zero on the basis of the mass balance, and we obtain

$$\frac{d}{dt}\int_{\mathscr{V}} \rho\mathbf{v}_r \, dV + \int_{A_e} (\rho\mathbf{v}_r)\mathbf{v}_r \cdot \mathbf{n} \, dA = \int_{\mathscr{V}} \rho\mathbf{g} \, dV + \int_{\mathscr{A}} \mathbf{t}_{(n)} \, dA \qquad (7.9\text{-}8)$$

Because $\mathbf{w}$ is constant, the control volume $\mathscr{V}_a(t)$, while moving through space, does not change size or shape, and to the moving observer it appears fixed in space. For this reason, the limits on the integrals in Eq. 7.9-8 are written as though the control volume were fixed in space.

In attacking the macroscopic mechanical energy balance, we must start with the stress equations of motion for a moving observer,

$$\rho\left(\frac{d\mathbf{v}_r}{dt} + \mathbf{v}_r \cdot \nabla\mathbf{v}_r\right) = \rho\mathbf{g} + \nabla \cdot \mathbf{T} \qquad (7.9\text{-}9)$$

and form the scalar product with $\mathbf{v}_r$ to obtain

$$\frac{d}{dt}\left(\tfrac{1}{2}\rho v_r^2\right) + \mathbf{v}_r \cdot \nabla\left(\tfrac{1}{2}\rho v_r^2\right) = \rho\mathbf{g} \cdot \mathbf{v}_r + \mathbf{v}_r \cdot (\nabla \cdot \mathbf{T}) \qquad (7.9\text{-}10)$$

where the density is taken as constant. Expressing the gravity vector as the gradient of a scalar, and noting that

$$\nabla \cdot \mathbf{v}_r = 0 \qquad (7.9\text{-}11)$$

for incompressible flows, we may write Eq. 7.9-10 as

$$\frac{d}{dt}\left(\tfrac{1}{2}\rho v_r^2\right) + \nabla \cdot \left(\tfrac{1}{2}\rho v_r^2\mathbf{v}_r\right) = -\nabla \cdot (\rho\phi\mathbf{v}_r) + \mathbf{v}_r \cdot (\nabla \cdot \mathbf{T}) \qquad (7.9\text{-}12)$$

Following Eq. 7.3-12 we write

$$\mathbf{v}_r \cdot (\nabla \cdot \mathbf{T}) = \nabla \cdot (\mathbf{v}_r \cdot \mathbf{T}) - \nabla\mathbf{v}_r : \mathbf{T} \qquad (7.9\text{-}13)$$

However,

$$\nabla\mathbf{v}_r = \nabla\mathbf{v} \qquad (7.9\text{-}14)$$

since $\nabla\mathbf{w}$ is zero, and Eq. 7.9-13 becomes

$$\mathbf{v}_r \cdot (\nabla \cdot \mathbf{T}) = \nabla \cdot (\mathbf{v}_r \cdot \mathbf{T}) - \nabla\mathbf{v} : \mathbf{T} \qquad (7.9\text{-}15)$$

Substitution of Eq. 7.9-15 into Eq. 7.9-12 and use of Φ to represent the viscous dissipation yield

$$\frac{d}{dt}\left(\tfrac{1}{2}\rho v_r^2\right) + \nabla \cdot \left(\tfrac{1}{2}\rho v_r^2\mathbf{v}_r\right) = -\nabla \cdot (\rho\phi\mathbf{v}_r) + \nabla \cdot (\mathbf{v}_r \cdot \mathbf{T}) - \Phi \qquad (7.9\text{-}16)$$

Integration over the volume $\mathscr{V}_a(t)$ and application of the divergence theorem yield

$$\int_{\mathscr{V}_a(t)} \frac{d}{dt} (\tfrac{1}{2}\rho v_r^2)\, dV + \int_{\mathscr{A}_a(t)} (\tfrac{1}{2}\rho v_r^2)\mathbf{v}_r \cdot \mathbf{n}\, dA = -\int_{\mathscr{A}_a(t)} \rho\phi\mathbf{v}_r \cdot \mathbf{n}\, dA$$

$$+ \int_{\mathscr{A}_a(t)} \mathbf{v}_r \cdot \mathbf{t}_{(n)}\, dA - \dot{E}_v \tag{7.9-17}$$

We have so far only made use of the definition given by Eq. 7.9-3, and we have not yet restricted ourselves to a control volume moving at a constant velocity. If we now make the restriction that $\mathscr{V}_a(t)$ moves at the constant velocity $\mathbf{w}$, we may make use of a special form of the general transport theorem referred to in Prob. 3-14 to write

$$\int_{\mathscr{V}_a(t)} \frac{d}{dt} (\tfrac{1}{2}\rho v_r^2)\, dV = \frac{d}{dt} \int_{\mathscr{V}_a(t)} (\tfrac{1}{2}\rho v_r^2)\, dV \tag{7.9-18}$$

Because all the solid surfaces move at the velocity $\mathbf{w}$, $\mathbf{v}_r$ is zero at the solid surfaces and Eq. 7.9-17 reduces to

$$\frac{d}{dt} \int_{\mathscr{V}_a(t)} (\tfrac{1}{2}\rho v_r^2)\, dV + \int_{A_e(t)} (\tfrac{1}{2}\rho v_r^2)\mathbf{v}_r \cdot \mathbf{n}\, dA$$

$$= \int_{A_e(t)} \mathbf{v}_r \cdot \mathbf{t}_{(n)}\, dA - \int_{A_e(t)} \rho\phi\mathbf{v}_r \cdot \mathbf{n}\, dA - \dot{E}_v \tag{7.9-19}$$

We note that there is no work term in this equation inasmuch as a moving observer sees no moving surfaces. The actual work done is given by

$$\dot{W} = \int_{A_s(t)} \mathbf{w} \cdot \mathbf{t}_{(n)}\, dA \tag{7.9-20}$$

For this special type of control volume, $\dot{W}$ is most easily determined by application of the momentum balance.

Analysis of a turbojet engine

Figure 7.9-1 shows a turbojet engine moving through still air at a constant velocity, v_0. The problem may also be represented as the engine fixed in space and the air entering the diffuser with a velocity v_0. As the air enters the diffuser it slows down and the pressure rises. The compressor further increases the pressure as the air is forced into the combustion chamber where fuel is added and combustion takes place. The combustion mixture passes

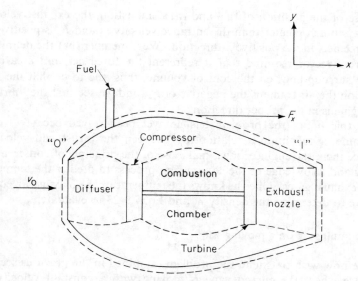

Fig. 7.9-1. Turbojet engine.

through the turbine driving the compressor and expands in the exhaust nozzle. It leaves the nozzle close to atmospheric pressure and at a higher velocity than the entering air. If we assume steady flow, the momentum balance in the x-direction may be written

$$\mathbf{i} \cdot \int_{A_e} (\rho \mathbf{v}_r) \mathbf{v}_r \cdot \mathbf{n} \, dA = \int_{\mathscr{A}} \mathbf{i} \cdot \mathbf{t}_{(n)}^* \, dA \qquad (7.9\text{-}21)$$

Assuming that the pressure at the surface of the control volume is atmospheric, the net stress $\mathbf{t}_{(n)}^*$ results only from the stress on the motor mount (presumably the fuel line would not be subjected to any stresses). If we take the velocity profiles at 0 and 1 to be flat, Eq. 7.9-21 reduces to

$$-\rho_0 v_0^2 A_0 + \rho_1 v_1^2 A_1 = F_x \qquad (7.9\text{-}22)$$

We notice there is no contribution to the momentum equation from the fuel added to the system, because the x-component of the fuel velocity vector is zero at the surface of the control volume. The mass balance requires that

$$\rho_0 v_0 A_0 + \dot{m}_f = \rho_1 v_1 A_1 \qquad (7.9\text{-}23)$$

where $\dot{m}_f$ is the mass flow rate of the fuel. Making use of Eq. 7.9-23 allows us to write the force F_x as

$$F_x = \rho_0 v_0 A_0 [v_1 (1 + \alpha) - v_0]$$

where

$$\alpha = \frac{\dot{m}_f}{\rho_0 v_0 A_0} \qquad (7.9\text{-}24)$$

Because of the addition of fuel and the combustion, the exhaust velocity v_1 is always much greater than the entrance velocity v_0 and F_x is positive—i.e., the force acts in the positive x-direction. We remember that the definition of the stress vector required that it represent the force per unit area exerted by the surroundings on the control volume, thus, the force that the engine exerts on the air frame is the negative of F_x, and we see that the "thrust" of the engine is in the proper direction.

At this point, the problem has not yet been solved because we must determine v_1 to obtain a relationship between the thrust and velocity. In practice then, the engineer must make use of the principle of conservation of energy and knowledge of the combustion process to predict the temperature of the exhaust gases. Once he knows the temperature, he may use an equation of state to determine the density ρ_1 and Eq. 7.9-23 to evaluate v_1.

Jet impinging on a moving vane

We now wish to extend the problem examined in the previous section to the case where the curved vane is moving with a constant velocity. This system is illustrated in Fig. 7.9-2.† We may attack this problem in two ways:

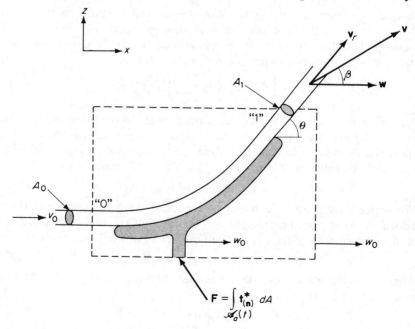

Fig. 7.9-2. Jet impinging on a moving vane.

† Note carefully that the jet *leaving* the vane is drawn as it would be seen by a *moving observer*. Here we have made use of the intuitive idea that $\mathbf{v}_r$ should be tangent to the vane.

from the point of view of an observer fixed in space and applying the general macroscopic mass, momentum and mechanical energy balances; or from the point of view of an observer moving with the control volume and applying Eqs. 7.9-6, 7.9-8, and 7.9-19. We shall use the second approach, but we need to discuss the first to gain some insight into the difficulties encountered in treating moving control volume problems.

Starting with Eq. 7.2-10,

$$\frac{d}{dt} \int_{\mathscr{V}_a(t)} \rho \mathbf{v} \, dV + \int_{A_e(t)} \rho \mathbf{v}(\mathbf{v} - \mathbf{w}) \cdot \mathbf{n} \, dA = \int_{\mathscr{V}_a(t)} \rho \mathbf{g} \, dV + \int_{\mathscr{A}_a(t)} \mathbf{t}_{(\mathbf{n})}^* \, dA \quad (7.9\text{-}25)$$

we neglect gravitational effects and note that the momentum of the control volume is constant to obtain

$$\int_{A_e(t)} \rho \mathbf{v}(\mathbf{v} - \mathbf{w}) \cdot \mathbf{n} \, dA = \mathbf{F} \quad (7.9\text{-}26)$$

In solving this problem, we will wish to determine the x- and z-components of the force $\mathbf{F}$; thus, we might first take the scalar product of Eq. 7.9-26 with the unit vector $\mathbf{i}$ to obtain

$$-\rho v_0 (v_0 - w_0) A_0 + \rho (v_1 \cos \beta)(v_1 \sin \beta) \left(\frac{A_1}{\sin \theta} \right) = F_x \quad (7.9\text{-}27)$$

We can now start to see some of the difficulties in this approach. The momentum entering the control volume is easily calculated; however, the terms describing the momentum leaving are not so easy to work with. We note first that the fluid velocity vector $\mathbf{v}$ is not tangent to the vane, requiring that the angle β be calculated. To do so we must know the relative velocity, $\mathbf{v}_r$, of the fluid leaving the jet. If we carry this problem much further, we see very shortly that the task of computing the momentum leaving the system becomes cumbersome; however if the fluid stream left the control volume in a direction either parallel or perpendicular to the vector $\mathbf{w}$, we would have no difficulty in calculating the momentum flux.

If we now switch our attack on this problem to a frame of reference moving with the control volume, we start with Eq. 7.9-8 and neglect gravitational effects to obtain

$$\int_{A_e} (\rho \mathbf{v}_r) \mathbf{v}_r \cdot \mathbf{n} \, dA = \mathbf{F} \quad (7.9\text{-}28)$$

Making use of Bernoulli's equation along a streamline in a moving coordinate system, Eq. 7.9-5, we find that the magnitude of the relative velocity vector v_r is a constant at points 0 and 1. Using this fact and taking the scalar product of Eq. 7.9-28 with **i** and **k**, we get

$$-\rho v_r^2 A_0 + \rho(v_r \cos \theta) v_r A_1 = F_x \tag{7.9-29}$$

$$\rho (v_r \sin \theta) v_r A_1 = F_z \tag{7.9-30}$$

where A_1 is the cross-sectional area of the jet and not the area of the exit, which is $A_1/\sin \theta$. The mass balance gives

$$A_0 = A_1 \tag{7.9-31}$$

and if we write the magnitude of the relative velocity vector as

$$v_r = v_0 - w_0 \tag{7.9-32}$$

the components of the force exerted by the vane on the jet are

$$\rho(v_0 - w_0)^2 A_0 (1 - \cos \theta) = -F_x \quad \begin{array}{l}\text{Force exerted by the} \\ \text{vane on the jet}\end{array} \tag{7.9-33}$$

$$-\rho(v_0 - w_0)^2 A_0 \sin \theta = -F_z \quad \begin{array}{l}\text{Force exerted by the} \\ \text{vane on the jet}\end{array} \tag{7.9-34}$$

The power $-\dot{W}$ generated by the action of the jet on the vane is the scalar product of the force $-\mathbf{F}$ times the velocity **w**.

$$\text{power} = \rho(v_0 - w_0)^2 w_0 A_0(1 - \cos \theta) \tag{7.9-35}$$

Note that if $\theta = 0$, no force is exerted on the vane and no power is generated. If $\theta = \pi$—i.e., the vane directs the jet back upon itself—the power generated is a maximum.

If we compare Eqs. 7.9-27 and 7.9-35, we can see that a rather large amount of algebraic effort must be expended to reduce Eq. 7.9-27 to the simple form given by Eq. 7.9-35. It is apparent that visualizing the problem in terms of a moving coordinate system leads to an easy solution.

Moving water scoop

Figure 7.9-3 illustrates a water scoop used by a fast-moving train to pick up water from a trough set between the tracks. We would like to know the rate at which the train takes on water and the drag on the train resulting from this process. The width of the scoop is b and the thickness of the water film is h. In this example, we will view the problem as observers fixed in space and apply Eqs. 7.1-7 and 7.2-10. In applying the macroscopic mass balance

$$\frac{d}{dt} \int_{\mathcal{V}_a(t)} \rho \, dV + \int_{A_e(t)} \rho(\mathbf{v} - \mathbf{w}) \cdot \mathbf{n} \, dA = 0 \tag{7.9-36}$$

we note that the fluid velocity **v** is equal to the velocity of the control volume **w** everywhere except in the water, where $\mathbf{v} = 0$. The time rate of change of

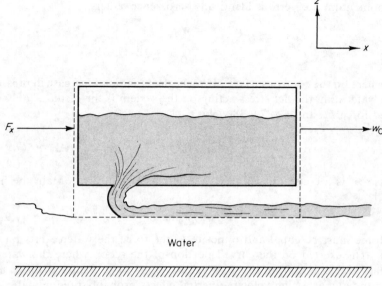

Fig. 7.9-3. Moving water scoop.

the mass of the control volume results only from the accumulation of water; thus, Eq. 7.9-36 yields

$$\frac{d}{dt}(\rho V_{H_2O}) - \rho w_0 h b = 0 \qquad (7.9\text{-}37)$$

or

$$\begin{Bmatrix} \text{rate at which} \\ \text{water is taken} \\ \text{onto the train} \end{Bmatrix} = \rho w_0 h b$$

Forming the scalar product of the macroscopic momentum balance with the unit vector $\mathbf{i}$ gives

$$\frac{d}{dt}\int_{\mathscr{V}_a(t)} \rho v_x \, dV + \int_{A_e(t)} \rho v_x (\mathbf{v} - \mathbf{w}) \cdot \mathbf{n} \, dA = \int_{\mathscr{A}_a(t)} \mathbf{i} \cdot \mathbf{t}^*_{(n)} \, dA \qquad (7.9\text{-}38)$$

The velocity of the water in the moving tank is not constant because it must enter the tank at a velocity greater than w_0; however, the average velocity in the tank must be w_0, and the first term on the left-hand side of Eq. 7.9-38 becomes

$$\frac{d}{dt}\int_{\mathscr{V}_a(t)} \rho v_x \, dV = \frac{d}{dt}(\rho V_{H_2O} w_0) \qquad (7.9\text{-}39)$$

The momentum flux term is identically zero, since either

$$\mathbf{v} = \mathbf{w}$$

or

$$v_x = 0$$

everywhere on the control surface. If we neglect the small increase in pressure in the water film, the net stress acting on the system is the result of only the applied force F_x, and Eq. 7.9-38 yields

$$\frac{d}{dt}(\rho V_{H_2O} w_0) = F_x \tag{7.9-40}$$

Because w_0 is a constant, we may use the mass balance to obtain the final result,†

$$F_x = \rho w_0^2 h b \tag{7.9-41}$$

This force must be equal and opposite to the force the water exerts on the scoop. It is exerted on the curved portion of the scoop where the water is suddenly accelerated from rest to a velocity somewhat greater than w_0. For a train moving at a high velocity, inertial effects probably predominate, and Eq. 7.9-41 is a reasonable solution. On the other hand, velocity gradients at the leading edge of the scoop will be large and viscous effects could be important if a very accurate answer is desired.

The accelerating water tank

Another application of the mass and momentum balances for moving control volumes is the accelerating water tank shown in Fig. 7.9-4. Inasmuch as the jet leaves the tank in a direction parallel to the velocity of the control volume, we will have no difficulty in determining the momentum flux term; however, if the jet issued from the tank in some direction other than that shown, the problem would be a great deal more complicated.

The tank contains a supply of compressed air regulated so that the flow rate leaving the tank through the nozzle is constant; thus,

$$\frac{d}{dt}(\rho V_{H_2O}) = -\dot{m} \tag{7.9-42}$$

where

$$\dot{m} = \text{a positive constant}$$
$$V_{H_2O} = \text{the volume of water in the tank}$$

† This result can be deduced intuitively from the linear momentum principle since the force F_x is just equal to the time rate of change of momentum; i.e., $(\rho w_0)(w_0 h b) = $ momentum per unit volume × volume per unit time.

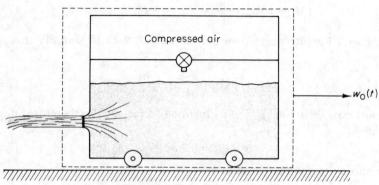

Fig. 7.9-4. Accelerating water tank.

We assume:

1. No friction occurs between the wheels and the solid surface.
2. The velocity profile in the emerging jet is flat.

The mass of the control volume, excluding the water, is M, and the volume of the water in the control volume at zero time is V_0. Application of the macroscopic mass balance gives

$$\rho(\mathbf{v} - \mathbf{w}) \cdot \mathbf{n}\big|_{\text{nozzle}} A_0 = \dot{m} \tag{7.9-43}$$

where A_0 is the area of the nozzle. Forming the scalar product of the momentum balance with the unit vector $\mathbf{i}$ and neglecting viscous and inertial effects in the surrounding air, we get

$$\frac{d}{dt} \int_{\mathcal{V}_a(t)} \rho v_x \, dV + \int_{A_e(t)} \rho v_x (\mathbf{v} - \mathbf{w}) \cdot \mathbf{n} \, dA = 0 \tag{7.9-44}$$

We now assume that the velocity everywhere inside the control volume is $\mathbf{w}$. This is not strictly correct because the fluid is moving towards the nozzle; however, if the amount of fluid in the tank is large and the flow rate through the nozzle is small, it may be a reasonable approximation. Making use of Eq. 7.9-43 and the above assumption allows us to write

$$\frac{d}{dt} (Mw_0 + \rho V_{\text{H}_2\text{O}} w_0) + v_x\big|_{\text{nozzle}} \dot{m} = 0 \tag{7.9-45}$$

Carrying out the differentiation gives

$$(M + \rho V_{H_2O}) \frac{dw_0}{dt} + w_0 \frac{d}{dt} (\rho V_{H_2O}) + v_x|_{nozzle}\, \dot{m} = 0 \qquad (7.9\text{-}46)$$

which may be simplified by the use of Eq. 7.9-42 to yield

$$(M + \rho V_{H_2O}) \frac{dw_0}{dt} + (v_x - w_0)|_{nozzle}\, \dot{m} = 0 \qquad (7.9\text{-}47)$$

Since $n = -i$ at the nozzle, we may use Eq. 7.9-43 to simplify this result further

$$(M + \rho V_{H_2O}) \frac{dw_0}{dt} - \frac{(\dot{m})^2}{\rho A_0} = 0 \qquad (7.9\text{-}48)$$

We must now solve for V_{H_2O} as a function of time, and we therefore integrate Eq. 7.9-42

$$\rho V_{H_2O} = -\dot{m}t + C_1 \qquad (7.9\text{-}49)$$

and impose the boundary condition

B.C. 1: $\qquad\qquad V_{H_2O} = V_0, \qquad t = 0 \qquad\qquad (7.9\text{-}50)$

to obtain

$$\rho V_{H_2O} = (\rho V_0 - \dot{m}t) \qquad (7.9\text{-}51)$$

Substitution of Eq. 7.9-51 into Eq. 7.9-48 and separation of the variables give

$$dw_0 = \frac{(\dot{m})^2}{\rho A_0 (M_0 - \dot{m}t)}\, dt \qquad (7.9\text{-}52)$$

where

$$M_0 = M + \rho V_0$$

which integrates to

$$w_0 = -\left(\frac{\dot{m}}{\rho A_0}\right) \ln (M_0 - \dot{m}t) + C_2 \qquad (7.9\text{-}53)$$

The boundary condition, or "initial condition" as it is sometimes called, will be specified as

B.C. 2: $\qquad\qquad w_0 = 0, \qquad t = 0 \qquad\qquad (7.9\text{-}54)$

and the final result is

$$w_0 = \left(\frac{\dot{m}}{\rho A_0}\right) \ln \left(\frac{M_0}{M_0 - \dot{m}t}\right) \qquad (7.9\text{-}55)$$

This solution is meaningful only for instances such that $\dot{m}t < \rho V_0$, because for larger times there is no water left in the tank according to Eq. 7.9-51.

7.10   Differential-Macroscopic Balances

The title of this section seems somewhat contradictory, for up to this point we have only examined differential equations (in Chaps. 2 and 5) and macroscopic equations (always referred to as "balances" to help distinguish them from differential equations). In obtaining the macroscopic balances, we integrated the differential equations over a volume $\mathcal{V}_a(t)$, and thus obtained *volume-averaged* versions of the differential equations. It would have been possible, and it is very practical in certain problems, to integrate the equations over an area $A_a(t)$ and thus obtain *area-averaged* versions of the differential equations. For practical purposes it is easier to obtain the area-averaged equations by applying the macroscopic balances to a volume of thickness Δx and then letting $\Delta x \to 0$.

Once the method has been outlined, the student will have no difficulty in formulating these balances for special problems; however, students often have difficulty in recognizing when the differential-macroscopic balance should be applied instead of the macroscopic balance. The rule to be followed in this case follows:

> If some quantity such as the pressure or average velocity varies continuously in the x-direction (for example), and we wish to determine this variation, the macroscopic balance must be made differential in the x-direction.

We will apply this idea to the rectangular channel illustrated in Fig. 7.10-1. The end of this channel is closed, and one side is made of a porous material that allows fluid to be drawn off. We will assume that by one technique or another the fluid can be removed uniformly. Under these

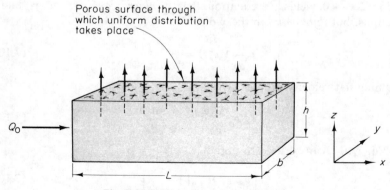

Fig. 7.10-1. Flow in a porous channel.

conditions, the volumetric flow rate in the channel is given by

$$Q(x) = Q_0\left(1 - \frac{x}{L}\right) \tag{7.10-1}$$

and the volumetric flow rate per unit length through the porous surface is

$$q = \frac{Q_0}{L} \tag{7.10-2}$$

We will assume that the flow is turbulent so that the flat velocity profile assumption can be made; viscous effects will be neglected. We now wish to determine the pressure as a function of x, and we therefore need to develop a differential-macroscopic balance in the x-direction. We do so by applying Eq. 7.2-11 to the control volume shown in Fig. 7.10-2. Neglecting viscous effects and dotting Eq. 7.2-11 with $\mathbf{i}$, we get

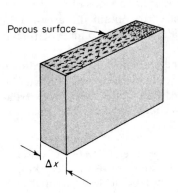

Porous surface

Δx

Fig. 7.10-2. Differential control volume.

$$\int_{A_e} \rho v_x \mathbf{v} \cdot \mathbf{n}\, dA = -\int_{\mathscr{A}} \mathbf{n} \cdot \mathbf{i} p\, dA \tag{7.10-3}$$

Application to the control volume gives

$$-\rho\langle v_x^2\rangle A\big|_x + \rho\langle v_x^2\rangle A\big|_{x+\Delta x}$$
$$= \langle p\rangle A\big|_x - \langle p\rangle A\big|_{x+\Delta x} \tag{7.10-4}$$

Because the area is constant we may divide by $A\,\Delta x$ to obtain

$$\rho\,\frac{\langle v_x^2\rangle\big|_{x+\Delta x} - \langle v_x^2\rangle\big|_x}{\Delta x} = -\frac{\langle p\rangle\big|_{x+\Delta x}\langle p\rangle\big|_x}{\Delta x} \tag{7.10-5}$$

Letting $\Delta x \to 0$ yields an equation that is *macroscopic* in the y- and z-directions, but *differential* in the x-direction.

$$\rho\,\frac{d}{dx}\left(\langle v_x^2\rangle\right) = -\frac{d\langle p\rangle}{dx} \tag{7.10-6}$$

Assuming flat velocity profiles gives

$$2\rho\langle v_x\rangle\,\frac{d\langle v_x\rangle}{dx} = -\frac{d\langle p\rangle}{dx} \tag{7.10-7}$$

and Eq. 7.10-1 can be used to obtain

$$\langle v_x\rangle = \langle v_x\rangle_0\left(1 - \frac{x}{L}\right) \tag{7.10-8}$$

where

$$\langle v_x \rangle_0 = \frac{Q_0}{A}$$

Use of Eq. 7.10-8 allows us to write Eq. 7.10-7 in the form

$$\frac{2\rho\langle v_x \rangle_0^2}{L}\left(1 - \frac{x}{L}\right) = \frac{d\langle p \rangle}{dx} \qquad (7.10\text{-}9)$$

which is easily integrated to obtain

$$\langle p \rangle_x = \langle p \rangle_0 + 2\rho\langle v_x \rangle_0^2\left[\frac{x}{L} - \frac{1}{2}\left(\frac{x}{L}\right)^2\right] \qquad (7.10\text{-}10)$$

This result indicates that the pressure increases continuously from $\langle p \rangle_0$ at the entrance of the channel to $\langle p \rangle_0 + \rho\langle v_x \rangle_0^2$ at the end of the channel. Differential-macroscopic balances present no serious difficulties provided we can recognize when they must be used.

PROBLEMS

7-1. Make use of the continuity equation and the material derivative to show that the stress equations of motion given by Eq. 7.2-3 are identical to those given by Eq. 4.4-13.

7-2. If

$$\int_{A_e(t)} \mathbf{v} \cdot \mathbf{n}\, dA = 0$$

and the flow is incompressible, show that the macroscopic mechanical energy balance may be written as

$$\frac{d}{dt}\int_{\mathscr{V}_a(t)} \left(\frac{1}{2}\,\rho v^2\right) dV + \int_{A_e(t)} \left(\frac{1}{2}\,\rho v^2\right) (\mathbf{v} - \mathbf{w}) \cdot \mathbf{n}\, dA$$

$$= \int_{A_e(t)} \mathbf{v} \cdot \mathbf{t}_{(\mathbf{n})}^*\, dA - \int_{\mathscr{A}_a(t)} \rho\phi\mathbf{v} \cdot \mathbf{n}\, dA + \dot{W} - \dot{E}_v$$

7-3. A hydraulic brake that consists of a cylindrical ram displacing fluid from a slightly larger cylinder is shown in Fig. 7-3. The velocity of the ram is specified as u_0 and we wish to know the force F required to maintain this motion. Neglect viscous effects and use both the momentum and the mechanical energy balances to obtain two answers. State carefully the assumptions that must be made in order to obtain a solution.

Ans: The mechanical energy balance gives

$$F = \frac{\rho u_0^2(\pi D_1^2/4)}{2[(D_1/D_0)^2 - 1]^2}$$

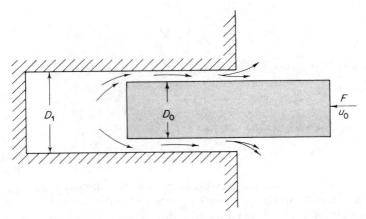

Fig. 7-3. The hydraulic ram.

7-4. A jet of water issues from a 1-in. I.D. nozzle at a velocity of 30 ft/sec and strikes a flat plate moving away from the jet at 17 ft/sec, as illustrated in Fig. 7-4. What force does the water jet exert on the plate?

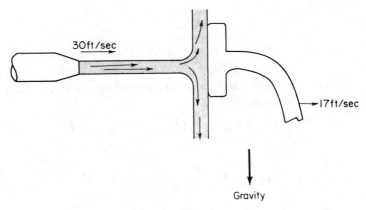

Gravity

Fig. 7-4

7-5. Water issues from a pipe imbedded in a concrete wall as shown in Fig. 7-5. If the velocity leaving the pipe is 20 ft/sec and the cross-sectional area is 1 in.², what are the components of the resultant force exerted on the pipe by the wall? Assume that the pressure drop from the wall to the end of the pipe is negligible.

Ans: $F_x = 0.72 \text{ lb}_f$, $F_y = 2.70 \text{ lb}_f$

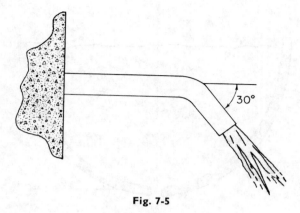

Fig. 7-5

7-6. A very simple device for pumping fluids is the ejector pump illustrated in Fig. 7-6. The fluid to be pumped is called the primary fluid, and *momentum* (instead of the *force* supplied by mechanical pumps) is supplied by the secondary fluid issuing through the nozzle. The momentum exchange takes place via viscous effects, and the viscous dissipation term in the mechanical

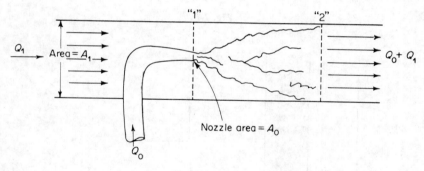

Fig. 7-6

energy balance cannot be neglected. However, the viscous surface forces can be neglected if the flow is turbulent and a satisfactory design of an ejector pump can be obtained with the momentum balance. Derive an expression for the pressure rise between points 1 and 2, and note the effect of reducing the nozzle area A_0 while maintaining the secondary flow rate Q_0 constant. Assume that the secondary fluid is the same as the primary fluid.

7-7. The Egyptians reportedly used water clocks similar to that illustrated in Fig. 7-7. The radius r_0 of the circular bowl is a function of z, the distance from the bottom of the bowl. Determine the functional dependence of r_0 on z required if the depth of the liquid is to be a linear function of time.

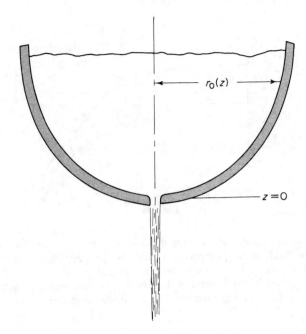

Fig. 7-7

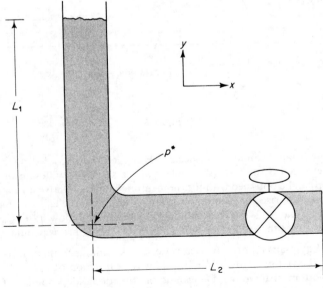

Fig. 7-8

7-8. If the valve on the pipe shown in Fig. 7-8 is opened rapidly, the pressure at the elbow will decrease suddenly. The problem is a complex one but can be solved for very short times when the velocity may be set equal to zero and viscous effects are negligible. Determine p^* for short times after the valve is opened. *Hint:* Two scalar components of the momentum equation must be used.

Ans: $p^* = p_0 + \rho g L_1 L_2 / (L_1 + L_2)$

7-9. A standard method for determining turbulent flow rates in conduits consists of measuring the pressure difference across a flow nozzle such as that shown in Fig. 7-9. Derive an expression for the volumetric flow Q in terms of A_1, A_2,

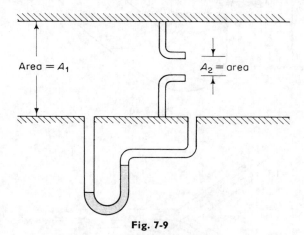

Fig. 7-9

and the pressure difference measured by the manometer. Consider carefully the relative merits of the momentum and mechanical energy balances, for one is much superior to the other for this particular analysis.

7-10. What is the resultant force at the connection between the nozzle assembly and the pipe in Fig. 7-10, because of the water issuing from the jet? The average velocity in the 2-in. I.D. section is 10 ft/sec, the mass of the nozzle assembly is 7 lb_m, and the interior volume is 38 in.^{3}

7-11. The device illustrated in Fig. 7-11 is used to mix two miscible fluids. Determine the resultant horizontal force on this device owing to the entering and leaving fluid streams.
Given:

$$\rho_A = 70 \ lb_m/ft^3$$
$$\rho_B = 59 \ lb_m/ft^3$$

gauge pressure at A = 15 psig
gauge pressure at B = 20 psig
gauge pressure at C = 0

The average velocity at A is 10 ft/sec; at B, it is 15 ft/sec.

Ans: $F_x = -28 \ lb_f$

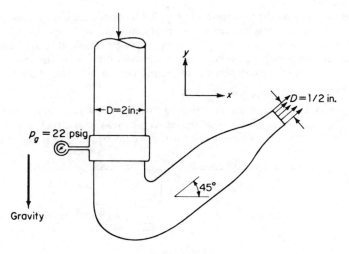

Fig. 7-10

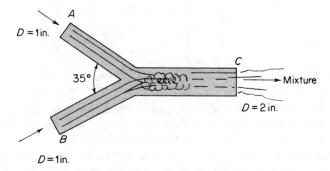

Fig. 7-11

7-12. Water is being pumped into a tank as shown in Fig. 7-12 at a rate of 8 ft³/sec. If the diameter of the pipe is 6 in. and the inside diameter of the tank is 30 in., what is the force required to hold the tank in position for h equal 24 in., excluding the gravitational force acting on the tank itself?

7-13. In solving macroscopic balance problems, we always attempt to place the surface of the control volume so that the streamlines are parallel and the momentum flux is easily determined. As an example of the error that may occur if the streamlines are not parallel, compute the momentum flux at the exit of a circular diverging section assuming (a) the streamlines are straight lines converging at point 0, and (b) the streamlines are parallel. (*Note:* the magnitude of the velocity vector must be adjusted so that the volumetric flow

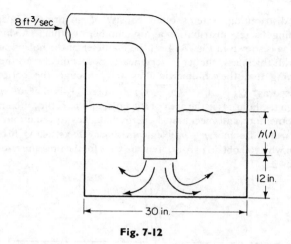

Fig. 7-12

rate is the same in both cases.) Express the ratio of momentum fluxes as a function of θ, and assume that the magnitude of the velocity vector is constant over the surface of the exit as indicated in Fig. 7-13a for assumption (a) and Fig. 7-13b for assumption (b).

Ans: $\dfrac{\text{momentum flux (a)}}{\text{momentum flux (b)}} = \dfrac{1}{2}\left[\dfrac{1 - \cos^2\theta}{(1 - \cos\theta)^2}\right]\ln(\sec\theta)$

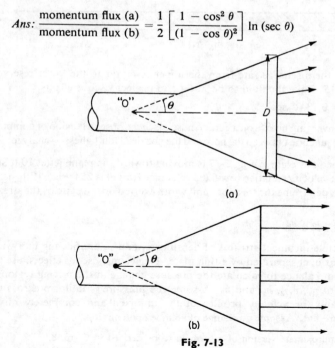

(a)

(b)

Fig. 7-13

7-14. Fluid distributing systems often consist of an array of perforated pipes providing discrete distribution at any number of points. A single perforation in a pipe is shown in Fig. 7-14. If the diameter of the hole is smaller than the pipe-wall thickness, the jet is very nearly perpendicular to the main stream. Assuming that the volumetric flow rate through the perforation can be expressed as† $Q_0 = A_0 \sqrt{2(p_1 - p_0)/\rho}$, where Q_0 is the volumetric flow rate through the hole, A_0 is the area of the hole, and p_0 is the ambient pressure, use the momentum and mechanical energy balances to obtain an expression for the pressure difference, $p_1 - p_2$. Neglect viscous effects, take Q_0 to be specified, and explain why you obtain two different answers for the pressure rise between points "1" and "2."

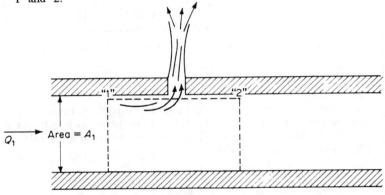

Fig. 7-14

7-15. Calculate the discharge rate from the upper reservoir to the lower reservoir in Fig. 7-15. Take the fluid to be water and neglect viscous effects.

Ans: $Q = 0.18$ ft^3/sec.

7-16. Does a converging nozzle on a garden hose place the hose in tension or compression at the junction between the hose and the nozzle? Don't guess—analyze.

7-17. The inclined flat plate in Fig. 7-17 is moving toward the plane jet at 10 ft/sec, and the jet velocity (relative to a fixed reference frame) is 25 ft/sec. If the jet is 1 in. thick, determine the force per unit width exerted on the plate by the stream of water.

Ans: $f_x = 148$ lb$_f$/ft

7-18. Two miscible turbulent streams of densities ρ_1 and ρ_2 are flowing in a wide, rectangular duct separated by a thin plate. Neglecting viscous effects, use the momentum balance to calculate the pressure change in the mixing region in terms of $\langle v_z \rangle_1$, $\langle v_z \rangle_2$, h_1, and h_2. Assume the pressure is uniform across the channel and the velocity profiles of the unmixed and completely mixed streams are flat. Assume no change of volume upon mixing.

† This is an approximate version of a formula to be derived in Chap. 8.

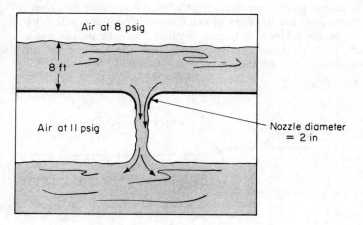

Fig. 7-15

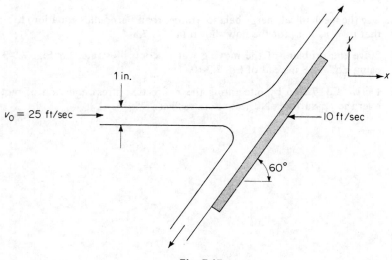

Fig. 7-17

Fig. 7-18. Mixing of two turbulent streams.

7-19. A laminar jet of water issues from a horizontal nozzle as shown in Fig. 7-19. The velocity profile of the jet as it emerges from the nozzle is parabolic, but the profile becomes flat some distance from the nozzle owing to viscous effects. Neglect the effect of gravity and the ambient air and derive an expression for the final area A_f.

Ans: $A_f/A_0 = \frac{3}{4}$

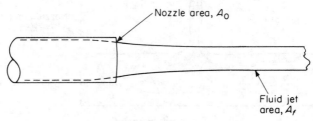

Nozzle area, A_0

Fluid jet area, A_f

Fig. 7-19. The laminar jet.

7-20. Use the mechanical energy balance (rather than Bernoulli's equation) to show that $v_1 = v_2 = v_3$ for the flow shown in Fig. 7.8-4.

7-21. Solve the problem of the moving water scoop illustrated in Fig. 7.9-3 by using Eq. 7.9-8 instead of Eq. 7.2-10.

7-22. Derive Eq. 7.10-6 by integrating the x-direction stress equation of motion over the y,z-surface. Neglect viscous effects.

Macroscopic Balances: Viscous Effects

8

In Chap. 6, we presented a qualitative description of turbulent flow and showed that the time-averaged stress equations of motion took the same form as the instantaneous stress equations of motion. However, the time-averaged equations could not be used to determine time-averaged velocity profiles, because the dependence of the turbulent stress $\bar{\tau}^{(t)}$ on the time-averaged velocity is unknown. Empirical expressions, such as the Prandtl mixing length equation, may be used to determine velocity profiles; however, they cannot be applied to any arbitrary geometry and their usefulness is limited.

In solving turbulent flow problems under conditions where viscous effects are important, we will always require some experimental data. The objective of this chapter is the formulation of a consistent method of interpreting experimental data and the application of this result to some problems where viscous effects must be considered.

*8.1 Friction Factors—Definition

In examining the momentum and mechanical energy balances (Eqs. 7.2-10 and 7.3-27), we see that knowledge of the integrals

$$\int_{\mathscr{A}_a(t)} \mathbf{t}_{(n)} \, dA \quad \text{and} \quad \int_{\mathscr{V}_a(t)} \Phi \, dV$$

285

is required if we are to obtain satisfactory solutions to these equations. In the previous chapter, viscous effects were neglected and these integrals were easily evaluated. While reasonable results were obtained for a variety of problems, the flows investigated were restricted to cases for which we knew a priori that inertial effects predominated. In accounting for viscous effects, we must relate the surface stress integral and the dissipation integral to experimentally determined pressure drops and flow rates.

A flowing fluid will exert a force on the solid surfaces that it contacts. In this chapter we are primarily interested in the component of this force in the direction of the mean flow, and it will be helpful to define a unit vector $\boldsymbol{\lambda}$ which points in the direction of the mean flow

$$\boldsymbol{\lambda} = \frac{\langle \mathbf{v} \rangle}{\langle \bar{v} \rangle} \tag{8.1-1}$$

Before defining the drag or friction force that the fluid exerts on the solid, Eq. 7.2-10 will be rewritten in a form which is especially convenient for interpreting experimental data. Substituting Eqs. 7.3-7, 7.8-15, and 7.8-20 into Eq. 7.2-10, and using the divergence theorem for a scalar, we get

$$\frac{d}{dt} \int_{\mathscr{V}_a(t)} \rho \mathbf{v} \, dV + \int_{A_e(t)} \rho \mathbf{v}(\mathbf{v} - \mathbf{w}) \cdot \mathbf{n} \, dA$$
$$= \int_{\mathscr{A}_a(t)} \{ -\mathbf{n}[(p - p_0) + \rho\phi] + \mathbf{n} \cdot \boldsymbol{\tau} \} \, dA \tag{8.1-2}$$

provided the density is constant. It should be kept in mind that for turbulent flow, $\boldsymbol{\tau}$ represents $\bar{\boldsymbol{\tau}} + \bar{\boldsymbol{\tau}}^{(t)}$, and p represents $\bar{p}$. Splitting the area integral on the right-hand side of Eq. 8.1-2 into the area of entrances and exits $A_e(t)$ and the area of solid surfaces (both fixed and moving) $A_s + A_s(t)$, we get

$$\frac{d}{dt} \int_{\mathscr{V}_a(t)} \rho \mathbf{v} \, dV + \int_{A_e(t)} \rho \mathbf{v}(\mathbf{v} - \mathbf{w}) \cdot \mathbf{n} \, dA = \int_{A_e(t)} \{ -\mathbf{n}[(p - p_0) + \rho\phi] + \mathbf{n} \cdot \boldsymbol{\tau} \} \, dA$$
$$+ \int_{A_s+A_s(t)} \{ -\mathbf{n}[(p - p_0) + \rho\phi] \} \, dA + \int_{A_s+A_s(t)} \mathbf{n} \cdot \boldsymbol{\tau} \, dA \tag{8.1-3}$$

We now define the drag force F_D as the force which the *fluid exerts on* the *solid* in the $\boldsymbol{\lambda}$-direction.†

$$F_D = \boldsymbol{\lambda} \cdot \int_{A_s+A_s(t)} \mathbf{n}[(p - p_0) + \rho\phi] \, dA - \boldsymbol{\lambda} \cdot \int_{A_s+A_s(t)} \mathbf{n} \cdot \boldsymbol{\tau} \, dA \tag{8.1-4}$$

† In the design of airfoils, an engineer is naturally interested in a *lift force*, the force the fluid exerts on the solid in a direction perpendicular to $\boldsymbol{\lambda}$.

For convenience, the total drag force is split into a *form force* and a *friction force*

$$F_{\text{form}} = \boldsymbol{\lambda} \cdot \int_{A_s + A_s(t)} \mathbf{n}[(p - p_0) + \rho\phi]\, dA \qquad (8.1\text{-}5)$$

$$F_{\text{friction}} = -\boldsymbol{\lambda} \cdot \int_{A_s + A_s(t)} \mathbf{n} \cdot \boldsymbol{\tau}\, dA \qquad (8.1\text{-}6)$$

The drag force contains the *negative* of the last two terms in Eq. 8.1-3, because it is defined as a force the *fluid exerts on the solid*, while the terms in Eq. 8.1-3 represent the force which the *surroundings exert on the fluid*. Because of the way in which the drag force has been defined, the normal vector **n** in Eqs. 8.1-4 through 8.1-6 is directed from the fluid into the solid.

The separation of the drag force into a *form force* and a *friction force* is made because the former depends mainly on inertial effects and is roughly proportional to ρu_0^2, while the latter depends on viscous effects and is roughly proportional to μu_0. The word "form" results from the fact that this portion of the drag force is greatly influenced by the *geometry* of the solid surface, while the word "friction" indicates that this portion of the drag force depends primarily on the *area* of the solid surface.

The drag force for flow in closed conduits is generally represented and correlated in terms of a dimensionless *friction factor f* defined by

$$f = \frac{F_D}{A^* KE^*} \qquad (8.1\text{-}7)$$

where

$A^* = $ a characteristic area

$KE^* = $ a characteristic kinetic energy per unit volume

There are many important processes dealing with the flow of fluids through conduits of constant cross-sectional area. For such conduits the characteristic kinetic energy per unit volume and characteristic area are generally given by

$$KE^* = \tfrac{1}{2}\rho\langle \bar{v}_z \rangle^2 \qquad (8.1\text{-}8)$$

$$A^* = \tfrac{1}{4} \text{ wetted surface} \qquad (8.1\text{-}9)$$

Because $\boldsymbol{\lambda}$ will be orthogonal to the outwardly directed unit normal at the solid surfaces, F_D is given by

$$F_D = -\boldsymbol{\lambda} \cdot \int_{A_s} \mathbf{n} \cdot \boldsymbol{\tau}\, dA \qquad (8.1\text{-}10)$$

for conduits having a constant cross-sectional area. Equation 8.1-10 is valid only for mathematically smooth conduits and thus is only an approximation for real conduits.

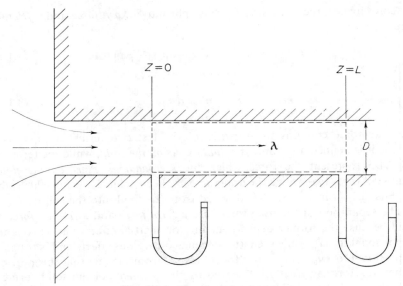

Fig. 8.1-1. Flow in a circular tube.

As an example, we will apply these ideas to flow in the circular tube shown in Fig. 8.1-1. The characteristic area is given by

$$A^* = \tfrac{1}{4}\pi DL \tag{8.1-11}$$

and substitution of Eqs. 8.1-8, 8.1-10, and 8.1-11 into Eq. 8.1-7 allows us to express the friction factor as

$$f = \frac{F_D}{A^* KE^*} = \frac{-\boldsymbol{\lambda} \cdot \displaystyle\int_{A_s} \mathbf{n} \cdot \boldsymbol{\tau}\, dA}{(\tfrac{1}{4}\pi DL)(\tfrac{1}{2}\rho \langle \bar{v}_z \rangle^2)} \tag{8.1-12}$$

For a mathematically smooth circular tube, there is only one nonzero component of the outwardly directed normal at the solid surface,

$$
\left.
\begin{aligned}
n_1 &= n_r = 1 \\
n_2 &= n_\theta = 0 \\
n_3 &= n_z = 0
\end{aligned}
\right\} \text{ at the tube wall}
$$

$$
\begin{aligned}
&(8.1\text{-}13\text{a}) \\
&(8.1\text{-}13\text{b}) \\
&(8.1\text{-}13\text{c})
\end{aligned}
$$

and $\boldsymbol{\lambda}$ has only one nonzero component.

$$\lambda_1 = \lambda_r = 0 \tag{8.1-14a}$$

$$\lambda_2 = \lambda_\theta = 0 \tag{8.1-14b}$$

$$\lambda_3 = \lambda_z = 1 \tag{8.1-14c}$$

Assuming that the stress at the wall is independent of θ and z, we may write the numerator of Eq. 8.1-12 as

$$-\boldsymbol{\lambda}\cdot\int_{A_s}\mathbf{n}\cdot\boldsymbol{\tau}\,dA = -\lambda_i(n_j\tau_{ji})\pi DL = -\tau_{rz}\pi DL \qquad (8.1\text{-}15)$$

The wall shear stress τ_0 was previously defined in Sec. 6.5 as

$$\tau_0 = -\tau_{rz}, \qquad \text{at} \quad r = r_0 \qquad (8.1\text{-}16)$$

and we may use this definition to express the friction factor as

$$f = \frac{4\tau_0}{\frac{1}{2}\rho\langle\bar{v}_z\rangle^2} \qquad (8.1\text{-}17)$$

This result simply indicates that the friction factor may be interpreted as a dimensionless wall shear stress.

The momentum balance

It will be helpful at this point to apply the momentum balance to the flow shown in Fig. 8.1-1. A rather careful analysis of the stress terms will be presented here, and future discussions of the momentum balance will presume that these points are understood. For the control volume indicated in Fig. 8.1-1, the momentum balance reduces to

$$0 = \int_{A_e} \{-\mathbf{n}[(p - p_0) + \rho\phi] + \mathbf{n}\cdot\boldsymbol{\tau}\}\,dA$$

$$+ \int_{A_s} -\mathbf{n}[(p - p_0) + \rho\phi]\,dA + \int_{A_s}\mathbf{n}\cdot\boldsymbol{\tau}\,dA \qquad (8.1\text{-}18)$$

Here, we have assumed that the velocity profiles at points 1 and 2 are identical, so that the momentum flux term in Eq. 8.1-3 is identically zero. Forming the scalar product with $\boldsymbol{\lambda}$ and using the definition of F_D, we reduce Eq. 8.1-18 to

$$F_D = \boldsymbol{\lambda}\cdot\int_{A_e} -\mathbf{n}[(p - p_0) + \rho\phi]\,dA + \boldsymbol{\lambda}\cdot\int_{A_e}\mathbf{n}\cdot\boldsymbol{\tau}\,dA \qquad (8.1\text{-}19)$$

Dividing by A^*KE^*, we obtain the following expression for the friction factor:

$$f = \frac{D}{L}(\mathscr{P}_1 - \mathscr{P}_2) + \left[\boldsymbol{\lambda}\cdot\int_{A_{\text{entrance}}}\mathbf{n}_1\cdot\boldsymbol{\tau}\,dA + \boldsymbol{\lambda}\cdot\int_{A_{\text{exit}}}\mathbf{n}_2\cdot\boldsymbol{\tau}\,dA\right]\Big/ A^*KE^*$$
$$(8.1\text{-}20)$$

In obtaining this result we have used the definition

$$\mathscr{P} = \frac{(\langle \bar{p} \rangle - p_0) + \rho \langle \phi \rangle}{\tfrac{1}{2}\rho \langle \bar{v}_z \rangle^2} \tag{8.1-21}$$

and the area integral over the entrance and exit has been represented as two separate integrals.

The stress terms are best treated in terms of index notation,

$$\boldsymbol{\lambda} \cdot (\mathbf{n} \cdot \boldsymbol{\tau}) = \lambda_i n_j \tau_{ji} \tag{8.1-22}$$

where

$$\tau_{ji} = \bar{\tau}_{ji} + \bar{\tau}_{ji}^{(t)}$$

Remembering that the turbulent stress was given in Sec. 6.2 as

$$\bar{\tau}_{ji}^{(t)} = -\overline{\rho v_j' v_i'}$$

and the time-averaged viscous stress is given by

$$\bar{\tau}_{ji} = \frac{\mu}{2}\left(\frac{\partial \bar{v}_j}{\partial x_i} + \frac{\partial \bar{v}_i}{\partial x_j}\right)$$

we may write Eq. 8.1-22 as

$$\boldsymbol{\lambda} \cdot (\mathbf{n} \cdot \boldsymbol{\tau}) = \lambda_i n_j \left[\frac{\mu}{2}\left(\frac{\partial \bar{v}_j}{\partial x_i} + \frac{\partial \bar{v}_i}{\partial x_j}\right) - \overline{\rho v_j' v_i'}\right] \tag{8.1-23}$$

We now wish to evaluate this quantity at the entrance and exit where $\mathbf{n}$ has only one nonzero component

$$n_1 = n_r = 0 \tag{8.1-24a}$$

$$n_2 = n_\theta = 0 \quad \text{at the entrance and exit} \tag{8.1-24b}$$

$$n_3 = n_z = \pm 1 \tag{8.1-24c}$$

Carrying out the summations indicated in Eq. 8.1-23, and making use of Eqs. 8.1-14 and 8.1-24, we get

$$\boldsymbol{\lambda} \cdot (\mathbf{n} \cdot \boldsymbol{\tau}) = \pm \left(\mu \frac{\partial \bar{v}_z}{\partial z} - \overline{\rho v_z' v_z'}\right) \tag{8.1-25}$$

In obtaining this result, we have assumed that the velocity field is described by

$$\bar{v}_r = \bar{v}_\theta = 0, \qquad \bar{v}_z \neq 0$$

$$v_r', v_\theta', v_z' \neq 0$$

The time-averaged velocity in the z-direction will be independent of z for all points downstream of the entrance region (i.e., in the region of one-dimensional flow); thus,

$$\frac{\partial \bar{v}_z}{\partial z} = 0 \tag{8.1-26}$$

and Eq. 8.1-20 may be written as

$$f = \frac{D}{L}(\mathscr{P}_1 - \mathscr{P}_2) - \frac{1}{A^* KE^*}\left(\langle \rho \overline{v_z' v_z'}\rangle_1 - \langle \rho \overline{v_z' v_z'}\rangle_2\right)\frac{\pi D^2}{4} \qquad (8.1\text{-}27)$$

If the structure of the turbulence does not change from 1 to 2, the turbulent stress terms will cancel and we are left with the result

$$f = (\mathscr{P}_1 - \mathscr{P}_2)\frac{D}{L} \qquad (8.1\text{-}28)$$

Thus, the friction factor may also be interpreted as a dimensionless pressure drop.

Dimensional analysis for the friction factor

Before examining the experimental values of f, it will be wise to make use of dimensional analysis to determine what parameters will influence the friction factor. Writing out Eq. 8.1-12 gives

$$f = \frac{\displaystyle\int_0^L \int_0^{2\pi} \left(-\mu \frac{\partial \bar{v}_z}{\partial r}\right)_{r=r_0} r_0\, d\theta\, dz}{(\tfrac{1}{4}\pi DL)(\tfrac{1}{2}\rho \langle \bar{v}_z\rangle^2)} \qquad (8.1\text{-}29)$$

Forming the dimensionless variables

$$Z = \frac{z}{D}$$

$$R = \frac{r}{D}$$

$$\bar{U}_z = \frac{\bar{v}_z}{\langle \bar{v}_z\rangle}$$

$$N_{\text{Re}} = \frac{\rho \langle \bar{v}_z\rangle D}{\mu}$$

allows us to express Eq. 8.1-29 as

$$f = \left(\frac{8}{\pi}\right)\left(\frac{D}{L}\right)\left(\frac{1}{N_{\text{Re}}}\right)\int_0^{L/D}\int_0^{2\pi}\left(-\frac{\partial \bar{U}_z}{\partial R}\right)_{R=1/2} R\, d\theta\, dZ \qquad (8.1\text{-}30)$$

This result indicates immediately that f depends upon the ratio L/D and the Reynolds number, but we must know upon what parameters $\partial \bar{U}_z/\partial R$ depends to complete the investigation. The continuity equation and the Navier-Stokes equations in dimensionless form are given by

$$\mathbf{\nabla} \cdot \mathbf{U} = 0 \tag{8.1-31}$$

$$\frac{\partial \mathbf{U}}{\partial \Theta} + \mathbf{U} \cdot \mathbf{\nabla} \mathbf{U} = -\mathbf{\nabla} \mathscr{P} + \frac{1}{N_{\text{Re}}} \nabla^2 \mathbf{U} \tag{8.1-32}$$

The boundary conditions for this flow may be expressed in both dimensional and dimensionless form as follows:

B.C. 1:　　　　　　$\mathbf{v} = 0, \qquad r = \dfrac{D}{2}$

$$\mathbf{U} = 0, \qquad R = \frac{1}{2} \tag{8.1-33}$$

B.C. 2:　　　　　$\mathbf{v} = \mathbf{v}_1(r, \theta, t), \qquad z = 0$

$$\mathbf{U} = \mathbf{U}_1(R, \theta, \Theta), \qquad Z = 0 \tag{8.1-34}$$

B.C. 3:　　　　　$\mathbf{v} = \mathbf{v}_2(r, \theta, t), \qquad z = L$

$$\mathbf{U} = \mathbf{U}_2(R, \theta, \Theta), \qquad Z = \frac{L}{D} \tag{8.1-35}$$

B.C. 4:　　　　　$p = p_1 - \rho\phi_1, \qquad z = 0$

$$\mathscr{P} = \mathscr{P}_1, \qquad Z = 0 \tag{8.1-36}$$

Although we cannot solve Eqs. 8.1-31 and 8.1-32 for $\mathbf{U}$ and $\mathscr{P}$, we can state that these two dependent variables are functions of the independent variables (R, θ, Z, Θ), the parameters in the differential equations (N_{Re}), and the parameters in the boundary conditions (L/D). Thus, we can write

$$\mathbf{U} = \mathbf{U}\left(R, \theta, Z, \Theta, N_{\text{Re}}, \frac{L}{D}\right) \tag{8.1-37a}$$

$$\mathscr{P} = \mathscr{P}\left(R, \theta, Z, \Theta, N_{\text{Re}}, \frac{L}{D}\right) \tag{8.1-37b}$$

If the time-average flow is steady, $\bar{\mathbf{U}}$ will be independent of the dimensionless time Θ, and the gradient at the wall may be expressed as

$$\left. \frac{\partial \bar{U}_z}{\partial R} \right|_{R=1/2} = \text{function of} \quad \left(\theta, Z, N_{\text{Re}}, \frac{L}{D}\right) \tag{8.1-38}$$

In Eq. 8.1-30, the θ and Z dependence will be eliminated by integration, and the functional dependence of the friction factor is

$$f = f\left(N_{\text{Re}}, \frac{L}{D}\right) \tag{8.1-39}$$

If the velocity profile is fully developed at $Z = 0$, the velocity gradient will be independent of Z. Integration with respect to Z in Eq. 8.1-30 will then yield the factor L/D, which just cancels the multiplying factor, D/L. The entrance length for turbulent flow is nearly independent of the Reynolds number and is on the order of 50 tube diameters. For large values of L/D, we may neglect the effect of the entrance region and write

$$f = f(N_{Re}) \qquad \text{For large } L/D \qquad (8.1\text{-}40)$$

*8.2   Friction Factors: Experimental

If the friction factor is measured using a variety of pipes all having large values of L/D, we soon discover that the experimental values of f cannot be represented by a single plot of f versus N_{Re} as Eq. 8.1-40 implies. Darcy[1] performed the first experimental studies leading to this conclusion, and we immediately wonder, "Where did our dimensional analysis go wrong?" As is often the case with a mathematical analysis, the trouble lies with one of the boundary conditions. In Eq. 8.1-33 we specified that the velocity was zero at $r = D/2$, and while this seems like quite a reasonable statement, it is true only for a mathematically smooth tube. In actual fact, we should have written

B.C. 1′: $\qquad\qquad \mathbf{v} = 0, \qquad r = \dfrac{D}{2} + e(\theta, z) \qquad (8.2\text{-}1)$

where the roughness function $e(\theta, z)$ is some unknown function of θ and z that describes the roughness of the conduit. For most commercial pipes the magnitude of e is of the order of 0.001 of the pipe diameter. Surely this is a "small effect," but for turbulent flow in pipes we will find that "small causes *do not* lead to small effects." This example should be remembered well, for it is a classic example of a plausible intuitive hypothesis leading to an erroneous conclusion.

The early work by Darcy and others led Nikuradse[2] to carry out a detailed experimental study of the friction factor for smooth and artificially roughened tubes. The rough tubes were obtained by covering the surface as tightly as possible with sand of a definite grain size glued onto the wall. In this manner, Nikuradse obtained a roughness considerably more uniform than that encountered in commercially available pipe. The experimental results are plotted as the friction factor versus the Reynolds number in Fig. 8.2-1. The results are characterized by the relative roughness parameter, ε/D, where ε

1. H. P. G. Darcy; for an account, see H. Rouse and S. Ince, *History of Hydraulics* (New York: Dover Publications, Inc., 1963), p. 170.

2. J. Nikuradse, *VDI-Forschungsh.* 361, Ausgabe B, Band 4, 1933. A translation of the original paper is available as *NACA Tech. Mem.* 1292, 1950.

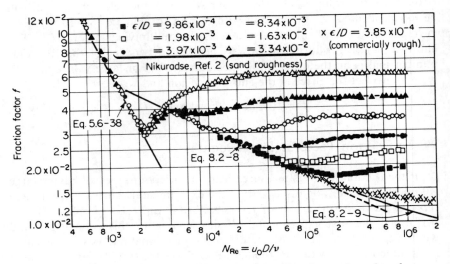

Fig. 8.2-I. Friction factor versus Reynolds number for sand-roughened tubes.

is the height of the sand grain. Because all the tubes were roughened in the same manner—i.e., the sand grains were placed as close together as possible—the single parameter ε/D was sufficient to characterize the roughness.

The student should give some serious thought to these results, for they are a clear indication that we can easily perform an apparently rigorous analysis, which in fact neglects important effects. It is quite common in engineering analysis to treat surfaces as mathematically smooth and impose boundary conditions of the type given by boundary condition 1. Generally, such an approach is satisfactory (as it is for laminar flow); however, for turbulent flow in tubes, a small effect such as wall roughness can lead to a striking effect in the pressure drop-flow rate relationship. In the absence of experimental studies, the average investigator is not likely to formulate the boundary condition as indicated by boundary condition 1'; thus, we must be constantly on the alert for flaws and limitations in a mathematical analysis. Several aspects of this friction factor plot must be discussed before we continue with the results for commercial pipes.

Laminar region

We note first that all the data in the laminar flow region fall on a single line, the equation for which was derived in Chap. 5,

$$f = \frac{64}{N_{\text{Re}}} \tag{8.2-2}$$

This equation is an indication that the values of ε/D were never large enough to affect severely the parabolic velocity profile. By using extremely rough pipes (say, $\varepsilon/D > 0.10$), we could certainly find an effect of ε/D on the laminar friction factor; however, this case is not of great practical importance. If we use Eq. 8.1-17, in conjunction with Eq. 8.2-2, to express the wall shear stress, we obtain

$$\tau_0 = \frac{8\mu \langle \bar{v}_z \rangle}{D} \qquad \text{for laminar flow} \qquad (8.2\text{-}3)$$

indicating that the drag force is proportional to the product of the viscosity and the velocity. Under these conditions, the drag force results entirely from the friction force; hence,

$$F_D = F_{\text{friction}}, \qquad \text{for laminar flow} \qquad (8.2\text{-}4)$$

Critical region

Pipe roughness is not a factor in determining the critical Reynolds number, and the transition to turbulent flow starts at $N_{\text{Re}} = 2100$. The critical Reynolds number may depend strongly on the inlet conditions to the pipe, upstream conditions such as valves and bends, and the presence of spurious disturbances such as building vibrations. It is well established that there is a lower bound for the critical Reynolds number of about 2100; however, recent studies[3] have shown that laminar flow can be maintained up to Reynolds numbers of 2×10^4 by taking extreme care to keep the inlet flow free of disturbances. In practical cases, there are numerous sources of disturbance and the transition to turbulent flow starts at $N_{\text{Re}} = 2100$. The region between $N_{\text{Re}} = 2100$ and $N_{\text{Re}} = 4000$ is called the critical region and it is here that the transition is completed. The transition is not a sharp one, and in the critical region the flow alternates between the laminar and turbulent regimes.

Transition and rough-pipe regions

For smooth tubes there is only one more region of flow in addition to the two previously mentioned—i.e., the region of fully developed turbulent flow existing for $N_{\text{Re}} > 4 \times 10^3$. However, for rough pipes the nature of the flow continues to change as the Reynolds number is increased. Provided the relative roughness is less than 0.01, the friction factor curve follows the smooth pipe curve for a region in which the rough pipe could be considered

3. R. J. Leite, *J. Fluid Mech.*, 1959, 5:81.

hydraulically smooth. As the Reynolds number is increased, each curve eventually departs from the smooth pipe curve, progresses through a transition region, and finally reaches a constant value depending only on the relative roughness. This latter region will be called the rough-pipe region of flow, and the zone between the smooth-pipe and rough-pipe regions will be called the transition region.

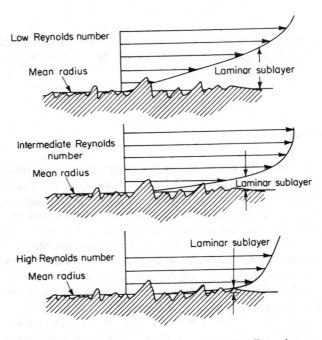

Fig. 8.2-2. Qualitative description of wall effects in turbulent flow.

We can explain the existence of the transition and rough-pipe regions only in a *qualitative* manner; however, the explanation will help to explain the nature of turbulent pipe flow and should be valuable for this reason alone. At low Reynolds numbers the laminar sublayer is generally thicker than the average roughness ε, and the wall shear stress τ_0 consists primarily of viscous stresses. As the Reynolds number is increased, the energy of the turbulent eddies increases, and they penetrate more closely to the wall. This process causes the thickness of the laminar sublayer to decrease, and the irregularities of the tube wall begin to protrude through the laminar sublayer, as Fig. 8.2-2 illustrates. When the turbulent eddies come into contact with these protrusions, the interaction of the fluid and solid changes. At high Reynolds numbers, the major source of resistance to flow is the interaction of the turbulent eddies with the wall roughness and friction drag becomes small compared to the form drag. In the rough-pipe region of flow, the friction factor is constant, and Eq. 8.1-17 indicates that the wall shear stress is proportional to the density times the velocity squared.

$$\tau_0 = \left(\frac{f}{8}\right)\rho\langle\bar{v}_z\rangle^2 \quad \begin{array}{l}\text{In the rough-pipe region}\\\text{of turbulent flow}\end{array} \qquad (8.2\text{-}5)$$

Comparing Eqs. 8.2-3 and 8.2-5, we see that two very distinct mechanisms of momentum transport exist in pipe flow—one a result of viscous effects and the other of inertial effects. Also, it is of interest to compare Eq. 8.2-5 with the formula developed in Chap. 7 for the force exerted by a jet on a plate, which indicated that

$$\left\{\begin{array}{l}\text{force exerted}\\\text{on the plate}\end{array}\right\} = \rho v^2 A \qquad (8.2\text{-}6)$$

where v and A are the velocity and area of the jet, respectively. For comparison, we might interpret Eq. 8.2-5 as

$$\left\{\begin{array}{l}\text{force per unit area}\\\text{exerted on the}\\\text{protrusions}\end{array}\right\} = \left(\frac{f}{8}\right)\rho\langle\bar{v}_z\rangle^2 \qquad (8.2\text{-}7)$$

There is obviously some similarity between the two flows.

Commercial pipes

Pipes and tubes used in engineering practice can neither be regarded as smooth nor be considered rough in the same sense as Nikuradse's sand-roughened pipes. The roughness in commercial pipes is not uniform, nor is it subject to direct measurement. However, a value of ε/D can be assigned to any given pipe if the friction factor is known in the rough-pipe region. Moody[4] has made an extensive investigation of friction factors for commercial pipes, the results of which appear in Fig. 8.2-3. This particular chart is widely used in engineering design and is often called the Moody chart. Values of the relative roughness are given in Fig. 8.2-4 for various types of pipe.

When using these charts, an engineer must keep in mind that the values of ε/D are only approximate and there may be significant variations in the relative roughness for any given type of pipe. Moody has indicated that the probable variation in f for smooth tubing is ± 5 per cent, and a variation of ± 10 per cent is to be expected for commercial steel pipe. Corrosion may also

4. L. F. Moody, "Friction Factors for Pipe Flow," *Trans. ASME*, 1944, 66:671.

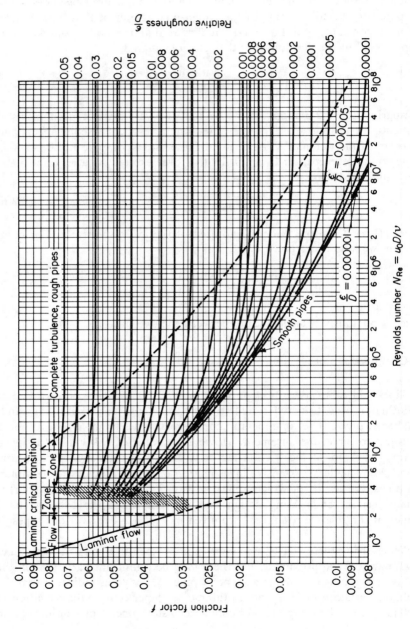

Fig. 8.2-3. Friction factors for commercial pipes.

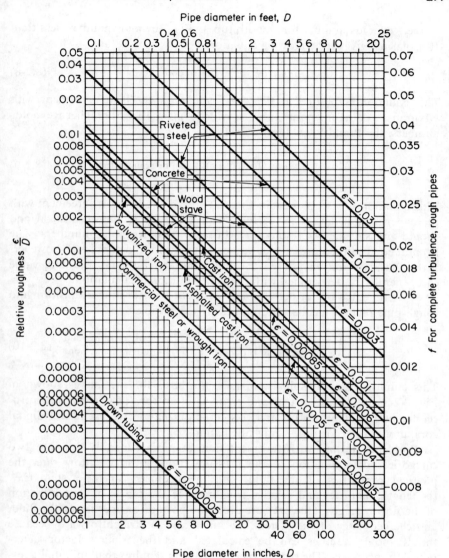

Fig. 8.2-4. Relative roughness for commercial pipes.

cause large variations in ε/D with time,[5] and we must be cautious when analyzing pipelines which have been in operation for an extended period of time.

There are two useful empirical formulas giving the friction factor in terms

5. C. F. Colebrook and C. M. White, "The Reduction of the Carrying Capacity of Pipes with Age," *J. Inst. Civ. Engrs.* (*London*), 1937, 7:99.

of the Reynolds number for smooth tubes. For Reynolds numbers less than 10^5, Blasius[6] gives the following equation

$$f = 0.316 N_{Re}^{-1/4} \quad \text{For smooth tubes} \tag{8.2-8}$$

This equation is plotted in Fig. 8.2-1 and is in excellent agreement with Nikuradse's data for smooth tubes provided $N_{Re} \leq 10^5$. For higher Reynolds numbers, the Prandtl equation[7] is useful:

$$\frac{1}{\sqrt{f}} = 2.0 \log(\sqrt{f} N_{Re}) - 0.8 \quad \text{For smooth tubes} \tag{8.2-9}$$

This equation is also plotted in Fig. 8.2-1, and shows good agreement with the experimental data. The derivation of Eq. 8.2-9 is semitheoretical and should give satisfactory results for arbitrarily high Reynolds numbers. The Prandtl equation requires a trial-and-error solution to determine f; however, if the Blasius equation is used to obtain the first estimate, the final value can generally be determined with only one additional calculation.

A useful equation for determining the friction factor in the transition and rough-pipe regions has been developed by Colebrook.[8]

$$\frac{1}{\sqrt{f}} = -2.0 \log\left(\frac{\varepsilon/D}{3.7} + \frac{2.51}{N_{Re}\sqrt{f}}\right) \quad \begin{array}{l}\text{For transition and}\\\text{rough-pipe regions}\end{array} \tag{8.2-10}$$

This empirical relationship is, in fact, the basis for the curves shown in Fig. 8.2-3. It requires a trial-and-error solution for f; however, such procedures are straightforward and this equation may prove useful if a digital computer is used for pipe-sizing calculations.

Problems dealing with turbulent flow in pipes generally fall into two categories: determination of the pressure drop, given the flow rate, the physical properties of the fluid, and the geometry of the system (i.e., the length, diameter and relative roughness of the pipe); or determination of the flow rate, given the pressure drop, the physical properties of the fluid, and the geometry of the system. The first case is straightforward because the Reynolds number can be calculated and the friction factor determined immediately. The second type of problem requires that an initial guess be made for f, allowing us to calculate the average velocity by Eq. 8.1-28. The

6. H. Blasius, "The Law of Similarity for Frictional Processes in Fluids," *Forsch. Arb. Ingr.-Wesen* (Berlin, 1913), 131:361.

7. L. Prandtl, "The Mechanics of Viscous Fluids," in *Aerodynamic Theory*, F. W. Durand, ed. (Berlin: Springer-Verlag, 1935), 3:143.

8. C. F. Colebrook, "Turbulent Flow in Pipes, with Particular Reference to the Transition Region between the Smooth and Rough-Pipe Laws," *J. Inst. Civ. Engrs.* (*London*), 1938, 11:133.

Reynolds number can then be determined, and the accuracy of the initial assumption for f may be examined. If the two values differ significantly, a second trial must be made. In the following example, we consider this type type of calculation.

Determination of the flow rate for a given pressure drop

Let us determine the volumetric flow rate of water at 75°F through a 750-ft length of 4-in. diameter (nominal) commercial steel pipe for a pressure drop of 23.5 $lb_f/in.^2$ We shall assume the pipe is horizontal so that gravitational effects need not be considered. It is given that

$$D = 4.03 \text{ in. (actual diameter)}$$
$$L = 750 \text{ ft}$$
$$\mu = 0.95 \text{ centipoise}$$
$$\rho = 62.4 \text{ lb}_m/\text{ft}^3$$
$$\Delta p = 23.5 \text{ lb}_f/\text{in.}^2$$
$$\frac{\varepsilon}{D} = 0.0004$$

We may rearrange Eq. 8.1-28 to yield

$$\langle v_z \rangle = \frac{1}{\sqrt{f}}\left(\frac{2\,\Delta p D}{\rho L}\right)^{1/2}$$

and the Reynolds number becomes

$$N_{Re} = \frac{\rho \langle v_z \rangle D}{\mu} = \frac{1}{\sqrt{f}}\left(\frac{2\,\Delta p \rho D^3}{\mu^2 L}\right)^{1/2}$$

For this example, we obtain

$$N_{Re} = \frac{1}{\sqrt{f}}\left\{\left[\frac{(2)(23.5 \text{ lb}_f/\text{in.}^2)(62.4 \text{ lb}_m/\text{ft}^3)(4.03 \text{ in.})^3}{(0.95 \text{ centipoise})^2(750 \text{ ft})}\right]\right.$$
$$\left.\times \left[\left(\frac{\text{centipoise–ft sec}}{0.672 \times 10^{-3} \text{ lb}_m}\right)^2\left(\frac{32.2 \text{ lb}_m\text{ft}}{\text{lb}_f \text{ sec}^2}\right)\left(\frac{\text{ft}}{12 \text{ in.}}\right)\right]\right\}^{1/2}$$

or

$$N_{Re} = \frac{4.13 \times 10^4}{\sqrt{f}}$$

Now we need only find the value of f for $\varepsilon/D = 0.0004$ that will satisfy this equation and the relationship between f and N_{Re} given in the Moody chart. The minimum value of f in this case is 0.016, which yields a value for the

Reynolds number of

$$N_{\text{Re}} = \frac{4.13 \times 10^4}{\sqrt{0.016}} = 3.26 \times 10^5$$

Examination of the friction factor chart for $\varepsilon/D = 0.0004$ and $N_{\text{Re}} = 3.26 \times 10^5$ gives

$$f = 0.0178$$

which in turn yields the second approximation for the Reynolds number,

$$N_{\text{Re}} = \frac{4.13 \times 10^4}{\sqrt{0.0178}} = 3.08 \times 10^5$$

Returning to the chart, we see that a Reynolds number of 3.08×10^5 gives a friction factor of 0.0178 for this particular relative roughness. Having established the Reynolds number, we may now determine the volumetric flow rate, Q.

$$Q = \left(\frac{\pi D^2}{4}\right)\langle v_z \rangle = \left(\frac{N_{\text{Re}} \pi D \mu}{4\rho}\right)$$

$$= \left[\frac{(3.08 \times 10^5)(3.14)(4.03 \text{ in.})(0.95 \text{ centipoise})}{(4)(62.4 \text{ lb}_{\text{m}}/\text{ft}^3)}\right]$$

$$\times \left[\left(\frac{0.672 \times 10^{-3} \text{ lb}_{\text{m}}}{\text{centipoise--ft sec}}\right)\left(\frac{\text{ft}}{12 \text{ in.}}\right)\right]$$

$$= 0.83 \text{ ft}^3/\text{sec}$$

Nominal pipe diameters

It is unfortunate but true that the nominal pipe diameter is not the actual pipe diameter; we must take this into account when specifying pipe diameters. In the previous example, the actual diameter of a 4-in. commercial steel pipe was 4.03 in. The difference between the nominal and actual diameters depends upon the diameter and the so-called *schedule number* of the pipe. The latter is simply a measure of the wall thickness and is therefore an indication of the pressure that the pipe can safely withstand. Information on

Nominal Pipe Size, in.	Outside Diameter, in.	Schedule No.	Inside Diameter, in.
6	6.62	5S	6.41
		10S	6.36
		40ST, 40S	6.06
		80XS, 80S	5.76
		120	5.50
		160	5.19
		XX	4.90

pipe sizes is available in handbooks,[9-10] and only a single example (see foot of facing page) will be cited here for a 6-in. diameter steel pipe.

The variation in inside diameter is significant and must be considered in designing any real system. Throughout the remainder of this text the nominal dimensions of any system are assumed to be identical to the actual dimensions.

Flow in closed conduits of noncircular cross section

Closed conduits of noncircular cross section are occasionally used, although they have received much less attention than circular tubes. For laminar flow, each noncircular conduit must be looked upon as a separate problem, for the result from one case cannot be extended to others. Knudsen and Katz[11] list several solutions of the Navier-Stokes equations for one-dimensional laminar flow in noncircular conduits. Dryden, Murnaghan, and Bateman[12] give a more thorough discussion of these problems and present several solutions. Since an engineer is generally concerned with only the pressure drop-flow rate relationship, the approximate method of solution suggested by Gaydon and Nuttal[13] is of great value in obtaining solutions for odd-shaped conduits. The method requires only a small computational effort to determine the pressure drop-flow rate relationship to within a few per cent.

Turbulent flow has been studied by several investigators[14-16] for triangular, rectangular and circular notched conduits; the experimental results are shown in Fig. 8.2-5. For each conduit, the friction factor is defined by

$$f = \frac{F_D}{A^* KE^*} \qquad (8.2\text{-}11)$$

where A^* and KE^* are given by Eqs. 8.1-8 and 8.1-9, and the Reynolds number is given by

$$N_{Re} = \frac{4\rho \langle v_z \rangle R_h}{\mu} \qquad (8.2\text{-}12)$$

9. *Chemical Engineers' Handbook*, 4th ed. (New York: McGraw-Hill Book Company, Inc., 1963), Sec. 6.

10. L. S. Marks, ed. *Mechanical Engineers Handbook*, 6th ed. (New York: McGraw-Hill Book Company, Inc., 1958).

11. J. G. Knudsen and D. L. Katz, *Fluid Dynamics and Heat Transfer* (New York: McGraw-Hill Book Company, Inc., 1958), Chap. 4.

12. H. L. Dryden, F. D. Murnaghan, and H. Bateman, *Hydrodynamics* (New York: Dover Publications, Inc., 1956), Chap. 2.

13. F. A. Gaydon and H. Nuttal, "Viscous Flow Through Tubes of Multiply Connected Cross Sections," *Trans. ASME Ser. E* 81, 1959, 4:573.

14. L. Schiller, *Z. Angew. Math. Mech.*, 1923, 3:2.

15. J. Nikuradse, *Ingr.-Arch.*, 1930, 1:306.

16. L. Prandtl, *Proc. Intern. Congr. Appl. Mech.*, Zürich, 1927.

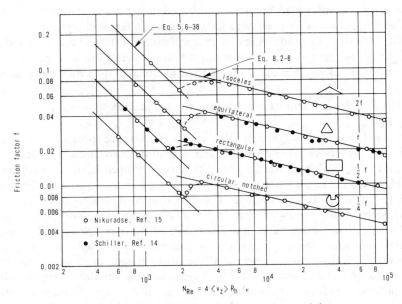

Fig. 8.2-5. Friction factors for noncircular conduits.

where R_h is the hydraulic radius. The results illustrated in Fig. 8.2-5 indicate excellent agreement with the Blasius equation; in addition, the values in the laminar flow region fall on the line given by

$$f = \frac{64}{N_{\mathrm{Re}}} \qquad (8.2\text{-}13)$$

These results must not be construed as verification of the friction factor chart for all shapes of closed conduits, for it is well known that laminar flows may deviate significantly from Eq. 8.2-13. However, we may conclude that if the shape of the conduit is not far removed from circular the friction factor chart can be used to obtain satisfactory results.

Drag coefficients for spheres and cylinders

The friction factor for solid bodies immersed in a flowing fluid is traditionally referred to as a dimensionless drag coefficient and defined by

$$C_D = \frac{F_D}{A^* KE^*} \qquad (8.2\text{-}14)$$

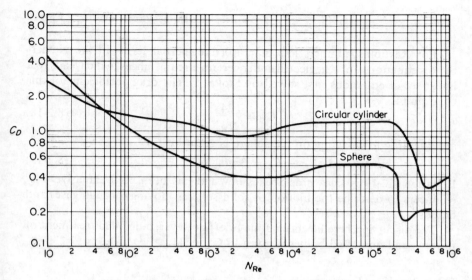

Fig. 8.2-6. Drag coefficients for spheres and cylinders.

The characteristic area A^* for immersed bodies is generally taken as the projected area in the direction of flow; thus,

$$A^* = \frac{\pi D^2}{4}, \qquad \text{for a sphere} \tag{8.2-15a}$$

$$A^* = DL, \qquad \text{for a cylinder} \tag{8.2-15b}$$

The characteristic kinetic energy is taken to be $\frac{1}{2}\rho u_\infty^2$, where u_∞ is the fluid velocity far removed from the immersed body. On the basis of Eqs. 8.2-14 and 8.2-15, the drag force acting on a sphere is

$$F_D = C_D\left(\tfrac{1}{2}\rho u_\infty^2\right)\left(\frac{\pi D^2}{4}\right) \tag{8.2-16}$$

and the drag force acting on a cylinder of length L and diameter D is

$$F_D = C_D(\tfrac{1}{2}\rho u_\infty^2)(DL) \tag{8.2-17}$$

Experimental values of C_D for spheres and cylinders are shown in Fig. 8.2-6. Dimensional analysis would again lead us to the conclusion that C_D is a function of Reynolds number and relative roughness. The effect of roughness has not been studied extensively because engineers are generally concerned with reducing the drag on immersed bodies; keeping them smooth is a means of accomplishing this end.†

† This is not always the case, for sometimes *increasing* the roughness can *decrease* the drag. This phenomenon, along with the curves shown in Fig. 8.2-6, will be discussed in detail in Chap. 11.

For Reynolds numbers less than 1.0, the inertial terms in the Navier-Stokes equation can be neglected under certain circumstances, which leads to a linear set of equations first solved by Stokes.[17] The drag coefficient for this condition is

$$C_D = \frac{24}{N_{\text{Re}}} \tag{8.2-18}$$

and the drag force acting on the sphere is given by

$$F_D = 3\pi\mu u_\infty D \tag{8.2-19}$$

Equation 8.2-19 is known as Stokes law and has been used extensively by engineers to describe the motion of solid spheres moving through gases and liquids.

The discussion here has been quite brief; however, a detailed treatment of flow around immersed bodies is given in Chap. 11.

8.3 Pipeline Systems

One of the standard problems that an engineer may encounter is the design of a piping system such as the one illustrated in Fig. 8.3-1. In the design of a new system, the flow rate and the physical properties of the fluid are generally given, and the engineer must determine the pipe size and the power requirement for the pump. The final solution will naturally be subject to certain economic constraints beyond the scope of this text. The main economic problem hinges on the fact that the cost of pumps and pipes depend on the size and that the final design of the system should satisfy the physical conditions at a minimum cost.

The mechanical energy balance is the most suitable macroscopic balance to use in solving pipeline problems, because the troublesome viscous effects are nicely lumped into a positive dissipation term. If we restrict ourselves to steady flow, fixed control surfaces *at entrances and exits,* and incompressible fluids, the mechanical energy balance (Eq. 7.3-27) takes the form

$$\underset{\substack{\text{Net outflow of}\\ \text{kinetic energy}}}{\int_A (\tfrac{1}{2}\rho v^2)\mathbf{v} \cdot \mathbf{n}\, dA} = \int_{A_e} \mathbf{v} \cdot \mathbf{t}_{(n)}\, dA \qquad \substack{\text{Rate of work done on the}\\ \text{system at the entrances}\\ \text{and exits}}$$

$$-\int_{A_e} \rho\phi\mathbf{v} \cdot \mathbf{n}\, dA \qquad \substack{\text{Rate of work done by}\\ \text{gravitational forces,}\\ \text{or the net outflow of}\\ \text{potential energy}} \tag{8.3-1}$$

$$+\, \dot{W} \qquad \substack{\text{Rate of work done on the}\\ \text{system by moving solid}\\ \text{surfaces}}$$

$$-\, \dot{E}_v \qquad \substack{\text{Rate of viscous}\\ \text{dissipation to}\\ \text{internal energy}}$$

17. G. G. Stokes; for an account, see H. Lamb, *Hydrodynamics,* 6th ed. (New York: Dover Publications, Inc., 1945), pp. 597–604.

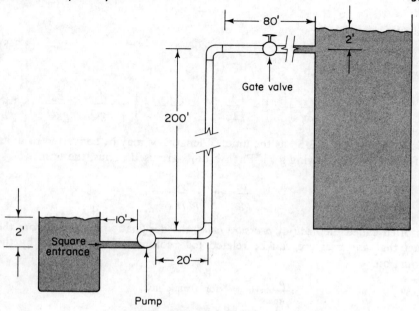

Fig. 8.3-1. Pipeline system.

If we now take the positive z-coordinate to be oppositely directed to the gravity vector, the potential energy function, ϕ, takes the form

$$\phi = gz \qquad (8.3\text{-}2)$$

In addition, we will consider control volumes such that the velocity at the entrances and exits is normal to the control surface; thus,

$$\int_{A_e} \mathbf{v} \cdot \mathbf{t}_{(n)} \, dA = -\int_{A_e} p\mathbf{v} \cdot \mathbf{n} \, dA \qquad (8.3\text{-}3)$$

Substituting Eqs. 8.3-2 and 8.3-3 into Eq. 8.3-1, and considering a control volume with one entrance (designated by 1) and one exit (designated by 2), we obtain

$$\tfrac{1}{2}\rho\langle v^3\rangle_2 A_2 - \tfrac{1}{2}\rho\langle v^3\rangle_1 A_1 + \rho g z_2 \langle v\rangle_2 A_2 - \rho g z_1 \langle v\rangle_1 A_1$$
$$= -p_2\langle v\rangle_2 A_2 + p_1\langle v\rangle_1 A_1 + \dot{W} - \dot{E}_v \qquad (8.3\text{-}4)$$

If the velocity profiles are nearly flat, we may use the macroscopic mass balance

$$\langle v \rangle_2 A_2 = \langle v \rangle_1 A_1 \tag{8.3-5}$$

to reduce Eq. 8.3-4 to

$$\left\{ \frac{1}{2g} \langle v \rangle_2^2 + \frac{p_2}{\rho g} + z_2 \right\} - \left\{ \frac{1}{2g} \langle v \rangle_1^2 + \frac{p_1}{\rho g} + z_1 \right\} = \frac{\dot{W}}{\rho g Q} - \frac{\dot{E}_v}{\rho g Q} \tag{8.3-6}$$

Each term in Eq. 8.3-6 has the units of length, or may be converted to units of length by multiplying g_c, if English units are used. Thus, the term

$$\frac{p}{\rho g} \quad \text{or} \quad \frac{p}{\rho g / g_c}$$

is often called the *head* or *pressure head*, the designation resulting from the fact that any pressure can be related to a column of static liquid by the equation,

$$\frac{p}{\rho g} = h, \qquad \text{for a static fluid}$$

and the fact that the height of a static liquid above a datum plane is traditionally referred to as the *liquid head*. The combination of terms, $p/\rho g + z$, is called the *piezometric head*, and $\langle v \rangle^2 / 2g$ is referred to as the *velocity head*. In keeping with this traditional nomenclature, the dissipation term $\dot{E}_v$ divided by $\rho g Q$ is called the *head loss*, and is generally separated into two terms, h_f and h_m. We will use h_f to refer to frictional head losses in straight sections of conduits having a uniform cross section, and h_m to refer to head losses occurring at sudden expansions, gate valves, etc. These losses are often called *minor losses* because the major source of viscous dissipation is in the comparatively long sections of straight conduit. The change in head $\dot{W}/\rho g Q$ owing to the power supplied by a pump or the power delivered to a turbine, is designated as H_w, the subscript w indicating that this term refers to the rate of *work* done on or by the fluid. The term H_w will be positive for pumps that supply energy to the fluid and negative for turbines that extract energy from the fluid. Using this nomenclature and simplifying the subscripts for the entrance and exit, we may rewrite Eq. 8.3-6 in the form

$$\left\{ \frac{\langle v_z \rangle^2}{2g} + \frac{p}{\rho g} + z \right\}_2 - \left\{ \frac{\langle v \rangle^2}{2g} + \frac{p}{\rho g} + z \right\}_1 = H_w - h_f - h_m \tag{8.3-7}$$

Before discussing the head loss terms in detail, it will be helpful to indicate the method of application of Eq. 8.3-7. Let us consider a pipeline to be split up into $N - 1$ separate sections, each of which contains either a straight section of conduit or one of the numerous special elements such as an elbow, a valve, a pump, etc. Writing Eq. 8.3-7 for each section of the system gives

$$\left\{ \frac{\langle v \rangle^2}{2g} + \frac{p}{\rho g} + z \right\}_2 - \left\{ \frac{\langle v \rangle^2}{2g} + \frac{p}{\rho g} + z \right\}_1 = \{ H_w - h_f - h_m \}_1$$

$$\left\{ \frac{\langle v \rangle^2}{2g} + \frac{p}{\rho g} + z \right\}_3 - \left\{ \frac{\langle v \rangle^2}{2g} + \frac{p}{\rho g} + z \right\}_2 = \{ H_w - h_f - h_m \}_2$$

- -

$$\left\{ \frac{\langle v \rangle^2}{2g} + \frac{p}{\rho g} + z \right\}_{N-1} - \left\{ \frac{\langle v \rangle^2}{2g} + \frac{p}{\rho g} + z \right\}_{N-2} = \{ H_w - h_f - h_m \}_{N-2}$$

$$\left\{ \frac{\langle v \rangle^2}{2g} + \frac{p}{\rho g} + z \right\}_N - \left\{ \frac{\langle v \rangle^2}{2g} + \frac{p}{\rho g} + z \right\}_{N-1} = \{ H_w - h_f - h_m \}_{N-1}$$

Summing all these equations, we see that only the first and the Nth terms remain on the left-hand side, while the right-hand side consists of the sum of the head loss and H_w terms.

$$\left\{ \frac{\langle v \rangle^2}{2g} + \frac{p}{\rho g} + z \right\}_N - \left\{ \frac{\langle v \rangle^2}{2g} + \frac{p}{\rho g} + z \right\}_1 = \sum_N H_w - \sum_N (h_f + h_m) \quad (8.3\text{-}8)$$

Using Δ to indicate differences between the outlet and the inlet, we obtain

$$
\underset{\substack{\text{Change in} \\ \text{velocity} \\ \text{head}}}{\Delta \left\{ \frac{\langle v \rangle^2}{2g} \right\}} + \underset{\substack{\text{Change in} \\ \text{pressure} \\ \text{head}}}{\frac{\Delta p}{\rho g}} + \underset{\substack{\text{Change in} \\ \text{elevation}}}{\Delta z} = \sum_N H_w
$$
Sum of head losses or gains for pumps and turbines

$$- \sum_N h_f$$
Sum of losses for all straight sections   (8.3-9)

$$- \sum_N h_m$$
Sum of losses for all values, fittings, etc.

At this point, the student should begin to appreciate all the effort involved in the derivation of the Navier-Stokes equations, the differential mechanical energy equation, and the macroscopic mechanical energy balance, because each was an important, logical step in arriving at Eq. 8.3-9. If we consider the complexity of flow through a pipeline, it is an achievement to be able to analyze such a system with the ease and simplicity suggested by the above result. With the aid of experimentally determined friction factors and loss coefficients we can use Eq. 8.3-9 to design a new pipeline or analyze an existing system.

To determine the friction head loss, h_f, we must apply both the macroscopic momentum and mechanical energy balances to the control volume shown in Fig. 8.1-1. The momentum balance is given by Eq. 8.1-28, which we may rearrange to get

$$\left\{\frac{p}{\rho g}+z\right\}_1 - \left\{\frac{p}{\rho g}+z\right\}_2 = f\left(\frac{L}{D}\right)\frac{\langle v\rangle^2}{2g} \qquad (8.3\text{-}10)$$

where

$$\langle v\rangle = \langle v_z\rangle_1 = \langle v_z\rangle_2$$

Substitution of this result into Eq. 8.3-7, H_w and h_m being zero, gives

$$h_f = f\left(\frac{L}{D}\right)\frac{\langle v\rangle^2}{2g}, \qquad \text{for circular tubes} \qquad (8.3\text{-}11)$$

This result is called the Darcy-Weisbach[18] formula. For noncircular conduits, we must remember that the term L/D resulted from

$$\frac{\tfrac14\ \text{wetted surface}}{\text{cross-sectional area}} = \frac{\tfrac14\pi DL}{\dfrac{\pi D^2}{4}} = \frac{L}{D}$$

Making use of the definition of the hydraulic radius R_h, we have a more general form of Eq. 8.3-11,

$$h_f = f\left(\frac{L}{4R_h}\right)\frac{\langle v\rangle^2}{2g}, \qquad \begin{array}{l}\text{for circular and noncircular}\\ \text{conduits.}\end{array} \qquad (8.3\text{-}12)$$

Equation 8.3-12 and the friction factor-Reynolds number chart provide us with sufficient information to determine the friction head losses in a pipeline.

The minor losses must also be determined experimentally and tabulated for all the different types of fittings. The equation for h_m for a Newtonian fluid is

$$h_m = \frac{\dot{E}_v}{\rho g Q} = \frac{\displaystyle\int_{\mathscr{V}} \Phi\, dV}{\rho g\langle v\rangle A} = \frac{2\mu \displaystyle\int_{\mathscr{V}} \nabla\mathbf{v}:\mathbf{d}\, dV}{\rho g\langle v\rangle A} \qquad (8.3\text{-}13)$$

Using R_h as a characteristic length and $\langle v\rangle$ as the characteristic velocity, we may put the volume integral in dimensionless form to obtain†

$$h_m = \frac{\langle v\rangle^2}{2g}\left\{\frac{4}{\dfrac{\rho\langle v\rangle A}{\mu R_h}}\int_{\mathscr{V}} \nabla\mathbf{U}:\mathbf{D}\, dV\right\} \qquad (8.3\text{-}14)$$

Since $\rho\langle v\rangle A/\mu R_h$ is directly proportional to the Reynolds number, we may

† Here the volume dV is actually dimensionless so that the term enclosed by braces { } is dimensionless.

18. H. Darcy, "Experimental Researches on the Flow of Water in Pipes," *Compt. Rend.*, 1854, 38:1109.

condense the expression for h_m to the traditional form,

$$h_m = K \frac{\langle v \rangle^2}{2g} \tag{8.3-15}$$

where K is a function of the Reynolds number and any dimensionless groups that enter into the boundary conditions.

The sudden expansion

The sudden expansion in a pipeline, shown in Fig. 8.3-2, is one case for which we can compute the head loss h_m directly. In Sec. 7.5 we found that the momentum balance predicted the pressure rise with reasonable accuracy;

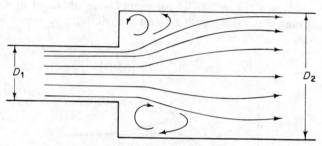

Fig. 8.3-2. Sudden expansion.

thus, we may make use of both the momentum and mechanical energy balance to determine h_m. The dimensionless pressure difference is given by

$$\Delta P = 2 \left[\left(\frac{D_1}{D_2} \right)^2 - 1 \right] \left(\frac{D_1}{D_2} \right)^2 \qquad \begin{array}{l}\text{Momentum balance}\\\text{(Eq. 7.5-13)}\end{array}$$

and

$$\Delta P = \left[\left(\frac{D_1}{D_2} \right)^4 - 1 \right] + \frac{8 \dot{E}_v}{\pi D_1^2 \rho \langle v_z \rangle_1^3} \qquad \begin{array}{l}\text{Mechanical energy balance}\\\text{(Eq. 7.5-31)}\end{array}$$

Equating the two results gives an expression for $\dot{E}_v / \rho g Q$,

$$h_m = \frac{4 \dot{E}_v}{\pi D_1^2 \rho g \langle v_z \rangle} = \left[1 - \left(\frac{D_1}{D_2} \right)^2 \right]^2 \frac{\langle v \rangle_1^2}{2g} \tag{8.3-16}$$

and the predicted loss coefficient, K, is given as

$$K = \left[1 - \left(\frac{D_1}{D_2} \right)^2 \right]^2 \tag{8.3-17}$$

The result is in error by about 20 per cent and may be used only for large Reynolds numbers.

When a pipe discharges into a large tank or a reservoir, $K = 1$, and the loss is 1 velocity head,

$$h_m = \frac{\langle v \rangle^2}{2g} \tag{8.3-18}$$

This amount is termed the exit loss and physically represents the complete dissipation of kinetic energy to internal energy by viscous forces.

The diffuser

If a gradual enlargement or diffuser is used to accomplish the transition from a smaller pipe to a larger one, the loss can be reduced significantly over that obtained for a sudden expansion. The experimentally determined coefficient C_ℓ is shown in Fig. 8.3-3. These results were obtained by Gibson[19-20] for water at high Reynolds numbers, and the friction and minor losses were represented as

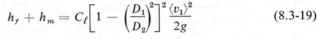

$$h_f + h_m = C_\ell \left[1 - \left(\frac{D_1}{D_2} \right)^2 \right]^2 \frac{\langle v_1 \rangle^2}{2g} \tag{8.3-19}$$

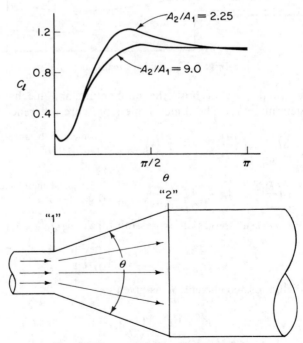

Fig. 8.3-3. Gradual expansion or diffuser.

19. A. H. Gibson, *Proc. Roy. Soc. (London) Ser. A*, 1910, 83:366.
20. A. H. Gibson, *Engineering*, 1912, 93:205.

It is convenient to express the head loss in this form, because the loss coefficient K may be represented as

$$K = C_\ell \left[1 - \left(\frac{D_1}{D_2} \right)^2 \right]^2 \qquad (8.3\text{-}20)$$

and C_ℓ should tend toward 1.0 as $\theta \to \pi$. As $\theta \to 0$, the coefficient $C\ell$ first decreases indicating a decrease in the minor losses as the system becomes more streamlined. For values of θ equal to approximately 7°, the friction loss and the minor loss are of comparable magnitude and C_ℓ begins to increase. Note that the form of Eq. 8.3-19 requires the $C_\ell \to \infty$ as $\theta \to 0$, because the term in brackets tends to zero while the friction loss remains finite.

Generally the losses in sudden expansions are explained in terms of the vortex formation that occurs when flow separation takes place. Energy must be supplied to maintain the vortex motion against the action of viscous forces, and this energy dissipation shows up in the term, h_m. It is not difficult to visualize an increase in vortex motion as the angle θ is increased,† and we therefore expect C_ℓ to increase with increasing θ. However, values of C_ℓ larger than 1.0 present a puzzling situation, for it indicates a more intense vortex motion than that occurring in a sudden expansion. Furthermore, the increasing values of C_ℓ with decreasing values of A_2/A_1 do not seem reasonable. Gibson suggested a possible explanation for this phenomenon, but he based his arguments on the assumption that the flow field is symmetric (see Birkhoff intuitive hypothesis III, Sec. 1.3), and it is not, for intermediate values of θ. It would be difficult to describe the flow phenomenon, and the previously mentioned movie "Flow Visualization" is strongly recommended.‡ Aside from providing an excellent description of the flow field in a diffuser, this movie drives home the point that we must have some idea of the flow topology before we can construct a meaningful analysis.

The reducer

The loss in head at a gradual reduction or reducer differs markedly from that for a diffuser. The difference results from the fact that flow separation, and hence vortex formation, does not occur. The loss in a reducer can be accounted for by the friction loss h_f, and we need not include the term, h_m.

The sudden contraction

The sudden contraction illustrated in Fig. 8.3-4 is very different from the reducer, for the abrupt change in cross-sectional area does lead to vortex

---

† It is a plausible intuitive hypothesis regarding the flow topology.

‡ Prepared by Professor S. J. Kline of Stanford University and distributed by Educational Services, Inc., 47 Galen St., Watertown 72, Mass.

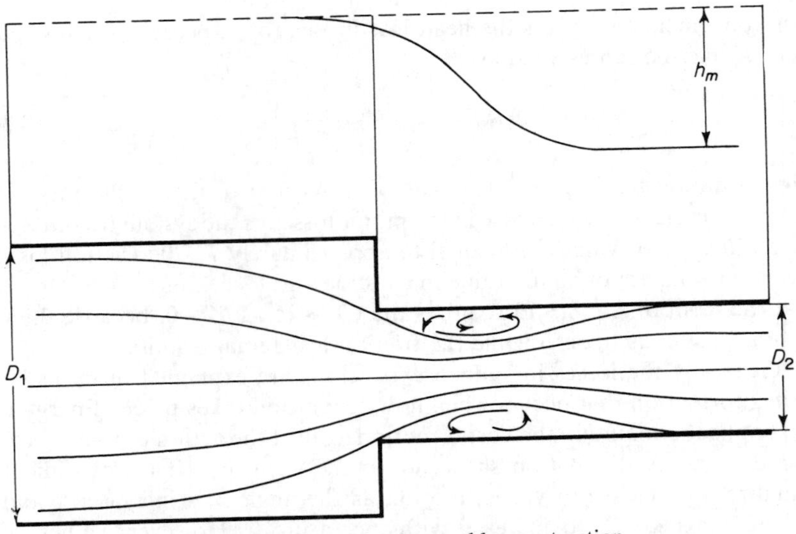

Fig. 8.3-4. Head loss in a sudden contraction.

formation. The loss coefficient K determined by Weisbach[21] is tabulated in Table 8.3-1.

An important point to notice in Fig. 8.3-4 is that the major portion of the loss takes place downstream from the abrupt change in cross-sectional area. The jet formed by the sudden contraction attains a minimum area about one

Table 8.3-1

LOSS COEFFICIENTS FOR A SUDDEN CONTRACTION

K	0.37	0.35	0.32	0.27	0.22	0.17	0.10	0.06	0.02	0
A_2/A_1	0.1	0.2	0.3	0.4	0.5	0.6	0.7	0.8	0.9	1.0

diameter (D_2) downstream from the contraction. This minimum area is called the vena contracta. Further downstream, viscous effects cause the jet to spread and fill the conduit.

Obviously the loss in a contraction is severely influenced by the geometry of the contraction, for the geometry controls the degree of vortex motion and hence energy dissipation. Three pipeline entrances from a large reservoir are illustrated in Fig. 8.3-5 along with approximate values for the head loss. The loss coefficient for a square-edged entrance is generally taken as $K \approx 0.5$, while the coefficient for a well-rounded entrance is $K \approx 0.04$ and the losses can be neglected. In this latter case, as in the gradual reduction in a pipeline, streamlining prevents the occurrence of a vena contracta and the accompanying vortex formation. The re-entrant opening is the extreme case, giving

21. J. Weisbach, *Die Experimental Hydraulik* (Freiberg, Germany: J. S. Englehardt, 1855), p. 133.

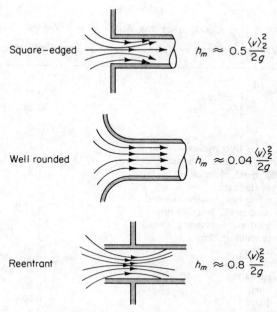

Square-edged $h_m \approx 0.5 \dfrac{\langle v \rangle_2^2}{2g}$

Well rounded $h_m \approx 0.04 \dfrac{\langle v \rangle_2^2}{2g}$

Reentrant $h_m \approx 0.8 \dfrac{\langle v \rangle_2^2}{2g}$

Fig. 8.3-5. Losses at pipeline entrances.

a minimum cross-sectional area for the vena contracta and a maximum degree of vortex motion, which, of course, gives rise to a maximum head loss.

In practice, these minor head losses do not play an important role; however, we can learn from these examples that streamlining may greatly reduce the vortex motion and the accompanying energy losses. While relatively unimportant in pipeline problems, these ideas will be of primary importance in the study of flow around immersed bodies.

Numerous types of fittings may be present in a pipeline; loss coefficients for several appear in Table 8.3-2. The head losses for these fittings have not been studied as thoroughly as the simple expansion and contraction, and there may be considerable variation between the value of K listed in Table 8.3-2 and the actual value for a given piece of equipment.

Regarding the actual design of a new pipeline, or the analysis of an existing pipeline, the engineer may be confronted with several possibilities. The essential elements of the problem are:

(a) geometry of the system (pipe length and diameter, valves and fittings, entrances and exits);
(b) pumping or power requirements;
(c) fluid properties (μ, ρ) and flow rates;
(d) the economic constraint.

Table 8.3-2

LOSS COEFFICIENTS FOR FITTINGS AND VALVES[a]

Type of Fitting or Valve	Loss Coefficient, K
45° ell	
standard	0.35
long radius	0.20
90° ell	
standard	0.75
long radius	0.45
square or miter	1.3
180° bend, close return	1.5
Tee, standard	
along run, branch blanked off	0.4
used as ell, entering run	1.3
used as ell, entering branch	1.5
branching flow	~1
Coupling	0.04
Union	0.04
Gate valve	
open	0.20
¾ open	0.90
½ open	4.5
¼ open	24.0
Diaphragm valve	
open	2.3
¾ open	2.6
½ open	4.3
¼ open	21.0
Globe valve	
open	6.4
½ open	9.5

[a] From *Chemical Engineers' Handbook*, 4th ed. (New York: McGraw-Hill Book Company, Inc., 1963), Sec. 5, p. 33.

The route to a solution simply requires the application of the macroscopic mass and mechanical energy balances, along with experimental values of the various head loss coefficients and friction factors. In the analysis of existing systems, the economic constraint is often of little or no concern and the engineer needs to determine either (b) or (c). In the design of new systems, (c) is usually given and the economic constraint requires that the job be done at a "minimum cost." This generally involves a multitude of factors and makes the application of the economic constraint the most difficult part of the problem. However, the physics of the design are adequately taken care of by Eq. 8.3-9, which is all we concern ourselves with in this text.

Power requirements for a pipeline system

In this example, we wish to determine the power requirements for the system shown in Fig. 8.3-1 if it is to handle a maximum flow rate of 100 gal/min of oil. The following are the specifications:

$Q = 100$ gal/min (volumetric flow rate)
$\rho = 60$ lb$_m$/ft^3 (density)
$\mu = 10$ centipoise (viscosity)
$D = 4$ in. (pipe diameter)

The gate valve is fully open, and the pipe is to be considered hydraulically smooth. The average velocity in the pipe is

$$\langle v \rangle = \frac{4Q}{\pi D^2} = \frac{4(100 \text{ gal/min})}{(3.14)(4 \text{ in.})^2} \frac{(231 \text{ in.})^3}{\text{gal}}$$

$$= 1840 \text{ in./min}$$

and the Reynolds number is

$$N_{Re} = \frac{\rho \langle v \rangle D}{\mu} = \left\{ \frac{(60 \text{ lb}_m/\text{ft}^3)(1840 \text{ in./min})(4 \text{ in.})}{(10 \text{ centipoise})} \right\}$$

$$\times \left\{ \left(\frac{4.78 \times 10^4 \text{ centipoise}}{\text{lb}_f\text{-sec/ft}^2} \right) \left(\frac{\text{ft}^2}{144 \text{ in.}^2} \right) \left(\frac{\text{min}}{60 \text{ sec}} \right) \left(\frac{\text{lb}_f \text{ sec}^2}{32 \text{ lb}_m \text{ ft}} \right) \right\} = 7600$$

Under these conditions the flow is turbulent, and we may use the head loss formulas discussed in this section. The smooth pipe curve on the Moody diagram yields a friction factor of

$$f = 0.033$$

From the macroscopic mechanical energy balance given by Eq. 8.3-9 we note

$$\Delta \left\{ \frac{\langle v \rangle^2}{2g} \right\} = 0 \qquad \text{initial and final velocities are zero}$$

$$\frac{\Delta p}{\rho g} = 0 \qquad \text{The pressure in the reservoirs at the entrance and exit levels is a constant}$$

$$\Delta z = 200 \text{ ft}$$

$$\sum h_f = \frac{f}{D} \frac{\langle v \rangle^2}{2g} \sum L$$

$$= \frac{(0.033)}{(4 \text{ in.})} \frac{(1840 \text{ in./min})^2}{(2)(32.2 \text{ ft/sec}^2)} (310 \text{ ft})$$

$$= 3.11 \text{ ft}$$

The sum of the minor losses takes a particularly simple form because the pipe diameter is constant.

$$\sum h_m = \frac{\langle v \rangle^2}{2g} \sum K = \frac{\langle v \rangle^2}{2g} \left\{ \underset{\text{Elbows}}{2(0.75)} + \underset{\substack{\text{Gate} \\ \text{valve}}}{0.2} + \underset{\substack{\text{Entrance} \\ \text{loss}}}{0.5} + \underset{\substack{\text{Exit} \\ \text{loss}}}{1.0} \right\}$$

$$= \frac{(1840 \text{ in./min})^2}{(2)(32.2 \text{ ft/sec}^2)}(3.2) = 0.32 \text{ ft}$$

As often happens, the minor losses are quite small, and, in fact, disregarding these losses would have caused an error of only 10% in the viscous losses.

Substitution of these results into Eq. 8.3-9 yields

$$\sum H_w = 200 \text{ ft} + 3.11 \text{ ft} + 0.32 \text{ ft}$$
$$= 203 \text{ ft}$$

Solving for the power required, $\dot{W}$, gives

$$\dot{W} = (203 \text{ ft})(\rho g Q)$$
$$= 2{,}720 \text{ lb}_f \text{ ft/sec}$$

or

$$\dot{W} = 5.0 \text{ hp}$$

Hence the pump must be capable of delivering 5.0 hp *to the fluid* if the maximum flow rate is to be obtained.

In studying this example, the student should stop and give some thought to the ideas behind it. We might list them as follows:

1. the *laws of mechanics* leading to the Navier-Stokes equations and the mechanical energy equation;
2. the principle of *conservation of mass*;
3. *kinematics*—the Reynolds transport theorem leading to the Navier-Stokes equations;
4. the concept of *stress*;
5. *mathematics*—the general transport theorem leading to the macroscopic balances.

The solution of pipeline problems by Eq. 8.3-9 is obviously a straightforward problem; however, *understanding* what one is doing is by no means a simple matter.

Pipeline networks

Very often piping systems may be much more complex than the one illustrated in Fig. 8.3-1, and the flow from a given outlet may come from several sources. Such a system is illustrated in Fig. 8.3-6, the design of which

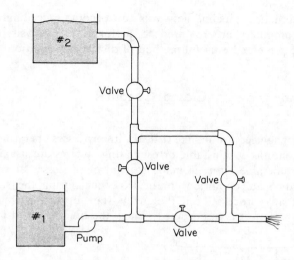

Fig. 8.3-6. Pipeline network.

would require specification of either the pipe or pump size required to provide a given flow rate at the single outlet. In pipeline networks, the following three conditions must be satisfied.

1. The sum of the pressure drops around each circuit must be zero—i.e., the pressure is a continuous, single-valued function.
2. The mass balance must be satisfied at each junction.
3. The mechanical energy balance must be satisfied for each section.

In single pipelines, only condition 3 has to be considered; however, 1 and 2 represent obvious physical concepts, and the problem of designing pipeline networks is simply one of algebraic complexity.

The problem is solved by first specifying the flow rates of all streams that enter and leave the system and of the streams within the system. These initial values are chosen so that the mass balance requirement is satisfied. The assumed flow distribution is used to determine the pressure everywhere in the system that generally does not satisfy condition 1. On the basis of the first calculation, adjustments are made and the process repeated until all the conditions are satisfied. An efficient method, worked out by Cross,[22] is described by Venard,[23] and we shall not discuss this subject further in this text.

22. H. Cross, "Analysis of Flow in Networks of Conduits or Conductors," *Univ. Illinois Eng. Expt. Sta. Bull.*, 286, 1936.

23. J. K. Venard, "One-Dimensional Flow," *Handbook of Fluid Mechanics*, V. L. Streeter, ed. (New York: McGraw-Hill Book Company, Inc., 1961).

In industrial practice, pipeline networks can become exceedingly complex, and digital computers are required to perform the analysis. Ingels and Powers[24] have presented a useful method of digital computation.

8.4 Unsteady Flow in Closed Conduits

In general, engineers would like to deal with processes operating at or near steady state conditions. Unstable or oscillating systems are usually undesirable, and considerable effort is made to control processes at some steady state. Unsteady state conditions naturally occur during the start-up and shut-down of any process, or if the steady-state operating conditions are changed. Very often it is important to know the time required to reach the

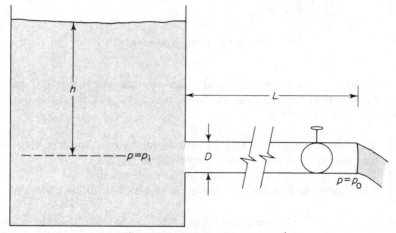

Fig. 8.4-1. Unsteady flow in a pipeline.

steady state, and we will apply the mechanical energy balance to two transient flows to illustrate the important steps in the analysis. Figure 8.4-1 illustrates a supply and pipeline arrangement for which we wish to determine the time required for the flow to reach the steady state value.

If the flow is always laminar, and the entrance length is small compared to the tube length, the differential equations of motion reduce to

$$\rho \frac{\partial v_z}{\partial t} = -\frac{\partial p}{\partial z} + \mu \frac{1}{r}\frac{\partial}{\partial r}\left(r\frac{\partial v_z}{\partial z}\right) \qquad (8.4\text{-}1)$$

24. D. M. Ingels and J. E. Powers, "Analysis of Pipeline Networks," *Chem. Eng. Prog.*, 1964, 60:65.

The boundary conditions for this problem are

B.C. 1: $v_z = 0$, $t = 0$,   for $0 \leq r \leq r_0$

B.C. 2: v_z is finite,   for $0 \leq r \leq r_0$

B.C. 3: $v_z = 0$, $r = r_0$

B.C. 4: $\dfrac{\partial p}{\partial z} = -\dfrac{(p_i - p_0)}{L}$, $t > 0$

The solution of this equation is beyond the scope of this text, for it requires a knowledge of partial differential equations. The result has been presented by Szymanski,[25] and it may be expressed as

$$\frac{\langle v_z \rangle}{\langle v_z \rangle_\infty} = 1 - \left(0.963 e^{-0.36 \Theta f \infty} + 0.036 e^{-1.90 \Theta f \infty} + \cdots\right) \tag{8.4-2}$$

where $\langle v_z \rangle_\infty$ is the average velocity for $t = \infty$. The complete solution consists of an infinite series of exponential terms, but only the first two are necessary for satisfactory results. The dimensionless time Θ is defined as

$$\Theta = \frac{t \langle v_z \rangle_\infty}{D} \tag{8.4-3}$$

and f_∞ is the friction factor at $t = \infty$.

$$f_\infty = \frac{64}{N_{\mathrm{Re},\infty}} \tag{8.4-4}$$

If the final flow is turbulent, the transition will be a complex process involving an initial transition in the laminar region and a final transition in the turbulent region. If the final Reynolds number is large (say, 10^6), the flow will be turbulent during most of the transition period, and we may obtain an approximate solution by the mechanical energy balance.

If the liquid depth h undergoes a negligible change during the transition, the pressure drop in the tube may be expressed as

$$\frac{\Delta p}{\rho g} = f_\infty \left(\frac{L}{D}\right) \frac{\langle v_z \rangle_\infty^2}{2g} \tag{8.4-5}$$

where

$$\frac{\Delta p}{\rho g} = h$$

Taking the tube as the control volume, the mechanical energy balance gives

$$\frac{d}{dt} \int_{\mathscr{V}} \left(\tfrac{1}{2} \rho v^2\right) dV = \int_{A_e} \mathbf{v} \cdot \mathbf{t}_{(n)} \, dA - \dot{E}_v \tag{8.4-6}$$

25. P. Szymanski, "Some Exact Solutions of the Equations of Motion for Flow in a Cylindrical Tube," *J. Math. Pures Appl. Ser.* 9, 1932, 11:67.

Assuming the velocity profile to be flat (it certainly won't be during the early stages), and representing the stress vector at the entrance and exit as

$$\mathbf{t}_{(n)} = -\mathbf{n}p \tag{8.4-7}$$

we find

$$\frac{d}{dt}\left\{\tfrac{1}{2}\rho\langle v_z\rangle^2 AL\right\} = \langle v_z\rangle \, \Delta p A - \dot{E}_v \tag{8.4-8}$$

Carrying out the differentiation and dividing by $\rho\langle v_z\rangle Ag$, we have

$$\left(\frac{L}{g}\right)\frac{d\langle v_z\rangle}{dt} = \frac{\Delta p}{\rho g} - \frac{\dot{E}_v}{\rho g Q} \tag{8.4-9}$$

If we remember that

$$\frac{\dot{E}_v}{\rho g Q} = h_f = f\left(\frac{L}{D}\right)\frac{\langle v_z\rangle^2}{2g}$$

and if we substitute Eq. 8.4-5 into Eq. 8.4-9 and use the dimensionless time Θ, we can write Eq. 8.4-9 in the form

$$2\left(\frac{dU_z}{d\theta}\right) = \left[1 - \left(\frac{f}{f_\infty}\right)U_z^2\right]f_\infty \tag{8.4-10}$$

Solving this equation would be a difficult task because of the complex variation of the friction factor f with the Reynolds number. A numerical solution would be straightforward (and might make an interesting class project), but to obtain an analytic solution we will assume

$$\frac{f}{f_\infty} \approx 1 \tag{8.4-11}$$

We separate variables and integrate to obtain

$$2\int \frac{dU_z}{1 - U_z^2} = f_\infty \int d\Theta + C \tag{8.4-12}$$

The approximation given by Eq. 8.4-11 will not be valid at short times when the flow is laminar; on the other hand, if the major portion of the transient time is associated with the rough-pipe region of flow, the approximation might be quite satisfactory. Integration of Eq. 8.4-12, and application of the boundary condition

B.C. 1: $U_z = 0,$ $\Theta = 0$ \hfill (8.4-13)

yield the final solution

$$U_z = \left(\frac{e^{\Theta f_\infty} - 1}{e^{\Theta f_\infty} + 1}\right) \tag{8.4-14}$$

Both Eqs. 8.4-14 and 8.4-2 indicate that the final velocity is not reached until the time becomes infinite; however, for practical purposes it is satisfactory to say that steady state has been reached when the velocity is within 1 per cent of the final value. The time is therefore given as

$$\Theta_{99\%} = \frac{11.8}{f_\infty}, \qquad \text{laminar flow}$$

$$\Theta_{99\%} = \frac{5.3}{f_\infty}, \qquad \text{turbulent flow}$$

It is difficult to comment on these two values, for they represent the transient time for two distinct types of flow. The real times for the two cases are

$$t_{99\%} = \frac{11.8\,D}{\langle v_z \rangle_\infty f_\infty}, \qquad \text{laminar}$$

$$t_{99\%} = \frac{5.3\,D}{\langle v_z \rangle_\infty f_\infty}, \qquad \text{turbulent}$$

To gain some familiarity with the orders of magnitude of these times, we could say for turbulent flow†

$$f_\infty = 0\,(0.005)$$
$$D = 0\,(1\ \text{ft})$$
$$\langle v_z \rangle = 0\,(1\ \text{ft/sec})$$

Under these conditions, the time would be

$$t_{99\%} = 0\left[\frac{(5.3)(1\ \text{ft})}{(0.005)(1\ \text{ft/sec})}\frac{\text{min}}{60\ \text{sec}}\right]$$

$$= 0[1.77\ \text{min}]$$

From this order of magnitude calculation we see that the transient time only becomes significant for large diameter tubes and low flow rates. Remember that this analysis assumed that the length of the pipe was long compared to the entrance length and is therefore not valid for short pipes.

Oscillating systems—the U-tube manometer

Various fluid systems are subject to upsets which may give rise to oscillatory motion. Actual processes may become extremely complex, and large analogue or digital computers may be required to determine the fluid motion even approximately. The purpose of studying the U-tube manometer is to gain some insight into the important aspects of oscillatory systems. In

† Read $0(0.005)$ as "on the order of magnitude of 0.005."

addition, this example is of some interest because it can easily be studied experimentally, thus introducing the student to the errors incurred in an approximate solution.

The U-tube manometer to be analyzed is shown in Fig. 8.4-2. Once again, the differential equations describing the motion are too complex to be solved, and the mechanical energy balance is required. We start with the complete equation and note that $\dot{W}$ is zero to obtain

$$\frac{d}{dt}\int_{\mathscr{V}_a(t)}(\tfrac{1}{2}\rho v^2)\,dV+\int_{A_e(t)}(\tfrac{1}{2}\rho v^2)(\mathbf{v}-\mathbf{w})\cdot\mathbf{n}\,dA$$

$$=\int_{A_e(t)}\mathbf{v}\cdot\mathbf{t}_{(\mathbf{n})}\,dA-\int_{\mathscr{A}_a(t)}\rho gz\mathbf{v}\cdot\mathbf{n}\,dA-\dot{E}_v \quad (8.4\text{-}15)$$

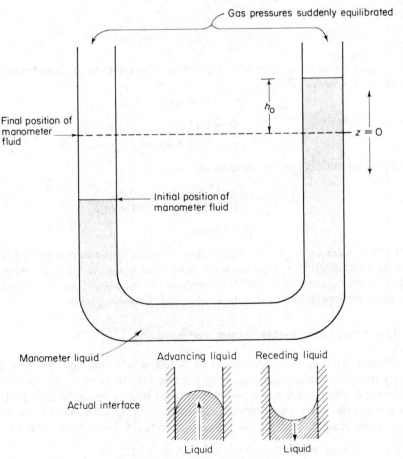

Fig. 8.4-2. U-tube manometer.

For the moving control volume $\mathscr{V}_a(t)$ we choose the fluid itself and assume that the gas-liquid interface is horizontal and well defined as shown in Fig. 8.4-2. Actually, it is not because the fluid adheres to the tube wall, and the interface will be as shown in the inset.

Considering Eq. 8.4-15, we note that

$$\mathbf{v} = \mathbf{w} \qquad \text{on} \quad \mathscr{A}_a(t)$$

and the convective transport term on the left-hand side of the mechanical energy balance is identically zero. If viscous effects at the gas-liquid interface are neglected, we may assume that

$$\mathbf{v} \cdot \mathbf{t}_{(n)} \big|_{\text{left}} = -\mathbf{v} \cdot \mathbf{t}_{(n)} \big|_{\text{right}} \tag{8.4-16}$$

and the first term on the right-hand side of Eq. 8.4-15 is also zero. This assumption is open to question, because the nature of the interface obviously depends upon whether it is advancing or receding. However, we must either solve the detailed problem associated with the moving interface, or we must assume it is flat and make the assumption indicated by Eq. 8.4-16 to obtain

$$\frac{d}{dt}\int_{\mathscr{V}_a(t)} (\tfrac{1}{2}\rho v^2)\, dV = -\int_{\mathscr{A}_a(t)} \rho g z\, \mathbf{v} \cdot \mathbf{n}\, dA - \dot{E}_v \tag{8.4-17}$$

If the flow in the manometer were turbulent, the various velocities in Eq. 8.4-17 could be replaced by average velocities and the energy dissipation term could be expressed as in the previous example. However, oscillating flow in a manometer is likely to be laminar, and we must devise an approximate analysis for laminar flow. Assuming the flow to be quasi-steady and one-dimensional, we write

$$v(r, t) = 2\langle v\rangle \left[1 - \left(\frac{r}{r_0}\right)^2 \right] \tag{8.4-18}$$

Here, $v(r, t)$ represents the component of the velocity vector along the tube. Expressing the transient velocity profile in terms of the steady state solution is a common technique (and one which should be used with caution) for obtaining approximate solutions to engineering problems. The success of this method depends on the variations with time being small enough so that the velocity profile is never far from parabolic. After obtaining the solution, we shall explore the validity of this assumption.

The average velocity $\langle v\rangle$ in Eq. 8.4-18 is a function of time, and will be defined as positive when the flow is from left to right. Since

$$\mathbf{v} \cdot \mathbf{n} \big|_{\text{left}} = -\mathbf{v} \cdot \mathbf{n} \big|_{\text{right}} \tag{8.4-19}$$

and the position of the two interfaces is given by,

$$z = -h \big|_{\text{left}}, \qquad z = +h \big|_{\text{right}} \tag{8.4-20}$$

We may simplify the area integral in Eq. 8.4-17 to obtain

$$\frac{d}{dt}\left\{4\rho\pi L\langle v\rangle^2\int_0^{r_0}\left[1-\left(\frac{r}{r_0}\right)^2\right]^2 r\,dr\right\} = -2\rho gh\langle v\rangle\pi r_0^2 - \int_{\mathscr{V}_{a(t)}}\Phi\,dV \quad (8.4\text{-}21)$$

From Table 7.3-1, we find the dissipation function to be

$$\Phi = 2\mu\left[\frac{\partial v_r^2}{\partial r} + \left(\frac{1}{r}\frac{\partial v_\theta}{\partial\theta} + \frac{v_r}{r}\right)^2 + \left(\frac{\partial v_z}{\partial z}\right)^2\right]$$

$$+ \mu\left[r\frac{\partial}{\partial r}\left(\frac{v_\theta}{r}\right) + \frac{1}{r}\left(\frac{\partial v_r}{\partial\theta}\right)\right]^2 + \mu\left[\frac{1}{r}\left(\frac{\partial v_z}{\partial\theta}\right) + \left(\frac{\partial v_\theta}{\partial z}\right)\right]^2$$

$$+ \mu\left[\left(\frac{\partial v_r}{\partial z}\right) + \left(\frac{\partial v_z}{\partial r}\right)\right]^2$$

In this case, there is only one component of velocity, $v_z = v$, and Φ reduces to

$$\Phi = 16\mu\langle v\rangle^2\left(\frac{r}{r_0^2}\right)^2 \quad (8.4\text{-}22)$$

Substituting this result into Eq. 8.4-21 and carrying out the integration, we get

$$\frac{d}{dt}\left\{\tfrac{2}{3}\rho\pi r_0^2 L\langle v\rangle^2\right\} = -2\rho gh\langle v\rangle\pi r_0^2 - 8\mu\pi L\langle v\rangle^2 \quad (8.4\text{-}23)$$

Because the time rate of change of height of the gas-liquid interface is equal to the average velocity,

$$\frac{dh}{dt} = \langle v\rangle$$

We may rearrange Eq. 8.4-23 to obtain

$$\frac{d^2h}{dt^2} + \left(\frac{6v}{r_0^2}\right)\frac{dh}{dt} + \left(\frac{3g}{2L}\right)h = 0 \quad (8.4\text{-}24)$$

This equation is to be solved subject to the boundary conditions

B.C. 1: $h = h_0, \qquad t = 0$ (8.4-25a)

B.C. 2: $\dfrac{dh}{dt} = 0, \qquad t = 0$ (8.4-25b)

It will be helpful to put the differential equation and the boundary conditions in dimensionless form. To do so, we define a dimensionless distance H and time Θ as,

$$H = \frac{h}{h_0}$$

$$\Theta = t\sqrt{\frac{3g}{2L}}$$

and Eq. 8.4-24 reduces to

$$\frac{d^2H}{d\Theta^2} + 2\beta \frac{dH}{d\Theta} + H = 0 \tag{8.4-26}$$

where

$$\beta = \frac{3v}{r_0^2}\sqrt{\frac{2L}{3g}}$$

In terms of the dimensionless variables, the boundary conditions are

B.C. 1': $H = 1, \qquad \Theta = 0$ (8.4-27a)

B.C. 2': $\dfrac{dH}{d\Theta} = 0, \qquad \Theta = 0$ (8.4-27b)

The solution of this second-order, ordinary, differential equation is obtained by assuming solutions of the form

$$H = e^{m\Theta} \tag{8.4-28}$$

which when substituted into Eq. 8.4-26 gives

$$e^{m\Theta}(m^2 + 2\beta m + 1) = 0 \tag{8.4-29}$$

This equation will be satisfied, and Eq. 8.4-28 will be a solution of the differential equation, if m is chosen so that

$$m^2 + 2\beta m + 1 = 0 \tag{8.4-30}$$

Thus, m has two possible values, given by

$$m_1 = -(\beta + \sqrt{\beta^2 - 1}) \tag{8.4-31a}$$

$$m_2 = -(\beta - \sqrt{\beta^2 - 1}) \tag{8.4-31b}$$

Provided m_1 and m_2 are distinct (i.e., $\beta \neq 1$), the general solution is

$$H = C_1 e^{m_1\Theta} + C_2 e^{m_2\Theta} \tag{8.4-32}$$

However, if the roots of Eq. 8.4-30 are not distinct, the solution is[26]

$$H = (C_1 + C_2\Theta)e^{-\Theta} \tag{8.4-33}$$

26. L. R. Ford, *Differential Equations* (New York: McGraw-Hill Book Company, Inc., 1933), p. 70.

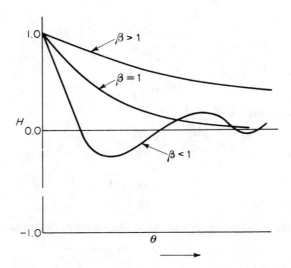

Fig. 8.4-3. Position of the gas-liquid interface for an oscillating manometer.

The motion of the fluid in the manometer may have three distinct modes depending on the value of β. The three types of motion are illustrated graphically in Fig. 8.4-3. We may discuss them as follows.

1. $\beta > 1$. For this case, both m_1 and m_2 are real negative numbers, and the constants of integration in Eq. 8.4-27 are readily determined to yield

$$H = \frac{(m_2 e^{m_1\Theta} - m_1 e^{m_2\Theta})}{(m_2 - m_1)} \tag{8.4-34}$$

This type of motion is called "over damped," and the fluid approaches its equilibrium position exponentially.

2. $\beta = 1$. Here, the roots are indistinct, and the solution is obtained by application of the boundary conditions to Eq. 8.4-33, yielding

$$H = (1 + \Theta)e^{-\Theta} \tag{8.4-35}$$

The fluid motion is similar to the previous case in that the equilibrium position is approached exponentially. However, this solution represents the most rapid approach to equilibrium without "overshooting" the equilibrium position. Such motion is called "critically damped."

3. $\beta < 1$. Under these conditions, the roots become complex, and we must take special care in obtaining a solution. We write the roots as

$$m_1, m_2 = -(\beta \pm i\sqrt{1 - \beta^2}), \qquad \beta < 1 \tag{8.4-36}$$

The solution is again given by Eq. 8.4-32; however, the result is a complex function containing both real and imaginary parts. The real part independently satisfies the differential equation and the boundary conditions, and takes the form

$$H = e^{-\beta\Theta}\left[\cos\left(\Theta\sqrt{1-\beta^2}\right) + \frac{\beta}{\sqrt{1-\beta^2}}\sin\left(\Theta\sqrt{1-\beta^2}\right)\right], \qquad \beta < 1$$

$$(8.4\text{-}37)$$

This result indicates that H takes on both positive and negative values which decrease exponentially with time. This motion is called "under damped."

Without the preceding analysis, we might easily guess that such motions could occur in a manometer. If viscous effects predominate, it seems natural that the fluid should slowly and steadily approach the equilibrium position. But if inertial effects predominate, we would certainly expect the system to behave somewhat like a pendulum, oscillating around the equilibrium position. Since β is, in effect, the ratio of viscous forces to inertial forces, the dependence of the motion on β is just what we would expect to find. Even though the analysis agrees with our intuition, we should still ask the important question, "Under what conditions can we expect this result to be accurate?" We can answer this question, in part, by performing an order of magnitude analysis.

Order of magnitude analysis

Two major assumptions were imposed on this analysis.

1. The gas-liquid interface was flat.
2. The velocity profile was parabolic—i.e., quasi-steady flow.

The first assumption is best investigated experimentally, but the validity of the second assumption can be discussed mathematically. At some distance away from the interface and the curved portion of the manometer tube, the flow will be one-dimensional, and the equations of motion reduce to

$$\rho\frac{\partial v}{\partial t} = -\frac{\partial p}{\partial z} + \rho g_z + \mu\frac{\partial}{\partial r}\left(r\frac{\partial v_z}{\partial r}\right) \qquad (8.4\text{-}38)$$

From previous work we know that if the local acceleration term is small compared to the viscous term, the velocity profile will be parabolic.

Making use of Eq. 8.4-18, we can perform the following order of magnitude analysis using the solution to Eq. 8.4-26 to estimate the magnitude of the terms in Eq. 8.4-38. Attacking the local acceleration term first, we write†

$$\rho\frac{\partial v}{\partial t} = 0\left(\rho\frac{\partial\langle v\rangle}{\partial t}\right) = 0\left(\rho\frac{d^2 h}{dt^2}\right) \qquad (8.4\text{-}39)$$

The viscous terms are expressed as

$$\mu\frac{1}{r}\frac{\partial}{\partial r}\left(r\frac{\partial v_z}{\partial r}\right) = 0\left(\frac{\mu\langle v\rangle}{r_0^2}\right) = 0\left(\frac{\mu}{r_0^2}\frac{dh}{dt}\right) \qquad (8.4\text{-}40)$$

Our requirement that the local acceleration term be small compared to the viscous term immediately leads us to the inequality,

$$\left|\frac{d^2 h}{dt^2}\right| \ll \left|\frac{v}{r_0^2}\frac{dh}{dt}\right| \qquad (8.4\text{-}41)$$

or, in dimensionless form,

$$\left|\frac{d^2 H}{d\Theta^2}\right| \ll \left|\beta\frac{dH}{d\Theta}\right| \qquad (8.4\text{-}42)$$

If the system is under damped ($\beta < 1$), the first derivative $dH/d\Theta$ takes on zero values; at these times the inequality can never be satisfied. For the under damped case, we can expect only qualitative agreement between the derived result and a real manometer.

For the critically damped case our solution indicates that

$$\frac{d^2 H}{d\Theta^2} = -(1-\Theta)e^{-\Theta}, \qquad \frac{dH}{d\Theta} = -\Theta e^{-\Theta}$$

Thus,

$$\left|\frac{d^2 H}{d\Theta^2}\right| \gg \left|\frac{dH}{d\Theta}\right|, \qquad \text{for} \quad \Theta \to 0$$

$$\left|\frac{d^2 H}{d\Theta^2}\right| \ll \left|\frac{dH}{d\Theta}\right|, \qquad \text{for} \quad \Theta \to \infty$$

and we can again expect only qualitative agreement between theory and experiment. This situation is left rather wide open, as it should be. If the agreement between theory and experiment were poor, we should not be surprised. Neither should we be surprised if the agreement were good, for it would only mean that significant deviations from the parabolic profile did not greatly alter the value of the viscous dissipation term.

The analysis for the over damped flow ($\beta > 1$) is more complex than the other two cases; however, if $\beta \gg 1$ we may write

$$\frac{\left|\dfrac{d^2 H}{d\Theta^2}\right|}{\left|\beta\dfrac{dH}{d\Theta}\right|} = \frac{2e^{-\beta\Theta}}{1 - e^{-2\beta\Theta}}$$

† The symbol 0 should be read as "the order of magnitude of." This type of analysis will be discussed in detail in Sec. 11.3.

Here we see that the inequality given by Eq. 8.4-42 is not satisfied for $\Theta \to 0$, but will be satisfied for all dimensionless times greater than β^{-1}. For over damped flows we may expect reasonably good agreement between theory and experiment, except for very short times.

8.5   Flow Rate Measurement

There are several common devices—such as the orifice meter, Venturi meter, Pitot tube, and the sharp-crested wier—used to measure flow rates and velocities. It is of interest to analyze these systems as an introduction to engineering practice, and since these metering devices have been studied experimentally, we have an opportunity to compare analysis with experiment.

Venturi meter

The Venturi meter, illustrated in Fig. 8.5-1, consists of a relatively abrupt constriction that accelerates the flow and produces a decrease in the fluid pressure; this process is followed by a gradual expansion allowing the head loss to be minimized. The pressure difference between points 1 and 2 can be related to the flow rate by the application of the macroscopic balances. This presents a situation for which we should definitely *not* use the momentum balance because the pressure (and thus the surface force) varies

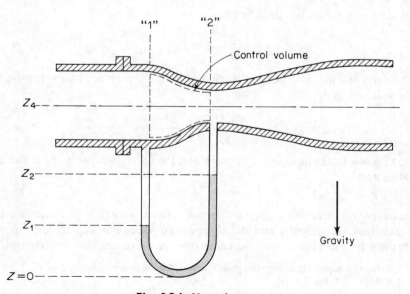

Fig. 8.5-1. Venturi meter.

from 1 to 2 in an unspecified manner.† The mechanical energy balance is well suited to this type of problem, and for steady, incompressible flow, the various terms in Eq. 7.3-31 are

$$\int_{A_e} \tfrac{1}{2}\rho v^2 \mathbf{v} \cdot \mathbf{n}\, dA = -\tfrac{1}{2}\rho\langle v^3\rangle_1 A_1 + \tfrac{1}{2}\rho\langle v^3\rangle_2 A_2 \tag{8.5-1}$$

$$\int_{A_e} \mathbf{v} \cdot \mathbf{t}_{(n)}\, dA = +\langle pv\rangle_1 A_1 - \langle pv\rangle_2 A_2 \tag{8.5-2}$$

$$\int_{A_e} \rho\phi \mathbf{v} \cdot \mathbf{n}\, dA = -\rho\langle \phi v\rangle_1 A_1 + \rho\langle \phi v\rangle_2 A_2 \tag{8.5-3}$$

For the present, we shall assume that viscous effects are negligible and write

$$\dot{E}_v = 0 \tag{8.5-4}$$

Substituting Eqs. 8.5-1 through 8.5-4 into Eq. 7.3-31, and assuming flat velocity profiles, we find

$$\tfrac{1}{2}\rho[\langle v\rangle_2^3 A_2 - \langle v\rangle_1^3 A_1] = \langle v\rangle_1\langle p\rangle_1 A_1 - \langle v\rangle_2\langle p\rangle_2 A_2$$
$$- \rho[\langle \phi\rangle_2\langle v\rangle_2 A_2 - \langle \phi\rangle_1\langle v\rangle_1 A_1] \tag{8.5-5}$$

Application of the macroscopic mass balance

$$\langle v\rangle_2 A_2 = \langle v\rangle_1 A_1 \tag{8.5-6}$$

allows Eq. 8.5-5 to be simplified to

$$\langle v\rangle_2^2 - \langle v\rangle_1^2 = \frac{2}{\rho}[\langle p + \rho\phi\rangle_1 - \langle p + \rho\phi\rangle_2] \tag{8.5-7}$$

The mass balance may be used to eliminate $\langle v\rangle_1$ and obtain an expression for the volumetric flow rate

$$Q = \langle v\rangle_2 A_2 = A_2\sqrt{\frac{2[\langle p + \rho\phi\rangle_1 - \langle p + \rho\phi\rangle_2]}{\rho[1 - (A_2/A_1)^2]}} \tag{8.5-8}$$

Now, ϕ is a linear function in z; therefore, the average value is the centerline value, and

$$\langle \phi\rangle_1 - \langle \phi\rangle_2 = 0 \tag{8.5-9}$$

However, the pressure at point 2 is not a linear function of z because the streamlines are curved,‡ and strictly speaking we cannot replace the average pressure by the pressure at the centerline. A more detailed analysis might

† Does this suggest a differential-macroscopic balance as a possibility?
‡ See Sec. 7.4, Eq. 7.4-21.

include an estimate of the effect of the curved streamlines on the average pressure; however, we shall neglect this effect and replace the average pressure by the centerline pressure to obtain

$$Q = A_2 \sqrt{\frac{2(p_1 - p_2)}{\rho[1 - (A_2/A_1)^2]}} \qquad (8.5\text{-}10)$$

If this formula is expressed in terms of the height of the manometer fluid, $z_2 - z_1$ yields

$$Q = A_2 \sqrt{\frac{2(\rho_m - \rho)g(z_2 - z_1)}{\rho[1 - (A_2/A_1)^2]}} \qquad (8.5\text{-}11)$$

where ρ_m is the density of the manometer fluid.

Experimental studies indicate that Eq. 8.5-11 is not always sufficiently accurate for engineering practice, and a discharge coefficient C_d is introduced to give

$$Q = C_d A_2 \sqrt{\frac{2(\rho_m - \rho)g(z_2 - z_1)}{\rho[1 - (A_2/A_1)^2]}} \qquad (8.5\text{-}12)$$

A plot of C_d versus Reynolds number is shown in Fig. 8.5-2 for a Venturi meter with $(A_2/A_1) = 0.25$. We see that at high Reynolds numbers the analysis is good because C_d is nearly unity. For Reynolds numbers less than 2300, we should not expect the analysis to hold because the flow is laminar and the velocity profiles are no longer flat. A more careful analysis, taking the velocity profile into account, can lead to the conclusion that C_d should decrease rapidly as laminar flow is approached; however this problem will be left as an exercise for the student.

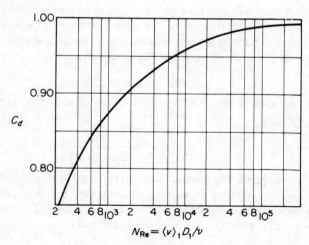

Fig. 8.5-2. Venturi discharge coefficient.

Orifice meter

The sharp-edged orifice shown in Fig. 8.5-3 is another device for accelerating the flow and obtaining a measurable pressure difference related to the flow rate. The orifice is often used as a metering device in preference to a Venturi meter because of its versatility and low cost of construction and installation. Because the area of the jet at point 3 (the vena contracta) is

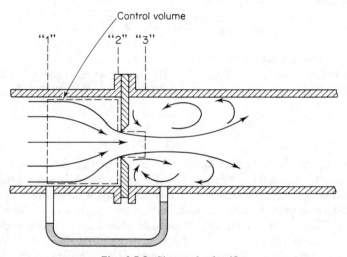

Fig. 8.5-3. Sharp-edged orifice.

unknown, the solution to this flow problem will not be as accurate as that for the Venturi meter. Calibration of orifice meters is therefore a necessity, and, in general, they are considered less reliable than Venturi meters.

If we express the area of the jet at the vena contracta as

$$A_3 = C_c A_2 \qquad (8.5\text{-}13)$$

where A_2 is the area of the orifice and C_c is the *contraction coefficient*, the flow rate is given by

$$Q = C_c A_2 \sqrt{\frac{2(p_1 - p_3)}{\rho[1 - (C_c A_2/A_1)^2]}} \qquad (8.5\text{-}14)$$

Here we have applied the mechanical energy balance, neglected viscous effects, and replaced average pressures with centerline pressures. Because the contraction coefficient is a function of the ratio of areas A_2/A_1, the equation is generally written in terms of a discharge coefficient

$$Q = C_d A_2 \sqrt{2(p_1 - p_3)/\rho} \qquad (8.5\text{-}15)$$

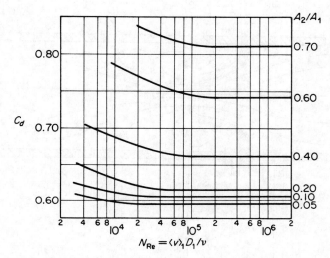

Fig. 8.5-4. Discharge coefficients for a sharp-edged orifice.

Our analysis would indicate that

$$C_d = \frac{C_c}{\sqrt{[1 - (C_c A_2/A_1)^2]}} \qquad (8.5\text{-}16)$$

Because C_c changes with A_2/A_1 it is rather difficult to compare our analysis with experimental results. However, as A_2/A_1 becomes small, the discharge coefficient should equal the contraction coefficient, and matters are somewhat simplified. Figure 8.5-4 shows some experimental values of C_d for a standard sharp-edged orifice. For small values of A_2/A_1, the discharge coefficient is approximately 0.6, a reasonable value of the contraction coefficient. Once again the analysis is only satisfactory at high Reynolds numbers.

Flow nozzle

A flow nozzle, such as that illustrated in Fig. 8.5-5, does not offer the difficulty of an unknown contraction coefficient, because the streamlines are parallel as the fluid emerges from the nozzle. The mechanical energy balance is applied as before to yield

$$Q = C_d A_2 \sqrt{\frac{2(p_1 - p_2)}{\rho[1 - (A_2/A_1)^2]}} \qquad (8.5\text{-}17)$$

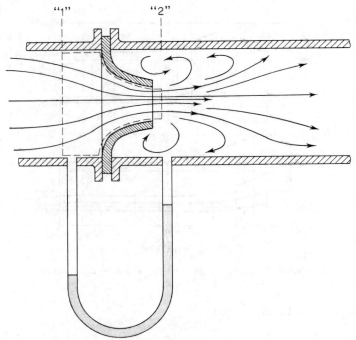

Fig. 8.5-5. Flow nozzle.

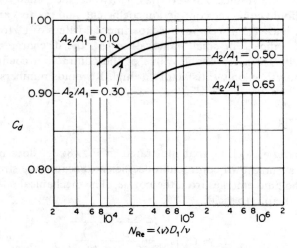

Fig. 8.5-6. Discharge coefficients for a flow nozzle.

The experimental values of C_d shown in Fig. 8.5-6 indicate that the analysis is in error by about 10 per cent or less, depending upon the ratio of the nozzle area to the duct area, A_2/A_1. As the ratio becomes smaller the fluid is accelerated more severely, and inertial effects very definitely predominate, provided the Reynolds number is greater than 10^5. For lower Reynolds numbers, viscous dissipation begins to show its effect and the discharge coefficient decreases.

Pitot-static tube

The pitot-static tube shown in Fig. 8.5-7 is a device for measuring fluid velocities at a point; it may be used to determine the flow rate if the velocity profile is flat or if the entire profile is measured. The tube has a small opening at point 2 which is the stagnation point, i.e., the velocity is zero. A series of holes are drilled around the periphery of the tube at point 3 to measure the static pressure. The pressure at point 2 is called the dynamic pressure and the difference between these two pressures may be measured by the manometer and related to the fluid velocity. In this particular system, we wish to compute the pressure along two streamlines rather than over a control surface, and we

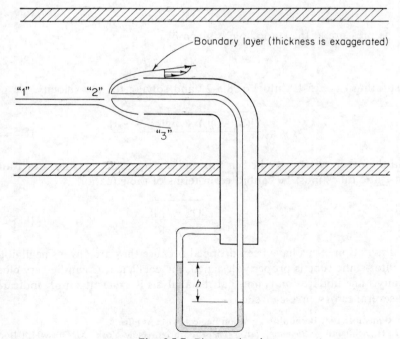

Fig. 8.5-7. Pitot-static tube.

shall use Bernoulli's equation. Application of Eq. 7.4-17 to the streamline between 1 and 2 yields†

$$p_1 + \tfrac{1}{2}\rho v_1^2 + \rho g z_1 = p_2 + \tfrac{1}{2}\rho v_2^2 + \rho g z_2 \qquad (8.5\text{-}18)$$

Since $v_2 = 0$, the pressure at point 2 is

$$p_2 = p_1 + \tfrac{1}{2}\rho v_1^2 + \rho g(z_1 - z_2) \qquad (8.5\text{-}19)$$

Along the streamline from points 1 to 3 we write

$$p_1 + \tfrac{1}{2}\rho v_1^2 + \rho g z_1 = p_3 + \tfrac{1}{2}\rho v_3^2 + \rho g z_3 \qquad (8.5\text{-}20)$$

To continue this analysis, we must know something about the flow field around the tube. We need not guess the flow topology, for experimental and theoretical studies have been carried out[27] indicating there is a thin region (called the boundary layer) around the tube where the velocity changes rapidly from the free stream value to zero. At high Reynolds numbers, the boundary layer thickness is small and the pressure difference across it is negligible. Under these conditions, the pressure at point 3 is very nearly equal to the pressure at the static hole at the surface of the Pitot-tube. We take the streamline from points 1 to 3 to be outside the boundary layer; thus,

$$v_3 = v_1 \qquad (8.5\text{-}21)$$

and the pressure at the static hole is given by

$$p_3 = p_1 + \rho g(z_1 - z_3) \qquad (8.5\text{-}22)$$

Substituting Eq. 8.5-19 into Eq. 8.5-22 and solving for the velocity, we get

$$v_1 = \sqrt{\frac{2[(p_2 - p_3) + \rho g(z_2 - z_3)]}{\rho}} \qquad (8.5\text{-}23)$$

As in the other systems studied in this section, the analysis is not exact and Pitot-static tubes must be calibrated in terms of the equation,

$$v_1 = C \sqrt{\frac{2(p_2 - p_3)}{\rho}} \qquad (8.5\text{-}24)$$

The gravitation terms have been dropped because they are always negligible. If a Pitot-static tube is properly designed, the coefficient C can be very close to unity. The implication is not that the analysis is exact; it simply indicates that several errors have cancelled.

† Remember that Bernoulli's equation neglects viscous effects.
27. H. Schlichting, *Boundary Layer Theory*, 4th ed. (New York: McGraw-Hill Book Company, Inc., 1955).

Sharp-crested weir

Flow rates in open channels may be measured by a weir, an obstruction in the channel over which the fluid must flow. There are several types of commonly used weirs, but we will consider only the sharp-crested weir shown in Fig. 8.5-8. It represents a rather complicated flow problem, and in the absence of experience and knowledge, it is not at all obvious how we should

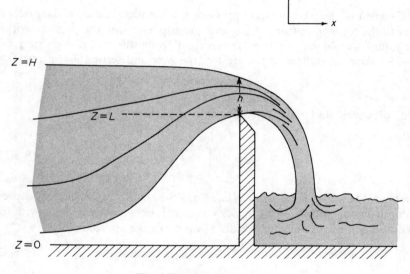

Fig. 8.5-8. Sharp-crested weir.

attack the problem. Both the momentum and mechanical energy balance would seem to be suitable tools for the analysis, but we will use Bernoulli's equation and leave the application of the macroscopic balances as an exercise.

Along any streamline we may write

$$p + \tfrac{1}{2}\rho v^2 + \rho g z = C_s \tag{8.5-25}$$

provided viscous effects are negligible. If the channel is deep compared to the thickness of the jet at the weir ($H \gg h$), the velocity far upstream from the weir will be small. Under these conditions, the constant C_s may be specified by applying Eq. 8.5-25 at some point far upstream from the weir.

$$C_s = p + \rho g z \tag{8.5-26}$$

Since the velocity in the z-direction is negligible there, the pressure is just the hydrostatic pressure,

$$p = p_0 + \rho g(H - z) \tag{8.5-27}$$

and we see that every streamline has the same constant given by

$$C_s = p_0 + \rho g H \tag{8.5-28}$$

We may now write Eq. 8.5-25 as

$$p + \tfrac{1}{2}\rho v^2 + \rho g z = p_0 + \rho g H \tag{8.5-29}$$

At the crest of the weir the fluid pressure is unknown; however, the pressure at both the top and bottom of the jet is atmospheric, and the pressure within the liquid should not be too far removed from this value. Applying Eq. 8.5-29 to the streamlines at the crest of the weir and setting $p = p_0$, we find

$$v = \sqrt{2g(H - z)} \tag{8.5-30}$$

The volumetric flow rate over the weir is given by

$$Q = b \int_{z=L}^{z=L+h} \mathbf{v} \cdot \mathbf{i}\, dz \tag{8.5-31}$$

where b is the width of the weir. While Eq. 8.5-30 may be a satisfactory expression for the magnitude of the velocity vector, it does not provide us with the x-component of the velocity vector. If we make the approximation

$$v = \mathbf{v} \cdot \mathbf{i} \tag{8.5-32}$$

Eq. 8.5-30 may be substituted into Eq. 8.5-31 and the integration carried out to yield

$$Q = \tfrac{2}{3}b\sqrt{2g}\{[H - L]^{3/2} - [H - (L + h)]^{3/2}\} \tag{8.5-33}$$

In practice, the height of the weir L is known, and the depth far upstream H is measured with a depth gauge; however, the position of the free surface at the weir remains as an unknown. Traditionally, we assume

$$H - (L + h) \ll H - L \tag{8.5-34}$$

and introduce a discharge coefficient to obtain

$$Q = \tfrac{2}{3}C_d b\sqrt{2g}(H - L)^{3/2} \tag{8.5-35}$$

We expect the discharge coefficient to be less than unity, and experiments indicate that

$$C_d \approx 0.6 \tag{8.5-36}$$

While experiments must be carried out to determine the discharge coefficient, this analysis does have value in that it predicts the correct dependence of flow rate on $(H - L)$. In Chap. 9, we will analyze the broad-crested weir, and show how practical flow rate measuring devices can be altered to fit available theory, thus providing a more reliable method of measurement.

The results presented in this section are brief; we must refer to handbooks on fluid metering[28-30] to obtain both accurate values for discharge coefficients and a thorough discussion of the many metering devices and their applications.

PROBLEMS

8-1. To determine the pressure drop-flow rate relationship for flow through a tube bundle used in heat transfer equipment, experiments are performed on configurations similar to that shown in Fig. 8-1. The tubes are arranged in a triangular pattern with the mean flow directed along the diagonal of the square. Describe how you would interpret the experimental results obtained in such a system—i.e., how would you define the friction factor, what parameters would f be a function of, etc.? Neglect wall effects and assume the tubes are infinitely long.

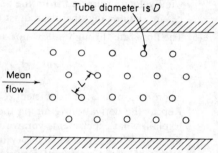

Fig. 8-1. Flow through a tube bundle.

8-2. Derive an integral expression for the pressure drop in the expanding circular tube shown in Fig. 8-2. Express Δp as a function of Q, A_1, A_2, and f. The

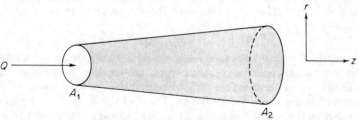

Fig. 8-2. Flow in an expanding tube.

28. "Flowmeter Computational Handbook," *Am. Soc. Mech. Engrs. Research Publication*, New York, 1961.

29. "Fluid Meters: Their Theory and Application," *Am. Soc. Mech. Engrs. Paper*, New York, 1959.

30. H. W. King and E. F. Brater, *Handbook of Hydraulics* (New York: McGraw-Hill Book Company, Inc., 1963).

cross-sectional area is given by

$$A = A_1 + (A_2 - A_1)\left(\frac{x}{L}\right)$$

and you are to assume that f is constant and the flow is turbulent.

8-3. Water is pumped through a 1-in. diameter pipe 100 ft long at a rate of 120 in.^{3}/sec. Neglecting entrance effects, calculate the pressure drop for a relative roughness ε/D of 0.002.

8-4. Calculate the pressure drop for the conditions in Prob. 8-3 if the pipe is replaced by a square duct, 1 in. on a side.

8-5. Crop-dusting of the artichoke fields around Castroville, California, is traditionally done by pilots flying at an altitude of 17 ft. If the particles of insecticide are approximately spherical with an average diameter of 10^{-2} cm, and a density of 127 lb m/ft, how long does it take them to fall to the ground? If the nearest population center is 1 mi from the fields, what is the maximum wind velocity (directed from the field toward the town) that can be tolerated before the dusting operation must be stopped?

8-6. The flow rate through a flow nozzle was given in Sec. 8.5 by

$$Q = C_d A_2 \sqrt{\frac{2(p_1 - p_2)}{\rho[1 - (A_2/A_1)^2]}}$$

where the discharge coefficient C_d had to be determined experimentally. Repeat the derivation retaining the viscous dissipation term in the analysis. Explain what experiments you would perform, and how you would correlate the data to obtain a satisfactory method of predicting flow rates by a flow nozzle. The assumption of flat velocity profiles is a reasonably good one and should be incorporated in your analysis.

8-7. The pump illustrated in Fig. 8-7 has an output given by

$$Q = Q_0 + a_Q \sin \omega t$$

where Q_0 is the time averaged flow rate, and a_Q represents the amplitude of the volumetric flow rate variations. The frequency of these variations is ω. If

$$a_Q \ll Q_0$$

the friction factor may be taken as a constant. In the absence of a surge tank, the fluctuations occurring at the process are identical to those at the pump and the process is therefore difficult to control. You are asked to design a surge tank which will reduce the amplitude of the fluctuations by a factor of 10. Set up the problem in a general fashion, locating a surge tank of diameter D_1 at a distance αL ($0 \le \alpha \le 1$) from the pump. Neglect minor losses and inertial effects. An exact solution is difficult to obtain; however, if the depth in the surge tank is represented by a steady term and a time-dependent term

$$h = h_0 + h'(t)$$

where

$$h'(t) \ll h_0$$

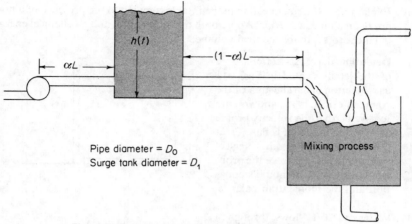

Fig. 8-7. Use of a surge tank to damp pump functions.

an approximate solution for the amplitude of the fluctuations in the surge tank $h'(t)$ may be obtained. Determine the value of α that will provide the maximum damping, and comment on the effect of increasing the ratio D_1/D_0. *Hint:* Assume a solution for $h'(t)$ of the form

$$h'(t) = a_h \sin(\omega t - \theta)$$

and make use of the approximation

$$\sqrt{h} = \sqrt{h_0}\left(1 + \frac{1}{2}\frac{h'(t)}{h_0}\right)$$

8-8. Apply the momentum and mechanical energy balances to derive an expression for the flow rate over the sharp-crested weir discussed in Sec. 8.5. Carefully list the assumptions that must be made to obtain a solution in each case.

8-9. Determine the water flow rate for the siphon shown in Fig. 8-9. The inlet to the siphon is placed 10 ft below the water level and the outlet is even with the bottom of the tank. The pipe diameter is 1 ft, the total length of the piping is 450 ft, and the relative roughness is 0.02. The fittings in the line are standard 90° elbows. Assume that the level of the water in the tank is constant.

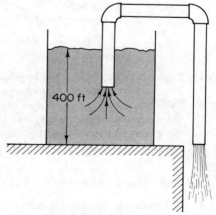

Fig. 8-9. Flow in a siphon.

8-10. Explain how you might estimate the total loss owing to the presence of a flow nozzle in a pipeline. *Hint:* Apply both the momentum and mechanical energy balances to a suitable control volume.

8-11. Determine the cross-sectional area of the jet illustrated in Fig. 8-11 as a function of z. The area of the rounded orifice is A_0, and you are to assume that the velocity profile everywhere in the jet is flat. Treat the flow as quasi-steady. Neglect viscous effects and solve the problem using both Bernoulli's equation and the momentum balance.

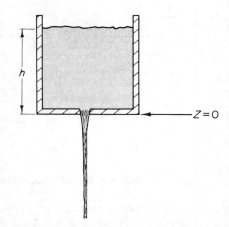

Fig. 8-11. Flow through a rounded orifice in a tank.

8-12. Water at 70°F flows through a Venturi meter as shown in Fig. 8-12. Cavitation occurs when the local pressure falls below the vapor pressure of the liquid, allowing vapor bubbles to form. The vapor pressure of water at 70°F is 0.36 psia. Calculate the maximum flow rate that this meter can handle without cavitation.

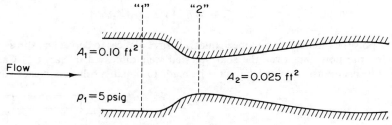

Fig. 8-12. Flow through a Venturi meter.

8-13. Figure 8-13 shows a pipeline system for pumping sea water into a reservoir. The Venturi meter has a discharge coefficient of 0.96 and a throat area one-half that of the pipe. The pipes are 4-in. and 6-in. I.D. commercial steel, and the manometer fluid is mercury. Determine the horsepower requirement of the pump and the volumetric flow rate. The density of sea water may be taken as 68.5 lb_m/ft^3 and the viscosity as 1.2 centipoise.

8-14. A $\frac{1}{2}$-in. plastic sphere ($\rho = 38\ lb_m/ft^3$) is released from the bottom of a deep lake. What is the terminal velocity?

8-15. Calculate the horsepower delivered by the pump to maintain a steady flow of water in the system shown in Fig. 8-15. All piping is 6-in. I.D. commercial

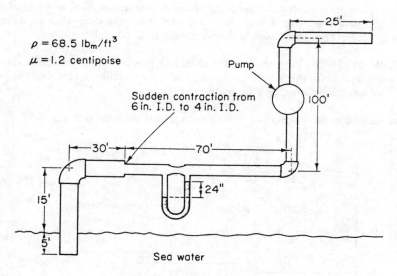

$\rho = 68.5\ lb_m/ft^3$
$\mu = 1.2$ centipoise

Pump

Sudden contraction from
6 in. I.D. to 4 in. I.D.

25'

100'

30'   70'

15'

24"

5'

Sea water

Fig. 8-13. Flow in a pipeline.

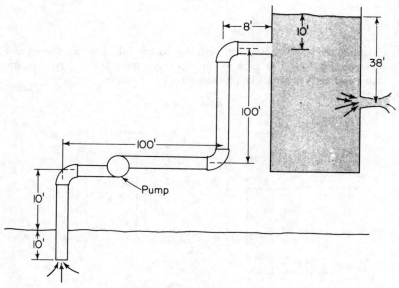

8'

10'

38'

100'

100'

Pump

10'

10'

Fig. 8-15. Flow in a pipeline.

steel, and all fittings are 90° standard elbows. Assume a value of 0.7 for the contraction coefficient of the 4-in. diameter orifice in the side of the tank.

8-16. Electrical transmission towers are placed at 1000-ft intervals, and $\frac{1}{2}$-in. diameter cables are strung between them. Determine the drag force on a single cable between two towers if the wind velocity is 60 mph.

8-17. When 15 ft³/sec of water flow in a 12-in. I.D. pipeline, 85 hp are lost in viscous dissipation for every 1000 ft of pipe. For these conditions, calculate the head loss, friction factor, and shear stress at the pipe wall.

8-18. Calculate the flow rate of water from the tank illustrated in Fig. 8-18.

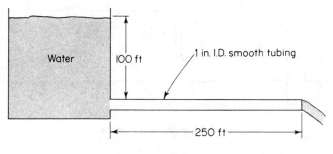

Fig. 8-18

8-19. Calculate the smallest flow rate required to keep the pipeline shown in Fig. 8-19 running full. The pipe is 1-in. I.D. commercial steel. Neglect minor losses and keep in mind the phenomenon of cavitation.

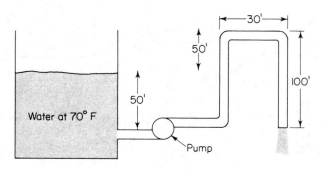

Fig. 8-19. Flow in a pipeline.

8-20. Calculate the flow rate through the submerged orifice in Fig. 8-20. The orifice diameter is 2 in. Estimate the discharge coefficient.

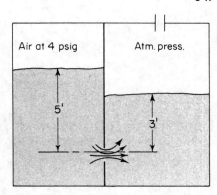

8-21. Derive an expression for the volumetric flow rate in a Venturi meter (see Sec. 8.5), assuming the velocity profile is always parabolic. Compare your result with the experimental values of the discharge coefficient shown in Fig. 8.5-2.

Fig. 8-20. Flow through a submerged orifice.

Open Channel Flow

9

The study of open channel flow is primarily directed toward applications in irrigation, flood control, and water supply. The analysis of flow in open channels is more complex than the analysis of flow in closed conduits for two reasons: the existence of a free surface complicates the analysis; and the actual channels encountered in practice are comparatively complex. A large portion of the flow in closed conduits is restricted to pipe flow, where the diameter and relative roughness describe the geometry fairly well. However, in dealing with flow in open channels we may encounter anything from a carefully constructed aquaduct to a grass-lined irrigation ditch. The flow characteristics of the former are fairly well known; however, those of the latter must be studied experimentally for every individual case if accurate results are desired. The study of open channel flow could easily be the subject of an entire course, and in a single chapter we can only hope to comment on the most important aspects.

These flows may be classified as either steady or unsteady, uniform or nonuniform. With the exception of the solitary shallow-water wave studied in Sec. 9.3, all the flows investigated in this chapter will be steady. A uniform flow is one for which the fluid depth h above the channel bed is constant. Nonuniform flows can be further classified into gradually varied flows, where the curvature of the free surface† is small compared to the depth of the fluid, and rapidly varied flows, where the curvature is comparable to the fluid depth.

In the study of flow in closed conduits, we sought equations relating the flow rate, pressure drop, and geometry $(Q, \Delta p, L, r_0)$, while in this chapter we will seek a relationship between the flow rate, fluid depth, and channel geometry $[Q, h(x), b(x), \eta(x)]$. We shall first analyze a simple uniform flow in terms of the macroscopic mass, momentum, and mechanical energy balances, and then go on to consider the flow in a channel with a changing geometry. This will lead us to equations defining gradually varied flows, after which we shall analyze rapidly varied flows, such as the hydraulic jump.

9.1   Uniform Flow

Consider the flow in a rectangular channel formed downstream from a sluice gate, such as that illustrated in Fig. 9.1-1. Just downstream from the gate, the flow will be nonuniform and rapidly varying; however, at some

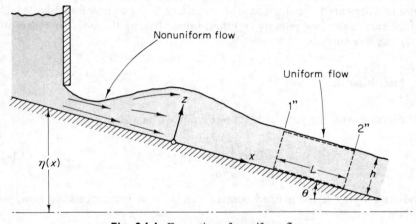

Fig. 9.1-1. Formation of a uniform flow.

distance downstream, a balance between gravitational and viscous forces will be achieved and the flow will become uniform. The velocity profile for a representative rectangular channel is shown in Fig. 9.1-2, and the curves indicate a rather curious situation. Because the drag force occurring at the wetted surface is the only force opposing the gravitational force, intuition leads us to expect the maximum velocity to occur at the centerline on the free

---

† The term "free surface" denotes an air-water interface, and has the characteristic that the tangential stress is zero and the normal stress is $-\mathbf{n}p_0$.

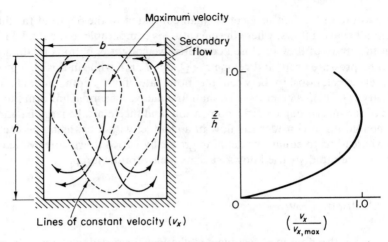

Fig. 9.1-2. Velocity profiles in a rectangular channel.

surface; however, the maximum velocity is located below the free surface. This anomaly appears to result from the *secondary flow* (indicated in Fig. 9.1-2), which carries the low velocity (v_x) fluid upward along the sides and then out over the free surface.

Mass balance

Starting with the general macroscopic mass balance,

$$\frac{d}{dt} \int_{\mathscr{V}_a(t)} \rho \, dV + \int_{A_e(t)} \rho(\mathbf{v} - \mathbf{w}) \cdot \mathbf{n} \, dA = 0 \tag{9.1-1}$$

and simplifying it for a fixed control volume and incompressible flow, we obtain

$$\int_{A_e} \mathbf{v} \cdot \mathbf{n} \, dA = 0 \tag{9.1-2}$$

Application of Eq. 9.1-2 to the control volume illustrated in Fig. 9.1-1 yields the obvious result

$$\langle v_x \rangle_2 A_2 - \langle v_x \rangle_1 A_1 = 0 \tag{9.1-3}$$

Since $A_2 = A_1 = bh$, we obtain

$$\langle v_x \rangle_2 = \langle v_x \rangle_1 \tag{9.1-4}$$

Time-averaging of all the equations used in this chapter is understood, because the open channel flows of practical importance are almost always turbulent. The general macroscopic momentum balance†

$$\frac{d}{dt}\int_{\mathcal{V}_{a}(t)} \rho\mathbf{v}\, dV + \int_{A_e(t)} \rho\mathbf{v}(\mathbf{v} - \mathbf{w})\cdot\mathbf{n}\, dA = \int_{\mathcal{V}_{a}(t)} \rho\mathbf{g}\, dV + \int_{\mathcal{A}_{a}(t)} \mathbf{t}_{(\mathbf{n})}^{*}\, dA \qquad (9.1\text{-}5)$$

can be dotted with $\mathbf{i}$ and applied to the fixed control volume to yield

$$\rho\langle v_x^2\rangle_2 A - \rho\langle v_x^2\rangle_1 A = \rho g_x A L + \int_{\mathcal{A}} \mathbf{t}_{(\mathbf{n})}^{*}\cdot\mathbf{i}\, dA \qquad (9.1\text{-}6)$$

Because the flow is uniform,

$$\langle v_x^2\rangle_2 = \langle v_x^2\rangle_1 \qquad (9.1\text{-}7)$$

and Eq. 9.1-6 reduces to a balance of surface forces and body forces,

$$0 = \rho g_x A L + \int_{\mathcal{A}} [-\mathbf{i}\cdot\mathbf{n}p_g + \mathbf{i}\cdot(\mathbf{n}\cdot\boldsymbol{\tau})]\, dA \qquad (9.1\text{-}8)$$

Assuming that the shear stress at the solid walls is independent of x (as it should be for uniform flow), Eq. 9.1-8 becomes

$$0 = \rho g_x A L + (\langle p_g\rangle_1 - \langle p_g\rangle_2)A + L\int_{S} \mathbf{i}\cdot(\mathbf{n}\cdot\boldsymbol{\tau})\, ds \qquad (9.1\text{-}9)$$

where S is the wetted perimeter, $b + 2h$. Once again uniform flow requires that

$$\langle p_g\rangle_1 = \langle p_g\rangle_2 \qquad (9.1\text{-}10)$$

Defining an average wall shear stress as

$$\tau_0 = -\frac{1}{S}\int_{S} \mathbf{i}\cdot(\mathbf{n}\cdot\boldsymbol{\tau})\, ds \qquad (9.1\text{-}11)$$

we obtain

$$0 = \rho g \sin\theta\, AL - \tau_0 SL \qquad (9.1\text{-}12)$$

Following the procedure used in the analysis of closed conduits flow, we arrange this equation in dimensionless form to obtain

$$\underset{\substack{\text{Dimensionless}\\\text{wall shear stress}}}{\frac{4\tau_0}{\tfrac{1}{2}\rho\langle v_x\rangle^2}} = \underset{\substack{\text{Dimensionless}\\\text{body force}}}{\frac{8g\sin\theta R_h}{\langle v_x\rangle^2}} = f \qquad (9.1\text{-}13)$$

† The use of the net stress vector is a convenience in analyzing open channel flow inasmuch as $\mathbf{t}_{(\mathbf{n})}^{*}$ is zero at a free surface.

where the hydraulic radius is given by

$$R_h = \frac{\text{cross-sectional area}}{\text{wetted perimeter}} = \frac{bh}{S}$$

Several empirical expressions exist for the friction factor, f. The most popular is the work of Manning,[1] which we may write in the form

$$f = 116 \frac{n^2}{R_h^{1/3}} \tag{9.1-14}$$

The coefficient n is a measure of the roughness, and values for several types of surfaces are listed in Table 9.1-1. Since f is dimensionless, we must be

Table 9.1-1
TABLE OF ROUGHNESS COEFFICIENTS n[a]

Type of Channel	n, ft$^{1/6}$
Artificial Channels of Uniform Cross Section	
Sides and bottom lined with well-planed timber evenly laid	0.009
Neat cement plaster, smoothest pipes	0.010
Cement plaster (3 cement to 1 sand), smooth iron pipes	0.011
Unplaned timber evenly laid, ordinary iron pipes	0.012
Ashlar masonry, best brickwork, well-laid sewer pipe[b]	0.013
Average brickwork, foul planks, foul iron pipes, ordinary sewer pipes after average uneven settlement and average fouling	0.015
Good rubble masonry, concrete laid in rough forms, poor brickwork, heavily incrusted iron pipes	0.017
Channels Subject to Nonuniformity of Cross Section	
Excellent clean canals in firm gravel, of fairly uniform section; rough rubble, "drying paving"	0.020
Ordinary earth canals and rivers in good order, free from large stones and heavy weeds	0.025
Canals and rivers with many stones and weeds	0.03–0.04

[a] Data from L. Marks and T. Baumeister, eds., *Marks' Mechanical Engineers' Handbook*. 6th ed. (New York: McGraw-Hill Book Company.Inc. 1958), pp. 3–81. A more thorough list of values is given in Ref. 2.
[b] This last value should be used for the previous categories, if doubt exists as to the excellence of construction and the maintenance free from slime, rust, or other growths and deposits.

careful to remember that n has units of ft$^{1/6}$. Note that the value of f given by Eq. 9.1-14 is independent of the Reynolds number, indicating that it is only valid for the "rough-pipe" region of flow where inertial effects predominate. A detailed discussion of the drag force is given by Chow.[2]

    1. R. Manning, "On the Flow of Water in Open Channels and Pipes," *Trans. Inst. Civ. Engrs. Ireland*, 1891, 20:161.
    2. V. T. Chow, *Open Channel Hydraulics* (New York: McGraw-Hill Book Company, Inc., 1959), Chap. 1.

Flow rate—channel depth calculations for
uniform flow

If the geometry and fluid depth for a channel are given, the determination
of the flow rate is straightforward. If we substitute Eq. 9.1-14 into Eq. 9.1-13
and solve for $\langle v_x \rangle$, we get

$$\langle v_x \rangle = \sqrt{\frac{8g \sin \theta \; R_h^{4/3}}{116n^2}} \tag{9.1-15}$$

From the channel geometry and fluid depth, we may readily compute the
volumetric flow rate. For a rectangular channel,

$$Q = bh \sqrt{\frac{8g \sin \theta \; R_h^{4/3}}{116n^2}}, \qquad \text{rectangular channel} \tag{9.1-16}$$

If the volumetric flow rate and channel geometry are given and the fluid depth
is to be determined, we use a trial-and-error solution. For a rectangular
channel, we multiply Eq. 9.1-15 by bh, express the hydraulic radius as

$$R_h = \frac{bh}{2h + b}$$

and rearrange to obtain

$$h = \frac{1}{b}\left[(2h + b)\left(\frac{116Q^2 n^2}{8g \sin \theta} \right)^{3/4} \right]^{2/5} \tag{9.1-17}$$

If we assume a value of h, we can then use Eq. 9.1-17 to calculate a second
value of h and test the validity of the assumption. A few trials will quickly
yield close agreement between the assumed and calculated values, and the
fluid depth is determined. More complex geometries, such as a trapezoidal
channel, lead to a more tedious trial-and-error calculation, but the method
is straightforward.

Mechanical energy balance

If the flow is incompressible and there are no solid moving surfaces, we
may use the results of Prob. 7-2 to write the mechanical energy balance as

$$\frac{d}{dt} \int_{\mathscr{V}_a(t)} (\tfrac{1}{2}\rho v^2) \, dV + \int_{A_e(t)} (\tfrac{1}{2}\rho v^2)(\mathbf{v} - \mathbf{w}) \cdot \mathbf{n} \, dA$$

$$= \int_{A_e(t)} \mathbf{v} \cdot \mathbf{t}_{(n)}^* \, dA - \int_{A_e(t)} \rho \phi \mathbf{v} \cdot \mathbf{n} \, dA - \dot{E}_v \tag{9.1-18}$$

For the case under consideration, Eq. 9.1-18 quickly reduces to

$$\int_{A_e} (\tfrac{1}{2}\rho v^2)\mathbf{v} \cdot \mathbf{n}\, dA = -\int_{A_e} p_g \mathbf{v} \cdot \mathbf{n}\, dA - \int_{A_e} \rho\phi \mathbf{v} \cdot \mathbf{n}\, dA - \dot{E}_v \quad (9.1\text{-}19)$$

Here we have used the arguments presented in Sec. 8.1 to reduce the stress on the entrance and exit to a simple pressure term, $-\mathbf{n}p_g$. Writing the gravitational potential as

$$\phi = g[\eta(x) + z\cos\theta] \quad (9.1\text{-}20)$$

and expressing the gauge pressure as

$$p_g = \rho g[(h - z)\cos\theta] \quad (9.1\text{-}21)$$

we may combine the pressure and gravitational terms in Eq. 9.1-19 to obtain

$$-\int_{A_e} p_g \mathbf{v} \cdot \mathbf{n}\, dA - \int_{A_e} \rho\phi \mathbf{v} \cdot \mathbf{n}\, dA = -\rho g \int_{A_e} (\eta + h\cos\theta)\mathbf{v} \cdot \mathbf{n}\, dA \quad (9.1\text{-}22)$$

Application of Eqs. 9.1-19 and 9.1-22 to the control volume indicated in Fig. 9.1-1 gives

$$\tfrac{1}{2}\rho\langle v_x^3\rangle_2 A_2 - \tfrac{1}{2}\rho\langle v_x^3\rangle_1 A_1$$
$$= -\rho g[(\eta_2 + h_2\cos\theta)\langle v_x\rangle_2 A_2 - (\eta_1 + h_1\cos\theta)\langle v_x\rangle_1 A_1] \quad (9.1\text{-}23)$$

Inasmuch as the flow is uniform,

$$\langle v_x^3\rangle_2 A_2 = \langle v_x^3\rangle_1 A_1$$
$$\langle p_g v_x\rangle_2 A_2 = \langle p_g v_x\rangle_1 A_1$$
$$\langle z v_x\rangle_2 A_2 = \langle z v_x\rangle_1 A_1$$
$$\langle v_x\rangle_2 A_2 = \langle v_x\rangle_1 A_1$$

The mechanical energy balance reduces to

$$0 = \rho g[\eta\,|_{x=x_1} - \eta\,|_{x=x_2}]\langle v_x\rangle A - \dot{E}_v \quad (9.1\text{-}24)$$

Dividing by $\rho g Q$ and noting that

$$\eta\,|_{x=x_1} - \eta\,|_{x=x_2} = L\sin\theta \quad (9.1\text{-}25)$$

we can rewrite Eq. 9.1-24 as

$$L\sin\theta = h_f \quad (9.1\text{-}26)$$

Thus, the *viscous dissipation* is just equal to the *decrease in potential energy* for uniform flow. The head loss can be expressed in more familiar terms by substituting $\sin\theta$ from Eq. 9.1-13 to obtain

$$h_f = \frac{f}{4}\left(\frac{L}{R_h}\right)\left(\frac{\langle v_x\rangle^2}{2g}\right) \quad (9.1\text{-}27)$$

However, the physical significance of the viscous dissipation is best expressed by Eq. 9.1-26.

9.2   Gradually Varied Flow

In this section, the macroscopic balances will be applied to the channel illustrated in Fig. 9.2-1. The width and slope are allowed to vary giving rise to a variable fluid depth $h(x)$.† The variations in channel slope and width shown in Fig. 9.2-1 are exaggerated, because the analysis presented here is valid

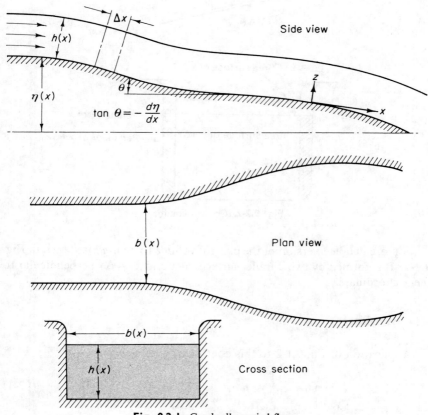

Fig. 9.2-1. Gradually varied flow.

only if the geometry is changing slowly—i.e., the curvature of the walls of the channel must be small compared to the width of the channel, and the curvature of the channel bed must be small compared to the fluid depth. We can therefore treat the flow as one-dimensional, even though the streamlines are curved.

† The phrase, "variable fluid depth" is the clue indicating that differential-macroscopic balances are in order.

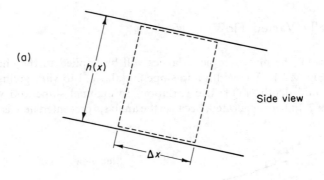

(a)

$h(x)$

Side view

Δx

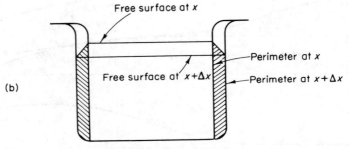

Free surface at x

Free surface at $x+\Delta x$

Perimeter at x

Perimeter at $x+\Delta x$

(b)

Fig. 9.2-2. Control volume.

A more detailed version of the control volume to be used is shown in Fig. 9.2-2. It is formed by two parallel surfaces at x and $x + \Delta x$ perpendicular to the x-coordinate.

Mass balance

Application of Eq. 9.1-2 to this control volume yields

$$\int_{A_e(x)} \mathbf{v} \cdot \mathbf{n} \, dA = \int_{A_e(x)} \mathbf{v} \cdot \mathbf{n} \, dA \bigg|_x + \int_{A_e(x)} \mathbf{v} \cdot \mathbf{n} \, dA \bigg|_{x+\Delta x} = 0 \qquad (9.2\text{-}1)$$

where the cross-sectional area of flow, $A_e(x)$, may be expressed as

$$A_e(x) = bh \qquad (9.2\text{-}2)$$

Note that $\mathbf{v} \cdot \mathbf{n}$ must be zero at the free surface for the flow to be steady. Assuming that the flow is one-dimensional, we may write

$$\mathbf{v} \cdot \mathbf{n} = \pm v_x \qquad \begin{array}{l}\text{At the entrance or exit of} \\ \text{the control volume}\end{array} \qquad (9.2\text{-}3)$$

and Eq. 9.2-1 reduces to

$$\langle v_x \rangle bh \,\big|_{x+\Delta x} - \langle v_x \rangle bh \,\big|_x = 0 \tag{9.2-4}$$

Dividing by Δx and taking the limit $\Delta x \to 0$, we find the differential macroscopic mass balance,

$$\frac{d}{dx}\left(\langle v_x \rangle bh \right) = 0 \tag{9.2-5}$$

Momentum balance

For steady flow, we may dot Eq. 9.1-5 with $\mathbf{i}$ to obtain

$$\int_{A_e} \rho v_x \mathbf{v} \cdot \mathbf{n} \, dA = \int_{\mathscr{V}} \rho g_x \, dV + \int_{\mathscr{A}} \mathbf{i} \cdot \mathbf{t}_{(n)}^{*} \, dA \tag{9.2-6}$$

Starting with the momentum flux term, we apply this equation to the differential control volume to obtain

$$\int_{A_e} \rho v_x \mathbf{v} \cdot \mathbf{n} \, dA = \rho \langle v_x^2 \rangle bh \,\big|_{x+\Delta x} - \rho \langle v_x^2 \rangle bh \,\big|_x \tag{9.2-7}$$

The body force term yields

$$\int_{\mathscr{V}} \rho g_x \, dV = \rho g_x bh \, \Delta x \tag{9.2-8}$$

The area integral of the stress vector may be expressed as

$$\int_{\mathscr{A}} \mathbf{i} \cdot \mathbf{t}_{(n)}^{*} \, dA = -\int_{\mathscr{A}} \mathbf{i} \cdot \mathbf{n} p_g \, dA + \int_{\mathscr{A}} \mathbf{i} \cdot (\mathbf{n} \cdot \boldsymbol{\tau}) \, dA \tag{9.2-9}$$

Directing our attention to the pressure term, we note the following:

1. $p_g = 0$, on the free surface;
2. $\mathbf{i} \cdot \mathbf{n} = 0$, on the bottom of the channel;
3. $\mathbf{i} \cdot \mathbf{n} = -\frac{1}{2}\dfrac{db}{dx}$, on the sides of the channel, provided $\dfrac{db}{dx} \ll 1$.

Under these conditions, we may write

$$\int_{\mathscr{A}} \mathbf{i} \cdot \mathbf{n} p_g \, dA = \int_{A_e(x)} p_g \, dA \,\bigg|_{x+\Delta x} - \int_{A_e(x)} p_g \, dA \,\bigg|_x \qquad \text{\small Pressure forces on the entrance and exit of the control volume}$$

$$\tag{9.2-10}$$

$$- \left(\frac{db}{dx}\right)\Delta x \int_0^{h(x)} p_g \, dz \qquad \text{\small Pressure forces on the sides of the channel}$$

It should be noted that the last term in Eq. 9.2-10 is easily overlooked, for our attention is generally directed to the forces at the entrance and exit of the control volume.

If we further assume that p_g is independent of position across the channel, Eq. 9.2-10 takes the form

$$\int_{\mathscr{A}} \mathbf{i} \cdot \mathbf{n} p_g \, dA = \int_0^{h(x)} p_g b \, dz \bigg|_{x+\Delta x} - \int_0^{h(x)} p_g b \, dz \bigg|_x - \frac{db}{dx} \Delta x \int_0^{h(x)} p_g \, dz \qquad (9.2\text{-}11)$$

The viscous shear stress term is easily handled by the definition of τ_0 given in Eq. 9.1-11

$$\int_{\mathscr{A}} \mathbf{i} \cdot (\mathbf{n} \cdot \boldsymbol{\tau}) \, dA = -S \, \Delta x \, \tau_0 \qquad (9.2\text{-}12)$$

Collecting the various terms in the momentum balance yields

$$\rho \langle v_x^2 \rangle bh \big|_{x+\Delta x} - \rho \langle v_x^2 \rangle bh \big|_x = \rho g_x bh \, \Delta x$$

$$- \left\{ \int_0^{h(x)} p_g b \, dz \bigg|_{x+\Delta x} - \int_0^{h(x)} p_g b \, dz \bigg|_x - \left(\frac{db}{dx}\right) \Delta x \int_0^{h(x)} p_g \, dz \right\} - S \, \Delta x \, \tau_0 \qquad (9.2\text{-}13)$$

Dividing by Δx and taking the limit $\Delta x \to 0$, we get

$$\rho \frac{d}{dx} (\langle v_x^2 \rangle bh) = \rho g_x bh - \frac{d}{dx} \int_0^{h(x)} p_g b \, dz + \left(\frac{db}{dx}\right) \int_0^{h(x)} p_g \, dz - \tau_0 S \qquad (9.2\text{-}14)$$

Expressing the gauge pressure as

$$p_g = \rho g_z [h(x) - z] \qquad (9.2\text{-}15)$$

carrying out the indicated integration and differentiation, and using the approximation†

$$\langle v_x^2 \rangle = \langle v_x \rangle^2 \qquad (9.2\text{-}16)$$

we get

$$\rho \langle v_x \rangle bh \frac{d\langle v_x \rangle}{dx} = \rho g_x bh - \rho g_z \frac{d}{dx}\left(\frac{bh^2}{2}\right) + \rho g_z \frac{h^2}{2} \frac{db}{dx} - \tau_0 S \qquad (9.2\text{-}17)$$

Here we have made use of the fact that

$$Q = \langle v_x \rangle bh = \text{constant} \qquad (9.2\text{-}18)$$

Differentiating Eq. 9.2-18 or Eq. 9.2-5 to obtain

$$bh \frac{d\langle v_x \rangle}{dx} + \langle v_x \rangle b \frac{dh}{dx} + \langle v_x \rangle h \frac{db}{dx} = 0 \qquad (9.2\text{-}19)$$

† Chow (Ref. 2, p. 28) indicates that Eq. 9.2-16 may be in error by as much as 20 per cent; hence, any study of real systems must incorporate the necessary correction factor.

and applying this result to Eq. 9.2-17, we can obtain the following dimension-less form of the differential-macroscopic momentum balance,

$$\frac{dh}{dx}\left[\frac{g_z}{g} - \frac{\langle v_x \rangle^2}{gh}\right] - \frac{\langle v_x \rangle^2}{gh}\left(\frac{h}{b}\right)\frac{db}{dx} = \frac{g_x}{g} - \frac{\tau_0 S}{\rho g b h} \qquad (9.2\text{-}20)$$

For practical purposes, gradually varied flows are restricted to cases where θ is less than $10°$, and under these conditions

$$\frac{g_z}{g} = \cos\theta \approx 1$$

$$\frac{g_x}{g} = \sin\theta \approx \tan\theta = -\left(\frac{d\eta}{dx}\right)$$

which leads to

$$\frac{dh}{dx}(1 - N_{Fr}) - N_{Fr}\left(\frac{h}{b}\right)\frac{db}{dx} = -\left(\frac{d\eta}{dx} + \frac{\tau_0 S}{\rho g b h}\right) \qquad (9.2\text{-}21)$$

We have replaced $\langle v_x \rangle^2/gh$ with the Froude number, so that it becomes clear the surface profile depends on whether N_{Fr} is greater or less than one. Flows for which $N_{Fr} = 1$ are called *critical flows*; $N_{Fr} > 1$ represents a *supercritical flow* and $N_{Fr} < 1$ a *subcritical flow*.

Mechanical energy balance

Starting with Eq. 9.1-19, we express the kinetic energy flux term as

$$\int_{A_e} (\tfrac{1}{2}\rho v^2)\mathbf{v} \cdot \mathbf{n} \, dA = \tfrac{1}{2}\rho\langle v_x^3 \rangle A\Big|_{x+\Delta x} - \tfrac{1}{2}\rho\langle v_x^3 \rangle A\Big|_{x} \qquad (9.2\text{-}22)$$

Using Eq. 9.1-20 to express ϕ and writing the gauge pressure as

$$p_g = \rho g[(h - z)\cos\theta] \qquad (9.2\text{-}23)$$

we can combine the pressure and gravitational terms in Eq. 9.1-19

$$-\int_{A_e} p_g \mathbf{v} \cdot \mathbf{n} \, dA - \int_{A_e} \rho\phi \mathbf{v} \cdot \mathbf{n} \, dA = -\rho g \int_{A_e} (\eta + h\cos\theta)\mathbf{v} \cdot \mathbf{n} \, dA \qquad (9.2\text{-}24)$$

Applying this result to the differential volume element in Fig. 9.2-2, and collecting the terms in Eq. 9.1-19, we get

$$\tfrac{1}{2}\rho\left(\langle v_x^3 \rangle A\Big|_{x+\Delta x} - \langle v_x^3 \rangle A\Big|_{x}\right) = -\rho g\left[(\eta + h\cos\theta)\langle v_x \rangle A\Big|_{x+\Delta x}\right.$$

$$\left. - (\eta + h\cos\theta)\langle v_x \rangle A\Big|_{x}\right] - \dot{E}_v \qquad (9.2\text{-}25)$$

Dividing by Δx and taking the limit $\Delta x \to 0$, we have the differential macroscopic mechanical energy balance

$$\tfrac{1}{2}\rho \frac{d}{dx}\left(\langle v_x^3\rangle A\right) = -\rho g \frac{d}{dx}\left[(\eta + h \cos\theta)\langle v_x\rangle A\right] - \dot{e}_v \qquad (9.2\text{-}26)$$

where

$$\dot{e}_v = \lim_{\Delta x \to 0}\left(\frac{\dot{E}_v}{\Delta x}\right) \qquad (9.2\text{-}27)$$

Assuming that

$$\langle v_x^3\rangle = \langle v_x\rangle^3 \qquad (9.2\text{-}28)$$

and using Eqs. 9.2-18 and 9.2-19, we can rearrange Eq. 9.2-26 to obtain

$$\frac{d}{dx}\left[\frac{\langle v_x\rangle^2}{2g} + h\right] = -\left(\frac{d\eta}{dx} + \frac{\dot{e}_v}{\rho g Q}\right) \qquad (9.2\text{-}29)$$

providing θ is less than $10°$. Referring to Eq. 9.1-26, we see that the viscous dissipation per unit length $\dot{e}_v$ for uniform flow is given by

$$\frac{\dot{e}_v}{\rho g Q} = \frac{\dot{E}_v}{\rho g Q L} = \sin\theta = -\frac{d\eta}{dx} \quad \text{for uniform flow} \qquad (9.2\text{-}30)$$

If the viscous dissipation for gradually varied flow is very nearly the same as for uniform flow, we may expect the right-hand side of Eq. 9.2-29 to be small. Integration of Eq. 9.2-29 gives

$$\frac{\langle v_x\rangle^2}{2g} + h = -\int\left(\frac{d\eta}{dx} + \frac{\dot{e}_v}{\rho g Q}\right) dx + \text{constant} \qquad (9.2\text{-}31)$$

which is generally written

$$\frac{\langle v_x\rangle^2}{2g} + h = E_{\text{sp}} \qquad (9.2\text{-}32)$$

E_{sp} is known as the *specific energy*, and it should be very nearly constant for gradually varied flow, although the changes in the geometry and roughness of the channel will certainly lead to small variations.

If the flow rate and channel width are given and values for τ_0 are available, either Eqs. 9.2-21 and 9.2-18 or Eqs. 9.2-29 and 9.2-18 can be used to solve for the two unknowns, $\langle v_x\rangle$ and h. In general, the process requires numerical integration, although analytic methods may be used to obtain approximate solutions for simple cases.

The mechanical energy balance is not as powerful a tool for solving open channel flow problems as it was for solving closed conduit problems; however, it can be used to good advantage to illustrate some important characteristics of open channel flow. Combination of Eqs. 9.2-18 and 9.2-32 to eliminate the velocity gives

$$\frac{Q^2}{2gb^2h^2} + h = E_{\text{sp}} \tag{9.2-33}$$

For a given volumetric flow rate and specific energy, Eq. 9.2-33 is a cubic in
h. Exluding negative and complex values of h, this equation yields either two
values of h or none. The solutions are shown in Fig. 9.2-3, where we see that
for each value of $Q^2/2gb^2$ there is a minimum value of E_{sp} below which there
is no solution for h. By inspection of Eq. 9.2-33, we can see that as E_{sp} becomes large the fluid depth may tend toward either zero or E_{sp}.

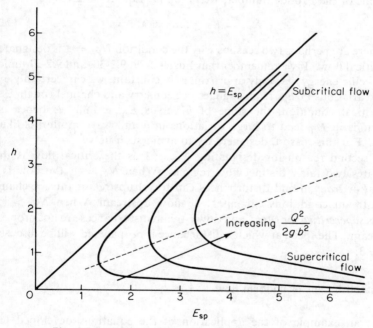

Fig. 9.2-3. Fluid depth as a function of specific energy.

We may determine the value of h for the minimum value of E_{sp} by setting
the derivative dE_{sp}/dh equal to zero and solving for h.

$$\frac{dE_{\text{sp}}}{dh} = 1 - \left(\frac{Q^3}{gb^2h^3}\right) = 0 \tag{9.2-34}$$

This condition corresponds to what is called critical flow, and the specific
energy, fluid depth, and velocity all assume their critical values. Expressing

Eq. 9.2-34 in terms of the velocity, we find the critical depth h_c to be

$$h_c = \frac{\langle v_x \rangle_c^2}{g} \qquad\qquad (9.2\text{-}35)$$

and the critical velocity is

$$\langle v_x \rangle_c = \sqrt{gh_c} \qquad\qquad (9.2\text{-}36)$$

Substitution of these results into Eq. 9.2-33 indicates that the critical specific energy is always three halves the critical depth

$$\tfrac{3}{2}\, h_c = (E_{sp})_c \qquad\qquad (9.2\text{-}37)$$

In terms of the Froude number, we note that Eq. 9.2-35 gives

$$N_{Fr} = 1 \qquad \text{for critical flow} \qquad\qquad (9.2\text{-}38)$$

There are perhaps two reasons why the condition $N_{Fr} = 1$ is designated as the critical flow. If we remember that Eqs. 9.2-29, 9.2-30, and 9.2-31 indicated the specific energy was only approximately constant, we can certainly expect small variations in E_{sp} from changes in geometry and channel roughness. At the critical condition, the slope of h versus E_{sp} is infinite; hence, small variations in E_{sp} lead to large variations in h and wave motion is likely to occur. For this reason, designers try to avoid such flows.

A second reason for designating $N_{Fr} = 1$ as the critical flow is that it separates two fairly distinct flow regimes. When $N_{Fr} < 1$, the flow is *subcritical* or *tranquil* and disturbances can travel upstream; thus, a change in downstream conditions can alter the flow upstream. When $N_{Fr} > 1$, the flow is *supercritical* or *rapid*, and downstream disturbances are not propagated upstream. The speed at which a disturbance is propagated will be discussed in Sec. 9.3.

Establishment of uniform flow

As an example of the application of the equations developed in this section, we will investigate the gradually varied flow indicated in Fig. 9.2-4 to determine the length required for establishing uniform flow. This example will also serve to introduce the student to the variety of surface profiles he may encounter for any particular flow system.

We start with the differential momentum balance, expressing the Froude number in terms of the volumetric flowrate and restricting the analysis to a rectangular channel of constant width.

$$\frac{dh}{dx}\left(1 - \frac{Q^2}{gb^2h^3}\right) = -\left(\frac{d\eta}{dx} + \frac{\tau_0 S}{\rho gbh}\right) \qquad\qquad (9.2\text{-}39)$$

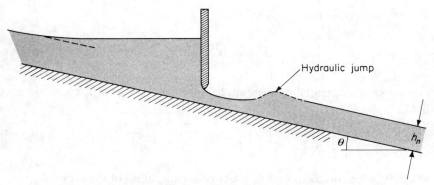

Fig. 9.2-4. Establishment of uniform flow.

Assuming that the Manning formula can be applied to gradually varied flows, we can combine Eqs. 9.1-13 and 9.1-14 and express the result in terms of the volumetric flow rate to obtain

$$\tau_0 = 14.5\rho \,\frac{Q^2 n^2}{b^2 h^2 R_h^{1/3}} \qquad (9.2\text{-}40)$$

If we further restrict the analysis to very wide channels, $b \gg h$, we can make the approximations

$$R_h \approx h$$
$$S \approx b$$

Under these conditions, we can combine Eqs. 9.2-39 and 9.2-40 to find

$$\frac{dh}{dx}\left(1 - \frac{Q^2}{gb^2 h^3}\right) = \sin\theta - 14.5\,\frac{Q^2 n^2}{gb^2 h^{10/3}} \qquad (9.2\text{-}41)$$

We have replaced $-d\eta/dx$ with $\sin\theta$. The left-hand side of this result may be simplified somewhat by noting that

$$\frac{Q^2}{gb^2} = \left(\frac{Q^2}{gb^2 h_c^3}\right)h_c^3 = h_c^3 \qquad (9.2\text{-}42)$$

because $Q^2/gb^2 h_c^3$ is the Froude number for critical flow and is therefore equal to one. Equation 9.2-41 can now be arranged in the form

$$\frac{dh}{dx}\left[1 - \left(\frac{h_c}{h}\right)^3\right] = \sin\theta\left(1 - \frac{14.5 Q^2 n^2}{gb^2 h^{10/3}\sin\theta}\right) \qquad (9.2\text{-}43)$$

If we designate h_n† as the fluid depth for uniform flow ($h \to h_n$ as $x \to \infty$),

† The subscript n is used because the depth under uniform flow conditions is often called the *normal depth*.

we may rearrange Eq. 9.1-16 to obtain

$$h_n = \left(\frac{14.5 Q^2 n^2}{g b^2 \sin \theta}\right)^{3/10} \tag{9.2-44}$$

Our original differential momentum balance may now be written in compact form

$$\frac{dh}{dx}\left[1 - \left(\frac{h_c}{h}\right)^3\right] = \sin \theta \left[1 - \left(\frac{h_n}{h}\right)^{10/3}\right] \tag{9.2-45}$$

which is to be solved subject to a boundary condition of the type

B.C. 1: $h = h_0, \qquad x = 0$ (9.2-46)

Surface profiles

Before going on to obtain an approximate solution to Eq. 9.2-45, we will discuss the possible surface profiles this equation may describe. Our purpose is not to acquaint the student with the nine specific surface profiles associated with the flow downstream from a sluice gate, but rather to drive home the point that flows in open channels can assume many possible forms. In his discussion of gradually varied flow, Chow (Ref. 2, p. 222) lists several dozen commonly encountered surface profiles. Thus, in analyzing flow in open channels it is extremely important to have knowledge of experimentally observed surface profiles, for it is especially difficult to "guess the flow topology" if the various possibilities are unknown.

For a given volumetric flow in a given channel, it should be intuitively obvious that the normal depth h_n will decrease with increasing slope. This idea is expressed quantitatively in Eq. 9.2-44 and leads us to classify channels as *mild*, i.e., having a slope small enough so that the normal depth is greater than the critical depth, $(h_n > h_c)$, *critical* $(h_n = h_c)$, and *steep* $(h_n < h_c)$. These conditions are illustrated in Fig. 9.2-5, and the flow at the critical slope is wavy or undular in agreement with our previous comment on the instability of critical flow. We now wish to examine Eq. 9.2-45 for mild, critical, and steep channels downstream and upstream from a sluice gate.

For mild channels, $h_n > h_c$, and we must consider three possibilities in the gradually varied flow region.

M1. $h > h_n > h_c$, subcritical flow;
M2. $h_n > h > h_c$, subcritical flow;
M3. $h_n > h_c > h$, supercritical flow.

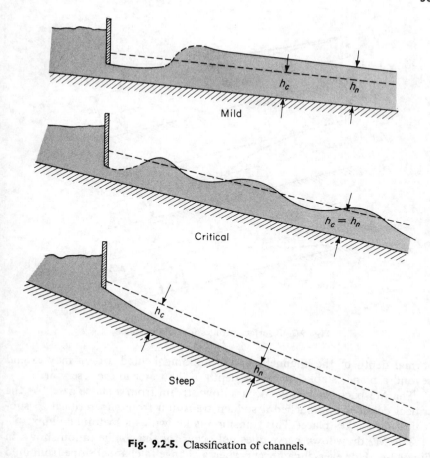

Fig. 9.2-5. Classification of channels.

Examining Eq. 9.2-45, we find the following restrictions on dh/dx:

M1. $dh/dx > 0$, backwater curve;
M2. $dh/dx < 0$, drawdown curve;
M3. $dh/dx > 0$, backwater curve.

The condition that h increases with increasing distance down the channel is called a backwater curve, while a decrease in h is called a drawdown curve. The three profiles for mild channels are illustrated in Fig. 9.2-6. As the depth approaches the critical depth, the profile is drawn with a dashed line, because, as Eq. 9.2-45 indicates, the flow cannot be gradually varied as $h \to h_c$.

The M1 backwater curve is the type of profile that exists upstream from a dam (or the sluice gate shown in Fig. 9.2-4). Knowledge of the backwater curve is important to reservoir design, because the profile lies above the

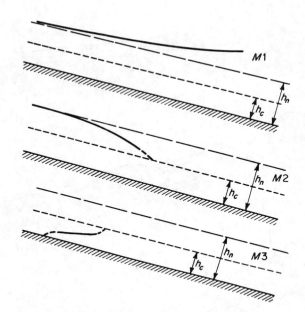

Fig. 9.2-6. Surface profiles for mild channels.

normal depth of the channel and the flooding behind a dam may extend beyond a plane established by the depth of the water in the reservoir.

The M3 backwater curve occurs downstream from a sluice gate. As the critical depth is approached a sudden transition from supercritical to subcritical flow takes place. This transition is known as a hydraulic jump.

The M2 drawdown curve does not occur for the configuration shown in Fig. 9.2-4. However, it can occur when a change in channel slope from mild to critical takes place.

For critical channels, $h_n = h_c$, and again we have three possibilities in the gradually varied flow region.

C1. $h > h_n = h_c$, subcritical flow;
C2. $h_n = h_c = h$, critical flow;
C3. $h_n = h_c > h$, supercritical flow.

Examination of Eq. 9.2-45 for this channel indicates:

C1. $dh/dx > 0$,   backwater curve;
C2. $dh/dx > 0$,† backwater curve;
C3. $dh/dx > 0$,   backwater curve.

The three profiles for critical channels are illustrated in Fig. 9.2-7.

† This result is easily obtained by application of l'Hospital's rule to Eq. 9.2-45; however, the actual existence of such a profile is open to question.

The C1 and C2 backwater curves occur upstream from a dam, and both may exhibit hydraulic jump. The C3 backwater curve may exist downstream from a sluice gate, and a mild, or undular, jump occurs at the transition from supercritical to critical flow.

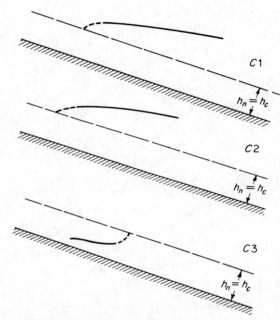

Fig. 9.2-7. Surface profiles for critical channels.

For steep channels, $h_c > h_n$, and the possible types of flow follow:

S1. $h > h_c > h_n$, subcritical flow;
S2. $h_c > h > h_n$, supercritical flow;
S3. $h_c > h_n > h$, supercritical flow.

These conditions lead to the following surface profiles:

S1. $dh/dx > 0$, backwater curve;
S2. $dh/dx < 0$, drawdown curve;
S3. $dh/dx > 0$, backwater curve.

These surface profiles are illustrated in Fig. 9.2-8.

The S1 backwater curve is the type that may occur upstream from a dam. The S2 and S3 profiles can occur downstream from a sluice gate, the S2 profile being similar to that illustrated in Fig. 9.2-5.

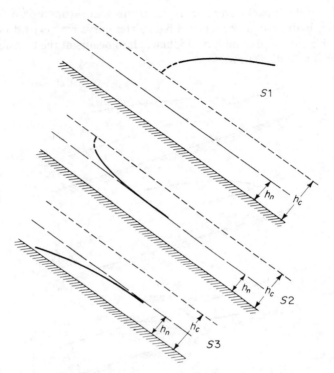

Fig. 9.2-8. Surface profiles for steep channels.

Once again, the point to be made in this discussion is that a variety of surface profiles are possible for a given geometrical configuration and it is necessary to have some idea what to expect before plunging into an analysis.

Returning now to Eq. 9.2-45, we wish to extract an approximate solution for the approach to uniform flow downstream from a sluice gate. The flow at the sluice gate cannot be classified as gradually varied; however, at a short distance downstream from the gate the variations in fluid depth are more gradual and Eq. 9.2-45 is satisfactory. Defining the dimensionless quantities

$$H = \frac{h}{h_n}, \quad \text{dimensionless fluid depth}$$

$$X = \frac{x \sin \theta}{h_n}, \quad \text{dimensionless length}$$

$$\mathscr{R} = \frac{h_c}{h_n}, \quad \text{ratio of critical to normal depth}$$

allows us to write Eq. 9.2-45 as

$$\frac{dH}{dX}\left(1 - \frac{\mathscr{R}^3}{H^3}\right) = \left(1 - \frac{1}{H^{10/3}}\right) \tag{9.2-47}$$

To extract an analytic solution from this equation we must make the approximation

$$H^{10/3} \approx H^3 \tag{9.2-48}$$

If $\frac{1}{2} < H < 2$, this approximation will lead to an error of about 25 per cent; however, it is not excessive when compared to the percentage of error incurred in the use of Eqs. 9.2-16 and 9.2-28 and the Manning formula for the friction factor.

Simplifying Eq. 9.2-47, separating variables, and integrating, we get

$$\int \left(\frac{H^3 - \mathscr{R}^3}{H^3 - 1}\right) dH = X + C \tag{9.2-49}$$

where C is the constant of integration to be determined by application of

B.C. 1': $H = H_0,$ $X = 0$ $\tag{9.2-50}$

The integral in Eq. 9.2-49 is available,[3] and the result, after applying boundary condition 1', is

$$(\overline{H} - H_0) + \frac{(\mathscr{R}^3 - 1)}{6}\left\{\ln\left[\left(\frac{1 + H + H^2}{1 + H_0 + H_0^2}\right)\left(\frac{1 - H_0}{1 - H}\right)^2\right]\right.$$

$$\left. + \frac{6}{\sqrt{3}}\left[\tan^{-1}\left(\frac{2H + 1}{\sqrt{3}}\right) - \tan^{-1}\left(\frac{2H_0 + 1}{\sqrt{3}}\right)\right]\right\} = X \tag{9.2-51}$$

For practical purposes, we can assume that uniform flow has been reached when h is within 1 per cent of h_n or H is within 1 per cent of unity. The length required to achieve uniform flow will be called the entrance length and designated by L_e.

Entrance lengths

For mild channels, only the M3 profile occurs downstream from a sluice gate, and a hydraulic jump occurs in the neighborhood of $H = \mathscr{R}$. For this type, $\mathscr{R} < 1$, and the maximum entrance length will be obtained for $\mathscr{R} \to 1$ because the term in braces ({ }) is always positive. Letting $\mathscr{R} = 1$ to obtain

---

3. H. B. Dwight, *Tables of Integrals and Other Mathematical Data* (New York: The Macmillan Company, 1961), p. 42.

an upper bound gives

$$L_e = \frac{(0.99 - H_0)h_n}{\sin \theta} \qquad (9.2\text{-}52)$$

and an order of magnitude estimate of the entrance length is

$$L_e = 0\left(\frac{h_n}{\sin \theta}\right) \qquad (9.2\text{-}53)$$

Since h_n is generally on the order of feet, and $\sin \theta$ may be 0.01 or less, the entrance length is on the order of 100 ft or more for mild channels.

For critical channels, $\mathscr{R} = 1$ and the entrance length is given by Eq. 9.2-52.

For steep channels, we see from Fig. 9.2-8 that there are two possible profiles leading to a uniform flow.:

S2. $\mathscr{R} \geq H \geq 1$;

S3. $\mathscr{R} \geq 1 \geq H$.

For these two limiting cases we will take $H_0 \gg 1$ and $H_0 \ll 1$, respectively, to obtain;

S2. $L_e = (h_n/\sin \theta) [1.44\mathscr{R}^3 + (1.01 - H_0)]$; $\qquad (9.2\text{-}54a)$

S3. $L_e = (h_n/\sin \theta) [2.02\mathscr{R}^3 + 0.99]$. $\qquad (9.2\text{-}54b)$

In both cases, the entrance length can be hundreds of feet long, and it should be apparent that uniform flow is the exception and varied flow the rule for most practical cases.

9.3 The Solitary Wave

To understand some of the phenomena encountered in open channel flow, we must determine the speed at which a disturbance to the surface profile moves. We first consider a disturbance caused by a movable wall which bounds an initially quiescent body of water. This process is illustrated in Fig. 9.3-1, and a sketch of the control volume to be used in the analysis is shown in Fig. 9.3-2. We assume that the wave profile is preserved and choose a differential control volume that moves with some specific portion of the wave. Note that the control volume is not a material volume, for it is the profile which moves, not the water. In this respect, Watts[4] has written that:

> "Buddhism has frequently compared the course of time to the apparent motion of a wave, wherein the actual water only moves up and down, creating the illusion of a 'piece' of water moving over the surface."

4. A. W. Watts, *The Way of Zen* (New York: Pantheon Books, Inc., 1957).

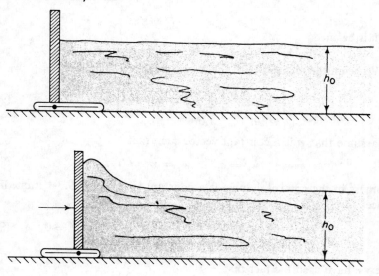

Fig. 9.3-1. Generation of a solitary wave.

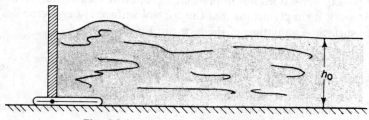

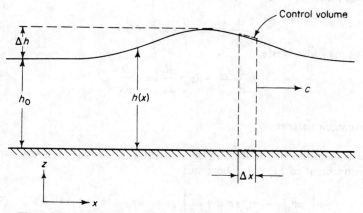

Fig. 9.3-2. Moving control volume for analysis of the solitary wave.

Mass balance

We begin the analysis with the macroscopic mass balance

$$\frac{d}{dt}\int_{\mathscr{V}_a(t)} \rho\, dV + \int_{A_e(t)} \rho(\mathbf{v} - \mathbf{w})\cdot\mathbf{n}\, dA = 0 \qquad (9.3\text{-}1)$$

and assume that $\mathbf{w}$ is a constant vector such that

$$w_x = c, \qquad w_y = w_z = 0 \qquad (9.3\text{-}2)$$

The mass in the control volume is a constant so that Eq. 9.3-1 immediately reduces to

$$\int_{A_e(t)} \rho(\mathbf{v} - \mathbf{w})\cdot\mathbf{n}\, dA\bigg|_{x+\Delta x} + \int_{A_e(t)} \rho(\mathbf{v} - \mathbf{w})\cdot\mathbf{n}\, dA\bigg|_{x} = 0 \qquad (9.3\text{-}3)$$

Here we have used the fact that

$$(\mathbf{v} - \mathbf{w})\cdot\mathbf{n} = 0 \quad \text{at the free surface} \qquad (9.3\text{-}4)$$

Note that Eq. 9.3-4 does not imply that the control volume moves with the fluid ($\mathbf{w} = \mathbf{v}$), it simply means that the control surface always coincides with the free surface. Evaluation of the terms in Eq. 9.3-3 gives

$$\int_0^{h(x)} (v_x - c)\, dz\bigg|_{x+\Delta x} - \int_0^{h(x)} (v_x - c)\, dz\bigg|_{x} = 0 \qquad (9.3\text{-}5)$$

where the density has been removed because the flow is incompressible. Dividing by Δx, expressing the integrals in terms of average velocities, and taking the limit $\Delta x \to 0$, we get

$$\frac{d}{dx}\left[(\langle v_x\rangle - c)h\right] = 0 \qquad (9.3\text{-}6)$$

which we may also write,

$$h\frac{d\langle v_x\rangle}{dx} + \langle v_x\rangle\frac{dh}{dx} = c\frac{dh}{dx} \qquad (9.3\text{-}7)$$

Momentum balance

The momentum of the fluid in the control volume will be a constant, so the x-component of Eq. 9.1-5 becomes

$$\int_{A_e(t)} \rho v_x(\mathbf{v} - \mathbf{w})\cdot\mathbf{n}\, dA = \int_{\mathscr{A}_a(t)} \mathbf{i}\cdot[-\mathbf{n}p_g + \mathbf{n}\cdot\boldsymbol{\tau}]\, dA \qquad (9.3\text{-}8)$$

Neglecting viscous effects and applying this equation to the control volume in Fig. 9.3-2, we have

$$\rho \frac{d}{dx} \left[\langle v_x(v_x - c) \rangle h \right] = -\frac{d}{dx} \int_0^{h(x)} p_g \, dz \qquad (9.3\text{-}9)$$

Expressing the gauge pressure as†

$$p_g = \rho g [h(x) - z] \qquad (9.3\text{-}10)$$

and carrying out the integration in Eq. 9.3-9, we find

$$\rho \frac{d}{dx} \left[\langle v_x(v_x - c) \rangle h \right] = -\rho g h \frac{dh}{dx} \qquad (9.3\text{-}11)$$

Assuming that the velocity profile is flat, and using Eq. 9.3-6, we get

$$(\langle v_x \rangle - c)h \frac{d\langle v_x \rangle}{dx} = -gh \frac{dh}{dx} \qquad (9.3\text{-}12)$$

Use of Eq. 9.3-7 to eliminate $d\langle v_x \rangle/dx$ leads us to

$$(c - \langle v_x \rangle)^2 = gh(x) \qquad (9.3\text{-}13)$$

or

$$c = \langle v_x \rangle \pm \sqrt{gh(x)} \qquad (9.3\text{-}14)$$

Provided the amplitude of the wave is small compared to the quiescent fluid depth $\Delta h \ll h_0$, the fluid velocity will be small compared to the wave speed‡ $\langle v_x \rangle \ll c$, and Eq. 9.3-14 reduces to

$$c = \pm\sqrt{gh(x)} \qquad (9.3\text{-}15)$$

The result of our analysis apparently contradicts one of the first assumptions—i.e., the wave profile is preserved—for Eq. 9.3-15 indicates that the speed of a particular point on the profile depends upon $h(x)$, which is not constant. However, our analysis does predict qualitatively the real behavior of waves in channels, for observation[5] indicates that the wave crest travels faster than the leading or trailing edge and that the wave tends to get steeper in front of the crest. However, if $\Delta h \ll h_0$, the speed will change only slightly over the wave, and a reasonable approximation for small amplitude waves is

$$c = \pm\sqrt{gh_0} \qquad (9.3\text{-}16)$$

† This equation assumes that the hydrostatic pressure variations are large compared to the variations caused by fluid motion in the z-direction.

‡ There is some tradition associated with the use of the word *celerity* to describe the time rate of change of position of the wave profile, reserving the word *velocity* for v and the word *speed* for $v = \sqrt{\mathbf{v} \cdot \mathbf{v}}$. However, the term *wave speed* or *wave velocity* is difficult to misinterpret.

5. J. J. Stoker, "The Formation of Breakers and Bores," *Comm. Appl. Math.*, 1948 1:1.

We must clarify the assumption associated with Eq. 9.3-10. Expressing the pressure as hydrostatic is satisfactory only if $\rho v_z^2/h_0$ is negligible compared to ρg (inertial effects are therefore small compared to gravitational effects). A careful study of wave motion[6] indicates that this assumption is satisfied when the wave length λ is long compared to the fluid depth. Such waves are often called *shallow-water waves*, and the wave speed is given correctly by Eq. 9.3-16. Waves for which the wave length is less than the fluid depth are called *gravity waves*, and their speed is given by

$$c = \pm \sqrt{\frac{g\lambda}{2\pi}}, \qquad \text{gravity waves } (\lambda < h_0) \qquad (9.3\text{-}17)$$

We see that gravity waves move at a slower velocity than shallow-water waves. If the wave length is very short—say, less than 1 cm—the wave velocity is governed by surface tension effects and these waves are called *ripples*. Their wave speed is given by

$$c = \pm \sqrt{\frac{2\pi\sigma}{\rho\lambda}}, \qquad \text{ripples } (\lambda < 1 \text{ cm}) \qquad (9.3\text{-}18)$$

Both Eqs. 9.3-17 and 9.3-18 are restricted to the condition that the wave amplitude is small compared to the wave length, $\Delta h \ll \lambda$; thus, the results are applicable only for small disturbances.

An important point to be cleared up before we discuss the result derived for shallow-water waves is the sign $\pm$ associated with the wave speed. There is nothing in the analysis which tells us whether the wave generated in Fig. 9.3-1 will travel to the left or to the right, but there is little doubt in our minds that it will move to the right. One might ask, "If our analysis is correct, why shouldn't it predict the direction in which the wave moves?" The answer is that one must investigate carefully the actual generation phenomena in order to predict the direction of wave propagation. Stoker[7] has presented a thorough treatment of this problem indicating that a disturbance always propagates into the "region of quiet," i.e., the undisturbed region. In our problem the undisturbed region is to the right of the movable wall; hence, the wave moves to the right.

An analysis of wave propagation in a flowing channel is similar to the development presented here and Eq. 9.3-14 is again obtained with the velocity $\langle v_x \rangle$ being the normal flow velocity. It is thus indicated that a disturbance may propagate downstream at a velocity equal to $\sqrt{gh}$ plus the stream velocity, and upstream at a velocity equal to $\sqrt{gh}$ minus the stream velocity. This situation is illustrated in Fig. 9.3-3 where a disturbance has been created by momentarily immersing a gate into the stream.

6. L. M. Milne-Thomson, *Theoretical Hydrodynamics*, 4th ed. (New York: The Macmillan Company, 1960), Chap. 14.

7. J. J. Stoker, *Water Waves* (New York: Interscience Publishers, Inc., 1957), p. 303.

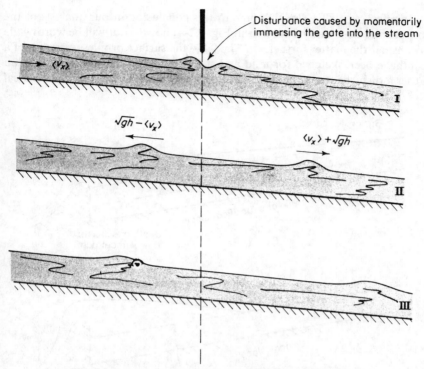

Fig. 9.3-3. Propagation of a disturbance in a mild channel.

The interesting case to consider is that of critical flow where the velocity is given by Eq. 9.2-36 as

$$\langle v_x \rangle = \sqrt{gh} \tag{9.3-19}$$

Thus, for critical flow a disturbance may remain fixed at a point in the channel; for subcritical flow (such as that illustrated in Fig. 9.3-3), a disturbance may propagate upstream; and for supercritical flow all small disturbances are carried downstream. Note that this latter statement also applies to gravity waves because they have a smaller velocity than shallow-water waves. Ripples may propagate upstream in a critical channel, provided

$$\lambda < \frac{2\pi\sigma}{\rho g h} \tag{9.3-20}$$

Thus, if the fluid depth is O(feet), the wave length must be about 10^{-2} cm. Such small waves are rapidly dissipated by viscous effects, and we conclude that shallow-water waves, gravity waves, and ripples are carried downstream in supercritical flow.

In effect, we have already come to this conclusion in our analysis of the flow profiles upstream of the weir in Fig. 9.2-4; however, it will be worthwhile to consider the matter further. In Fig. 9.3-4 the surface profiles upstream of a dam have been sketched for mild and steep channels. In each case, the dam causes a disturbance in the flow. For the mild channel, the flow is subcritical

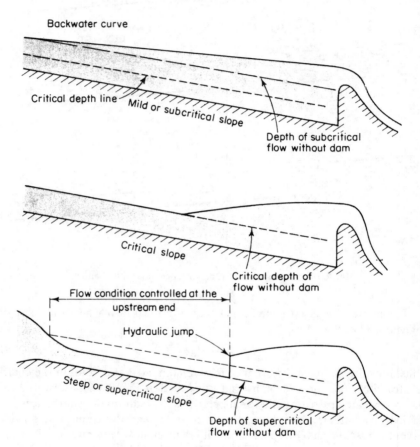

Fig. 9.3-4. Surface profiles upstream from a dam.

and the disturbance is propagated upstream forming the smooth backwater curve. In the steep channel, small disturbances are carried downstream; however, the dam presents a finite disturbance and a hydraulic jump is formed which propagates upstream at a velocity just equal to $\langle v_x \rangle$. The characteristics of hydraulic jumps will be treated in Sec. 9.5.

9.4 Flow Over Bumps, Crests, and Weirs

The presentation in this section is mainly qualitative, the objective being to examine the broad-crested weir and describe how it works.

Flow over a bump

We wish to examine the flow illustrated in Fig. 9.4-1 and determine whether the surface will hump or dip when passing over the bump in the channel. Intuition would naturally lead us to believe that a hump would appear but this assumption is not necessarily correct. We assume that there are no variations in channel width so that Eq. 9.2-21 reduces to

$$\frac{dh}{dx}(1 - N_{\text{Fr}}) = -\left(\frac{d\eta}{dx} + \frac{\tau_0 S}{\rho g b h}\right) \tag{9.4-1}$$

Upstream and downstream from the bump the flow is uniform,† and

$$\frac{dh}{dx} = 0 \tag{9.4-2}$$

Under these conditions,

$$\left(\frac{d\eta}{dx}\right) = -\left(\frac{\tau_0 S}{\rho g b h}\right) \tag{9.4-3}$$

The difficult question to answer is, "What happens to these quantities at the bump?" The behavior of $d\eta/dx$ is defined by the geometry; its absolute value decreases on the upstream side of the bump and increases on the downstream side. Our comments regarding τ_0 and h can only be vague generalizations, and for a start we shall assume that neither h nor τ_0 changes as the fluid flows over the bump. This statement is consistent with the assumption that a hump forms as illustrated in Fig. 9.4-1. Based on this assumption, we may write

$$\left(\frac{d\eta}{dx} + \frac{\tau_0 S}{\rho g b h}\right) > 0, \quad \text{on the upstream side} \tag{9.4-4a}$$

$$\left(\frac{d\eta}{dx} + \frac{\tau_0 S}{\rho g b h}\right) < 0, \quad \text{on the downstream side} \tag{9.4-4b}$$

We now consider two cases:

1. $N_{\text{Fr}} > 1$, supercritical flow;
2. $N_{\text{Fr}} < 1$, subcritical flow.

† This statement assumes that we do not have supercritical flow on a mild or critical channel.

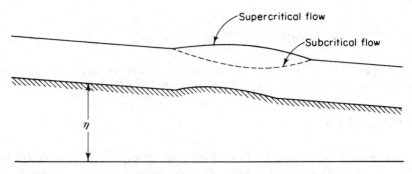

Fig. 9.4-1. Flow over a bump.

For case 1, Eqs. 9.4-1 and 9.4-4 indicate that

$$\frac{dh}{dx} > 0, \qquad \text{on the upstream side} \qquad (9.4\text{-}5a)$$

$$\frac{dh}{dx} < 0, \qquad \text{on the downstream side} \qquad (9.4\text{-}5b)$$

Thus, for supercritical flow the profile rises up over the bump, and our assumptions regarding h and τ_0 in the neighborhood of the bump *may* be correct.

For case 2, Eqs. 9.4-1 and 9.4-4 indicate that

$$\frac{dh}{dx} < 0, \qquad \text{on the upstream side} \qquad (9.4\text{-}6a)$$

$$\frac{dh}{dx} > 0, \qquad \text{on the downstream side} \qquad (9.4\text{-}6b)$$

Thus, for subcritical flow our analysis indicates that the profile dips down over the bump as indicated by the dashed curve in Fig. 9.4-1. This conclusion, of course, violates our assumption that h and τ_0 are constant in the neighborhood of the jump. However, if h decreases and τ_0 increases owing to the increased velocity, the inequalities given by Eqs. 9.4-4 still hold, and we conclude that the profile rises over a bump when the flow is supercritical and dips when the flow is subcritical. We must note that this discussion is very qualitative in nature, and the behavior of the surface profile in the neighborhood of a bump is best understood in terms of experimental observation. The analysis is put in its proper place if we simply state that it *does not contradict* the experimental observation.

Flow over a crest

We now wish to examine the problem of flow over a crest, as illustrated in Fig. 9.4-2. Water flows from a reservoir over the crest and into a second reservoir formed by an adjustable gate. In examining this problem, we shall take a chronological approach.

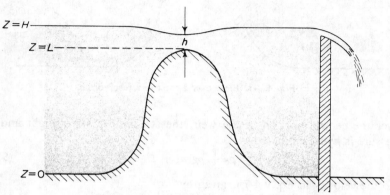

Fig. 9.4-2. Flow over a crest in a reservoir.

Let us consider first the case where the control gate is raised so that no flow occurs and the water in the reservoir is quiescent. If we lower the gate so that a small flow takes place, the flow will be subcritical and a dip in the profile will occur at the crest. Further lowering of the control gate will increase the flow rate until the critical velocity is reached. Up to this time the flow has been subcritical and controlled by the downstream conditions. However, once critical flow is reached small disturbances can no longer be propagated upstream, and further lowering of the control gate simply washes out the downstream portion of the dip in the profile at the crest. This situation is illustrated in Fig. 9.4-3, which shows the subcritical flow upstream of the crest, the critical flow at the crest, and the supercritical flow downstream of the crest.

The broad-chested weir

A broad-crested weir is shown in Fig. 9.4-4. Broad-crested weirs are used as flow rate measuring devices, and have a certain advantage over the previously discussed sharp-crested weir (Sec. 8.5). The initial portion of the analysis of this flow is identical to that presented for the sharp-crested weir where the application of Bernoulli's equation to any streamline gave us

$$p + \tfrac{1}{2}\rho v^2 + \rho g z = p_0 + \rho g H \tag{9.4-7}$$

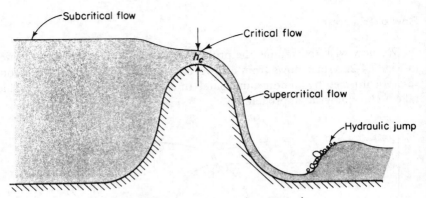

Fig. 9.4-3. Flow over a crest in a reservoir.

Over the central portion of the weir, the streamlines are straight and the pressure is hydrostatic,

$$p = p_0 + \rho g(h_c + L - z) \tag{9.4-8}$$

and the velocity in Eq. 9.4-7 is given by†

$$v = \sqrt{2g}\,\sqrt{(H - L) - h} \tag{9.4-9}$$

This equation could be used to determine the volumetric flow rate over a broad-crested weir if H and h were measured with depth gauges. Because the streamlines are straight, the volumetric flow rate per unit width is

$$q = h\sqrt{2g}\,\sqrt{(H - L) - h} \tag{9.4-10}$$

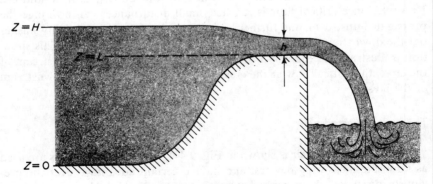

Fig. 9.4-4. Broad-crested weir.

† Remember that Bernoulli's equation neglects viscous effects; therefore, it is not unreasonable that Eq. 9.4-9 indicates a flat velocity profile.

The broad-crested weir has its greatest utility when the flow at the weir has reached the critical value. Under these conditions, the velocity is given by

$$v_c = \sqrt{gh_c} \tag{9.4-11}$$

and Eq. 9.4-9 is written as

$$v_c = \sqrt{2g}\,\sqrt{(H - L) - h_c} \tag{9.4-12}$$

We may now eliminate h_c, solve for v_c, and obtain the total volumetric flow rate,

$$Q = b\sqrt{g}[\tfrac{2}{3}(H - L)]^{3/2} \tag{9.4-13}$$

This result is similar in form to that obtained for the sharp-crested weir; however, in deriving this equation we have not had to introduce a discharge coefficient to correct the assumption of a flat velocity profile, and we have been able to specify the fluid depth at the weir.

The results obtained in this section are restricted to gradually varied flows and negligible viscous effects. Calculations made using these equations should be regarded only as estimates.

Calculation of flow rate

For a value of $H - L = 0.525$ ft, determine the volumetric flow rate per unit width, and the fluid depth on a broad-crested weir.

By Eq. 9.4-13 the volumetric flow rate per unit width is given by

$$q = \sqrt{g}[\tfrac{2}{3}(H - L)]^{3/2} = \sqrt{32.2 \text{ ft/sec}^2}[(\tfrac{2}{3})(0.525 \text{ ft})]^{3/2}$$

or

$$q = 1.17 \text{ ft}^3/\text{ft-sec}$$

Because the flow on the weir will be critical, we may express q as

$$q = v_c h_c = \sqrt{gh_c}h_c = \sqrt{g}[\tfrac{2}{3}(H - L)]^{3/2}$$

and solve for h_c:

$$h_c = \tfrac{2}{3}(H - L) = 0.35 \text{ ft}$$

Experiments described by Doeringsfeld and Barker[8] indicate that for these conditions,

$$q = 1.08 \text{ ft}^3/\text{ft-sec}$$
$$h_c = 0.28 \text{ ft}$$

Thus, the actual flow rate is within 8 per cent of the calculated value, while the measured fluid depth on the weir is 20 per cent smaller than the calculated value. In view of the simplifications made in the analyses, the agreement between measured and calculated flow rates is remarkable.

8. H. A. Doeringsfeld and C. L. Barker, *Trans. A.S.C.E.*, 1941, 106:934–46.

9.5   Hydraulic Jump

A hydraulic jump occurs at a transition from supercritical to subcritical flow. This transition may be brought about by a change in the slope of the channel, such as the jump illustrated in Fig. 9.4-3, or it may occur when a supercritical flow is formed on a mild channel by a sluice gate. This situation is illustrated in Fig. 9.2-4.

In analyzing the hydraulic jump, we will consider the flow shown in Fig. 9.5-1. As shown, it consists of a supercritical flow coming off a steep channel onto a mild channel. On the mild channel, the depth gradually increases and then undergoes a sudden change, which is called an hydraulic jump. We will, in the course of this analysis, show that the jump may be located as indicated here or up on the steep portion of the channel.

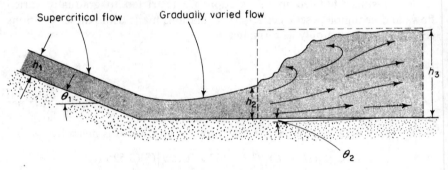

Fig. 9.5-I. Hydraulic jump.

Inasmuch as the hydraulic jump is highly turbulent and energy losses are large, the momentum balance provides the only route to a direct solution. Assuming steady flow and neglecting viscous and gravitational effects, Eq. 9.1-5 reduces to

$$\int_{A_e} \rho v_x \mathbf{v} \cdot \mathbf{n} \, dA = -\int_{\mathscr{A}} \mathbf{i} \cdot \mathbf{n} p_g \, dA \qquad (9.5\text{-}1)$$

when dotted with the unit vector $\mathbf{i}$. The assumption of nearly straight streamlines before and after the jump allows us to express the gauge pressure as

$$p_g = \rho g(h_2 - z), \qquad 0 \le z \le h_2$$
$$p_g = 0, \qquad h_2 < z \le h_3 \qquad (9.5\text{-}2)$$

before the jump, and

$$p_g = \rho g(h_3 - z), \qquad 0 \le z \le h_3 \qquad (9.5\text{-}3)$$

after the jump. Expressing the left-hand side of Eq. 9.5-1 in terms of averages, and evaluating the right-hand side, we get

$$\rho \langle v_x^2 \rangle_3 h_3 - \rho \langle v_x^2 \rangle_2 h_2 = \tfrac{1}{2}\rho g (h_2^2 - h_3^2) \tag{9.5-4}$$

Assuming flat velocity profiles and applying the macroscopic mass balance, we have

$$(h_2 - h_3)\left[(h_2 + h_3) - \frac{2q^2}{gh_2 h_3}\right] = 0 \tag{9.5-5}$$

There are two possible solutions to Eq. 9.5-5; either

$$h_2 = h_3 \tag{9.5-6}$$

or†

$$h_3 = -\frac{h_2}{2} + \sqrt{\frac{h_2^2}{4} + \left(\frac{q^2}{gh_2^3}\right)2h_2^2} \tag{9.5-7}$$

Here we have excluded the negative root for h_3 as physically impossible. It is not difficult to eliminate Eq. 9.5-6 as a possible solution by examining Eq. 9.2-21. For a supercritical flow on a mild channel, the right-hand side of Eq. 9.2-21 will be negative, as will be the term $(1 - N_{\mathrm{Fr}})$. Thus, we conclude that dh/dx is positive and Eq. 9.5-6 is not a possible solution.

Recognizing that q^2/gh_2^3 is the Froude number for the flow prior to the jump, Eq. 9.5-7 reduces to

$$h_3 = -\frac{h_2}{2} + \sqrt{\frac{h_2^2}{4} + 2N_{\mathrm{Fr}}h_2^2} \tag{9.5-8}$$

The nature of the jump depends very strongly on the Froude number of the approaching flow; Fig. 9.5-2 illustrates the four main types of jump. A brief description of these different types of jump is helpful.

1. $N_{\mathrm{Fr}} = 1$ to 3. Standing waves are formed and the jump is called an undular jump. The surface is smooth.
2. $N_{\mathrm{Fr}} = 3$ to 6. Rollers develop on the surface of the jump, but the downstream surface remains smooth. The jump is called a weak jump.
3. $N_{\mathrm{Fr}} = 6$ to 21. The high-speed flow entering the jump forms an unstable jet producing large waves of irregular period. These waves can travel for miles and cause serious damage.
4. $N_{\mathrm{Fr}} = 21$ to 80. The action of this jump is well balanced and the action and position are least sensitive to the downstream depth. The energy dissipation‡ ranges from 45 to 70 per cent.

† Work done by the Bureau of Reclamation (Ref. 9) indicates excellent agreement between Eq. 9.5-7 and experimental observations.
‡ The major effect of an hydraulic jump is the dissipation of kinetic energy.

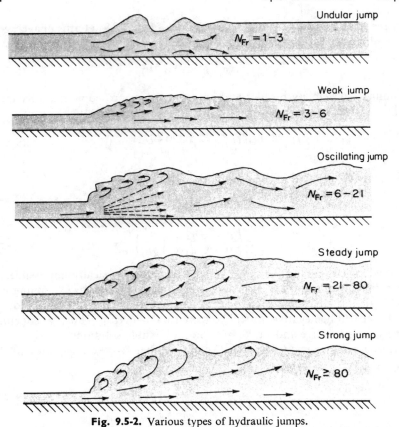

Fig. 9.5-2. Various types of hydraulic jumps.

5. $N_{Fr} \geq 80$. The jump action is rough, and energy dissipation may be as high as 85 per cent. Undesirable waves are formed which travel downstream.

It is important to have some idea how to locate the position of a jump; to outline the method, we shall study a specific example for the flow shown in Fig. 9.5-1.

Location of the hydraulic jump

Let us consider the problem of locating the position of the hydraulic jump shown in Fig. 9.5-1 for the following conditions:

    (a) $\theta_1 = 30°$;
    (b) $\theta_2 = 5'$;
    (c) $q = 20$ ft³/ft-sec;
    (d) channel width $\gg$ fluid depth;
    (e) n $= 0.014$ ft$^{1/6}$.

From Eq. 9.1-17, with $b \gg h$, we obtain the two uniform fluid depths

$$h_1 = 0.45 \text{ ft}$$
$$h_3 = 2.62 \text{ ft}$$

Knowing h_3 and the flow rate, we may rearrange Eq. 9.5-7 and solve for the fluid depth, h_2.

$$h_2 = 2.04 \text{ ft}$$

Obviously, the jump from 2.04 to 2.62 ft is not a strong one, and if we calculate the Froude number just upstream of the jump we find

$$N_{\text{Fr}} = 1.46$$

Under these conditions, we have an undular jump such as the one illustrated in Fig. 9.5-2. The velocity just upstream from the jump is 9.8 ft/sec, and we may think of the standing wave forming the undular jump as having a wave velocity of -9.8 ft/sec.

To determine the location of the jump, we first note that the fluid depth at the start of the mild channel is the same as that in the steep channel, i.e., 0.45 ft. This statement assumes that the change in channel slope gives rise to a gradually varied flow that does not allow disturbances to propagate upstream. Application of Eq. 9.2-51 indicates that the distance from the beginning of the mild channel to the hydraulic jump is 700 ft.

If we decrease the slope of the mild channel from $\theta = 5'$ to $\theta = 3'$, we obtain the conditions,

$$h_1 = 0.45 \text{ ft}$$
$$h_2 = 1.71 \text{ ft}$$
$$h_3 = 3.06 \text{ ft}$$

Obviously the jump is a stronger one, although the Froude number just upstream from the jump ($N_{\text{Fr}} = 2.5$) still indicates an undular jump. For this case, Eq. 9.2-41 indicates that the jump takes place 560 ft from the beginning of the mild channel. Further decreases in the mild channel slope will strengthen the hydraulic jump and move the position of the jump toward the start of the mild channel. When the calculated value of h_2 is 0.45 ft, the jump will occur at the beginning of the mild channel. If the slope of the mild channel is decreased even more, the jump will take place in the steep channel, as Fig. 9.5-3 illustrates. The jump is a good deal more difficult to analyze under these conditions, because it may take place over a region occupied by both the steep and mild channels. In any event, the location of the jump is fairly well established. A detailed experimental study of hydraulic jumps carried out by the Bureau of Reclamation[9] has provided accurate design data.

9. "Hydraulic Design of Stilling Basins and Energy Dissipators," *Engineering Monograph No. 25*, Hydraulics Laboratory Branch, U.S. Bureau of Reclamation, Denver, Colorado, 1958.

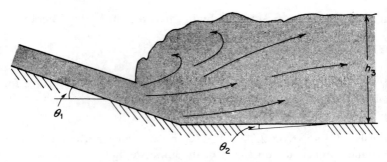

Fig. 9.5-3. Hydraulic jump.

PROBLEMS

9-1. Apply the same type of analysis used in examining the motion of a solitary wave to deduce the surface profile for the depression wave shown in Fig. 9-1. Remember that the disturbance will propagate into the undisturbed region. Comment on the shape of the disturbance as time progresses.

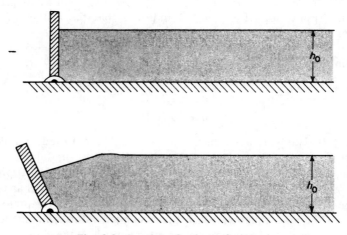

Fig. 9-1. Creation of a depression wave.

9-2. The positive surge, or elevation wave, shown in Fig. 9-2 may be formed in a riverbed by a cloudburst, or in an estuary by a rapidly advancing tidal front. In the laboratory, it can be formed by sudden changes in the position of a sluice gate. The positive surge is often called a moving hydraulic jump. Analyze the flow shown in Fig. 9-2 to obtain an expression for the velocity of the surge in terms of h_1 and h_2.

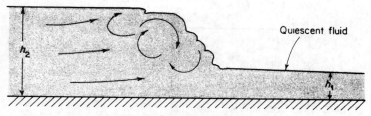

Fig. 9-2. The positive surge.

9-3. Determine the slope of the mild channel in the example in Sec. 9.5 such that the hydraulic jump takes place at the beginning of the mild channel.

Ans: $\theta_2 = 0.5 \times 10^{-4}$ radians

9-4. Apply the momentum balance to the flow illustrated in Fig. 9.3-3 to determine the wave speed in a flowing stream.

9-5. A uniform flow of water takes place in a rectangular channel constructed with evenly laid unplaned timber. If the angle between the channel and the horizontal is 6°, the channel is 10 ft wide, and the water is 2 ft deep, compute the velocity, flow rate, and Froude number.

9-6. The surface roughness and slope (i.e., sin θ) of a rectangular channel are fixed by design considerations; however, the width and depth are not. Calculate the ratio of the fluid depth to channel width, subject to the restriction that the area of flow is 100 ft², that will provide a maximum discharge.

9-7. How deep will the water flow in a 15-ft wide, smooth, concrete, rectangular channel if the slope is 0.001 and the volumetric flow rate is 87 ft³/sec. Determine the wall shear stress, τ_0, and the Froude number.

Ans: $h = 1.3$ ft, $\tau_0 = 0.065$ lb$_f$/ft², $N_{Fr} = 0.48$

9-8. Determine the volumetric flow rate in a 10-ft diameter sewer if the uniform flow depth is 3 ft and the slope is 0.0002.

9-9. Use the mechanical energy balance to derive an expression for the flow through the sluice gate shown in Fig. 9-9 in terms of the fluid depth h_1 and the depth at the gate, h_2. Because the streamlines are not parallel at the gate, a contraction or discharge coefficient must be included in the analysis (indicate clearly why this is so). Show how experimental measurements of the fluid depth h_3 could be used to determine the contraction coefficient.

9-10. The volumetric flow rate in a 10-ft wide channel is 300 ft³/sec. What is the minimum specific energy possible for this flow? What is the critical depth and the critical velocity?

Ans: $E_{sp} = 4.6$ ft, $h_c = 3.0$ ft, $v_2 = 10.0$ ft/sec

9-11. Rederive the differential-macroscopic mass and momentum balances incorporating the effects of a constant seepage into the channel. Express the

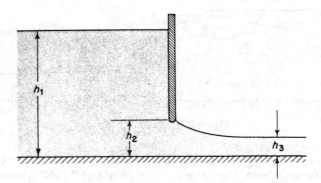

Fig. 9-9. Flow under a sluice gate.

volumetric flow rate into the channel as cubic feet per second per unit length of channel, and assume that the fluid enters the channel normal to the channel walls.

9-12. Perform a numerical integration of Eq. 9.2-47 and compare the results with Eq. 9.2-51 for the following three cases:

  1. $\mathscr{R} = 3.0,$ $H_0 = 2.0$

  2. $\mathscr{R} = 3.0,$ $H_0 = 0.5$

  3. $\mathscr{R} = 0.5,$ $H_0 = 0.1$

9-13. Water, at a velocity of 3 ft/sec and a depth of 2 ft, approaches a smooth rise in a channel as shown in Fig. 9-13. Estimate the depth of the stream after the 3 in. rise.

 Ans: h = 1.7 ft

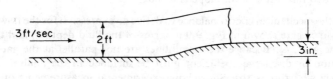

Fig. 9-13. Flow over a rise in a channel.

9-14. Apply the mechanical energy balance, in conjunction with the momentum balance, to an hydraulic jump in a rectangular channel to derive an expression for the energy dissipation. Express the loss as a fraction of the velocity head $v^2/2g$ and Froude number preceding the jump. Examine the derived expression for $N_{Fr} = 1$ and $N_{Fr} \to \infty$.

9-15. Apply the momentum balance to an hydraulic jump in a 90° V-shaped channel to obtain a relationship between the two fluid depths, h_1 and h_2, measured from the bottom of the channel.

9-16. Derive an expression for the horizontal force acting on the sluice gate shown in Fig. 9-9.

9-17. Water in a mild channel flows at a velocity of 0.8 ft/sec and at a depth of 8 ft from a holding basin to an irrigation distributing system 2 mi away. If an adjustment in a sluice gate at the holding basin produces a shallow-water wave, how long will it take for this disturbance to be felt at the distributing system?

   Ans: 10.4 min

9-18. If the amplitude of the wave in Prob. 9-17 is 6 in. and the wave length is 40 ft, estimate the distance it will travel before a pronounced skewness is formed in the initially symmetric wave profile.

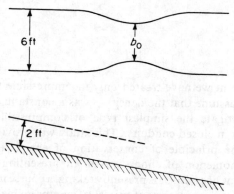

Fig. 9-19. Flow through a constriction.

9-19. A rectangular channel 6 ft wide has a uniform flow depth of 2 ft and a volumetric flow rate of 60 ft³/sec. A constriction occurs in the channel as illustrated in Fig. 9-19, and it may be assumed that inertial effects predominate in changing the surface profile at the constriction. Treat the flow as gradually varied on a mild channel.
   (a) Determine the minimum value of b_0 for which the upstream depth will remain undisturbed.
   (b) Describe the surface profile upstream and downstream from the constriction for values of b_0 greater than, or equal to, the minimum value.
   (c) If b_0 is decreased further than the minimum value, what will happen to the surface both upstream and downstream of the constriction?

Compressible Flow

10

Up to this point we have treated only incompressible flows, or flows for which we could assume that the density ρ was a constant. Our purpose here will be to investigate the simplest type of compressible flow—i.e., one-dimensional flow in closed conduits. This study will provide an introduction to the use of the principle of conservation of energy in fluid mechanics and to the phenomenon of shock waves. In presenting this material, we assume the student has had, or is presently taking, a course in thermodynamics.

Currently, the most important aspect of compressible flow is the supersonic motion of aircraft and missiles; however, this subject requires a more detailed study than we have time for in an introductory text. For a more comprehensive treatment, the student is referred to the two-volume work of Shapiro.[1]

10.1 The Governing Equations for Compressible Flow

In previous chapters the implied equation of state has been

$$\rho = \text{constant} \tag{10.1-1}$$

---

1. A. H. Shapiro, *The Dynamics and Thermodynamics of Compressible Flow*, Vols. 1 and 2 (New York: The Ronald Press Company, 1953).

Now, however, our problem has been expanded, and we must represent the density as a function of temperature and pressure.

$$\rho = \rho(p, T) \tag{10.1-2}$$

Thus, we find temperature as a new variable, and another equation must be introduced, which is, of course, the total energy equation.

Conservation of energy

The fundamental postulate of conservation of energy may be stated in words as

$$
\begin{Bmatrix} \text{the time rate of} \\ \text{change of internal} \\ \text{and kinetic energy} \\ \text{of a body} \end{Bmatrix}
=
\begin{Bmatrix} \text{the rate at which} \\ \text{heat is transferred} \\ \textit{to} \text{ the body} \\ \text{(energy transfer} \\ \text{through a rigid,} \\ \text{diathermal wall)} \end{Bmatrix}
+
\begin{Bmatrix} \text{the rate at which sur-} \\ \text{face work is done } \textit{on} \\ \text{the body (energy} \\ \text{transfer through} \\ \text{a movable} \\ \text{adiabatic wall)} \end{Bmatrix}
\tag{10.1-3}
$$

$$
+
\begin{Bmatrix} \text{the rate at which} \\ \text{work is done } \textit{on} \\ \text{the body by body} \\ \text{forces such as gravity} \end{Bmatrix}
$$

The reference to heat as energy transfer through a rigid, diathermal wall, and work as energy transfer through a movable, adiabatic wall is given to emphasize that heat and work are simply two different modes of energy transfer. We actually deal with "walls" or surfaces which may transfer energy by both mechanisms.

If we integrate Eq. 10.1-3 with respect to time, we obtain a result often written as

$$\Delta(U + KE) = Q - W \tag{10.1-4}$$

where $U =$ internal energy of the body
$KE =$ kinetic energy of the body
$Q =$ heat transferred *to* the body (*by* the surroundings)
$W =$ work done *by* the body (*on* the surroundings)

Equation 10.1-4 represents the first law of thermodynamics† as it applies to *closed systems* (i.e., material volumes). The only difference between the word statement of the principle of conservation of energy given here and the form usually encountered in thermodynamics texts is that work is taken as positive when the surroundings do work on the body. Since energy can be exchanged between the body and the surroundings in two ways (heat and work), it seems natural to retain the same sign convention for both these mechanisms. Thus energy transferred *to* the body is a positive quantity regardless of whether the transfer is accomplished by heat or work.

† Correctly speaking, Eqs. 10.1-4 and 10.1-3 are *definitions* of the internal energy; the *first law of thermodynamics* being that the internal energy is a *state function*.

The mathematical statement of Eq. 10.1-3 is

$$\underbrace{\frac{D}{Dt} \int_{\mathscr{V}_{m}(t)} \rho(e + \tfrac{1}{2}v^2)\, dV}_{\text{(a)}} = -\underbrace{\int_{\mathscr{A}_{m}(t)} \mathbf{q} \cdot \mathbf{n}\, dA}_{\text{(b)}} + \underbrace{\int_{\mathscr{A}_{m}(t)} \mathbf{t}_{(n)} \cdot \mathbf{v}\, dA}_{\text{(c)}} + \underbrace{\int_{\mathscr{V}_{m}(t)} \rho\mathbf{g} \cdot \mathbf{v}\, dV}_{\text{(d)}} \quad (10.1\text{-}5)$$

where e = internal energy per unit mass
$\mathbf{q}$ = heat flux vector

The term (a) in this equation represents the time rate of change of internal and kinetic energy of the material volume $\mathscr{V}_m(t)$—i.e., the *body*. Term (b) represents the heat transferred *to* the body. The negative sign results from the fact that if the heat flux vector is pointing inward toward the body, the quantity $\mathbf{q} \cdot \mathbf{n}$ will be negative. Thus the negative sign in front of the integral is required. In terms of the symbols† used in Eq. 10.1-4,

$$\dot{Q} = -\int_{\mathscr{A}_{m}(t)} \mathbf{q} \cdot \mathbf{n}\, dA \qquad (10.1\text{-}6)$$

Term (c) in Eq. 10.1-5 represents the rate at which work is done on the body by surface forces. Term (d) in Eq. 10.1-5 represents the rate at which work is done by the force of gravity. We will show shortly that this term can be represented as the material derivative of the potential energy of the body, thereby allowing us to include it on the left-hand side of Eq. 10.1-5. This form of the energy equation may have been encountered in thermodynamics texts where it would be written as

$$\Delta(U + KE + PE) = Q - W' \qquad (10.1\text{-}7)$$

Here W' represents only the work done by surface forces.

If we make use of the special form of the Reynolds transport theorem derived in Chap. 3,

$$\frac{D}{Dt} \int_{\mathscr{V}_{m}(t)} \rho \mathcal{S}\, dV = \int_{\mathscr{V}_{m}(t)} \rho\, \frac{D\mathcal{S}}{Dt}\, dV$$

and express the stress vector as

$$\mathbf{t}_{(n)} = \mathbf{n} \cdot \mathbf{T}$$

Eq. 10.1-5 may be written as

$$\int_{\mathscr{V}_{m}(t)} \rho\, \frac{D}{Dt}(e + \tfrac{1}{2}v^2)\, dV = -\int_{\mathscr{A}_{m}(t)} \mathbf{q} \cdot \mathbf{n}\, dA + \int_{\mathscr{V}_{m}(t)} \rho\mathbf{g} \cdot \mathbf{v}\, dV + \int_{\mathscr{A}_{m}(t)} (\mathbf{n} \cdot \mathbf{T}) \cdot \mathbf{v}\, dA$$

$$(10.1\text{-}8)$$

† As usual, the dot over Q indicates a time derivative.

Applying the divergence theorem to the second and fourth integrals allows us to put all the terms under one integral sign and extract the differential equation.

$$\rho \frac{D}{Dt}(e + \tfrac{1}{2}v^2) = -\nabla \cdot \mathbf{q} + \rho \mathbf{g} \cdot \mathbf{v} + \nabla \cdot (\mathbf{T} \cdot \mathbf{v}) \tag{10.1-9}$$

Expressing $\mathbf{g}$ as $-\nabla \phi$, we may write

$$\rho \mathbf{g} \cdot \mathbf{v} = -\rho \mathbf{v} \cdot \nabla \phi \tag{10.1-10}$$

Remembering the formula for the material derivative, we write

$$\frac{D\phi}{Dt} = \frac{\partial \phi}{\partial t} + \mathbf{v} \cdot \nabla \phi \tag{10.1-11}$$

Since the gravitational potential ϕ is independent of time, $\partial \phi / \partial t = 0$ and we may combine Eqs. 10.1-11 and 10.1-10·to obtain

$$\rho \mathbf{g} \cdot \mathbf{v} = -\rho \frac{D\phi}{Dt} \tag{10.1-12}$$

Substitution of this result into Eq. 10.1-9 yields the differential energy equation in terms of internal, kinetic, and potential energy.

Time rate of change of internal, kinetic and potential energy per unit volume	Rate of heat transfer per unit volume	Rate of surface work per unit volume

$$\rho \frac{D}{Dt}(e + \tfrac{1}{2}v^2 + \phi) = -\nabla \cdot \mathbf{q} + \nabla \cdot (\mathbf{T} \cdot \mathbf{v}) \tag{10.1-13}$$

We will refer to this result as the *total energy equation*. In Sec. 10.2, we will show how the *thermal energy equation* may be derived by subtracting the *mechanical energy equation* from Eq. 10.1-13.

In the analysis of compressible flows, the total energy equation is the most useful form of the principle of conservation of energy. In this brief introduction to compressible flow, we will only use the macroscopic total energy balance, and Eq. 10.1-13 must be integrated. The integration is complicated by the presence of the density ρ outside the material derivative; we must remedy this difficulty before proceeding. Letting Ω represent the total energy per unit mass,

$$\Omega = e + \tfrac{1}{2}v^2 + \phi \tag{10.1-14}$$

and expanding the material derivative in Eq. 10.1-13, we get

$$\rho \frac{\partial \Omega}{\partial t} + \rho \mathbf{v} \cdot \nabla \Omega = -\nabla \cdot \mathbf{q} + \nabla \cdot (\mathbf{T} \cdot \mathbf{v}) \tag{10.1-15}$$

Noting that $\Omega\,[(\partial\rho/\partial t) + \boldsymbol{\nabla}\cdot\rho\mathbf{v}]$ is zero by the continuity equation, we may add this term to the left-hand side of Eq. 10.1-15 to obtain a form suitable for integration.

$$\frac{\partial}{\partial t}(\rho\Omega) + \boldsymbol{\nabla}\cdot(\rho\mathbf{v}\Omega) = -\boldsymbol{\nabla}\cdot\mathbf{q} + \boldsymbol{\nabla}\cdot(\mathbf{T}\cdot\mathbf{v}) \qquad (10.1\text{-}16)$$

Carrying out the integration over the arbitrary moving volume $\mathscr{V}_a(t)$, and applying the divergence theorem to the second, third, and fourth integrals, we get

$$\int_{\mathscr{V}_a(t)}\frac{\partial}{\partial t}(\rho\Omega)\,dV + \int_{\mathscr{A}_a(t)}(\rho\mathbf{v}\Omega)\cdot\mathbf{n}\,dA = -\int_{\mathscr{A}_a(t)}\mathbf{q}\cdot\mathbf{n}\,dA + \int_{\mathscr{A}_a(t)}\mathbf{t}_{(n)}\cdot\mathbf{v}\,dA \quad (10.1\text{-}17)$$

Applying the general transport theorem, and noting that the convective energy flux term will be zero except over the area $A_e(t)$, we obtain the macroscopic total energy balance

$$\frac{d}{dt}\int_{\mathscr{V}_a(t)}\rho\Omega\,dV + \int_{A_e(t)}\rho\Omega(\mathbf{v}-\mathbf{w})\cdot\mathbf{n}\,dA = -\int_{\mathscr{A}_a(t)}\mathbf{q}\cdot\mathbf{n}\,dA + \int_{\mathscr{A}_a(t)}\mathbf{t}_{(n)}\cdot\mathbf{v}\,dA \quad (10.1\text{-}18)$$

Splitting the rate of work term into area integrals† over $A_s(t)$ and $A_e(t)$ allows us to write

$$\frac{d}{dt}\int_{\mathscr{V}_a(t)}\rho\Omega\,dV + \int_{A_e(t)}\rho\Omega(\mathbf{v}-\mathbf{w})\cdot\mathbf{n}\,dA = -\int_{\mathscr{A}_a(t)}\mathbf{q}\cdot\mathbf{n}\,dA + \dot{W} + \int_{A_e(t)}\mathbf{t}_{(n)}\cdot\mathbf{v}\,dA$$

$$(10.1\text{-}19)$$

Note that the term $\dot{W}$ used throughout this text always refers to the rate of work done *on* the system *by* solid moving surfaces. In thermodynamics texts, this concept is often referred to as the *useful work*, while the work done on the system at the entrance and exits (the last term in Eq. 10.1-19) is referred to as the *flow work*.

While Eq. 10.1-19 is a completely general form of the macroscopic total energy balance, we shall generally restrict ourselves in this chapter to fixed control surfaces at entrances and exits and steady state conditions. Under these conditions, Eq. 10.1-19 reduces to

$$\int_{A_e}\rho\Omega\mathbf{v}\cdot\mathbf{n}\,dA = -\int_{\mathscr{A}}\mathbf{q}\cdot\mathbf{n}\,dA + \dot{W} + \int_{A_e}\mathbf{t}_{(n)}\cdot\mathbf{v}\,dA \qquad \begin{array}{l}\text{for fixed control surfaces}\\ \text{at entrances and exits and}\\ \text{steady state conditions}\end{array}$$

$$(10.1\text{-}20)$$

It will be to our advantage to express this result in terms of the enthalpy per unit mass

$$h = e + \frac{p}{\rho} \qquad (19.1\text{-}21)$$

† This integral is zero over the fixed solid surface, A_s.

Adding and subtracting p/ρ from Ω yields

$$\int_{A_e} \rho\left(h + \tfrac{1}{2}v^2 + \phi - \frac{p}{\rho}\right)\mathbf{v} \cdot \mathbf{n}\, dA = \dot{Q} + \dot{W} + \int_{A_e} \mathbf{t}_{(n)} \cdot \mathbf{v}\, dA \qquad (10.1\text{-}22)$$

where the integral representing the rate of heat transfer to the system has been replaced by $\dot{Q}$.

As we have noted in several previous examples, the stress at entrances and exits may be approximated by

$$\mathbf{t}_{(n)} = -\mathbf{n}p \qquad (10.1\text{-}23)$$

Substitution of this expression for the stress vector into Eq. 10.1-22 leads to a cancellation of terms and we obtain

$$\int_{A_e} \rho(h + \tfrac{1}{2}v^2 + \phi)\mathbf{v} \cdot \mathbf{n}\, dA = \dot{Q} + \dot{W} \qquad (10.1\text{-}24)$$

If we neglect variations of h, v^2, and ϕ across the entrances and exits and restrict ourselves to a system having one entrance and one exit, we may write Eq. 10.1-24 as

$$\Delta(h + \tfrac{1}{2}v^2 + \phi) = \frac{\dot{Q} + \dot{W}}{\dot{m}} \qquad (10.1\text{-}25)$$

where $\dot{m}$ is the mass flow rate, and Δ indicates the difference between the exit conditions (where $\mathbf{v} \cdot \mathbf{n}$ is positive) and the entrance conditions (where $\mathbf{v} \cdot \mathbf{n}$ is negative).

With the mass, momentum, and energy balances at our disposal, we are ready to analyze the propagation of a weak sonic disturbance (a sound wave) and begin our investigation of compressible flows. However, before doing so, we should tie up some loose ends regarding the viscous dissipation term encountered in the derivation of the mechanical energy equation. In the next section, therefore, we will derive the thermal energy equation to show that the viscous dissipation does indeed appear as thermal energy.

10.2 The Thermal Energy Equation and the Entropy Equation

Our objective in this section is to put the total, thermal, and mechanical energy equations in proper perspective, and to derive the entropy equation. We start the analysis with the total energy equation,

$$\rho\frac{D}{Dt}(e + \tfrac{1}{2}v^2) = -\boldsymbol{\nabla} \cdot \mathbf{q} + \rho\mathbf{g} \cdot \mathbf{v} + \boldsymbol{\nabla} \cdot (\mathbf{T} \cdot \mathbf{v}) \qquad \text{total energy equation} \quad (10.2\text{-}1)$$

the stress equation of motion,

$$\rho \frac{D\mathbf{v}}{Dt} = \rho\mathbf{g} + \mathbf{\nabla} \cdot \mathbf{T} \tag{10.2-2}$$

and the continuity equation

$$\frac{\partial \rho}{\partial t} + \mathbf{\nabla} \cdot (\rho\mathbf{v}) = 0 \tag{10.2-3}$$

Forming the scalar product of Eq. 10.2-2 with the velocity **v** yields†

$$\rho \frac{D}{Dt}(\tfrac{1}{2}v^2) = \rho\mathbf{g} \cdot \mathbf{v} + \mathbf{v} \cdot (\mathbf{\nabla} \cdot \mathbf{T}) \tag{10.2-4}$$

The last term on the right-hand side may be expressed as‡

$$\mathbf{v} \cdot (\mathbf{\nabla} \cdot \mathbf{T}) = \mathbf{\nabla} \cdot (\mathbf{T} \cdot \mathbf{v}) - \mathbf{\nabla}\mathbf{v} : \mathbf{T} \tag{10.2-5}$$

Substitution of this expression into Eq. 10.2-4 yields the mechanical energy equation for compressible flow:

$$\rho \frac{D}{Dt}(\tfrac{1}{2}v^2) = \rho\mathbf{g} \cdot \mathbf{v} + \mathbf{\nabla} \cdot (\mathbf{T} \cdot \mathbf{v}) - \mathbf{\nabla}\mathbf{v} : \mathbf{T} \qquad \text{mechanical energy equation} \tag{10.2-6}$$

Subtracting this result from the total energy equation yields the thermal energy equation:

$$\rho \frac{De}{Dt} = -\mathbf{\nabla} \cdot \mathbf{q} + \mathbf{\nabla}\mathbf{v} : \mathbf{T} \qquad \text{thermal energy equation} \tag{10.2-7}$$

If we write the total stress tensor as

$$\mathbf{T} = -p\mathbf{I} + \boldsymbol{\tau}$$

the last term on the right-hand side of Eq. 10.2-7 may be expressed as§

$$\mathbf{\nabla}\mathbf{v} : \mathbf{T} = -p\mathbf{\nabla} \cdot \mathbf{v} + \Phi \tag{10.2-8}$$

Our general form of the thermal energy equation for compressible flow is now written as

$$\rho \frac{De}{Dt} = -\mathbf{\nabla} \cdot \mathbf{q} - p\mathbf{\nabla} \cdot \mathbf{v} + \Phi \tag{10.2-9}$$

Thus, viscous dissipation always gives rise to an increase in the internal energy and, therefore, the temperature of the fluid.

The thermal energy equation is most convenient to use when heat is being transferred to or from the system, and we wish to know inlet and outlet

† See Eqs. 7.3-2, 7.3-3, and 7.3-4.
‡ See Eqs. 7.3-9 through 7.3-12.
§ See Eqs. 7.3-13 through 7.3-17.

temperatures, or temperature profiles and heat fluxes. This equation is studied in detail in courses in heat transfer.

The total energy equation is generally used when significant changes in temperature *and* kinetic energy are taking place—the common situation, of course, for compressible flows.

We must be careful to remember that the mechanical energy equation is derived from the laws of mechanics, and that the total and thermal energy equations are two *distinct* equations. The fact that the total energy equation, under special restrictions, can degenerate into both the thermal energy equation and the mechanical energy equation, has led to some confusion regarding the role of the fundamental energy postulate in fluid mechanics.

Entropy equation

In the next two sections, we will be dealing with *isentropic* (constant entropy) *processes*. It is therefore important to derive the entropy equation so that we know what we mean by this term. Starting with the statement that the internal energy may be specified in terms of the entropy and density

$$e = e(s, \rho) \tag{10.2-10}$$

we may take the material derivative of e to obtain

$$\frac{De}{Dt} = \left(\frac{\partial e}{\partial s}\right)_\rho \frac{Ds}{Dt} + \left(\frac{\partial e}{\partial \rho}\right)_s \frac{D\rho}{Dt} = T \frac{Ds}{Dt} + \frac{p}{\rho^2} \frac{D\rho}{Dt} \tag{10.2-11}$$

Multiplying this equation by ρ yields

$$\rho \frac{De}{Dt} = T\rho \frac{Ds}{Dt} + \frac{p}{\rho} \frac{D\rho}{Dt} \tag{10.2-12}$$

Remembering now that the continuity equation may be written in the form†

$$\frac{D\rho}{Dt} + \rho \nabla \cdot \mathbf{v} = 0 \tag{10.2-13}$$

we may write Eq. 10.2-12 as

$$\rho \frac{De}{Dt} = T\rho \frac{Ds}{Dt} - p\nabla \cdot \mathbf{v} \tag{10.2-14}$$

Substitution of $\rho De/Dt$ from Eq. 10.2-9 and rearrangement give an expression for the rate of change of entropy

$$\rho \frac{Ds}{Dt} = \frac{1}{T} (-\nabla \cdot \mathbf{q} + \Phi) \tag{10.2-15}$$

† See Eq. 3.5-7.

We now wish to determine the time rate of change of the entropy of a material volume. Rearranging the right-hand side of Eq. 10.2-15 and forming the integral, we obtain

$$\int_{\mathscr{V}_m(t)} \rho \frac{Ds}{Dt}\, dV = -\int_{\mathscr{V}_m(t)} \boldsymbol{\nabla} \cdot \left(\frac{\mathbf{q}}{T}\right) dV + \int_{\mathscr{V}_m(t)} \left(\frac{-\mathbf{q}\cdot\boldsymbol{\nabla}T}{T^2} + \frac{\Phi}{T}\right) dV \quad (10.2\text{-}16)$$

Using the special form of the Reynolds transport theorem given by Eq. 3.5-12, and applying the divergence theorem to the first integral on the right-hand side, we have an expression for the rate of change of entropy.

$$\frac{D}{Dt}\int_{\mathscr{V}_m(t)} \rho s\, dV = -\int_{\mathscr{A}_m(t)} \frac{\mathbf{q}\cdot\mathbf{n}}{T}\, dA + \int_{\mathscr{V}_m(t)} \left(\frac{-\mathbf{q}\cdot\boldsymbol{\nabla}T}{T^2} + \frac{\Phi}{T}\right) dV \quad (10.2\text{-}17)$$

If a process is to be isentropic, the entropy of a body or of a material volume involved in the process must be constant† therefore,

$$\frac{D}{Dt}\int_{\mathscr{V}_m(t)} \rho s\, dV = 0, \qquad \text{for an isentropic process} \qquad (10.2\text{-}18)$$

This condition can be satisfied as follows:

1. $\mathbf{q}\cdot\mathbf{n} = 0$ on the surface, i.e., the process is adiabatic;
2. $\boldsymbol{\nabla}T = 0$ everywhere in the system, i.e., the process is "reversible";
3. $\Phi = 0$ everywhere in the system, i.e., "frictional" effects are negligible.

In analyzing the speed of sound in Sec. 10.3 and flow in nozzles in Sec. 10.4, we will assume that the processes are isentropic even though viscous dissipation cannot be identically zero and the temperature gradients are definitely finite. This assumption of isentropy greatly reduces the extent of the analysis while still allowing us to investigate the key features of the flow.

10.3 The Speed of Sound

We will determine the velocity of sound by analyzing the density variations that occur when a small disturbance is created at the end of a tube, such as that shown in Fig. 10.3-1. This process is comparable to what might happen if the closed end of a cylindrical tube were hit with a mallet. If the flow were incompressible, the density would be ρ_0 throughout the tube and the velocity would everywhere be equal to the velocity of the piston at the end of the tube. Since the flow is compressible, the density may increase above the value ρ_0;

† Strictly speaking this is a sufficient but not a necessary condition.

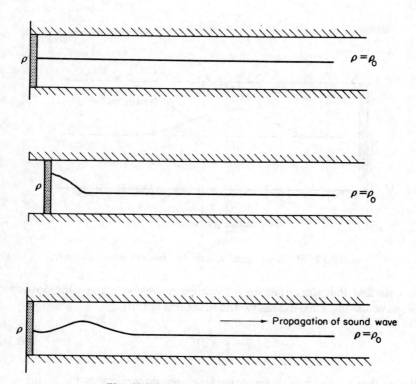

Fig. 10.3-1. Generation of a sound wave.

thus, the fluid far from the piston is initially undisturbed. Illustrative density profiles are indicated above the tube for each step of the process. The curves are comparable to the surface profiles for open channel wave formation shown in Fig. 9.3-1, and in what follows we shall see that the analysis of these two different wave propagation phenomena is similar.

We will analyze this problem in terms of the macroscopic mass and momentum balances, and because the variable of interest ρ (or p) changes in the x-direction, we must make the macroscopic balances differential in the x-direction. Figure 10.3-2 illustrates the differential control volume to be used. We assume that the speed of the density variation (or sound wave) is a constant given by c; thus the control volume moves with the sound wave.

Mass balance

Starting with the general macroscopic mass balance,

$$\frac{d}{dt}\int_{\mathscr{V}_a(t)} \rho \, dV + \int_{A_e(t)} \rho(\mathbf{v} - \mathbf{w}) \cdot \mathbf{n} \, dA = 0 \tag{10.3-1}$$

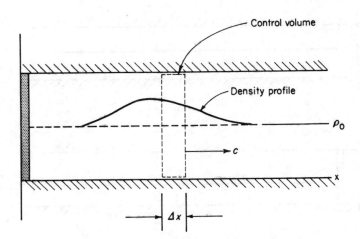

Fig. 10.3-2. Moving control volume for analysis of sound wave.

we note first that since the control volume moves with a specific portion of the wave having a fixed density, the first term is zero.

$$\frac{d}{dt} \int_{\mathcal{V}_a(t)} \rho \, dV = 0 \tag{10.3-2}$$

We see that $\mathbf{i} \cdot \mathbf{w} = c$, and the remaining area integral takes the form

$$\int_{A_e(t)} \rho(v_x - c) \, dA \bigg|_{x+\Delta x} - \int_{A_e(t)} \rho(v_x - c) \, dA \bigg|_x = 0 \tag{10.3-3}$$

While the wave velocity c may be quite large, the actual fluid velocity v_x will be small. Viscous effects may be neglected,† and the velocity profile may be assumed to be flat. Under these conditions, we may divide Eq. 10.3-3 by Δx and take the limit $\Delta x \to 0$ to obtain

$$\frac{d}{dx} [\rho(v_x - c)A] = 0 \tag{10.3-4}$$

which may be rearranged in two convenient forms,

$$\rho(v_x - c)A = \text{constant} \tag{10.3-5a}$$

$$\rho \frac{d}{dx} [(v_x - c)A] + (v_x - c)A \frac{d\rho}{dx} = 0 \tag{10.3-5b}$$

† This is an experimental observation. An analytical proof would be difficult.

Momentum balance

We start with the general momentum balance,

$$\frac{d}{dt}\int_{\mathscr{V}_a(t)} \rho\mathbf{v}\, dV + \int_{A_e(t)} \rho\mathbf{v}(\mathbf{v}-\mathbf{w})\cdot\mathbf{n}\, dA = \int_{\mathscr{V}_a(t)} \rho\mathbf{g}\, dV + \int_{\mathscr{A}_a(t)} \mathbf{t}_{(n)}\, dA \qquad (10.3\text{-}6)$$

and note that the momentum of the control volume is constant. We form the scalar product with $\mathbf{i}$ to obtain

$$\int_{A_e(t)} \rho v_x(\mathbf{v}-\mathbf{w})\cdot\mathbf{n}\, dA = \int_{\mathscr{A}_a(t)} \mathbf{i}\cdot\mathbf{t}_{(n)}\, dA \qquad (10.3\text{-}7)$$

Remembering that viscous effects are being neglected and $\mathbf{i}\cdot\mathbf{w} = c$, we apply Eq. 10.3-7 to the moving control volume in Fig. 10.3-2 and obtain

$$\int_{A_e(t)} \rho v_x(v_x - c)\, dA\bigg|_{x+\Delta x} - \int_{A_e(t)} \rho v_x(v_x - c)\, dA\bigg|_{x} = -\int_{A_e(t)} p\, dA\bigg|_{x+\Delta x} + \int_{A_e(t)} p\, dA\bigg|_{x}$$

$$(10.3\text{-}8)$$

Again assuming flat velocity profiles, dividing by Δx, and taking the limit $\Delta x \to 0$, we obtain

$$\frac{d}{dx}\big[\rho v_x(v_x - c)A\big] = -\left(\frac{dp}{dx}\right)A \qquad (10.3\text{-}9)$$

Using Eq. 10.3-5a allows us to simplify this result to

$$\rho(v_x - c)A\left(\frac{dv_x}{dx}\right) = -\left(\frac{dp}{dx}\right)A \qquad (10.3\text{-}10)$$

Taking the cross-sectional area A to be constant, we may use Eq. 10.3-5b to eliminate dv_x/dx from Eq. 10.3-10 and obtain

$$(v_x - c)^2\left(\frac{d\rho}{dx}\right) = \left(\frac{dp}{dx}\right) \qquad (10.3\text{-}11)$$

Solving for c gives

$$c = v_x \pm \sqrt{\frac{dp}{d\rho}} \qquad (10.3\text{-}12)$$

and, provided $v_x \ll \sqrt{dp/d\rho}$, our expression for the velocity of sound reduces to

$$c = \pm\sqrt{\frac{dp}{d\rho}} \qquad (10.3\text{-}13)$$

Note that the analysis indicates that the wave may propagate in either direction; however, we know intuitively that it will move from left to right as Fig. 10.3-2 indicates. A rigorous proof of this fact involves extensive analysis. Such a study has been carried out by Stoker[2] indicating that a disturbance always propagates into the "region of quiet."

If the process is adiabatic and reversible, the entropy, s, will be constant (i.e., the process is isentropic), and Eq. 10.3-13 is written as

$$c = \sqrt{\left(\frac{\partial p}{\partial \rho}\right)_s} = \{\text{the speed of sound}\} \qquad (10.3\text{-}14)$$

For air at atmospheric pressure and normal temperatures, Eq. 10.3-14 indicates that the speed of sound is about 1100 ft/sec. Our definition of a "weak disturbance" will be that v_x (in Eq. 10.3-12) is much smaller than the speed of sound. In the process under consideration, we may assume that the fluid velocity v_x is equal to, or less than, the velocity of the piston; our analysis will therefore be correct provided the velocity of the piston is much less than the speed of sound.

For a perfect gas, the pressure and density in an isentropic process are related by

$$\frac{p}{\rho^\gamma} = \text{constant} \qquad (10.3\text{-}15)$$

where $\gamma = c_p/c_v$, the ratio of specific heats. The equation of state for a perfect gas is generally expressed as

$$pV = n\mathscr{R}T \qquad (10.3\text{-}16)$$

where $\mathscr{R}$ is the universal gas constant and equal to 82.06 atm–cm^3/g-mole °K, and n is the number of moles. This form is generally encountered in thermodynamics texts where the quantity of material is specified in terms of the number of moles. In fluid mechanics, the mass is a more useful measure of the quantity of material contained in a system, and Eq. 10.3-16 is written in the form

$$pV = mRT \qquad (10.3\text{-}17)$$

where

$$R = \frac{\mathscr{R}}{\text{molecular weight}}$$

An even more convenient form results from dividing by V to yield

$$p = \rho RT \qquad (10.3\text{-}18)$$

Here we must remember that R is different for every gas. By differentiating Eq. 10.3-15 with respect to ρ, using Eq. 10.3-18 to eliminate p, and substituting the result into Eq. 10.3-14, we can express the velocity of sound as

$$c = \sqrt{\gamma RT} \qquad (10.3\text{-}19)$$

Values of R and γ for some common gases are listed in Table 10.3-1.

2. J. J. Stoker, *Water Waves* (New York: Interscience Publishers, Inc., 1957), p. 303.

Table 10.3-1

GAS CONSTANT R AND RATIO OF SPECIFIC HEATS γ FOR
SOME COMMON GASES

Gas	R, ft-lb$_f$/lb$_m$-°R	γ, standard conditions
Hydrogen, H_2	766.5	1.41
Helium, He	386.3	1.67
Nitrogen, N_2	55.15	1.40
Oxygen, O_2	48.29	1.39
Carbon dioxide, CO_2	35.12	1.29
Air	53.35	1.40
Water vapor, H_2O	85.8	1.33

This analysis has introduced us to the velocity of sound, a key parameter in the analysis of compressible flow. If the fluid velocity is much less than the velocity of sound, compressibility effects are *usually*† small, while fluid velocities comparable to, or greater than, the speed of sound lead to some unusual situations where the compressibility effects dominate the flow. Therefore, the ratio M of the fluid velocity to the speed of sound is an important measure of the compressibility effects; we call it the Mach number after the physicist, Ernest Mach.[3]

$$M = \frac{v}{c} \qquad (10.3\text{-}20)$$

The common designation of the flow regimes associated with various values of the Mach number are as follows:

$M \ll 1$,   incompressible flow

$\frac{1}{2} < M < 1$,   subsonic flow

$M \approx 1$,   transonic flow

$M > 1$,   supersonic flow

Because the velocity of sound in liquids is approximately 5000 ft/sec (3400 mph), compressibility effects are rarely of importance in liquids, and the treatment of compressible flows is generally restricted to gases.

† Remember that the circulation velocities occurring in a heated pan of water are small compared to the speed of sound.

3. H. Rouse and S. Ince, *History of Hydraulics* (New York: Dover Publications, Inc., 1963), p. 195.

Speed of sound in helium and air

We wish to compare the speed of sound in air and in helium at 72°F. For air, Eq. 10.3-19 gives

$$c_{\text{air}} = \left[(1.40) \left(\frac{53.35 \text{ ft-lb}_f}{\text{lb}_m\text{-}°R} \right) (532°R) \left(\frac{32.2 \text{ lb}_m\text{-ft}}{\text{lb}_f\text{-sec}^2} \right) \right]^{1/2}$$
$$= 1130 \text{ ft/sec}$$

Similarly, the velocity of sound in helium is calculated to be

$$c_{\text{He}} = 3330 \text{ ft/sec}$$

Thus, the velocity of sound in helium is approximately three times as large as that in air. This difference gives a curious quality to the voice if one speaks with a lung full of helium.

10.4 Isentropic Nozzle Flow

The simplest example of compressible flow is the isentropic flow from a large reservoir through a converging nozzle, such as that shown in Fig. 10.4-1. The assumption of constant entropy requires that the process be

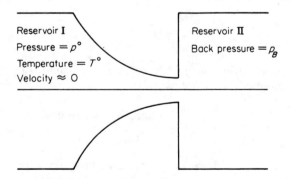

Fig. 10.4-1. Isentropic flow through a nozzle.

adiabatic, and that $\mathbf{q} \cdot \nabla T$ and Φ be negligible. The assumption of adiabatic flow is reasonable, and we may neglect viscous dissipation for flow in a nozzle without incurring much error. Because fairly large temperature changes take place in the nozzle, the assumption that $\mathbf{q} \cdot \nabla T$ is negligible must be based on the fact that the thermal conductivity of gases is small. Therefore,

$$\mathbf{q} = -k\nabla T \approx 0$$

Although our analysis in this section will be directed toward understanding the flow in a nozzle, the derived equations will be generally applicable to isentropic flows in ducts of variable cross-sectional area. It will be especially important to note precisely where the isentropic restriction is imposed, for

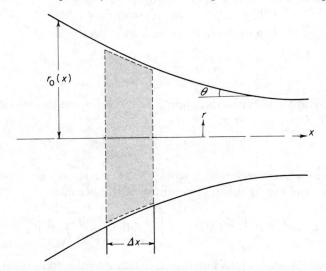

Fig. 10.4-2. Control volume for analysis of nozzle flow.

we will remove this restriction in our analysis of shock waves in Sec. 10.5. We shall now discuss the form that the governing equations take when applied to the differential control volume shown in Fig. 10.4-2.

Mass balance

Application of Eq. 10.3-1 to the differential control volume yields†

$$\frac{d}{dx}\left(\rho\langle v_x\rangle A\right) = 0 \tag{10.4-1a}$$

or

$$\rho\langle v_x\rangle A = \text{constant} \tag{10.4-1b}$$

Momentum balance

Starting with Eq. 10.3-6, we form the scalar product with $\mathbf{i}$ to obtain

$$\int_{A_e} \rho v_x^2\, dA\bigg|_{x+\Delta x} - \int_{A_e} \rho v_x^2\, dA\bigg|_{x} = \int_{\mathscr{A}} \mathbf{i}\cdot\mathbf{t}_{(n)}\, dA \tag{10.4-2}$$

† Here we have assumed that the density is constant at any given cross section of the nozzle.

In evaluating the term on the right-hand side of Eq. 10.4-2, we must remember that the outwardly directed unit normal **n** from the control volume is given by

$$\mathbf{i} \cdot \mathbf{n} = \pm 1, \qquad \text{at the entrance and exit}$$
$$\mathbf{i} \cdot \mathbf{n} = \sin \theta, \qquad \text{at the walls of the nozzle}$$

where

$$\theta = \tan^{-1}\left(-\frac{dr_0}{dx}\right)$$

To keep the analysis reasonably simple, we must impose the restriction that $dr_0/dx \ll 1$, so we may write

$$\sin \theta \approx \tan \theta = -\frac{dr_0}{dx} \tag{10.4-3}$$

Inasmuch as we are neglecting viscous effects, the stress vector is given by $\mathbf{t}_{(n)} = -\mathbf{n}p$, and the right-hand side of Eq. 10.4-2 becomes

$$\int_{\mathscr{A}} \mathbf{i} \cdot \mathbf{t}_{(n)}\, dA = -\int_{A_e} p\, dA\big|_{x+\Delta x} + \int_{A_e} p\, dA\big|_x + \left(\frac{dr_0}{dx}\right)\Delta x \int_S p\, ds \tag{10.4-4}$$

Substituting Eq. 10.4-4 into Eq. 10.4-2, dividing by Δx and taking the limit $\Delta x \to 0$, we obtain

$$\frac{d}{dx}\left(\rho\langle v_x^2\rangle A\right) = -\frac{d}{dx}\left(\langle p\rangle A\right) + 2\pi r_0\left(\frac{dr_0}{dx}\right)\bar{p} \tag{10.4-5}$$

Here $\bar{p}$ represents the mean pressure over the bounding circular strip of the control volume. If we now assume flat velocity profiles and a uniform pressure across the duct (i.e., $\langle p\rangle = \bar{p} = p$), this result reduces to

$$\frac{d}{dx}\left(\rho\langle v_x\rangle^2 A\right) = -A\left(\frac{dp}{dx}\right) \tag{10.4-6}$$

which we may simplify further by using Eq. 10.4-1b,

$$\rho\langle v_x\rangle \frac{d\langle v_x\rangle}{dx} = -\left(\frac{dp}{dx}\right) \tag{10.4-7}$$

Energy balance

We begin with the simplified form of the energy balance given by Eq. 10.1-24, and note that $\dot{W} = \dot{Q} = 0$ to obtain

$$\int_{A_e} \rho(h + \tfrac{1}{2}v^2 + \phi)\mathbf{v} \cdot \mathbf{n}\, dA = 0 \tag{10.4-8}$$

Provided the velocity profile is essentially flat and the enthalpy does not vary across the duct, Eq. 10.4-8 quickly reduces to

$$h + \tfrac{1}{2}\langle v_x \rangle^2 = \text{constant} \tag{10.4-9}$$

The assumption that $\langle v^2 \rangle = \langle v_x \rangle^2$ is reasonable in light of the restriction that $dr_0/dx \ll 1$. Further restriction of the analysis to gases for which the enthalpy is a linear function of temperature allows us to write

$$h = c_p T + \text{constant} \tag{10.4-10}$$

and Eq. 10.4-9 becomes

$$c_p T + \tfrac{1}{2}\langle v_x \rangle^2 = \text{constant} \tag{10.4-11}$$

The constant may be evaluated by applying this result to reservoir 1 where $\langle v_x \rangle = 0$ and $T = T^\circ$, which gives

$$c_p T + \tfrac{1}{2}\langle v_x \rangle^2 = c_p T^\circ \tag{10.4-12}$$

where T° is called the *stagnation temperature*. The use of "∘" as a superscript is unusual and is done to clearly designate T° as the stagnation temperature and not the temperature at point "∘." The stagnation temperature and pressure are the temperature and pressure that a fluid particle would attain if it were isentropically brought to rest. In the analysis of compressible flows, it is often convenient to specify local conditions in terms of the stagnation temperature and pressure and the Mach number; thus T° and p° are especially important quantities.

We now have at our disposal the mass, momentum, and energy equations along with the equation of state for a perfect gas, $p = \rho RT$. We may now solve for the four unknowns $(T, p, \rho, \langle v_x \rangle)$. Noting that

$$c_p = \frac{\gamma R}{\gamma - 1} \tag{10.4-13}$$

and

$$\langle v_x \rangle^2 = M^2 \gamma RT \tag{10.4-14}$$

Equation 10.4-12 can be used to express the local temperature as a function of the local Mach number and the stagnation temperature.

$$T = T^\circ \left(1 + \frac{\gamma - 1}{2} M^2 \right)^{-1} \tag{10.4-15}$$

Three assumptions led to this result: enthalpy is a linear function of temperature; the equation of state for the gas can be approximated by the perfect gas law; and the flow is one-dimensional. Thus, the restriction to isentropic flow has not yet been imposed.

Since $\gamma > 1.0$, Eq. 10.4-15 indicates that the temperature decreases as the velocity (and therefore the Mach number) increases. Intuitively we think of this conversion as one of thermal energy to kinetic energy.

Our next step in the analysis requires the restriction of isentropic flows. By a straightforward analysis, we can show that the temperature and pressure in an isentropic process are related by

$$\frac{p}{T^{\gamma/\gamma-1}} = \text{constant} \tag{10.4-16}$$

and we may use this result in conjunction with Eq. 10.4-15 to obtain an expression for the pressure

$$p = p^\circ \left(1 + \frac{\gamma - 1}{2} M^2 \right)^{\gamma/1-\gamma} \tag{10.4-17}$$

This equation is only valid for isentropic flows. We will obtain an interesting result if we use the binomial theorem[4] to expand the term in parentheses.

$$p = p^\circ \left[1 + \frac{\gamma}{1-\gamma} \frac{\gamma-1}{2} M^2 + \frac{\dfrac{\gamma}{1-\gamma}\dfrac{2\gamma-1}{1-\gamma}}{2!} \frac{(\gamma-1)^2}{4} M^4 + \cdots \right] \tag{10.4-18}$$

Making use of Eq. 10.4-14 and simplifying the terms somewhat, we obtain

$$p = p^\circ \left[1 - \frac{1}{2} \frac{\langle v_x \rangle^2}{RT} + \frac{\gamma(2\gamma-1)M^4}{8} + \cdots \right] \tag{10.4-19}$$

Application of the perfect gas law allows us to obtain a form somewhat reminiscent of Bernoulli's equation in the absence of gravitational effects

$$p^0 \left[1 + \frac{\gamma(2\gamma-1)}{8} M^4 + \cdots \right] \tag{10.4-20}$$

$$= p + \tfrac{1}{2} \rho \langle v_x \rangle^2 \left[1 + \left(\frac{\gamma-1}{2} \right) M^2 \right]^{1/\gamma-1}$$

Let us imagine now that we have a free stream of gas at a pressure p moving at a velocity $\langle v_x \rangle$, which impinges on a Pitot tube such as that illustrated in Fig. 8.5-7. It is not a bad assumption that the flow along the stagnation streamline is isentropic; thus, the pressure at the nose of the Pilot tube is the stagnation pressure, p°. If the flow were incompressible p° would be given by

$$p^\circ = p + \tfrac{1}{2}\rho \langle v_x \rangle^2 \tag{10.4-21}$$

However, Eq. 10.4-20 would certainly give a more accurate determination. This simple example provides us with an estimate of the effects of compressibility, for if $M < \tfrac{1}{2}$, Eqs. 10.4-20 and 10.4-21 will agree to within 1 per cent.

Returning now to the analysis of the nozzle, we designate the mass flow rate as $\dot{m}$ and write Eq. 10.4-1b as

$$\dot{m} = \rho \langle v_x \rangle A \tag{10.4-22}$$

4. H. B. Dwight, *Tables of Integrals and Other Mathematical Data* (New York: The Macmillan Company, 1961), p. 1.

Using the perfect gas law (Eq. 10.3-18) to express the density as a function of temperature and pressure, and representing the velocity as

$$\langle v_x \rangle = \left(\frac{\langle v_x \rangle}{c} \right) c = M\sqrt{\gamma R T} \tag{10.4-23}$$

we may write the mass flow rate as

$$\dot{m} = Ap \sqrt{\frac{\gamma}{RT}}\, M \tag{10.4-24}$$

Substitution of T and p from Eqs. 10.4-15 and 10.4-17 gives us

$$\dot{m} = Ap^\circ \sqrt{\frac{\gamma}{RT^\circ}} \left(1 + \frac{\gamma - 1}{2} M^2 \right)^{(\gamma+1)/2(1-\gamma)} M \tag{10.4-25}$$

So far, we have determined the temperature, pressure, and mass flow rate in terms of T°, p°, and M, and we need only specify the velocity to define the flow completely. Substitution of Eq. 10.4-15 into Eq. 10.4-23 gives us this result:

$$\langle v_x \rangle = M\sqrt{\gamma R T^\circ} \left(1 + \frac{\gamma - 1}{2} M^2 \right)^{-1/2} \tag{10.4-26}$$

Thus, T, p, $\dot{m}$, and $\langle v_x \rangle$ are known as functions of p°, T°, and M. While T° and p° are generally specified, the Mach number must be determined everywhere in the duct to specify the flow completely. For practical purposes, the back pressure in reservoir II is specified and a trial-and-error solution is necessary to determine the temperature, pressure, and Mach number distributions. We may do so by assuming a mass flow rate and using Eq. 10.4-25 to calculate the Mach number in the duct. Once we know M, we may determine the pressure distribution by Eq. 10.4-17. If the calculated pressure at the exit of the nozzle is different from the back pressure in reservoir II, we assume a new value of $\dot{m}$ and repeat the calculation.

Rather than doing so, we will examine the results of these equations by specifying the pressure ratio p/p° and determining the distribution of M and $\dot{m}/A$ throughout the nozzle. By working in terms of the mass flow rate per unit area, $\dot{m}/A$, we avoid specifying the geometry of the nozzle. For this example we have assumed that the gas is air and the stagnation temperature is 300°K. The results are shown in Fig. 10.4-3.

We want to think of the pressure ratio p/p° as being physically the back pressure divided by the stagnation pressure. When we look at it in this fashion, the points on the curve represent the values of M and $\dot{m}/A$ at the exit of the nozzle shown in Fig. 10.4-1. Let us imagine that the back pressure is initially

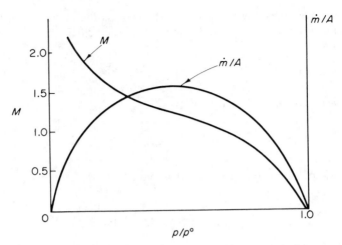

Fig. 10.4-3. Variation of M and $\dot{m}/A$ for isentropic flow.

equal to the stagnation pressure and that no flow takes place between the two reservoirs. In Fig. 10.4-3, then, $p/p° = 1$ and $M = \dot{m}/A = 0$. Now let us lower the pressure in reservoir II, which according to Fig. 10.4-3, causes an increase in both the Mach number and $\dot{m}/A$ entirely in accord with our intuition. When the pressure ratio reaches a value of about 0.5, the mass flow rate per unit area reaches a maximum and begins to decrease. As the back pressure tends to zero ($p/p° \to 0$), the flow rate tends to zero while the Mach number steadily increases to values greater than 10. This behavior is certainly not in accord with our intuition, and we had better reserve judgment on the validity of these curves.

Experimental evidence is in order here, and the results indicate that $\dot{m}/A$ is constant at the maximum value even though the back pressure is continually decreased. The Mach number at the exit of the nozzle is also constant at a value of 1.0, and the flow is termed *critical*. This situation is similar to the critical flow we encountered in the study of open channel flow in that the flow rate is not controlled by the back pressure (downstream conditions) for sonic (critical) or supersonic (supercritical) flows.

Figure 10.4-4 shows a Schlieren photograph of an air jet issuing from a convergent nozzle. The Mach number at the exit is 1.0 and the pressure at the exit is 105 times the back pressure. Under these conditions, there is a sudden expansion of the air stream as it leaves the nozzle and the flow is no longer one-dimensional. It has overexpanded and a shock wave has formed in the jet downstream from the nozzle exit. The performance curves for a convergent nozzle are shown in Fig. 10.4-5 and indicate the constant flow rate achieved for values of the pressure ratio less than the critical value.

Fig. 10.4-4. Flow issuing from a converging nozzle. Photograph courtesy NASA Langley Research Center, Va.

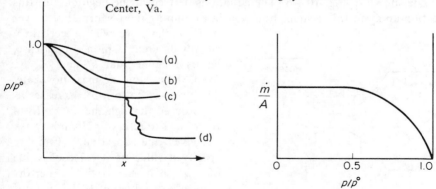

Fig. 10.4-5. Performance curves for a converging nozzle.

Choke flow

The condition of maximum flow rate observed in a converging nozzle is called *choke flow*, and all engineers who work with fluids should recognize its existence as a fact of life. It would be possible for an engineer, given a pressure ratio less than the critical value, to "plug and chug" with the appropriate equations and calculate a mass flow rate for converging nozzle that is less than the value occurring at the choke flow condition.

There are two other ways in which choke flow may occur. While these mechanisms are too complex for us to analyze in this limited treatment of compressible flow, they deserve a comment. In a converging nozzle, we *accelerated* the flow by decreasing the area of the duct; however, there are other ways in which the flow can be accelerated provided the flow is compressible.

Let us consider first the case of compressible, adiabatic flow in a long duct of constant cross-sectional area. The decrease in pressure gives rise to a decrease in the density, which in turn forces the velocity to increase. If the pressure drop is sufficiently large, the velocity may reach sonic velocity at some point in the duct and choke flow will occur because the downstream conditions can no longer influence the flow rate.

Choke flow may also be brought about by heating the gas. Such heating causes a decrease in density and an increase in velocity; thus, sonic velocity may be attained and a choked condition occurs. It also follows that cooling the gas may prevent the occurrence of choke flow.

Converging-diverging nozzles

We now consider isentropic flow through the converging-diverging nozzle shown in Fig. 10.4-6. The equations derived at the beginning of this section apply to this system; however, in examining the performance curves in Fig. 10.4-3 we will proceed in a slightly different fashion. In this case, let us imagine that p° and p_B are fixed, thus fixing the mass flow rate. The pressure ratio p/p° decreases as we proceed through the nozzle from reservoir I to reservoir II, and we ask ourselves the question, "Can we specify a value of A for each value of p/p° such that both the performance curves in Fig. 10.4-3 *and* our intuition are satisfied?"

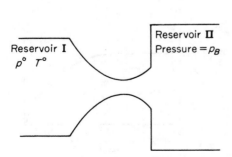

Reservoir I
p° T°

Reservoir II
Pressure $= p_B$

Fig. 10.4-6. Converging-diverging nozzle.

As we begin our progress through the nozzle, p/p° decreases and $\dot{m}/A$ increases because of the decrease in area. The Mach number also increases because the decrease in area accelerates the flow. When we reach the critical pressure ratio, the Mach number is 1.0 and $\dot{m}/A$ is a maximum. Now, if we are to continue along the performance curve, the area A *must* increase if $\dot{m}/A$ is going to decrease. In our previous example of a converging nozzle, intuition told us that points on the performance curve for supersonic flow were inadmissible. Experiments confirmed our intuition, and the idea of choke flow was introduced. In this case intuition does not restrict us from imagining an increased cross-sectional area giving rise to the predicted decrease in $\dot{m}/A$, but what about the Mach number (and therefore the velocity) continuing to increase while the area increases? This process is surely in opposition to our intuition, but if we again turn to experimental evidence we find the velocity does increase in the diverging section and supersonic velocities are obtained.

Subsonic and supersonic flow

The increasing velocity in the diverging portion of the nozzle is a curious phenomenon which we need to analyze further. Certainly it results from the density decreasing faster than the area increases, but we need to examine the process in concrete terms. Starting with the mass balance (Eq. 10.4-1a), we carry out the differentiation and divide by $\rho <v_x> A$ to obtain

$$\frac{1}{\rho}\left(\frac{d\rho}{dx}\right) + \frac{1}{\langle v_x \rangle}\frac{d\langle v_x \rangle}{dx} + \frac{1}{A}\frac{dA}{dx} = 0 \qquad (10.4\text{-}27)$$

Differentiation of the energy balance (Eq. 10.4-9) yields

$$\frac{dh}{dx} + \langle v_x \rangle \frac{d\langle v_x \rangle}{dx} = 0 \qquad (10.4\text{-}28)$$

which we may simplify further if we use the thermodynamic relationship

$$dh = T\,ds + \frac{1}{\rho}\,dp \qquad (10.4\text{-}29)$$

For isentropic flows, we may write

$$\left(\frac{dh}{dx}\right)_s = \frac{1}{\rho}\left(\frac{dp}{dx}\right)_s \qquad (10.4\text{-}30)$$

Substitution into Eq. 10.4-28 yields an interesting special form of the energy equation:

$$\langle v_x \rangle \left(\frac{d\langle v_x \rangle}{dx}\right)_s = -\frac{1}{\rho}\left(\frac{dp}{dx}\right)_s \qquad (10.4\text{-}31)$$

This result is identical to the momentum equation (Eq. 10.4-7) if the entropy is constant. Thus, one-dimensional isentropic flows may be solved by means of the mass and total energy equations, the momentum equation yielding no new information. Directing our attention now to Eq. 10.4-27, we specify that the flow be isentropic and write the density gradient as,

$$\left(\frac{d\rho}{dx}\right)_s = \left(\frac{\partial\rho}{\partial p}\right)_s\left(\frac{dp}{dx}\right)_s \tag{10.4-32}$$

and use Eq. 10.4-31 to eliminate the pressure gradient

$$\left(\frac{dp}{dx}\right)_s = -\rho\left(\frac{\partial\rho}{\partial p}\right)_s \langle v_x\rangle\left(\frac{d\langle v_x\rangle}{dx}\right)_s \tag{10.4-33}$$

Substitution of this result into Eq. 10.4-27, and use of Eq. 10.3-14 to express $(\partial\rho/\partial p)_s$ in terms of the speed of sound yield

$$\left(-\frac{1}{c^2} + \frac{1}{\langle v_x\rangle^2}\right)\langle v_x\rangle\frac{d\langle v_x\rangle}{dx} + \frac{1}{A}\frac{dA}{dx} = 0 \tag{10.4-34}$$

Expressing this result in terms of the Mach number, and rearranging, we obtain

$$\frac{d\langle v_x\rangle}{dA} = -\left[\frac{A}{\langle v_x\rangle}(1 - M^2)\right]^{-1} \tag{10.4-35}$$

From this result we see that if $M < 1$, the velocity increases if A decreases—i.e., the flow is accelerated in a converging section and decelerated in a diverging section. However, if the flow is supersonic, $M > 1$ and the velocity

Table 10.4-1

SUBSONIC AND SUPERSONIC FLOW IN
CONVERGING AND DIVERGING CONDUITS

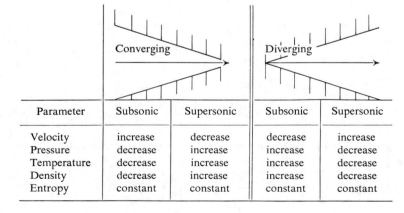

Parameter	Subsonic	Supersonic	Subsonic	Supersonic
Velocity	increase	decrease	decrease	increase
Pressure	decrease	increase	increase	decrease
Temperature	decrease	increase	increase	decrease
Density	decrease	increase	increase	decrease
Entropy	constant	constant	constant	constant

incréases with increasing cross-sectional area and decreases with decreasing cross-sectional area. We must keep in mind that these conclusions hold for isentropic flow that may not occur in long reaches of converging-diverging ducts. The other flow properties also behave differently when the flow changes from subsonic to supersonic; these are indicated in Table 10.4-1.

In studying the performance curves in Fig. 10.4-3, we specified a continuously decreasing pressure ratio $p/p°$, and found that values of $A(x)$ exist that lead to a converging-diverging nozzle. We now wish to look at the results for isentropic flow from still another point of view. Let us assume that $A(x)$ is *specified* so that the nozzle resembles the one shown in Fig. 10.4-6. If we specify the stagnation properties, $A(x)$, and $\dot{m}$, we can use the derived equations to determine the pressure at every point in the nozzle, starting at reservoir I where $p = p°$ and continuing to reservoir II where $p = p_B$. Such calculations lead to the curves shown in Fig. 10.4-7. The

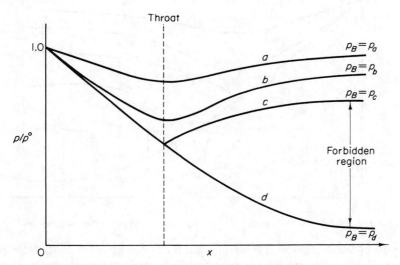

Fig. 10.4-7. Pressure ratio in a converging-diverging nozzle.

first two curves, a and b, are for low flow rates where the Mach number is always less than 1.0. Here, the nozzle acts like a Venturi meter, the pressure being low where the velocity is high and a pressure recovery taking place in the diverging section. The pressure recovery is incomplete because the downstream cross-sectional area is smaller than the upstream area. Curves (a), (b), and (c) indicate increasing mass flow rates with the latter flow causing a Mach number of 1.0 to be reached at the throat. This condition gives the maximum flow rate for the nozzle at these stagnation conditions, and the solution for the pressure is double valued and may follow either curve (c) or curve (d). In actual practice, the pressure distribution at this flow rate would be determined by whether the back pressure were equal to p_c or p_d.

But what of the "forbidden region" between p_c and p_d? Our analysis indicates that this condition simply cannot be reached, yet we know that experimentally we may adjust the back pressure to take on values between p_c and p_d. Once again, experimental evidence is in order, we find that if the back pressure is adjusted to some value between p_c and p_d, a shock wave develops and there is a sudden transition from supersonic to subsonic flow accompanied by an increase in entropy. The pressure distributions for such flows are indicated in Fig. 10.4-8. This phenomenon is similar to the sudden

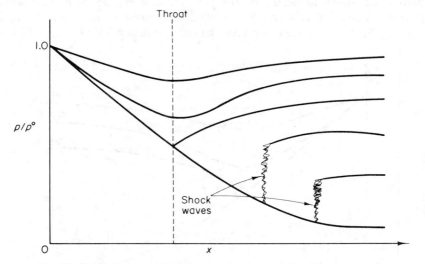

Fig. 10.4-8. Formation of shock waves in a converging-diverging nozzle.

transition that occurs at a hydraulic jump in open channel flow. Note that these shock waves are advancing into the flowing stream at speeds greater than the speed of sound just as the hydraulic jump advances into a flowing stream at speeds greater than $\sqrt{gh}$—i.e., the velocity of propagation for a small disturbance.

10.5 Shock Waves

In attacking this problem, we will make use of the experimental observation that shock waves occur over very thin regions† and show that a transition from supersonic to subsonic flow is permissible, provided the entropy

† The thickness of a shock wave depends on the Mach number, temperature, and pressure and is on the order of 10^{-4} in. (see Ref. 1, Vol. 1, p. 134).

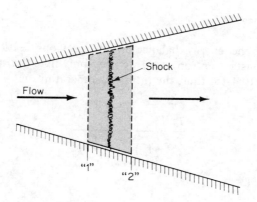

Fig. 10.5-1. Control volume for the analysis of a shock wave.

increases. We will now reformulate the mass, momentum, and energy equations for the control volume shown in Fig. 10.5-1 (which contains the shock wave) without imposing the restriction of constant entropy. Remember that in the previous section the momentum equation was not required to specify the flow; however, when we allow the entropy to vary we will find that the momentum equation is required.

Mass balance

Since $\rho \langle v_x \rangle A$ is a constant, the mass balance simply reduces to

$$\dot{m} = \rho_1 \langle v_x \rangle_1 A_1 = \rho_2 \langle v_x \rangle_2 A_2 \tag{10.5-1}$$

or by Eq. 10.4-24 we may write

$$p_1 M_1 \sqrt{\frac{\gamma}{RT_1}} = p_2 M_2 \sqrt{\frac{\gamma}{RT_2}} \tag{10.5-2}$$

Momentum balance

To obtain the momentum balance, we simply integrate Eq. 10.4-6 from x_1 to x_2 to obtain

$$\dot{m}(\langle v_x \rangle_2 - \langle v_x \rangle_1) = -A(p_2 - p_1) \tag{10.5-3}$$

Here we have assumed that the shock is so thin that variations in $A(x)$ may be neglected relative to variations in $\langle v_x \rangle$ and p.

Energy balance

We derived the energy balance in the previous section without the restriction of constant entropy, and we need only note that the temperature is given by Eq. 10.4-15; thus, the ratio of temperatures is

$$\frac{T_2}{T_1} = \frac{1 + \frac{\gamma - 1}{2} M_1^2}{1 + \frac{\gamma - 1}{2} M_2^2} \tag{10.5-4}$$

Entropy change

Starting with Eq. 10.2-10, we can quickly derive the thermodynamic relationship

$$dh = T\,ds + \frac{1}{\rho}\,dp \tag{10.5-5}$$

Rearranging and integrating ds between x_1 and x_2 gives

$$s_2 - s_1 = \int_1^2 ds = \int_1^2 \frac{dh}{T} - \int_1^2 \frac{dp}{\rho T} \tag{10.5-6}$$

Restricting our analysis to fluids that may be treated as perfect gases, we may carry out the integration to obtain

$$s_2 - s_1 = c_p \ln\left(\frac{T_2}{T_1}\right) - R \ln\left(\frac{p_2}{p_1}\right) \tag{10.5-7}$$

The ratio T_2/T_1 is already available in Eq. 10.5-4, and we need only find p_2/p_1 to determine the entropy change across the shock. It is easiest to do so by means of the mass balance and the perfect gas law. Rearranging Eq. 10.5-1 and neglecting the change in area from x_1 to x_2, we obtain

$$\frac{\rho_2}{\rho_1} = \frac{\langle v_x \rangle_1}{\langle v_x \rangle_2} \tag{10.5-8}$$

Expression of the velocities in terms of the Mach number (Eq. 10.4-23) before and after the shock wave yields

$$\frac{\rho_2}{\rho_1} = \frac{M_1}{M_2}\left(\frac{T_1}{T_2}\right)^{1/2} \tag{10.5-9}$$

and the perfect gas law may be used to express the pressure ratio as

$$\frac{p_2}{p_1} = \frac{\rho_2 T_2}{\rho_1 T_1} = \frac{M_1}{M_2}\left(\frac{T_2}{T_1}\right)^{1/2} \tag{10.5-10}$$

Substitution of this result into Eq. 10.5-7 and rearrangement give

$$s_2 - s_1 = (c_p - \tfrac{1}{2}R) \ln\left(\frac{T_2}{T_1}\right) - R \ln\left(\frac{M_1}{M_2}\right) \qquad (10.5\text{-}11)$$

We may now use Eq. 10.5-4 to express the temperature ratio in terms of the Mach numbers, and we obtain

$$s_2 - s_1 = (c_p - \tfrac{1}{2}R) \ln\left(\frac{1 + \dfrac{\gamma - 1}{2} M_1^2}{1 + \dfrac{\gamma - 1}{2} M_2^2}\right) - R \ln\left(\frac{M_1}{M_2}\right) \qquad (10.5\text{-}12)$$

Now, the second law of thermodynamics tells us that $\Delta s \geq 0$ for any adiabatic process; therefore, Eq. 10.5-12 indicates either

$$M_2 = M_1, \qquad \Delta s = 0$$

or

$$M_2 < M_1, \qquad \Delta s > 0$$

Our analysis indicates that *only* transitions that decrease the Mach number are *possible*. The analysis does not indicate that such transitions do occur, nor does it indicate that the transition should be from supersonic to subsonic.† It only states that such a transition is possible, and if it occurs, the entropy increases.

From the analysis of isentropic flows we know that there are certain conditions (i.e., a back pressure in the "forbidden region") which disallow the possibility of an isentropic flow. With this information in hand, one might ask, "Why isn't there a smooth, nonisentropic transition from supersonic to subsonic flow?" The answer to this question is apparently unavailable at present. We can only state that transitions from supersonic to subsonic flow occur abruptly.

PROBLEMS

10-1. Integrate Eq. 10.1-19 with respect to time to obtain the traditional form of the first law of thermodynamics for open systems. Carefully explain the meaning of each term.

10-2. Starting with Eq. 10.2-15, derive the general macroscopic entropy balance for a control volume, $\mathscr{V}_a(t)$.

10-3. Derive Eq. 10.4-7 by integrating the x-direction equation of motion over the cross-sectional area $A(x)$—i.e.,

$$\int_{A(x)} \mathbf{i} \cdot \rho\left[\frac{\partial \mathbf{v}}{\partial t} + \mathbf{v} \cdot \nabla \mathbf{v}\right] dA = -\int_{A(x)} \mathbf{i} \cdot \nabla p \, dA + \int_{A(x)} \mathbf{i} \cdot \rho \mathbf{g} \, dA + \mu \int_{A(x)} \mathbf{i} \cdot \nabla^2 \mathbf{v} \, dA$$

† Thus, we could have the situation $M_1 > M_2 > 1$.

Make the same simplifying assumptions as in Sec. 10.4, and use the Leibnitz rule (see Prob. 3-5) for interchanging integration and differentiation.

10-4. For a given value of $T°$, show that an upper limit exists for the velocity given by

$$\langle v_x \rangle < \sqrt{\frac{2R\gamma}{\gamma - 1} T°}$$

10-5. A perfect gas at T_1 and p_1 in a large reservoir flows isentropically through a convergent nozzle of area A_2 into the atmosphere where the pressure is p_0. Derive expressions for the mass flow rate $\dot{m}$ taking into account the phenomenon of choke flow. (This type of calculation would be a key step in the design of a safety valve for a high-pressure chemical reactor.)

10-6. If at a shock such as that shown in Fig. 10.5-1, $M_1 = 3.0$, $T_1 = 1000°R$ and $p_1 = 0.2$ atm, find the Mach number and pressure after the shock. Assume $\gamma = 1.5$.

10-7. For isentropic flow in a divergent channel, the density decreases 14 per cent ($\rho_2 = 0.86\rho_1$) for a 10 per cent increase in the cross-sectional area ($A_2 = 1.10 A_1$). Calculate the change in velocity between these two points.

10-8. A stream of air flows at a Mach number of 0.8. If a Pitot tube is used to measure the velocity, compute the error incurred by the use of the incompressible form of Bernoulli's equation.

10-9. Air flowing in a duct enters a nozzle at a velocity of 5000 ft/sec, a pressure of 100 psia, and a temperature of 800°F. The nozzle is designed to increase the pressure isentropically to 125 psia. If the mass flow rate is 10 lb_m/sec, what is the downstream cross sectional area of the nozzle?

10-10. Air is contained in a tank at 200 psia and 72°F. If the flow of air through the outlet valve is approximated as isentropic and one-dimensional, what is the maximum flow rate into the surrounding atmosphere? Take the cross-sectional area at the valve as 1.0 in.² and the ambient pressure as 14.7 psia. What would the flow rate be if the pressure in the tank were increased to 400 psia?

Flow Around
Immersed Bodies

11

The objectives of this chapter are to introduce the student to the phenomena associated with flow around immersed bodies and to provide him with a rational explanation of the drag coefficient-Reynolds number curves shown in Fig. 8.2-6 in Chap. 8. Boundary layer theory will be introduced, thus giving some practice in setting up and solving differential-macroscopic balances. We shall also use boundary layer theory to explore the method of performing an order of magnitude analysis.

11.1 Description of Flow

The study of flow around immersed bodies is an enormously difficult subject to discuss with any degree of exactness. The difficulty results from the fact that there are three distinct, and fairly complex regions of flow that influence the force exerted by the fluid on the body. Figure 11.1-1 illustrates the flow past a thin airfoil at a zero angle of inclination and a high Reynolds number. At high Reynolds numbers, inertial effects predominate everywhere except in a thin region close to the surface of the solid body. The flow outside this thin region is governed almost entirely by inertial effects and is called *irrotational*. As the name implies, fluid elements in this region undergo

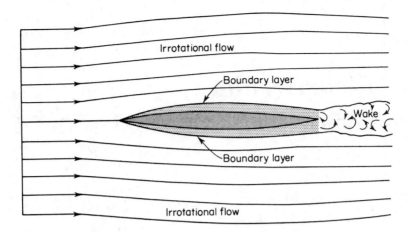

Fig. II.I-I. Flow regimes around an immersed body.

translation but do not rotate; therefore, there is no shear deformation and viscous effects are negligible. A great deal is known about irrotational flow, because in the absence of viscous effects the equations of motion can be solved by fairly simple mathematical techniques. While the study of ir-rotational flow is well within the student's capabilities, it will be treated only qualitatively here, and we will concentrate our attention on the boundary layer. The wake is extremely difficult to treat theoretically, and again we will restrict ourselves to qualitative comments regarding this region.

Near the solid surface, viscous effects become important, and this flow region is called the boundary layer. The equations of motion here reduce to what are known as the Prandtl boundary layer equations. In the next section, we will lay the ground work for both the derivation and the solution of these equations.

II.2 The Suddenly Accelerated Flat Plate

As an introduction to the analysis of boundary layers we will examine the fluid motion that results when an infinitely wide, infinitely long, flat plate is suddenly accelerated from rest to a constant velocity, u_0. We may rightly ask, "Why study a hypothetical flow that can never be realized in practice?" The answer is that by performing the analysis we will gain intuition—i.e., we may improve our skill at guessing the flow topology. In addition, the equations we will solve are identical to those describing transient heat and mass transfer into a semi-infinite medium; thus, the analysis has value beyond

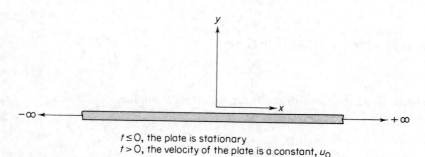

$t \leq 0$, the plate is stationary
$t > 0$, the velocity of the plate is a constant, u_0

Fig. 11.2-1. The suddenly accelerated flat plate.

the area of fluid mechanics. The system under consideration is illustrated in Fig. 11.2-1.

We start with the two-dimensional form of the Navier-Stokes equations

$$\rho\left(\frac{\partial v_x}{\partial t} + v_x \frac{\partial v_x}{\partial x} + v_y \frac{\partial v_x}{\partial y}\right) = -\frac{\partial p}{\partial x} + \mu\left(\frac{\partial^2 v_x}{\partial x^2} + \frac{\partial^2 v_x}{\partial y^2}\right) \qquad (11.2\text{-}1)$$

$$\rho\left(\frac{\partial v_y}{\partial t} + v_x \frac{\partial v_y}{\partial x} + v_y \frac{\partial v_y}{\partial y}\right) = -\frac{\partial p}{\partial y} - \rho g + \mu\left(\frac{\partial^2 v_y}{\partial x^2} + \frac{\partial^2 v_y}{\partial y^2}\right) \qquad (11.2\text{-}2)$$

and the continuity equation

$$\frac{\partial v_x}{\partial x} + \frac{\partial v_y}{\partial y} = 0 \qquad (11.2\text{-}3)$$

Since the plate is infinite in the x-direction, we can argue logically that v_x, v_y, and p are not functions of x. The continuity equation immediately reduces to

$$\frac{\partial v_y}{\partial y} = 0 \qquad (11.2\text{-}4)$$

and application of the boundary condition

B.C. 1: $v_y = 0, \quad y = 0$ (11.2-5)

leads us to the conclusion that v_y is zero everywhere. Under these conditions, the equations of motion reduce to

$$\rho\left(\frac{\partial v_x}{\partial t}\right) = \mu\left(\frac{\partial^2 v_x}{\partial y^2}\right) \qquad (11.2\text{-}6)$$

$$0 = -\left(\frac{\partial p}{\partial y}\right) - \rho g \qquad (11.2\text{-}7)$$

We need solve only the first of these to determine the velocity as a function of y and t. Defining the dimensionless velocity U_x as

$$U_x = \frac{v_x}{u_0} \tag{11.2-8}$$

we may write Eq. 11.2-6 in the form

$$\frac{\partial U_x}{\partial t} = \nu \left(\frac{\partial^2 U_x}{\partial y^2} \right) \tag{11.2-9}$$

which we must solve subject to the following boundary conditions

B.C. 2:	$U_x = 0,$	$t = 0,$	$0 \leq y \leq \infty$	(11.2-10)
B.C. 3:	$U_x = 1,$	$t > 0,$	$y = 0$	(11.2-11)
B.C. 4:	$U_x = 0,$	$y = \infty,$	$t \geq 0$	(11.2-12)

The boundary condition B.C. 2 is often referred to as an initial condition since it specifies the velocity field at some initial time. The boundary condition B.C. 3 indicates that for times greater than zero the plate is moving at a constant velocity, thus an infinite acceleration is required. While this is physically impossible, it provides us with some insight as to how disturbances originating at solid surfaces are propagated into the surrounding fluid.

Equation 11.2-9 is a partial differential equation. Until now such equations have been considered beyond the scope of this text; however, we can solve this one without expending too much effort, and in the process we can become acquainted with a fairly general method of solving partial differential equations. A solution may be obtained by means of Laplace transforms, but here we will use a technique known as a *similarity solution*. Thus, we define a new variable η in terms of powers of y and t,

$$\eta = y^a t^b \tag{11.2-13}$$

where a and b are as yet undetermined constants, and we seek a solution of the form

$$U_x(y, t) = U_x[\eta(y, t)] \tag{11.2-14}$$

If we find that U_x can, indeed, be represented in terms of the single variable η, we will have been successful. If we cannot represent U_x in terms of η, we must try other methods of solution.

We note first that the two partial differentials in Eq. 11.2-9 may be written

$$\frac{\partial U_x}{\partial t} = \left(\frac{dU_x}{d\eta} \right) \frac{\partial \eta}{\partial t} = \left(\frac{dU_x}{d\eta} \right) b y^a t^{b-1} \tag{11.2-15a}$$

$$\frac{\partial^2 U_x}{\partial y^2} = \frac{d^2 U_x}{d\eta^2} \left(\frac{\partial \eta}{\partial y} \right)^2 + \frac{dU_x}{d\eta} \left(\frac{\partial^2 \eta}{\partial y^2} \right)$$

$$= \frac{d^2 U_x}{d\eta^2} (a y^{a-1} t^b)^2 + \frac{dU_x}{d\eta} [a(a - 1) y^{a-2} t^b] \tag{11.2-15b}$$

At this point we can see that setting $a = 1$ will eliminate one term, thus simplifying our equation. Substituting Eqs. 11.2-15 into Eq. 11.2-9, and setting $a = 1$, we get

$$\left(\frac{dU_x}{d\eta}\right) by t^{b-1} = \nu\left(\frac{d^2U_x}{d\eta^2}\right) t^{2b} \qquad (11.2\text{-}16)$$

If we could somehow eliminate y and t from this equation, our problem would be reduced to solving an ordinary differential equation. We can accomplish this by setting $b = -\frac{1}{2}$, thereby defining η as,

$$\eta = yt^{-1/2} \qquad (11.2\text{-}17)$$

Equation 11.2-16 reduces to

$$\left(\frac{dU_x}{d\eta}\right) = -\frac{2\nu}{\eta}\left(\frac{d^2U_x}{d\eta^2}\right) \qquad (11.2\text{-}18)$$

Putting the boundary conditions in terms of η, we find

B.C. 2′: $\qquad\qquad U_x = 0, \qquad \eta = \infty \qquad\qquad (11.2\text{-}19)$

B.C. 3′: $\qquad\qquad U_x = 1, \qquad \eta = 0 \qquad\qquad (11.2\text{-}20)$

B.C.4′: $\qquad\qquad U_x = 0, \qquad \eta = \infty \qquad\qquad (11.2\text{-}21)$

Here we see that boundary conditions B.C. 2′ and B.C. 4′ become identical in terms of the transformation of variables from y and t to η.

We solve the differential equation by first reducing the order to obtain

$$P = -\frac{2\nu}{\eta}\left(\frac{dP}{d\eta}\right) \qquad (11.2\text{-}22)$$

where

$$P = \frac{dU_x}{d\eta}$$

Separating variables and integrating gives

$$\ln P = -\frac{\eta^2}{4\nu} + C_1$$

or

$$\frac{dU_x}{d\eta} = C_1' e^{-\eta^2/4\nu} \qquad (11.2\text{-}23)$$

Formation of the indefinite integral gives

$$U_x = C_1' \int_0^\eta e^{-\tau^2/4\nu}\, d\tau + C_2 \qquad (11.2\text{-}24)$$

where τ is the dummy variable of integration. It will be convenient to define a new dummy variable ξ by

$$\xi = \frac{\tau}{\sqrt{4\nu}}$$

allowing us to write Eq. 11.2-24 as

$$U_x = C_1'' \int_0^{\eta/\sqrt{4\nu}} e^{-\xi^2} \, d\xi + C_2 \qquad (11.2\text{-}25)$$

By boundary condition 3', $C_2 = 1$, and application of boundary condition 2' leads to the result

$$U_x = 1 - \frac{\displaystyle\int_0^{\eta/\sqrt{4\nu}} e^{-\xi^2} \, d\xi}{\displaystyle\int_0^{\infty} e^{-\xi^2} \, d\xi} \qquad (11.2\text{-}26)$$

The definite integral in Eq. 11.2-26 is known to be equal to $\sqrt{\pi}/2$, and our expression for the velocity becomes

$$U_x = 1 - \frac{2}{\sqrt{\pi}} \int_0^{\eta/\sqrt{4\nu}} e^{-\xi^2} \, d\xi \qquad (11.2\text{-}27)$$

The latter term in this equation is known as the *error function*, abbreviated $\mathrm{erf}(\eta/\sqrt{4\nu})$. Tabulated values of the error function are available,[1] and our final expression is

$$U_x = 1 - \mathrm{erf}\frac{y}{\sqrt{4\nu t}} \qquad (11.2\text{-}28)$$

This result is plotted in Fig. 11.2-2. The key point of this analysis is that U_x reaches 99 per cent of the undisturbed value for $y/\sqrt{4\nu t} = 1.8$, and we can use this fact to define a "boundary layer" thickness δ as

$$\delta = 3.6\sqrt{\nu t} \qquad (11.2\text{-}29)$$

For values of y larger than δ, the velocity is, for all practical purposes, zero. We may also interpret Eq. 11.2-29 by saying that the distance the disturbance penetrates into the quiescent fluid is proportional to the square root of time t, and the kinematic viscosity, ν. This result agrees with our intuition, which should tell us that a large viscosity leads to a rapid propagation of a disturbance, and a zero value of the viscosity would not allow the disturbance to be felt anywhere in the fluid.

1. M. Abramowitz and I. A. Stegun, eds., *Handbook of Mathematical Functions* (Washington, D.C.: National Bureau of Standards, 1964).

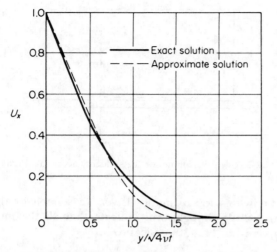

Fig. 11.2-2. Velocity profiles for the suddenly accelerated flat plate.

Approximate solution

We will now solve this problem again, by an approximate method, and compare the results with the exact solution. The student might well ask, "Why solve a problem with an approximate method when the exact solution is already available—especially when the problem is somewhat removed from any real situation?" Aside from keeping idle minds busy, the answer must be that by comparing an approximate result with the exact solution, we can gain some insight into the validity of the approximate method. In addition, it provides an interesting application of the macroscopic momentum balance.

The control volume for the approximate solution is illustrated in Fig. 11.2-3. The upper boundary is located at $y = \delta(t)$ and is moving in the y-direction. We start with the complete macroscopic momentum balance and dot it with $\mathbf{i}$ to obtain

$$\frac{d}{dt} \int_{\mathscr{V}_a(t)} \rho v_x \, dV + \int_{A_e(t)} \rho v_x (\mathbf{v} - \mathbf{w}) \cdot \mathbf{n} \, dA = \int_{\mathscr{A}_a(t)} \mathbf{i} \cdot \mathbf{t}_{(n)} \, dA \qquad (11.2\text{-}30)$$

We again impose the restriction that the velocity and pressure are independent of x, and make the approximation (A) that

A. 1: $\qquad\qquad\qquad\qquad v_x = 0, \qquad y \geqslant \delta(t) \qquad\qquad\qquad\qquad (11.2\text{-}31)$

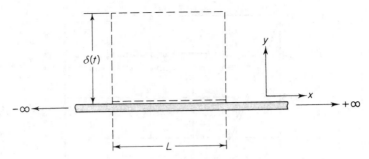

Fig. 11.2-3. Control volume for the suddenly accelerated flat plate.

Of course, we know this approximation is very reasonable on the basis of the exact solution. A little thought will indicate that all the momentum flux terms are zero, and Eq. 11.2-30 reduces to

$$\frac{d}{dt}\int_0^L\int_0^{\delta(t)}\rho v_x\,dy\,dx = \int_0^L\left[\tau_{yx}\Big|_{y=\delta(t)} - \tau_{yx}\Big|_{y=0}\right]dx \qquad (11.2\text{-}32)$$

Substitution of Newton's law of viscosity for τ_{yx} yields

$$\frac{d}{dt}\int_0^L\int_0^{\delta(t)}\rho v_x\,dy\,dx = \mu\int_0^L\left\{\left(\frac{\partial v_x}{\partial y}\right)_{y=\delta(t)} - \left(\frac{\partial v_x}{\partial y}\right)_{y=0}\right\}dx \qquad (11.2\text{-}33)$$

By approximation 1, we have specified $v_x = 0$ for $y \geq \delta(t)$. If we require the derivative $(\partial v_x/\partial y)$ to be a continuous function, then approximation 1 naturally leads us to the condition,†

$$\left(\frac{\partial v_x}{\partial y}\right) = 0, \qquad y = \delta(t) \qquad (11.2\text{-}34)$$

and Eq. 11.2-33 reduces to

$$\frac{d}{dt}\int_0^{\delta(t)}\rho v_x\,dy = -\mu\left(\frac{\partial v_x}{\partial y}\right)_{y=0} \qquad (11.2\text{-}35)$$

Here we have used the fact that v_x is independent of x; thus, the integration with respect to x can be dropped. This result states that, the force exerted by the plate on the fluid is equal to the time rate of change of the momentum of the fluid.

† One can also argue that all higher derivatives are zero at $y = \delta(t)$.

We now make the assumption that the velocity profiles are similar, allowing us to express the velocity as

A.2: $$v_x(y, t) = v_x\left[\frac{y}{\delta(t)}\right] \qquad (11.2\text{-}36)$$

Note that this equation is comparable to Eq. 11.2-14 if we designate η as

$$\eta = \frac{y}{\delta(t)}$$

We further assume that the functional dependence of v_x on $y/\delta(t)$ can be represented by a polynomial.

A.3: $$v_x = a + b\left(\frac{y}{\delta}\right) + c\left(\frac{y}{\delta}\right)^2 + d\left(\frac{y}{\delta}\right)^3 + \cdots \qquad (11.2\text{-}37)$$

To determine the constants in the polynomial, we require some specific information regarding the velocity profile, which is given as

$$v_x = 0, \qquad y = \delta(t) \qquad \text{(an intuitive approximation)} \qquad (11.2\text{-}38\text{a})$$

$$\frac{\partial v_x}{\partial y} = 0, \qquad y = \delta(t) \qquad \text{(continuity of stress)} \qquad (11.2\text{-}38\text{b})$$

$$v_x = u_0, \qquad y = 0 \qquad \text{(a bonafide boundary condition)} \qquad (11.2\text{-}38\text{c})$$

These three equations allow us to determine only three of the constants in Eq. 11.2-37. We could obtain more equations by requiring the higher derivatives of v_x to be zero at $y = \delta$; however, a key piece of information regarding the velocity profile can be obtained from the differential equation. Examining Eq. 11.2-1, keeping in mind that p and v_x are independent of x, we quickly conclude that

$$\frac{\partial^2 v_x}{\partial y^2} = 0, \qquad y = 0 \qquad \text{(from the differential equation)} \qquad (11.2\text{-}38\text{d})$$

Equations 11.2-38 may be used to determine the constants a, b, c, and d to obtain

$$v_x = u_0\left[1 - \frac{3}{2}\left(\frac{y}{\delta}\right) + \frac{1}{2}\left(\frac{y}{\delta}\right)^3\right] \qquad (11.2\text{-}39)$$

Defining dimensionless variables as

$$U_x = \frac{v_x}{u_0} \quad \text{and} \quad Y = \frac{y}{\delta} \qquad (11.2\text{-}40)$$

we see that the velocity is given by

$$U_x = 1 - \tfrac{3}{2}Y + \tfrac{1}{2}Y^3 \qquad (11.2\text{-}41)$$

Putting Eq. 11.2-35 into dimensionless form yields

$$\frac{d}{dt}\left\{\delta \int_0^1 U_x\, dY\right\} = -\frac{\nu}{\delta}\left(\frac{dU_x}{dY}\right)_{Y=0} \tag{11.2-42}$$

By substituting Eq. 11.2-41 and carrying out the differentiation and integration, we obtain a first-order differential equation for the boundary layer thickness.

$$d\delta = \left(\frac{4\nu}{\delta}\right) dt \tag{11.2-43}$$

Separating variables, integrating and imposing the boundary condition

B.C. 1: $\qquad\qquad\qquad \delta = 0, \qquad t = 0 \tag{11.2-44}$

we have an expression for the boundary layer thickness as a function of time,

$$\delta = 2.8\sqrt{\nu t} \tag{11.2-45}$$

While the boundary layer thickness predicted by the approximate solution is very different from the exact solution, the result is not as bad as it might seem. The comparison of velocity profiles is given in Fig. 11.2-2, and certainly the two profiles are in good agreement for values of $y/\sqrt{4\nu t}$ less than 1.0. We conclude that this type of approximate analysis should yield reasonably satisfactory results and we are now ready to attack the more complex boundary layer flow illustrated in Fig. 11.3-1.

11.3 The Boundary Layer on a Flat Plate

The flow we wish to consider in this section is illustrated in Fig. 11.3-1. It consists of an infinite stream flowing past a thin flat plate of length L. The plate is infinitely wide and the flow is uniform at a velocity of u_∞. This flow has some of the same characteristics of the suddenly accelerated flat plate, especially if we view the problem as a flat plate moving at a velocity u_∞ through an initially quiescent fluid. Under these conditions, the time t in the previous problem would be comparable to x/u_∞ where x is measured from the leading edge of the plate. For this reason we may use Eq. 11.2-29 to estimate the boundary layer thickness as

$$\delta \approx 3.6\sqrt{\nu x/u_\infty} \tag{11.3-1}$$

Our first objective in this section will be to perform an order of magnitude analysis of the equations of motion to obtain the Prandtl boundary layer equations. We will not solve the equations because the mathematical techniques required are beyond the scope of this text; however, the result

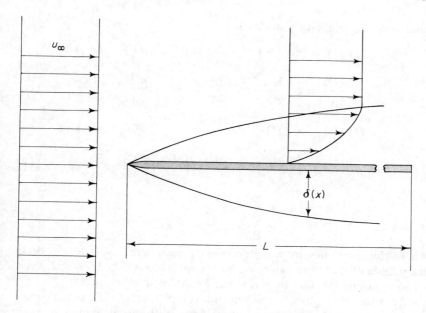

Fig. 11.3-1. Boundary layer flow over a flat plate.

will be given and compared with an approximate analysis. It should be understood that the order of magnitude analysis is a general tool of engineering analysis and has applications far beyond the development presented here.

We start with the two-dimensional Navier-Stokes equations and the continuity equation for steady, incompressible flow.

$$v_x\left(\frac{\partial v_x}{\partial x}\right) + v_y\left(\frac{\partial v_x}{\partial y}\right) = -\frac{1}{\rho}\left(\frac{\partial p}{\partial x}\right) + \nu\left(\frac{\partial^2 v_x}{\partial x^2} + \frac{\partial^2 v_x}{\partial y^2}\right) \qquad (11.3\text{-}2)$$

$$v_x\left(\frac{\partial v_y}{\partial x}\right) + v_y\left(\frac{\partial v_y}{\partial y}\right) = -\frac{1}{\rho}\left(\frac{\partial p}{\partial y}\right) + \nu\left(\frac{\partial^2 v_y}{\partial x^2} + \frac{\partial^2 v_y}{\partial y^2}\right) \qquad (11.3\text{-}3)$$

$$\frac{\partial v_x}{\partial x} + \frac{\partial v_y}{\partial y} = 0 \qquad (11.3\text{-}4)$$

We use the free stream velocity and the length of the plate to form the dimensionless variables

$$U_x = \frac{v_x}{u_\infty}, \qquad U_y = \frac{v_y}{u_\infty}, \qquad P = \frac{p - p_0}{\rho u_\infty^2}$$

$$X = \frac{x}{L}, \qquad Y = \frac{y}{L}, \qquad \delta' = \frac{\delta(x)}{L}, \qquad N_{\text{Re},L} = \frac{u_\infty L}{\nu}$$

and write the original equations as

(1) (1) $(\delta')\left(\dfrac{1}{\delta'}\right)$ (1') $\left(\dfrac{1}{\delta'^2}\right)$

$$U_x\frac{\partial U_x}{\partial X} + U_y\frac{\partial U_x}{\partial Y} = -\frac{\partial P}{\partial X} + \frac{1}{N_{\mathrm{Re},L}}\left(\frac{\partial^2 U_x}{\partial X^2} + \frac{\partial^2 U_x}{\partial Y^2}\right) \qquad (11.3\text{-}5)$$

(1) (δ') (δ') (1) (δ') $\left(\dfrac{1}{\delta'}\right)$

$$U_x\frac{\partial U_y}{\partial X} + U_y\frac{\partial U_y}{\partial Y} = -\frac{\partial P}{\partial Y} + \frac{1}{N_{\mathrm{Re},L}}\left(\frac{\partial^2 U_y}{\partial X^2} + \frac{\partial^2 U_y}{\partial Y^2}\right) \qquad (11.3\text{-}6)$$

(1)   (1)
$$\frac{\partial U_x}{\partial X} + \frac{\partial U_y}{\partial Y} = 0 \qquad (11.3\text{-}7)$$

where the quantities in parentheses over each term indicate the order of magnitude of that term. Here we have used what is called a *length Reynolds number*, noting this fact by giving the Reynolds number as $N_{\mathrm{Re},L}$.

An order of magnitude analysis of a complex set of differential equations can be an extremely profitable undertaking. With this technique an engineer may often reduce an essentially unsolvable problem to one which still contains the pertinent elements of the real world yet is amenable to analysis. The technique requires skill, daring, and luck, and the reward may be great. We start with the x-component of the dimensionless velocity, U_x. Its value ranges between 0 at $Y = 0$ and 1 for $Y \geq \delta'$, and we write the order of magnitude of U_x as

$$U_x = 0(1) \qquad (11.3\text{-}8)$$

The generally accepted meaning of this expression is that U_x is closer to 1.0 than it is to either 0.1 or 10.0.

An order of magnitude is perhaps best looked upon as an estimate of the average value of a function over the region under consideration. Viewing it in this way, we might express Eq. 11.3-8 as

$$U_x = 0\left(\frac{1}{\delta'}\int_0^1\int_0^{\delta'} U_x\, dY\, dX\right) = 0(1) \qquad (11.3\text{-}9)$$

To treat the estimate of a derivative, we need to expand the function in a Taylor series and develop some finite difference expressions. Expanding U_x around the point $X = X_0$ gives

$$U_x|_X = U_x|_{X_0} + (X - X_0)\frac{\partial U_x}{\partial X}\bigg|_{X_0} + \frac{(X - X_0)^2}{2!}\frac{\partial^2 U_x}{\partial X^2}\bigg|_{X_0}$$
$$+ \frac{(X - X_0)^3}{3!}\frac{\partial^3 U_x}{\partial X^3}\bigg|_{X_0} + \cdots \qquad (11.3\text{-}10)$$

Letting $(X - X_0)$ equal $+\Delta X$ and $-\Delta X$, respectively, gives

$$U_x\big|_{X_0+\Delta X} = U_x\big|_{X_0} + \Delta X \left(\frac{\partial U_x}{\partial X}\right)\bigg|_{X_0} + \frac{\Delta X^2}{2!}\left(\frac{\partial^2 U_x}{\partial X^2}\right)\bigg|_{X_0}$$

$$+ \frac{\Delta X^3}{3!}\left(\frac{\partial^3 U_x}{\partial X^3}\right)\bigg|_{X_0} + \cdots \qquad (11.3\text{-}11)$$

$$U_x\big|_{X_0-\Delta X} = U_x\big|_{X_0} - \Delta X \left(\frac{\partial U_x}{\partial X}\right)\bigg|_{X_0} + \frac{\Delta X^2}{2!}\left(\frac{\partial^2 U_x}{\partial X^2}\right)\bigg|_{X_0}$$

$$- \frac{\Delta X^3}{3!}\left(\frac{\partial^3 U_x}{\partial X^3}\right)\bigg|_{X_0} + \cdots \qquad (11.3\text{-}12)$$

Subtracting Eq. 11.3-12 from Eq. 11.3-11 yields an expression for the first derivative,

$$\left(\frac{\partial U_x}{\partial X}\right)_{X_0} = \frac{U_x\big|_{X_0+\Delta X} - U_x\big|_{X_0-\Delta X}}{2\,\Delta X} - \frac{1}{3!}\Delta X^2\left(\frac{\partial^3 U_x}{\partial X^3}\right)\bigg|_{X_0}$$

$$+ \text{ higher order terms} \quad (11.3\text{-}13)$$

Provided the higher order terms are not excessively large, a reasonable approximation is

$$\frac{\partial U_x}{\partial X}\bigg|_{X_0} \approx \frac{U_x\big|_{X_0+\Delta X} - U_x\big|_{X_0-\Delta X}}{2\,\Delta X} \qquad (11.3\text{-}14)$$

By adding Eqs. 11.3-11 and 11.3-12, we may also obtain an approximation for the second derivative.

$$\frac{\partial^2 U_x}{\partial X^2} \approx \frac{U_x\big|_{X_0+\Delta X} - 2U_x\big|_{X_0} + U_x\big|_{X_0-\Delta X}}{\Delta X^2} \qquad (11.3\text{-}15)$$

From these two equations, we conclude that the order of magnitude estimates for the derivatives may be expressed as

$$\frac{\partial U_x}{\partial X} = \frac{0(U_x)}{\Delta X} \qquad (11.3\text{-}16a)$$

$$\frac{\partial^2 U_x}{\partial X^2} = \frac{0(U_x)}{\Delta X^2} \qquad (11.3\text{-}16b)$$

Letting $X_0 = \frac{1}{2}$ and $\Delta X = \frac{1}{2}$, we find that

$$\frac{\partial U_x}{\partial X} = 0(1)$$

$$\frac{\partial^2 U_x}{\partial X^2} = 0(1)$$

In the second case, we are stretching our definition, for ΔX^2 could also be written

$$\Delta X^2 = \tfrac{1}{4} = O(10^{-1})$$

however, our final result would not be altered if we made this change.

To determine the order of magnitude of U_y, we note first that

$$\frac{\partial U_y}{\partial Y} = -\frac{\partial U_x}{\partial X} = O(1) \qquad (11.3\text{-}17)$$

Using a finite difference formula in conjunction with Eq. 11.3-17, we find that

$$\frac{\partial U_y}{\partial Y} = \frac{U_y|_{Y=\delta'} - U_y|_{Y=0}}{\delta'} = O(1) \qquad (11.3\text{-}18)$$

and we conclude that

$$U_y = \delta'[O(1)] = O(\delta')$$

The other order of magnitude estimates indicated in Eqs. 11.3-5 and 11.3-6 readily follow by similar techniques. In examining Eqs. 11.3-5 and 11.3-6, we see that the corresponding terms in Eq. 11.3-6 are of order of δ' less than those in Eq. 11.3-5. Thus, if δ' is about 10^{-2}, we can neglect the y-direction momentum equation and also $(\partial^2 U_x/\partial X^2)$ relative to $(\partial^2 U_x/\partial Y^2)$, which allows us to simplify the equations to†

$$U_x\frac{\partial U_x}{\partial X} + U_y\frac{\partial U_x}{\partial Y} = -\frac{dP}{dX} + \frac{1}{N_{\mathrm{Re},L}}\left(\frac{\partial^2 U_x}{\partial Y^2}\right) \qquad \begin{array}{l}\text{Prandtl}\\ \text{boundary}\\ \text{layer}\\ \text{equations}\end{array} \quad (11.3\text{-}19)$$

$$\frac{\partial U_x}{\partial X} + \frac{\partial U_y}{\partial Y} = 0 \qquad (11.3\text{-}20)$$

These equations represent an indeterminant set of equations, for we have three unknowns—U_x, U_y, and P—and only two equations. However, for this type of flow we know that

$$\frac{dP}{dX} = 0, \qquad Y \geq \delta'$$

and by our order of magnitude analysis we conclude that variations of P throughout the boundary layer must be small. This statement suggests that dP/dX within the boundary layer must be nearly zero, and we are led at last to the Prandtl boundary layer equations for flow past a flat plate:

$$U_x\frac{\partial U_x}{\partial X} + U_y\frac{\partial U_x}{\partial Y} = \frac{1}{N_{\mathrm{Re},L}}\left(\frac{\partial^2 U_x}{\partial Y^2}\right) \qquad (11.3\text{-}21)$$

$$\frac{\partial U_x}{\partial X} + \frac{\partial U_y}{\partial Y} = 0 \qquad (11.3\text{-}22)$$

† This step relies very heavily on the plausible intuitive hypothesis that "small causes produce small effects."

On the basis of the order of magnitude analysis presented here, we expect these equations to be valid only if $\delta' \leq 10^{-2}$. By Eq. 11.3-1, we may express this restriction in terms of a length Reynolds number as

$$\delta' = \frac{\delta}{L} \approx 3.6 \sqrt{\frac{\nu}{u_\infty x}} \left(\frac{x}{L}\right) = \frac{3.6}{\sqrt{N_{\text{Re},x}}} \left(\frac{x}{L}\right) \leq 10^{-2} \qquad (11.3\text{-}23)$$

or

$$N_{\text{Re},x} \geq (3.6)^2 \times 10^4 \qquad (11.3\text{-}24)$$

because x/L is always less than one. Thus, we expect the Prandtl boundary layer equations to be valid if the length Reynolds number is greater than 10^5.

The solution of Eqs. 11.3-21 and 11.3-22 requires more skill than we possess at the moment; however, they can be solved without a great deal of difficulty and the result is compared with experimental data in Fig. 11.3-2.

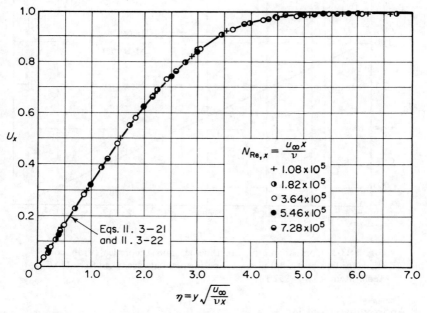

Fig. 11.3-2. Comparison of experimental and theoretical velocity profiles for flow past a flat plate.

The calculated and experimental values of the velocity are plotted as a function of the single variable $\eta = y\sqrt{u_\infty/\nu x}$, which arises when the partial differential equations are transformed to an ordinary differential equation. The length Reynolds number for the experimental points ranges from 1.08×10^5 to 7.28×10^5, large enough to satisfy the restriction given by Eq. 11.3-24.

We conclude that our order of magnitude analysis and simplification of the two-dimensional Navier-Stokes equations have been successful. The result indicates that the boundary layer thickness is given by

$$\delta = 4.9 \sqrt{\frac{\nu x}{u_\infty}}$$ (11.3-25)

which is not too different from the original estimate given by Eq. 11.3-1.

An interesting comparison between theory and experiment is the measured and calculated drag coefficients shown in Fig. 11.3-3. It becomes obvious that theory and experiment are not in agreement for values of $N_{Re,x}$ less than 10^3.

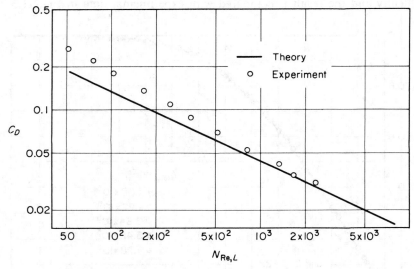

Fig. 11.3-3. Comparison of experimental and theoretical drag coefficients for flow past a flat plate. (Experimental data are taken from NACA Tech. Mem. 1316, 1951.)

Approximate solution

Although we have left the Prandtl boundary layer equations unsolved, we can analyze the flow with an approximate solution. The control volume to be used for the differential-macroscopic momentum balance is shown in Fig. 11.3-4. In this analysis, we will start directly with the macroscopic momentum balance; however, we could integrate the Prandtl boundary layer equations to obtain the same differential macroscopic momentum balance. This problem will be left as an exercise for the student.

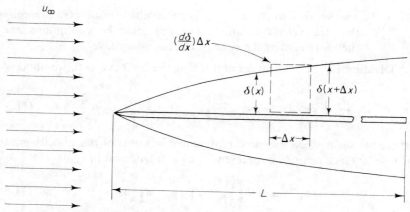

Fig. 11.3-4. Control volume for approximate solution.

For a fixed control volume and steady flow, the momentum balance takes the form

$$\int_{A_e} (\rho\mathbf{v})\mathbf{v}\cdot\mathbf{n}\,dA = \int_{\mathscr{V}} \rho\mathbf{g}\,dV + \int_{\mathscr{A}} \mathbf{t}_{(\mathbf{n})}\,dA \qquad (11.3\text{-}26)$$

Applying the x-component of this equation to the control volume yields

$$\underbrace{\int_0^\delta \rho v_x^2\,dy\Big|_{x+\Delta x}}_{\substack{\text{Momentum flux}\\\text{at } x + \Delta x}} - \left\{ \underbrace{\int_0^\delta \rho v_x^2\,dy\Big|_x}_{\substack{\text{Momentum flux}\\\text{at } x}} + \rho u_\infty^2 \left(\frac{d\delta}{dx}\right)\Delta x \right\} + \underbrace{\rho u_\infty v_y\,\Delta x\Big|_{y=\delta}}_{\substack{\text{Momentum flux}\\\text{at } y = \delta}}$$

$$= \underbrace{-\tau_{yx}\Big|_{y=0}\,\Delta x}_{\substack{\text{Surface force}\\\text{at } y = 0}} \qquad (11.3\text{-}27)$$

We have made the following assumptions in accord with the order of magnitude analysis that led to the Prandtl boundary layer equations.

A. 1: The viscous stress on the x-surfaces is neglected. This assumption may be stated

$$\tau_{xx} \ll \tau_{yx}$$

which is comparable to specifying that

$$\frac{\partial^2 v_x}{\partial x^2} \ll \frac{\partial^2 v_x}{\partial y^2}$$

A. 2: The pressures at x and $x + \Delta x$ are equal, and therefore do not contribute to the momentum balance. This assumption is derived from the facts that $(\partial p/\partial y)$ is negligible and that the pressure outside the boundary layer is constant.

A. 3: The viscous stress at $y = \delta$ is zero, which results from specifying that the velocity gradient $(\partial v_x/\partial y)$ must be continuous and is therefore zero at the edge of the boundary layer.

Dividing Eq. 11.3-27 by Δx and taking the limit $\Delta x \to 0$, we obtain

$$\frac{d}{dx}\int_0^{\delta} \rho v_x^2 \, dy - \rho u_\infty^2 \left(\frac{d\delta}{dx}\right) + \rho u_\infty v_y\bigg|_{y=\delta} = -\mu \frac{\partial v_x}{\partial y}\bigg|_{y=0} \qquad (11.3\text{-}28)$$

where the shear stress has been represented in terms of the velocity gradient at $y = 0$. Once again, we represent v_x as a polynomial in (y/δ)

$$v_x = a + b\left(\frac{y}{\delta}\right) + c\left(\frac{y}{\delta}\right)^2 + d\left(\frac{y}{\delta}\right)^3 + \cdots \qquad (11.3\text{-}29)$$

which is subject to the restrictions

$v_x = 0,$ $\quad y = 0$ $\quad$ (a bonafide boundary condition) $\qquad$ (11.3-30a)

$v_x = u_\infty,$ $\quad y = \delta$ $\quad$ (an intuitive approximation) $\qquad$ (11.3-30b)

$\dfrac{\partial v_x}{\partial y} = 0,$ $\quad y = \delta$ $\quad$ (continuity of stress) $\qquad$ (11.3-30c)

$\dfrac{\partial^2 v_x}{\partial y^2} = 0,$ $\quad y = 0$ $\quad$ (from the differential equation) $\qquad$ (113-30d)

These conditions allow us to determine the four constants in Eq. 11.3-29, and the velocity is given by

$$v_x = u_\infty\left(\tfrac{3}{2}Y - \tfrac{1}{2}Y^3\right) \qquad (11.3\text{-}31)$$

where

$$Y = \frac{y}{\delta}$$

To determine v_y at $y = \delta$, the continuity equation may be integrated

$$v_y\bigg|_{y=\delta} = -\int_0^{\delta}\left(\frac{\partial v_x}{\partial x}\right) dy \qquad (11.3\text{-}32a)$$

and substitution of Eq. 11.3-31 for v_x gives

$$v_y\bigg|_{y=\delta} = \frac{3u_\infty}{8}\left(\frac{d\delta}{dx}\right) \qquad (11.3\text{-}32b)$$

Substitution of Eqs. 11.3-31 and 11.3-32b into Eq. 11.3-28, and the changing of the variable of integration from y to Y, give

$$\frac{d}{dx}\left\{\delta\int_0^1 \left(\tfrac{3}{2}Y - \tfrac{1}{2}Y^3\right)^2 dY\right\} - \frac{5}{8}\left(\frac{d\delta}{dx}\right) = -\frac{3}{2\delta}\left(\frac{\nu}{u_\infty}\right) \qquad (11.3\text{-}33)$$

Carrying out the integration and differentiation yields

$$\frac{39}{280}\left(\frac{d\delta}{dx}\right) = \frac{3}{2\delta}\left(\frac{\nu}{u_\infty}\right) \qquad (11.3\text{-}34)$$

Separating variables, integrating, and applying the boundary condition

B. C. 1: $\qquad\qquad\qquad \delta = 0, \qquad x = 0 \qquad\qquad (11.3\text{-}35)$

we get an expression for the boundary layer thickness

$$\delta = 4.64\sqrt{\frac{\nu x}{u_\infty}} \qquad (11.3\text{-}36)$$

which is in excellent agreement with that given by the exact solution. The velocity profiles for the exact and approximate solutions are shown in Fig. 11.3-5, and the agreement is seen to be excellent—far better, in fact, than the agreement between the exact and approximate solutions for the suddenly accelerated flat plate.

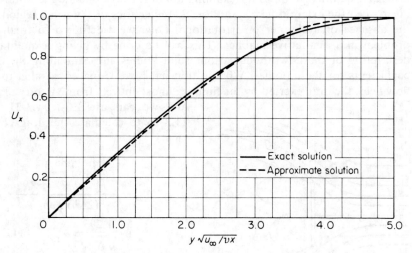

Fig. 11.3-5. Velocity profile for flow past a flat plate.

To gain some insight into the nature of the boundary layer, let us consider the following example. For the flat plate shown in Fig. 11.3-1, we assume the following conditions:

$u_\infty = 100$ mph
$\rho = 0.075$ lb$_m$/ft^3 (density of air)
$\mu = 3.8 \times 10^{-7}$ lb$_f$-sec/ft^2 (viscosity of air)
$L = 6$ in.

The length Reynolds number is 6×10^5, and the boundary layer thickness at $x = L$ is

$$\delta \approx (5) \frac{6 \text{ in.}}{\sqrt{6 \times 10^5}}$$

$$\approx 3.86 \times 10^{-2} \text{ in.}$$

The point here is that the boundary layer thickness is in general quite small for conditions that might be encountered for air flowing past solid objects. Since the kinematic viscosity ν of water is about a factor of 10 less than that of air, we can also expect boundary layers for the flow of water around solid objects to be very thin.

11.4 External Flows and Wakes

We are now in a position to understand the nature of the boundary layer flow, and we must go on to the examination of the flow outside the boundary layer—i.e., the external flow—and the characteristics of the wake region. In the absence of a chapter on irrotational flow, we are forced to treat this problem in a qualitative manner. This will be done by giving a qualitative description of the flow about various solid bodies and examining the drag coefficients for these bodies. When a thin flat plate is placed parallel to the flow field, the drag exerted by the fluid is almost entirely from viscous effects, and we can use Eqs. 11.3-31 and 11.3-36 to calculate the drag coefficient†

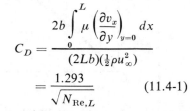

$$C_D = \frac{2b \int_0^L \mu \left(\frac{\partial v_x}{\partial y}\right)_{y=0} dx}{(2Lb)(\frac{1}{2}\rho u_\infty^2)}$$

$$= \frac{1.293}{\sqrt{N_{\text{Re},L}}} \qquad (11.4\text{-}1)$$

with considerable accuracy, provided the boundary layer flow remains laminar and $N_{\text{Re},L} \geq 10^3$. However, if the plate is placed perpendicular to the flow, an entirely different situation, depicted in Fig. 11.4-1, is created. For this case, the flow may be divided into an irrotational flow

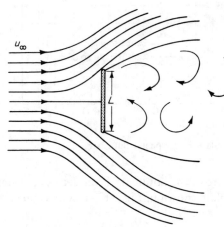

Fig. 11.4-1. Flow past a plate at high Reynolds numbers.

† The exact solution gives a coefficient of 1.328.

region, a wake region, and a stagnation region in front of the plate. The drag on the plate results almost entirely from the pressure difference on the front and back surfaces of the plate. Under these conditions, the drag is very nearly proportional to the density times the square of the free stream velocity.

$$\text{drag} \propto \rho u_\infty^2$$

This situation is comparable to the jet impinging on the flat plate (Sec. 7.8) and the rough-pipe region of flow (Sec. 8.2). The drag coefficient for a flat plate placed perpendicularly to the free stream is defined in terms of the projected area and the kinetic energy per unit volume of the free stream.

$$C_D = \frac{\text{drag force}}{(Lb)(\frac{1}{2}\rho u_\infty^2)} \tag{11.4-2}$$

Both mathematical[2-5] and experimental[6-8] values of the drag coefficient are available for a flat plate placed parallel and perpendicular to the flow. These results are shown in Fig. 11.4-2, and, as we would expect, there is a large difference in the drag coefficients for the two configurations.

For Reynolds numbers less than one, viscous effects predominate and the drag coefficients differ by less than 50 per cent. It is consistent with our intuition that the drag coefficient for the plate placed perpendicular to the flow is the larger of the two. For Reynolds numbers greater than 10, inertial effects predominate for the perpendicular plate and the drag coefficient is constant. The behavior of the parallel plate is quite different, and the drag coefficient continues to decrease with increasing Reynolds number. We must keep in mind that the drag force is not necessarily decreasing; it is simply *not increasing* as fast as ρu_∞^2. These results indicate clearly that there are two distinct types of drag forces to be considered for immersed bodies, just as there were two distinct mechanisms of drag to be considered for flow in rough pipes.

While the drag coefficient for the perpendicular plate remains constant

2. Y. H. Kno, "On the Flow of an Incompressible Viscous Fluid Past a Flat Plate at Moderate Reynolds Numbers," *J. Math. Phys.* 1953, 32:83.

3. S. Tomotika and T. Aoi, "The Steady Flow of a Viscous Fluid Past an Elliptic Cylinder and a Flat Plate at Small Reynolds Numbers," *Quart. J. Mech. Appl. Math.*, 1953, 6:290.

4. B. A. Boley and M. B. Friedman, "On the Viscous Flow Around the Leading Edge of a Flat Plate," *J. Aerospace Sci.* 1959, 26:453.

5. H. Schlichting, *Boundary Layer Theory* (New York: McGraw-Hill Book Company, Inc., 1955), Chap. 7.

6. Z. Janour, "Resistance of a Plate in Parallel Flow at Low Reynolds Numbers," *NASA Tech. Note* 1316, Nov., 1951.

7. S. Dhawan, "Direct Measurements of Skin Friction," *NACA* Rept. 1121, 1953.

8. S. F. Hoerner, *Aerodynamic Drag* (pub. by author, 148 Busteed, Midland Park, New Jersey), Chap. 3.

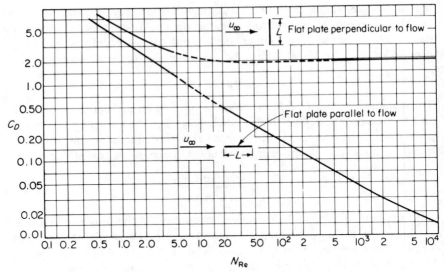

Fig. 11.4-2. Drag coefficients for thin, flat plates.

for Reynolds numbers higher than those in Fig. 11.4-2, an important change in the drag characteristics of the parallel plate occurs. This change is illustrated in Fig. 11.4-3, where we see that the drag coefficient for a flat plate behaves much like the friction factor for flow in a pipe. At a Reynolds number of about 3×10^5, the drag coefficient suddenly increases in an

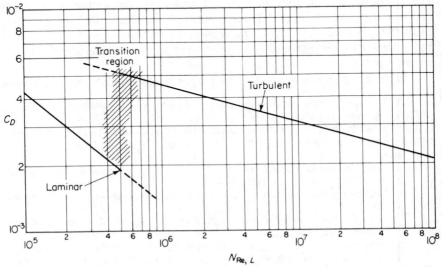

Fig. 11.4-3. Drag coefficient for a flat plate—the transition to turbulence.

erratic manner and then follows a smooth curve decreasing less rapidly than the curve for the lower Reynolds numbers. Obviously a change has occurred in the flow, and in view of our knowledge of the transition from laminar to turbulent flow in smooth tubes, it seems reasonable to attribute the change to the onset of turbulence.

Both experiment and theory[5] verify the onset of turbulence at $N_{\mathrm{Re},x} \approx 3 \times 10^5$, and a schematic drawing of the flow field is shown in Fig. 11.4-4.

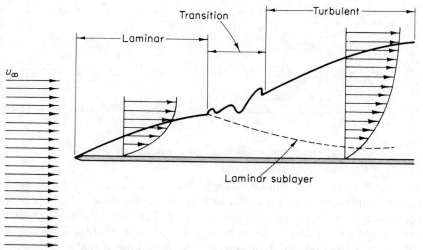

Fig. 11.4-4. Boundary layer formation on a flat plate.

As in the case of pipe flow, the transition Reynolds number depends on a variety of factors. Schubauer and Skramstad[9] found that an increase in the intensity of turbulence resulted in a transition at a lower Reynolds number, and by carefully eliminating the free stream turbulence, a transition Reynolds number of 3×10^6 was reached.

On the basis of our qualitative examination of the flow past a flat plate placed both parallel and perpendicular to a uniform stream, we are aware of three distinct types of drag forces: "form force" from the difference in pressure acting on the front and back (or leading and trailing) surfaces; a laminar "friction force"; and a turbulent "friction force." A clear understanding of these phenomena can be obtained only with a more detailed mathematical analysis and an extended survey of experimental results; however, the brief description presented here does touch on the key points we wish to bring out in this chapter.

The next step in the process of sharpening our intuition is to examine the

9. G. B. Schubauer and H. K. Skramstad, "Laminar Boundary Layer Oscillations and Transition on a Flat Plate." *NACA Rept.* 909, 1949.

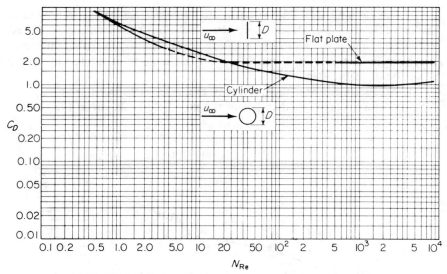

Fig. 11.4-5. Drag coefficients for a cylinder and a flat plate.

drag coefficients for a cylinder and a flat plate shown in Fig. 11.4-5. At low Reynolds numbers, the drag coefficients are nearly the same, with the cylinder showing a somewhat higher value for C_D. It is not at all obvious that the drag on these two rather different objects should be nearly identical in the low Reynolds number region. However, it appears that the degree of deformation suffered by the fluid as it flows past the plate and the cylinder is about the same, which leads to similar values for the drag coefficient. The drag on the flat plate results entirely from form drag even at low Reynolds numbers, while the total drag on the cylinder at low Reynolds numbers is evenly divided between form and friction drag.[3] From the results shown in Fig. 11.4-5, we conclude that the form drag for the cylinder must always be less than that for the flat plate, and that streamlining reduces the total drag at high Reynolds numbers.

Recalling that the boundary layer on the flat plate become turbulent at a high Reynolds number yielding an abrupt increase in the drag coefficient, we might expect a similar change in the drag coefficient-Reynolds number curve for the cylinder. The complete curve is shown in Fig. 11.4-6, and, indeed, there is an abrupt change in the drag coefficient. But while the drag increases for the flat plate, the drag on the cylinder undergoes an abrupt decrease! Here it seems appropriate to quote Shapiro,[10] who, at this point in his classic

10. A. H. Shapiro "The Fluid Mechanics of Drag," distributed by Educational Services, Inc., 47 Galen St., Watertown 72, Mass. A written version of the experiments and commentary contained in the film is available in the paperback book, A. H. Shapiro, *Shape and Flow— The Fluid Dynamics of Drag* (Garden City, New York: Anchor Books, Doubleday and Co. Inc., 1961).

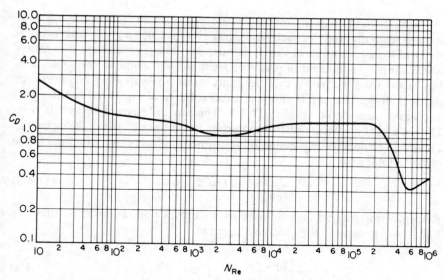

Fig. 11.4-6. Drag coefficient versus Reynolds number for a circular cylinder.

movies on drag, said, "Well, this is certainly unexpected." To explain this curious phenomenon we must examine the process of boundary layer separation for both laminar and turbulent flow, for it is the shifting of the separation point when the boundary layer becomes turbulent that gives rise to the abrupt decrease in the drag coefficient. Before considering boundary layer separation, we will present a brief, qualitative description of the flow field outside both the wake and the boundary layer.

The external flow

Both analysis and experiment indicate that the region outside the boundary layer can be described reasonably well if viscous effects are neglected entirely. For steady flow, the equations of motion reduce to

$$\rho \mathbf{v} \cdot \nabla \mathbf{v} = -\nabla p + \rho \mathbf{g} \qquad (11.4\text{-}3)$$

and the flow is termed irrotational. Equation 11.4-3 also describes the motion of what is called a *perfect fluid*, or an *inviscid fluid*. By definition, an inviscid fluid has a zero value of the viscosity coefficient; thus, $\mu = 0$. Equation 11.4-3 may also be obtained by postulating that the stress always acts normal to any surface, requiring the stress tensor to be given by

$$\mathbf{T} = -p\mathbf{I} \qquad (11.4\text{-}4)$$

and the stress equations of motion quickly reduce to Eq. 11.4-3.

Now, inviscid fluids do not exist in the real world. Yet there is much to be learned from the study of such fluids, just as we learned a great deal from the study of the suddenly accelerated, infinite, flat plate, even though it is a flow which cannot be realized in practice. Here, we will examine the solution of Eq. 11.4-3 for flow past a cylinder, only to obtain a limiting condition for the form drag. The results of one possible solution of Eq. 11.4-3 for flow past a cylinder are shown in Fig. 11.4-7. The streamlines are shown in Fig. 11.4-7a and the pressure distribution over the surface of the cylinder in Fig. 11.4-7b. The analytic expression for the dimensionless pressure on the surface of the cylinder[11] is

$$\frac{p - p_\infty}{\frac{1}{2}\rho u_\infty^2} = (1 - 4\sin^2\theta) \qquad (11.4\text{-}5)$$

Remembering that an inviscid fluid exerts only a normal force, we may use Eq. 10.4-5 to express the drag coefficient as

$$C_D = \frac{F_\text{form}}{(\frac{1}{2}\rho u_\infty^2)(bD)} = \boldsymbol{\lambda} \cdot \int_0^{2\pi} \mathbf{n}(1 - 4\sin^2\theta)\,d\theta \qquad (11.4\text{-}6)$$

Inasmuch as $\boldsymbol{\lambda} \cdot \mathbf{n} = -\cos\theta$, the drag coefficient is zero,

$$C_D = -\int_0^{2\pi} (1 - 4\sin^2\theta)\cos\theta\,d\theta = 0 \qquad (11.4\text{-}7)$$

This result, often known as D'Alembert's paradox,[12] caused considerable consternation among early researchers in fluid mechanics. Even in the absence of viscous forces, it was felt that a streaming fluid would exert some

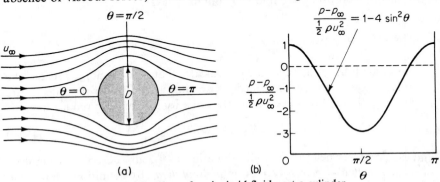

Fig. 11.4-7. Flow of an inviscid fluid past a cylinder.

11. L. M. Milne-Thomson, *Theoretical Hydrodynamics*, 4th ed. (New York: The Macmillan Company, 1960), p. 157.

12. H. Rouse and S. Ince, *History of Hydraulics* (New York: Dover Publications, Inc., 1963), p. 102.

force on an immersed body, for experience certainly indicated that immersed bodies experienced a drag at high Reynolds numbers where viscous effects were *presumably* negligible.

The two points of maximum pressure shown in Fig. 11.4-7 are often referred to as the forward ($\theta = 0$) and rear ($\theta = \pi$) stagnation points. The terminology is appropriate, because the velocity is zero at the points even if the fluid is inviscid and "slips" past solid surfaces. The degree to which the rear stagnation pressure approaches the forward stagnation pressure is sometimes called the *pressure recovery*. For the illustrated case, the pressure recovery is complete.

We now have some knowledge of the limiting behavior of the form drag, i.e., it is zero for the flow illustrated in Fig. 11.4-7. We can carry this qualitative description of inviscid flow somewhat further and perhaps gain more insight into the nature of the flow of real fluids past immersed bodies. The flow illustrated in Fig. 11.4-7 is just one of an infinite number of solutions to Eq. 11.4-3 subject to the boundary condition that the normal component of the velocity on the surface of the cylinder is zero.

There is a class of solutions for inviscid flow past immersed bodies known as Helmholtz flows,† or free streamline flows. A possible flow of this type is shown in Fig. 11.4-8 for flow past a cylinder. The pressure in the stagnant

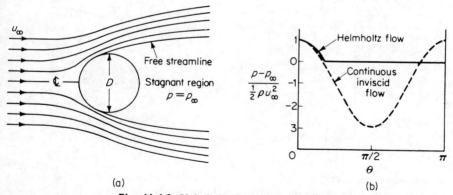

(a)   (b)

Fig. 11.4-8. Helmholtz flow past a cylinder.

wake region was taken to be the same as the free stream pressure. If the pressure in the wake is taken to be some value larger than p_∞, the point of separation moves toward the rear of the cylinder and the wake becomes progressively smaller. When the pressure in the wake is taken to be the forward stagnation pressure, the wake disappears and the Helmholtz flow collapses to the continuous flow.

† See Ref. 12, p. 201, and Ref. 11, Chap. 12.

Inasmuch as the pressure distribution in the Helmholtz flow is not symmetric, a positive drag force results; the flow is therefore in accord with our experience. In addition, the stagnant wake region also bears some resemblance to reality, although in actual fact it is unstable and a series of oscillating vortices are formed.

Our treatment here has been extremely qualitative; however, from the Helmholtz and continuous flow pressure distributions we may draw the following conclusion: *When the flow separates from the solid surface the pressure recovery is not complete and the form drag increases.*

Boundary layer separation

When a real fluid flows past a cylinder, a boundary layer forms, separating from the cylinder as shown in Fig. 11.4-9. A detailed sketch of the boundary layer separation is shown in Fig. 11.4-9, and a qualitative explanation of the

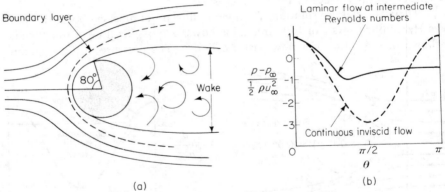

(a)   (b)

Fig. 11.4-9. Flow of a viscous fluid past a cylinder.

separation phenomenon follows. We imagine a rectangular coordinate system located on the surface of the cylinder as shown in Fig. 11.4-10, and write the x-direction equation of motion for steady flow and negligible gravitational effects.

$$\rho\left(v_x \frac{\partial v_x}{\partial x} + v_y \frac{\partial v_x}{\partial y}\right) = -\frac{\partial p}{\partial x} + \mu\left(\frac{\partial v_x^2}{\partial x^2} + \frac{\partial^2 v_x}{\partial y^2}\right) \qquad (11.4\text{-}8)$$

At the solid surface, v_x and v_y are both zero and Eq. 11.4-8 is simplified to

$$\frac{\partial p}{\partial x} = \mu \frac{\partial^2 v_x}{\partial y^2} \qquad (11.4\text{-}9)$$

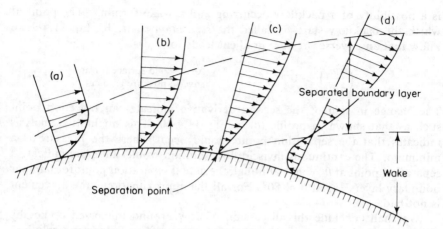

Fig. 11.4-10. Separation of a laminar boundary layer from a cylinder.

which indicates that the sign ($\pm$) of the second derivative depends upon whether the pressure gradient is positive or negative. Following the analysis of the boundary layer on a flat plate, we shall assume that the pressure gradient does not vary across the boundary layer; we can therefore determine $\partial p/\partial x$ at the solid surface by examining the inviscid flow outside the boundary layer.

Over the front surface of the cylinder, the velocity increases as x increases; by Bernoulli's equation, then, the pressure must be decreasing. Both fluid inertia and the pressure gradient are tending to propel the fluid forward against the effects of viscosity. A decreasing pressure leads to what is called a *favorable pressure gradient*, which gives rise to a boundary layer that remains attached to the solid surface. When the pressure gradient is favorable,

$$\frac{\partial p}{\partial x} < 0$$

and Eq. 11.4-11 indicates that

$$\left(\frac{\partial^2 v_x}{\partial y^2}\right) < 0 \qquad \begin{array}{l}\text{At the solid surface for a} \\ \text{favorable pressure gradient}\end{array} \qquad (11.4\text{-}10)$$

This condition is illustrated by profile (a) in Fig. 11.4-10.

Let us now consider the possibility that separation and wake formation did *not* take place, and that the flow outside the boundary layer was accurately described by the continuous, inviscid flow shown in Fig. 11.4-7. For values of $\theta > \pi/2$, the pressure would be increasing and a so-called *adverse pressure gradient* would be established. Both viscous *and* pressure forces would thereby be acting against the inertial force of the fluid, and there is a possibility of a backflow occurring and a wake forming. The point at which the backflow starts is called the *separation point*. By Eq. 11.4-9 we know that an adverse pressure gradient leads to

$$\left(\frac{\partial^2 v_x}{\partial y^2}\right) > 0 \qquad \begin{array}{l}\text{At the solid surface for an} \\ \text{adverse pressure gradient}\end{array} \qquad (11.4\text{-}11)$$

The change in sign of the second derivative indicates an inflection point such as that shown in profile (c) in Fig. 11.4-10. This qualitative analysis indicates that the separation point should occur where the pressure is a minimum. The continuous inviscid flow solution would therefore indicate a separation point at $\theta = 90°$, although the actual separation point for laminar boundary layers[13] is at $\theta \approx 80°$. For all the approximations, the agreement is not bad.

We shall conclude this discussion of flow around immersed bodies by examining all the flow regimes associated with uniform flow past a cylinder. In practice, the engineer will encounter a variety of shapes of immersed bodies, and limiting our discussion to cylinders certainly does not do justice to the subject. However, the pertinent aspects of the flow around immersed bodies are contained in this one example, and it should be a satisfactory introduction to the subject.

In Fig. 11.4-11, a series of flow fields is illustrated based on the observations and calculations of a number of investigators.[13-17] At Reynolds numbers less than one there is no wake and the flow follows the curved surface of the cylinder in much the same manner as the inviscid continuous flow. At a Reynolds number of about 4, a visible wake appears. As the Reynolds number increases, the wake grows in size and the separation point moves forward. At a Reynolds of about 40, the flow tends to become unstable, and the two vortices behind the cylinder are alternately shed to form what is known as Kármán's vortex trail. This flow pattern is illustrated in Fig. 11.4-12. The alternate shedding of vortices produces periodic transverse forces on the cylinder that may cause severe damage if shedding frequency is comparable to the resonant frequency of the cylinder. The "singing" of electrical transmission wires in a high wind is a familiar example of this

13. A. S. Grove, F. H. Shair, E. E. Petersen, and A. Acrivos, "An Experimental Investigation of the Steady Separated Flow Past a Circular Cylinder," *J. Fluid Mech.*, 1964, 19:60.

14. L. Prandtl and O. G. Tietjens, *Applied Hydro and Aeromechanics*, (New York: Dover Publications, Inc., 1957), p. 302.

15. I. Proudman and J. R. A. Pearson, "Expansions at Small Reynolds Numbers for Flow Past a Sphere and a Circular Cylinder," *J. Fluid Mech.*, 1957, 2:237.

16. A. Thom, "The Flow Past Circular Cylinders at Low Speeds," *Proc. Roy. Soc.* (*London*) *Ser. A.*, 1933, 141:651.

17. D. J. Tritton, "Experiments on the Flow Past a Circular Cylinder at Low Reynolds Numbers," *J. Fluid Mech.*, 1959, 6:547.

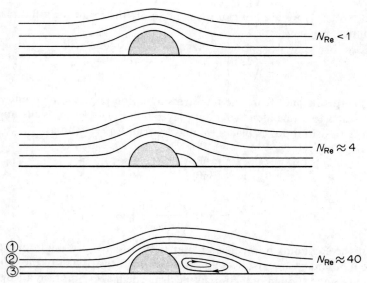

Fig. 11.4-11. Streamlines for flow past a cylinder.

phenomenon. The Kármán vortex trail is observed in the Reynolds number range of from about 60 to 5000. At higher Reynolds numbers, the motion tends to become more turbulent in nature and the distinct vortices are obscured.

As the Reynolds number increases further, it eventually reaches the point where a sudden decrease in the drag coefficient takes place. The main purpose of this section is to try to provide a rational explanation for this curious phenomenon, and by now we have sufficient knowledge to do so.

From our examination of the boundary layer on a flat plate, we know that a transition to turbulence takes place for a length Reynolds number of

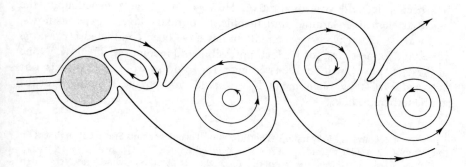

Fig. 11.4-12. The Kármán vortex trail.

about 3×10^5. If we are not cautious and apply the result for a flat plate to the cylinder, we may write

$$\left(\frac{u_\infty s}{\nu}\right)_{\text{transition}} = 3 \times 10^5 \qquad (11.4\text{-}12)$$

where s is the distance from the forward stagnation point to the point where the transition to a turbulent boundary layer takes place. If θ_t is the angle at which the transition takes place, we may rewrite Eq. 11.4-14 as

$$\left(\frac{u_\infty D}{\nu}\right)\left(\frac{\pi}{360°}\right)\theta_t = 3 \times 10^5 \qquad (11.4\text{-}13)$$

or

$$\theta_t = 360°\left(\frac{3 \times 10^5}{\pi N_{\text{Re}}}\right)$$

Thus, if the Reynolds number is greater than 3×10^5, we might expect the turbulent boundary to exist over a portion of the forward half of the cylinder. The fact that the sudden reduction in the drag coefficient occurs at a Reynolds number of about 3×10^5 certainly leads us to believe that this abrupt change is associated with the appearance of a turbulent boundary layer.

Careful experimental studies of this phenomenon[18-20] have clearly demonstrated that the appearance of the turbulent boundary layer causes the abrupt decrease in the drag coefficient, by the following mechanism. When the boundary layer becomes turbulent, the separation point moves to the rear of the cylinder, perhaps as much as 10°. This change reduces the area of the low pressure region, altering the pressure distribution around the cylinder so that the pressure at the rear stagnation point increases. Both these occurrences tend to reduce the form drag, and since it accounts for practically all the drag at these high Reynolds numbers, the drag abruptly decreases when the boundary layer becomes turbulent.

The description of flow around immersed bodies presented in this chapter has been brief and very qualitative. However, we have touched upon the essential elements—laminar and turbulent boundary layers, external flows, and wakes. Extensive experimental studies have been conducted for a large variety of solid bodies, for both compressible and incompressible flow. None of these, however, will be discussed here, for to do so would add little to our knowledge of flow phenomena if we could not pursue a more rigorous mathematical attack.

18. See Ref. 14, p. 96.

19. A. Fage and J. H. Warsap, "The Effects of Turbulence and Surface Roughness on the Drag of a Circular Cylinder," *Aero. Res. Council Rept.* 1283, Gr. Brit., 1930.

20. A. Roshko, "Experiments on the Flow Past a Circular Cylinder at Very High Reynolds Numbers," *J. Fluid Mech.*, 1961, 10:345.

PROBLEMS

11-1. Obtain an approximate solution for the suddenly accelerated flat plate (see Sec. 11.2) using a fourth order polynomial and the additional condition

$$\frac{\partial^2 v_x}{\partial y^2} = 0, \qquad y = \delta(t)$$

Compare the calculated boundary layer thickness with that obtained by the exact solution.

Ans: $\delta = 3.65 \sqrt{vt}$

11-2. Integrate the Prandtl boundary layer equations between $y = 0$ and $y = \delta(x)$, expressing v_x as a polynomial in $y/\delta(x)$, to derive an expression for $\delta(x)$. *Hint:* Start by forming the integral

$$\int_0^\delta \left(v_x \frac{\partial v_x}{\partial x} + v_y \frac{\partial v_x}{\partial y} \right) dy = v \int_0^\delta \frac{\partial^2 v_x}{\partial y^2}\, dy$$

and expressing v_x as

$$v_x = u_\infty \left[\frac{3}{2}\left(\frac{y}{\delta}\right) - \frac{1}{2}\left(\frac{y}{\delta}\right)^3 \right]$$

11-3. Obtain an approximate solution for flow past a flat plate, expressing the velocity as

$$v_x = u_\infty \left(\frac{y}{\delta}\right), \qquad 0 \leq y \leq \delta$$

Compare the calculated boundary layer thickness and drag coefficient with those given by the solution of the Prandtl boundary layer equations.

Ans: $\delta = 3.47 \sqrt{vx/u_\infty}$

11-4. Air at 72°F and 1 atm flows past a flat plate with a uniform free stream velocity of 30 ft/sec. What is the boundary layer thickness at a point 5 in. from the leading edge?

11-5. Consider an immersed body of mass M (such as a submarine) moving through an infinite, quiescent fluid at a velocity $\mathbf{w} = \lambda u_0$. Derive an expression for the power required to move the body in terms of C_D and u_0. Let A^* be the characteristic area used in defining C_D.

11-6. The turbulent boundary layer thickness on a smooth, flat plate can be determined approximately if we make use of experimental data for turbulent flow in smooth tubes. The velocity profile may be approximated by

$$v_x = u_\infty (y/\delta)^{1/7} \qquad 0 \leq y \leq \delta \qquad \text{(see Sec. 6.3)}$$

and the shear stress at the wall by

$$\tau_0 = \left(\frac{f}{8}\right)\rho\langle\bar{v}_x\rangle^2$$

(see Sec. 8.2)

$$f = 0.316\, N_{\mathrm{Re}}^{-1/4}$$

thus leading to

$$\tau_0 = \left(\frac{f}{8}\right)\rho u_\infty^2$$

$$f = 0.316\left(\frac{2\delta\, u_\infty}{\nu}\right)^{-1/4}$$

Here we have replaced the average velocity in a tube with the free stream velocity, and the tube diameter with 2δ. We can use the momentum equation to determine the turbulent boundary layer thickness. Consider carefully the boundary condition to be imposed on the derived differential equation for δ. Use these results to calculate a drag coefficient that may be compared with the experimental curve for C_D shown in Fig. 11.4-3.

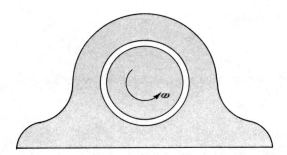

Fig. 11-7. Suddenly accelerated journal bearing.

11-7. A bearing, shown in Fig. 11-7, is initially at rest. At time $t = 0$ it is suddenly accelerated to a constant angular velocity, ω. If the viscosity of the oil in the bearing is 100 centipoise and the annular gap is 0.10 in., *estimate* the time required to obtain a steady velocity profile.

Index